D1279950

PRAISE FOR THE BOOKS BY MARK AND DELIA OWENS

Praise for *Cry of the Kalahari*

WINNER OF THE JOHN BURROUGHS MEDAL FOR BEST NATURAL HISTORY BOOK OF THE YEAR

"Extraordinary...How the couple overcame the hazards of the desert and came to appreciate its living richness makes fascinating reading...Read their remarkable book to be delighted, moved, and awed."—*People*

"For anyone interested in animals or in real live adventure, this book is a must."
—Jane Goodall

"Leaps off the page and sweeps you away."—*Los Angeles Times*

"Splendid...If [the Owenses'] survival is a wonder, so is their book—stirring, heartening, and elegiac all at once."—*Newsweek*

"One of the best testimonials to the perseverance, idealism, and general spunk of passionate animal students."—*Washington Post*

"Mark and Delia Owens's simple human passion and dedication are invigorating. This is a remarkable and important story."—Barry Lopez

Praise for *The Eye of the Elephant*

"Exciting hybrid of a book, part adventure story, part wildlife tale"
—*The Boston Globe*

"A provocative, disturbing, and eminently readable work."—*Natural History*

"Much tougher, more poignant than *Cry of the Kalahari*...Another good book by a remarkable pair."—*Chicago Tribune*

Praise for *Secrets of the Savanna*

"A moving account that documents their [the Owenses'] efforts, illustrates their courage and intelligence, and—no small achievement—makes for a terrific read."
—*Providence Journal*

"A fascinating look at the interplay of social and wildlife upheavals in Africa in the early 1990s and a worthy follow-up to the authors' *Cry of the Kalahari*."
—*Publishers Weekly*, starred review

"A stirring account by two dedicated and courageous conservationists."
—*Kirkus Reviews*

DELIA OWENS IN AFRICA:

A LIFE IN THE WILD

MARK OWENS
DELIA OWENS

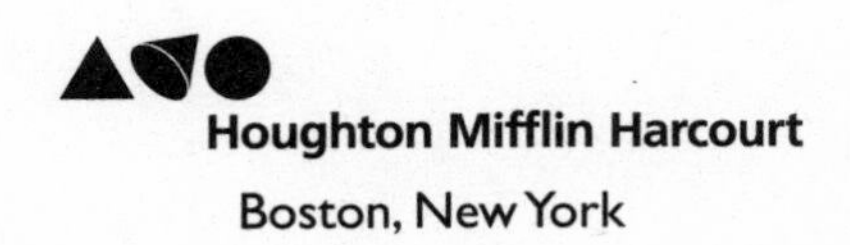
Houghton Mifflin Harcourt
Boston, New York

Cover photo by Shripal Daphtary on Unsplash

For information about permission to reproduce selections from this book,
write to Permissions, Houghton Mifflin Harcourt Publishing Company,
3 Park Avenue, 19th Floor, New York, NY 10016.

Visit our Web site:
www.hmhbooks.com

POB 3 Volume ISBN: 978-0-358-31516-2
Printed in the United States of America

CONTENTS

Cry *of the* KALAHARI

MARK *and* DELIA OWENS

We dedicate this book to
Dr. Richard Faust
and to
Ingrid Koberstein
of the Frankfurt Zoological Society
for all they have done for the animals
of this earth.

And to Christopher, who could not be with us.

Maps on pages 8-9 drawn by Lorraine Sneed.
Maps on pages 10, 339, and 341 prepared by Larry A. Peters

Library of Congress Cataloging in Publication Data
Owens, Mark.
Cry of the Kalahari.
Includes bibliographical references.
1. Zoology – Kalahari Desert. 2. Zoology – Botswana.
3. Kalahari Desert. I. Owens, Delia. II. Title.
QL337.K3095 1984 591.9681'1 84-10771
ISBN-13: 978-0-395-64780-6 (pbk.)
ISBN-10: 0-395-64780-0 (pbk.)

Printed in the United States of America

DOC 45 44 43 42 41

4500767958

CONTENTS

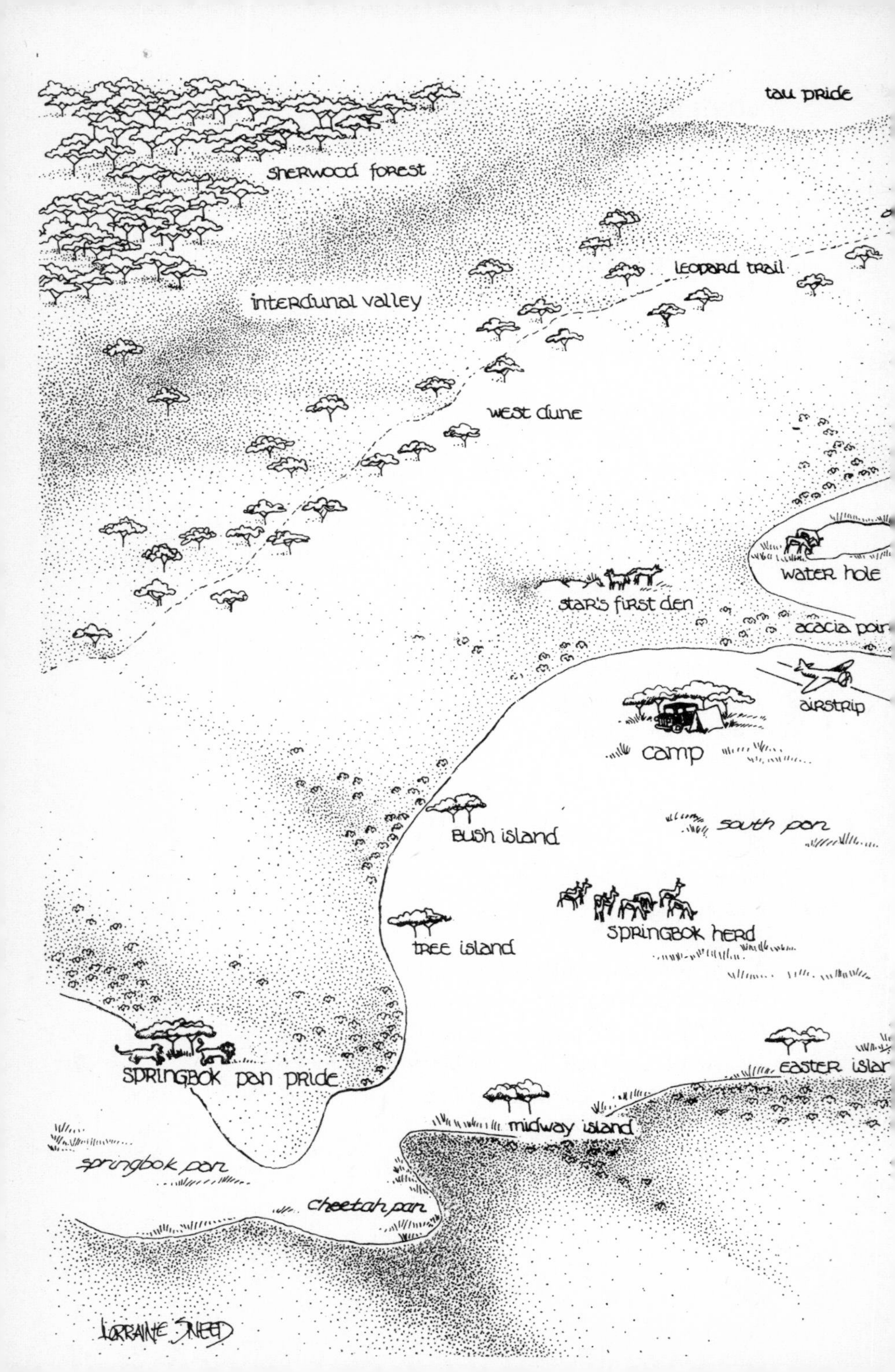
tau pride
sherwood forest
leopard trail
interdunal valley
west dune
water hole
star's first den
airstrip
camp
south pan
bush island
springbok herd
tree island
springbok pan pride
midway island
springbok pan
cheetah pan
Lorraine Sneed

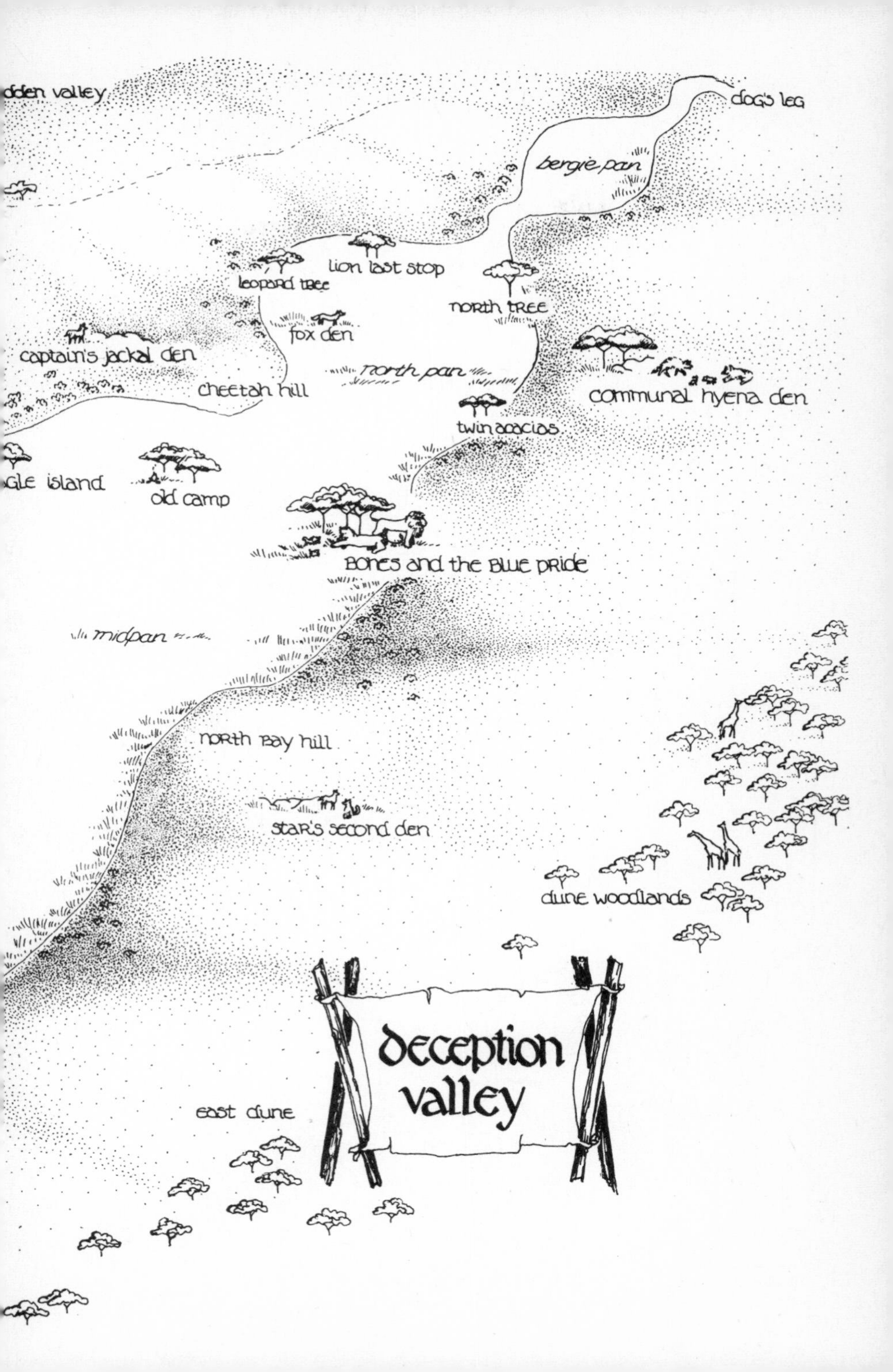
dden valley
dog's leg
bergie pan
lion last stop
leopard tree
north tree
fox den
captain's jackal den
north pan
cheetah hill
communal hyena den
twin acacias
gle island
old camp
bones and the blue pride
midpan
north bay hill
star's second den
dune woodlands
deception valley
east dune

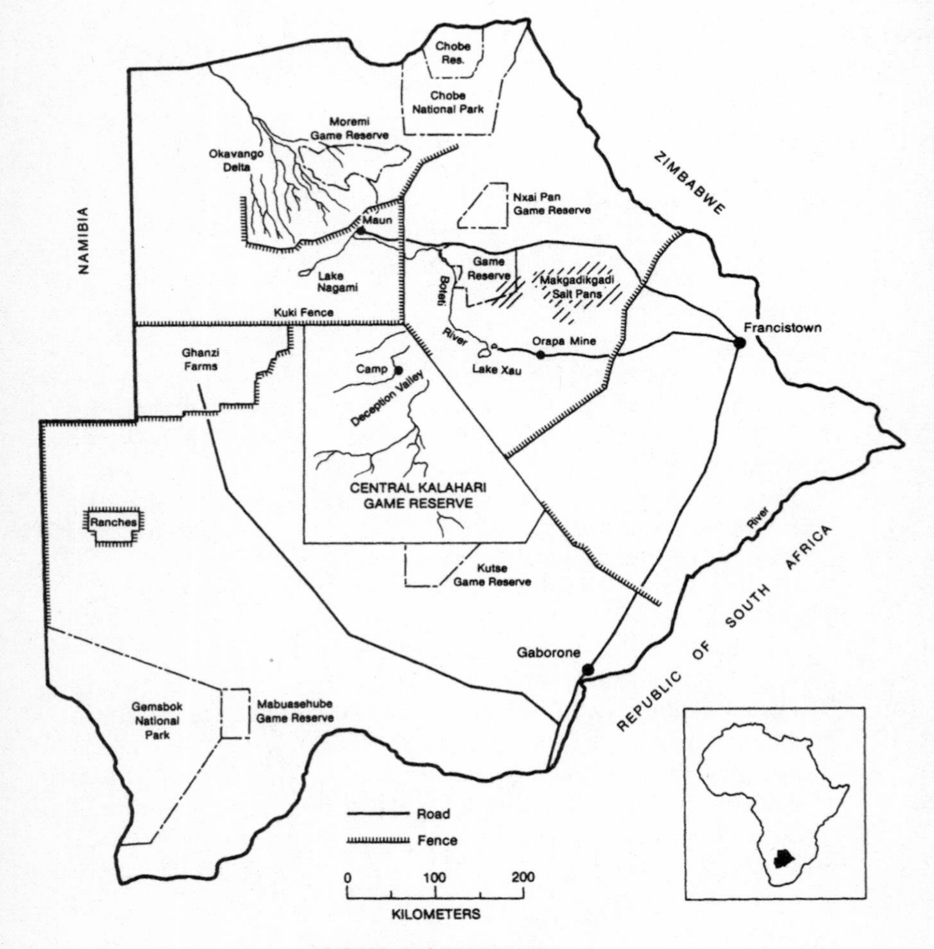

THE REPUBLIC OF BOTSWANA

Prologue

Mark

MY LEFT SHOULDER and hip ached from the hard ground. I rolled to my right side, squirming around on grass clumps and pebbles, but could not get comfortable. Huddled deep inside my sleeping bag against the chill of dawn, I tried to catch a few more minutes of sleep.

We had driven north along the valley the evening before, trying to home on the roars of a lion pride. But by three o'clock in the morning they had stopped calling and presumably had made a kill. Without their voices to guide us, we hadn't been able to find them and had gone to sleep on the ground next to a hedge of bush in a small grassy clearing. Now, like two large army worms, our nylon sleeping bags glistened with dew in the morning sun.

Aaoouu—a soft groan startled me. I slowly lifted my head and peered over my feet. My breath caught. It was a very big lioness—more than 300 pounds—but from ground level she looked even larger. She was moving toward us from about five yards away, her head swinging from side to side and the black tuft on her tail twitching deliberately. I clenched a tuft of grass, held on tight, and froze. The lioness came closer, her broad paws lifting and falling in perfect rhythm, jewels of moisture clinging to her coarse whiskers, her deep-amber eyes looking straight at me. I wanted to wake up Delia, but I was afraid to move.

When she reached the foot of our sleeping bags, the lioness turned slightly. "Delia! S-s-s-h-h-h—wake up! The lions are here!"

Delia's head came up slowly and her eyes grew wide. The long body of the cat, more than nine feet of her from nose to tuft, padded past our feet to a bush ten feet away. Then Delia gripped my arm and quietly pointed to our right. Turning my head just slightly, I saw another lioness four yards away, on the other side of the bush next to us . . . then another . . . and another. The entire Blue Pride, nine in all, surrounded us, nearly all of them asleep. We were quite literally in bed with a pride of wild Kalahari lions.

Like an overgrown house cat, Blue was on her back, her eyes closed, hind legs sticking out from her furry white belly, her forepaws folded over her downy chest. Beyond her lay Bones, the big male with the shaggy black mane and the puckered scar over his knee—the token of a hurried surgery on a dark night months before. Together with Chary, Sassy, Gypsy, and the others, he must have joined us sometime before dawn.

We would have many more close encounters with Kalahari lions, some not quite so amicable. But the Blue Pride's having accepted us so completely that they slept next to us was one of our most rewarding moments since beginning our research in Botswana's vast Central Kalahari Desert, in the heart of southern Africa. It had not come easily.

As young, idealistic students, we had gone to Africa entirely on our own to set up a wildlife research project. After months of searching for a pristine area, we finally found our way into the "Great Thirst," an immense tract of wilderness so remote that we were the only people, other than a few bands of Stone Age Bushmen, in an area larger than Ireland. Because of the heat and the lack of water and materials for shelter, much of the Central Kalahari has remained unexplored and unsettled. From our camp there was no village around the corner or down the road. There was no road. We had to haul our water a hundred miles through the bushveld, and without a cabin, electricity, a radio, a television, a hospital, a grocery store, or any sign of other humans and their artifacts for months at a time, we were totally cut off from the outside world.

Most of the animals we found there had never seen humans before. They had never been shot at, chased by trucks, trapped, or snared. Because of this, we had the rare opportunity to know many of them in a way few people have ever known wild animals. On a rainy-season morning we would often wake up with 3000 antelope grazing around our tent. Lions, leopards, and brown hyenas visited our camp at night, woke us up by tugging the tent guy ropes, occasionally surprised us in the bath boma, and drank our dishwater if we forgot to pour it out. Sometimes they sat in the moonlight with us, and they even smelled our faces.

There were risks—we took them daily—and there were near disasters that we were fortunate to survive. We were confronted by terrorists, stranded without water, battered by storms, and burned by droughts. We fought veld fires miles across that swept through our camp—and we met an old man of the desert who helped us survive.

We had no way of knowing, from our beginnings of a thirdhand Land Rover, a campfire, and a valley called "Deception," that we would learn new and exciting details about the natural history of Kalahari lions and brown hyenas: How they survive droughts with no drinking water and very little to eat, whether they migrate to avoid these hardships, and how members of these respective species cooperate to raise their young. We would document one of the largest antelope migrations on earth and discover that fences are choking the life from the Kalahari.

* * *

I don't really know when we decided to go to Africa. In a way, I guess each of us had always wanted to go. For as long as we can remember we have sought out wild places, drawn strength, peace, and solitude from them and wanted to protect them from destruction. For myself, I can still recall the sadness and bewilderment I felt as a young boy, when from the top of the windmill, I watched a line of bulldozers plough through the woods on our Ohio farm, destroying it for a superhighway—and changing my life.

Delia and I met in a protozoology class at the University of Georgia and it didn't take long to find out that we shared the same goal. By the end of the semester we knew that when we went to Africa, it would have to be together. During this time we heard a visiting scientist tell of Africa's disappearing wilderness: More than two-thirds of its wildlife had already been eliminated, pushed out of its habitats by large ranches and urban sprawl. In the southern regions, thousands of predators were being trapped, shot, snared, and poisoned to protect domestic stock. In some African nations, conservation policies and practices were virtually nonexistent.

These were frightening reports. We became determined to study an African carnivore in a large, pristine wilderness and to use the results of our research to help devise a program for the conservation of that ecosystem. Perhaps, also, we simply wanted to see for ourselves that such wild places still existed. But if we didn't go immediately, there might be little left to study.

Going to Africa as part of our graduate programs would mean years of delay, and since we had not finished our doctorates, we knew there was little chance of our getting a grant from a conservation organization. We decided to take a temporary, if prolonged, leave from university and to earn the money needed to finance the expedition. Once a study site had been chosen and our field research was under way, we thought surely someone would grant us the funds to continue.

After six months of teaching, we had saved nothing. I switched jobs and began operating the crusher at a stone quarry while Delia worked at odd jobs. At the end of another six months we had saved $4900, plus enough money for air fares to Johannesburg in South Africa. It was not nearly enough to begin a research project. But it was late 1973 and the Arabs had just pulled the plug on cheap oil; prices were skyrocketing. We had to go then, or not at all.

Trying desperately to scrape enough money together, we piled everything we owned—stereo, radio, television, fishing rod and reel, pots and pans—into our small station wagon and drove to the stone quarry one morning, just as the men were coming off the night shift. I stood on top of the car and auctioned it all away, including the car, for $1100.

On January 4, 1974, a year after we were married, we boarded a plane with two backpacks, two sleeping bags, one pup tent, a small cooking kit, a camera, one change of clothes each, and $6000. It was all we had to set up our research.

* * *

This book is *not* a detailed account of our scientific findings; that is being published elsewhere. Instead, it is the story of our lives with lions, brown hyenas, jackals, birds, shrews, lizards, and many other creatures we came to know, and how we survived and conducted research in one of the last and largest pristine areas on earth. The story was taken from our journals and is all true, including names and dialogue. Although each chapter is written in one voice, we developed every phase of the book together.

1

The Jumblies

Mark

They went to sea in a Sieve, they did,
In a Sieve they went to sea:
In spite of all their friends could say,
On a winter's morn, on a stormy day,
In a Sieve they went to sea!

. . . .

Far and few, far and few,
Are the lands where the Jumblies live;
Their heads are green, and their hands are blue;
And they went to sea in a Sieve.

—*Edward Lear*

SLEEPLESS, I rested my head against the thick double windowpane of the jet, staring into the blackness of the mid-Atlantic night. The world turned slowly below as the plane reached for the dawn of Africa.

With careful grace the cheetah strolls onto the plain. Head erect, its tail a gentle vane turning easily on the wind, it glides toward the stirring herd. Alert, the antelope prance back and forth, but do not run. The cat is hungry and begins loping forward.

The plane met and passed the dawn. Soon it was standing on asphalt, disgorging its passengers near a hazy city. Customs officials in short pants and spotless white shirts with bold black epaulets called orders and waved clipboards. We filled out long forms and questionnaires, waited in crowded halls, and gazed through chain-link fences. Plenty of time to daydream.

A perfect union of speed, coordination, balance, and form, the cheetah accelerates toward the dashing antelope and singles one out.

Others veer aside and the ageless footrace between predator and prey begins.

A smaller plane, a shorter ride—we had been traveling forever. On a train this time, again we stared numbly past our reflections in a window. Miles and miles of thornbush, all of it the same, rushed by in time with the clickety-clack of the rail sections as the train swayed along. "Clickety-clack, clickety-clack, you can't get off and you'll never go back; clickety-clack . . ."

The cheetah is a blur across the plain. Fifty, sixty, seventy miles per hour, the living missile streaks toward its target. At this moment, as it draws near the flashing rear quarters of its prey, the awesome beauty of their contest is inescapable. Each is a sculptor who, using eons of time as its maul and evolution as its chisel, has created, in the other, something of such form, such vitality, such truth that it can never be duplicated. This relationship is the best Nature has to offer; the ego of the natural world.

It is the moment of truth for the gazelle. The cheetah, still at full speed, reaches forward a clublike paw to destroy the balance of its prey. The antelope cuts sharply, and what was ultimate form is suddenly perverted. At seventy miles per hour the fence wire slices through the cheetah's nose, shatters its jaw, and snaps its head around. Before its momentum is spent on the mesh, its elegant neck is twisted and broken, the shank of a splintered white bone bursts through the skin of its foreleg. The fence recoils and spits the mutilated form, ruptured and bleeding, into the dirt.

With a hissing of air brakes the train lurched to a stop and interrupted the nightmare. We shouldered our backpacks and stepped down onto the sandy station yard in the black African night. From behind, the diesel rumbled and the car couplings clanged as the train pulled away. Standing alone by the ramshackle station house at two o'clock in the morning, it was as though we were in a long, dark tunnel. At one end a grimy sign beneath a dim yellow light read GABORONE BOTSWANA.

The quiet darkness seemed to swallow us. Alone in a strange country with too little money, all of it stuffed in the pocket of my backpack, we suddenly felt that the challenge was overwhelming: We had to find a four-wheel-drive truck and a study area and accomplish enough solid research to attract a grant before our money ran out. But we were exhausted from traveling, and before worrying about anything else, we needed sleep.

Across a dirt road from the train station, another weak light bulb dangled over the tattered screen door of the Gaborone Hotel—a sagging building with flakes of paint peeling from its walls, and tall grass fringing its foundation. The rooms were eight dollars a night, more than we could afford.

As we turned and began to walk away, the old night watchman beckoned to us from the hotel. A flickering candle cupped in his hands, he led us through the bare lobby into a small courtyard choked with weeds and thornscrub. Smiling broadly through teeth like rusted bolts, the old native patted my pack and then the ground. We bowed our thanks and within minutes we had pitched our small pack tent next to a thornbush and settled into our sleeping bags.

Morning came with the chatter of native Africans moving like columns of army ants through fields of tall grass and thornbush toward the town. Most of them wore unzipped and unbuttoned western shirts and dresses or pants of mix-matched, bright colors. Women swayed along with bundles balanced on their heads—a pint milk carton, a basket of fruit, or fifty pounds of firewood. One man had slabs of tire tread bound to his feet for sandals, a kaross of goatskin slung over his shoulders, and the spotted skin of a gennet cat, the tail hanging down, set at a rakish angle on his head. These people eked out their livelihoods by hawking carvings, walking sticks, and other artifacts to travelers through the windows of railroad coaches. They lived in shanties and lean-tos of corrugated tin or cardboard, old planks or mud bricks. One was made entirely of empty beer cans.

Looking over the scene, Delia muttered softly, "Where the devil are we?"

We made our way toward the haze of wood smoke that covered the town of Gaborone, which sprawled at the foot of some rocky hills. It is the capital of Botswana, known before its independence in 1967 as the British Bechuanaland Protectorate. Architecturally, it is a crossbred town: One avenue of small shops and a few three-story office buildings of Western design rise from a mishmash of mud-and-thatch huts called *rondavels*. Dusty paths were crowded with Africans in European clothes and Europeans in African prints.

It is an interesting blend of cultures, but nothing happens very fast in Gaborone, and for two months after our arrival in Botswana we were stuck there. Day after day we walked from one isolated government department to another, trying to arrange residence and research permits and meeting with people who might know something about a suitable study site. We were determined to find a place—one far from fences—where the behavior of the predators had not been affected by human settlements.

From all accounts, the best places for the type of study we had in mind were in the remote regions of northern Botswana, but none of the Wildlife Department personnel had ever been to the most inaccessible of those areas. Without anyone to guide us, the expedition seemed more difficult and risky than we had supposed. Even if we could find our own way into such an undeveloped part of Botswana, setting up and supplying a research camp would mean moving food, fuel, and other supplies over vast tracks of uncharted wilderness. Besides, practically the entire northern third of the country was under water from the heaviest rains in its recorded history. The only road to the north had been impassable for months.

One of our most immediate problems was how to find a vehicle among the population of battered four-wheel-drive trucks that rattled around the town. The best we could afford was an old thirdhand Land Rover with a concave roof, bush-scraped sides, and drab grey paint. We bought the "Old Grey Goose" for 1000 rands ($1500), overhauled the engine, installed a reserve gas tank, and built flat storage boxes in the back. Covered with a square of foam rubber, the boxes would also serve as our bed.

When we had finally finished outfitting the Grey Goose, it was already early March 1974; we hadn't been in the field yet, and we had only $3800 left, $1500 of which would be needed to get us home if we failed to get a grant. Every delay meant lost research time. If we were to have any chance of convincing some organization to fund us before our money ran out, we had to find a study site immediately and get to work. So, despite warnings that we would not get through to the north country, early one morning we headed out of Gaborone into the rolling thornbush savanna.

A few miles outside town, with a bone-jarring crash, we left the only pavement in Botswana behind us. As I swerved to dodge the ruts and chuckholes, the narrow dirt road led us deeper and deeper into the bushveld. I took a deep, satisfying breath of wild Africa; our project was finally under way. The sense of freedom and the exhilaration were almost intoxicating, and I reached across to pull Delia over next to me. She smiled up at me—a smile that washed away the tensions that had built over the long, frustrating weeks of preparation. Her eyes spoke her total confidence that we could handle any challenge that confronted us, and her confidence was itself a challenge.

Our destination, the village of Maun, lay where the waters of the Okavango River delta reach the sands of the Kalahari Desert, more than 450 miles to the north. There was only one narrow gravel road to follow through a territory that offered little shelter, except an occasional cluster of native huts. Because of the flooding, no one had driven the road for weeks. As we crawled north at ten to fifteen miles per hour, the savanna grew wetter and wetter until we were churning through deep black mud.

Near Francistown, the last large village on the east side of Botswana, we swung northwest toward Maun, still more than 300 miles away. Whole stretches of the road had completely washed away. In places I waded ahead through shallow lakes more than a mile across, searching under the water for firm ground with my bare feet as Delia followed in the Land Rover. Dodging ruts three or four feet deep, we passed the mud-caked hulks of trucks bellied-up in muck like dinosaurs in a tar pit. They had been abandoned for weeks. Time after time the Grey Goose sank to its undercarriage. Using a high-lift jack to raise it, we piled thornbush, stones, and logs under the wheels. Another few yards and we were down to the axles again.

At night, slapping at swarms of mosquitoes, we would squat next to a mudpuddle and wash the crust off our faces, arms, and legs. Then we would fall asleep on top of the boxes in the back of the Land Rover. We kept the truck parked in the middle of the roadbed because if I had driven off its crown, we would have become hopelessly mired. We had met only two or three other vehicles in several days, so it was unlikely that someone would need to pass by in the night.

In the morning we would be on our way once more. Dazed with fatigue, we would spin forward, sink, dig out, and spin forward again. Some days we made no more than a mile or two. But we had to keep going. Though we didn't talk about it, we both had the desperate feeling that if we couldn't even make it to Maun, we would surely fail in the field. Yet failure was an option we simply could not afford. We had invested all our savings—our dreams and our pride—in this venture. There was no reason to turn around; there was nothing to go back to.

Occasionally we saw goats, cattle, and donkeys drinking and wallowing in mudholes along the way. They were the only signs of animal life in the flat monotony of overgrazed thornscrub. It was depressing and disconcerting that we had come all this way to find in these remote areas no herds of wild antelope. Perhaps after all, we had chosen a country in which little wildlife was left. Even then we knew that much of Africa had been grazed to death by domestic stock.

Eleven days after we had set off from Gaborone, hollow-eyed and covered in mud, we stopped on the one-lane bridge over the Thamalakane River. On its banks was Maun, a village of reed-and-straw huts, donkeys, and sand. Herero tribeswomen had spread their lavish skirts, made of yards of different materials, on the emerald riverbanks to dry, like great butterflies fanned out in a riot of reds, yellows, blues, greens, and purples.

Delia's eyes were red and her face and hair spattered with grey mud. Her hands were deeply scratched from piling rocks and thornbush under the mired truck. But she grinned and gave a rebel yell. We had made it!

On sand tracks that ran between *rondavels* we drove to Riley's, a large compound including garage, general store, hotel, and bar, where we bought gasoline and a few supplies: lard, flour, mealie-meal, and sugar. Perishables such as milk, bread, and cheese were not available in northern Botswana, and when we arrived even staples were in short supply because no transport trucks had been able to get through in weeks. The people of the village were hungry. We avoided the eyes of the begging children, embarrassed that we had nothing we could give them, yet knowing we were wealthy by comparison.

Officials in the Department of Wildlife in Gaborone had advised us to ask professional hunters about a good place to start our research. One of the names we had scribbled in our journal was "Lionel Palmer—Maun." Lionel was well known at Riley's, where we asked for directions to his home. We made our way along deep sand tracks and through more mudholes until, about four miles north of the village, we found the Palmer homestead. Over the river hung tall fig trees with orange, red, and yellow bougainvillea spilling over their tops. Red-eyed bulbuls, grey hornbills, hoopoes, and a myriad other birds flitted about the canopy above the garden.

Lionel Palmer, deeply tanned, his dark hair brushed with grey, was dressed in baggy jeans, a cowboy shirt, and a bandana. He sauntered out to greet us, holding a glass of whisky in his hand. The oldest and most experienced professional hunter in the area, Lionel held considerable social positon in Maun. He was famous for his parties, where bedroom furniture sometimes ended up on the roof, and once a Land Rover had been hung in a fig tree—and for his capacity for Scotch. Once, after several days of intoxication, he woke up with a stabbing earache. The doctor at the clinic removed a two-inch-long sausage fly—a reddish-brown, tubelike, winged insect—which had taken up residence in Lionel's numbed ear while he slept off his drunkenness in a flowerbed. For a week Lionel carried the fly's carcass bedded down in a cotton-lined matchbox, proudly showing it to everyone he met, whether or not he knew them.

Sitting with us on the patio overlooking the river, Lionel suggested a few areas in northern Botswana where flooding was not too severe and where predators unaffected by man could be found. One, the Makgadikgadi Pans, is a great tract of remote bushveld wilderness more than 100 miles east and south of Maun. The pans are the remnants of an enormous inland lake that dried up some 16,000 years ago.

"Go ninety-nine miles east of Maun on the Nata road and find a palm tree broken off at the top. Look for an old spoor that runs south from the main track. There's no sign, but that's where the reserve begins. Nobody goes out there much—there's bugger-all there, except miles and miles of bloody Africa."

Most game reserves in Botswana are large tracts of totally undeveloped wilderness. There are no paved roads, fast-food stands, water fountains, campgrounds, restrooms, or any of the other "improvements" found in parks and reserves in more developed countries.

Two days later we found two faint tire tracks at a broken palm, turned off the main road, and left all traces of civilization behind us. Immediately we had a sense of being in Africa, the real Africa, the one we had always dreamed about. The vast untracked savanna, broken only by occasional isolated trees, made us feel frail, minuscule, vulnerable. It was beautiful, exciting—but also a little intimidating.

About thirty miles south of the main road, the track we had been following led us to the edge of a vast plain. Then it disappeared. Delia noted our compass heading, the mileage, and a lone thorntree we thought we might be able to recognize again. With no chart or guide, and with only fifteen gallons of water and the barest minimum of essential food, we set off across the Makgadikgadi.

The savanna was very rough, the grass tall and heavy with ripe seed, and it was hot. We made no more than three miles per hour for the rest of the day. Gradually the front of the Grey Goose was buried under a thick moving carpet of grass seed and insects that completely obscured the headlights and hood. Every quarter of a mile or so we had to brush off the front of the engine and cool the boiling radiator by pouring water over the top.

Around midmorning of the second day we came to an immense network of saucer-shaped salt pans interlaced with crescents of grass savanna, touches of woodland, and wisps of palm islands. Some pans were filled with brackish, unpotable water and flowery masses of orange, purple, green, and red algae; others were covered with a thin salt crust. We were at the edge of an alien world—no roads, no trails, no people. A shimmering mirage drew the tops of the palms into the sky.

"Whatever you do, don't drive across those pans or you'll go down like a bloody rock," Lionel had warned us. "The salt crust'll look firm, but it won't be, 'specially with all the rain we've had lately. Underneath there's nothing but mud for God knows how deep. Game Department lost a whole truck in one of them last year. No matter how much time you think you'll save by crossing, go around."

While I was skirting these enormous irregular depressions, Delia sketched a map of our route, noting compass headings and odometer readings at regular intervals, so that we would be able to find our way back to "Lone Tree."

Itching from grass seed and insects, I drove toward a large pan that looked as if it might contain enough fresh rainwater for bathing. We were coming over the rise above it—suddenly the truck dropped from under us. The chassis cracked like a rifleshot and we were thrown from our seats hard against the windshield. The engine stalled and a haze of dust rose in front of us. When it had cleared, the hood of the Land Rover stood at ground level, buried in a large antbear hole that had been hidden in tall grass. After checking to see that Delia was all right, I jacked the truck up and began shoveling a ton of sand under the wheels. When we were finally able to back out, I crawled under the Goose to check for damage. There were several new cracks in the chassis, one near a motor mount. Another bad hole could tear the engine loose. Still, we were lucky; if only one of the front wheels had gone in, it could have broken off.

I was sharply aware that if we lost the service of the Grey Goose in some way, our chances of ever leaving the Makgadikgadi alive were not good. I didn't trust my limited knowledge of mechanics, and we hadn't been able to afford all the backup spare parts we should have been carrying for an expedition like this. Furthermore, no one knew where we were or when to expect us back. Lionel knew only that we had left Maun headed for one of several areas he had mentioned.

We didn't discuss these risks, but they lingered in the backs of our minds. We washed in the brackish water of the pan, and after we had dried in the wind, our faces felt stretched tight, like overblown balloons.

For the rest of the day I walked ahead of the Land Rover, checking for holes in the long grass while Delia drove. Several times I stepped into rodent burrows, hoping that they weren't also the home of some poisonous snake. We carried no anti-venin, since it would have to be refrigerated.

That second night we camped next to a small tree not more than six feet high, the only one for miles around. We had been irresistibly drawn to it and had actually driven quite a way off course to get to it. Though we slept inside the truck, the tree gave us a vague sense of security. Our early primate ancestors would probably have been similarly pleased to find even this mere seedling on a nearly treeless plain, after they left the safety of the forests to venture onto the vast savannas millions of years ago.

We climbed a low rise late in the afternoon of the fourth day, and I was walking ahead. Suddenly I stopped. "My God! *Look* at that!" The sounds and smells of animals, tens of thousands of animals, carried to us on the light wind. For as far as we could see, the plains beyond were covered with zebra and wildebeest, grazing placidly near a large water hole. Fighting zebra stallions bit and kicked each other, puffs of dust rising from their hooves. Wildebeest tossed their heads and pranced and blew their alarm sounds. The great herds stirred, and my skin tingled at the spectacular display of life. If we never saw another sight like this, the months of working in a stone quarry and the hawking of all our belongings would have been worth this one glimpse of what much of Africa must once have been like.

We watched for hours, passing the binoculars back and forth between us, taking notes on everything we saw—how the herds mingled and moved, how many drank, how many fought—as though this signified in some way that our research had begun. We pitched camp near the top of the ridge, so we could watch for cheetahs or lions preying on the herds. When it was too dark to see, we sat heating a can of sausages over the kerosene lantern inside the Grey Goose and discussed establishing our research in the Makgadikgadi.

We went on watching the herds all the next day and into the evening. Then reality returned: Our water was getting low. Frustrated, anxious to get some solid field work done, and hating to leave the zebra and wildebeest, we began the long drive back across the plains. Following the reciprocal of compass headings and using the schematic diagram Delia had made of our course eastward, we would return to Lone Tree, get our bearings, then drive on to the Boteti River, thirteen miles farther west, for water.

For two days we retraced our course, but somewhere we went wrong. A great salt pan, unfamiliar to us, a dazzling white depression more than a mile across and miles long from north to south, blocked our way. Standing on the roof of the Land Rover and scanning with binoculars, we couldn't see any way around it.

After driving north, and then south for some distance along the bank, I decided to see how firm the surface was. I was more and more concerned about our dwindling gasoline and water supply. Perhaps with caution, we could drive across the pan instead of laboring over miles of rough terrain to skirt it. I dug a test hole with the spade. The clay beneath the salt crust seemed surprisingly dry and solid, and no matter how hard I jumped on it with my heels, I could barely make an impression. Next, I slowly drove the front wheels of the Grey Goose onto the pan; the crust held firm. Finally, I brought the full weight of the truck onto the surface, which was as hard as concrete pavement. So in spite of Lionel's warning, we decided to make the crossing.

Starting the run, I accelerated quickly. By driving fast in four-wheel drive, I hoped to skim over any soft spots we might encounter farther out.

I bent over the steering wheel, scanning the white salt crust ahead for dark patches, a sign that the pan had not dried out completely. But there was none. It was like driving over a billiard table, and I began to relax. Then, about 800 yards from the edge, we saw some timbers and poles sticking at odd angles from a depression in the grey, cracked surface. We got out to investigate. What could have made such a hole? And where had the timbers come from? There were no tracks or any other clues. Puzzled, I looked into the deep, ragged pit, to the place where the ends of the posts converged and then disappeared into an abyss of mud. My throat suddenly tightened—someone had tried, unsuccessfully, to save his truck. I glanced quickly at ours.

"My God! The truck's sinking! Get in—hurry—we've got to get out of here!"

Its wheels were slowly settling through the salt crust into a pocket in the softer clay beneath. The surface was giving way; in seconds our truck would break through.

I tried to drive forward, but the engine stalled. The wheels had sunk too deep. Working frantically, I restarted the motor and jammed the gearshift into low-range four-wheel drive. Spinning and throwing clay, the Land Rover churned forward until it heaved itself up onto the firm surface again. I quickly shifted to high range for better speed, spun around, and raced to the safety of the grass bank at the edge of the pan. We sat staring at each other and shaking our heads in dumb relief. I was furious with myself for having tried to make the crossing, but I had endangered us even more by stopping the truck in the middle of the pan. After consulting our sketch map, we headed north. It took an entire afternoon to drive around the rest of the pan.

On the morning of the fourth day of the return trip, we finally reached the west edge of the Makgadikgadi plain, and slipped beneath the cool, refreshing canopy of riverine forest. Spider webs were drawn like fishing nets from tree to tree, and their hairy black-and-yellow architects scrambled over the hood of the truck as we ploughed through heavy sand toward the river. Kudu watched from deep shadows.

At last we stood on the high banks of the Boteti River. Deep-blue water gently caressed its way around the lilies, hyacinths, and other water plants nodding in the sleepy current. At the top of a tall fig tree, a pair of fish eagles threw back their heads and called to the sky. We ran down the steep bank and plunged into the cool water.

Climbing the riverbank after our swim, we saw something red lying in the grass. It was a fifty-gallon drum—a great find! We had looked for one in Maun, but they were almost impossible to get in northern Botswana; everyone needed them. By lashing this one to the top of the Land Rover and filling it with water, we could greatly increase our range and endurance while searching remote areas for a study site. The drum looked sound enough. We never stopped to wonder why it had been abandoned.

In the late afternoon, heavy splashes began sounding from the river below. After living for weeks on mealie-meal, raw oatmeal, powdered milk, and an occasional tin of greasy sausages—so pale and limp we called them dead man's fingers—we both craved a thick, juicy piece of meat. Fresh fish would be scrumptious! I found a tangle of old fishing line the previous owner had left in the Land Rover, made a hook with a pair of pliers, and fashioned a spinning lure from the shiny top of a powdered-milk tin.

Delia had watched skeptically while I made my fishing rig, and now she began baking mealie bread in the three-legged iron pot. Heading down the riverbank, I snatched a corn cricket from the grass, put it on the hook, and threw it into the water. It was almost dusk, and the surface of the river was jumping with big fish. In a few seconds, shouting and laughing, I hauled in a beautiful bream, and then a big catfish.

Delia rolled the fillets in mealie-meal and flour before frying them, and soon we were sitting by the fire stuffing ourselves with big chunks of steaming mealie bread and tender white pieces of fish. Afterward, we sat high above the quiet waters of the river, talking over our Makgadikgadi adventure. Africa was seasoning us.

The next day we caught and ate more fish. Then we stocked up with river water, hauling jerricans up and down the steep bank. After filling the red drum, we set it on its side, and lashed it to the roof of the Land Rover. By noon we were on our way back into the Makgadikgadi to look for predators.

Four days later, back on "Zebra Hill," the thousands of antelope we had seen a week before were gone. We drove around for hours without finding a single one. And without prey, no lions, cheetahs, or other carnivores were likely to be around. It was depressing. We had seriously thought of settling in the Makgadikgadi to do our research, but considering the tremendous mobility—with no apparent focal point—of these great herds, and presumably of the predators, how would we locate and stay in contact with our study animals? We drove back to Maun for more supplies and more advice.

Over the next several weeks we made reconnaissance trips to Nxai Pan, the Savuti Marsh, and other areas on the fringes of the Okavango River delta. The marsh, pans, and forests all had alluring varieties of antelope and predators, but by and large these places were still flooded. The water would limit our operations severely. Often, as we crossed the *malopos*—reed-choked, swampy waterways—from one palm island to the next, water ran in over the floor of the truck, shorting out the motor. We spent hours digging the Land Rover out of black muck.

Discouraged, we turned back to Maun. With each unsuccessful reconnaissance and return for supplies, our operating funds were shrinking. Again it was the hunter Lionel Palmer who finally suggested, "Why don't you try the Kalahari? I've seen a place called Deception Valley from the air . . . has lots of game. 'Course, I've never hunted there myself; it's miles inside the game reserve."

On the one-to-a-million-scale map of Botswana, we could quickly see that the Central Kalahari Game Reserve was one of the largest wildlife protectorates in the world, more than 32,000 square miles of raw, untracked wilderness. And the wilderness didn't stop at the reserve boundaries; it extended for 100 miles farther in nearly every direction, interrupted only by an occasional cattle post or small village. According to Lionel, there was not one road, not a single building, no water, and no people, except for a few bands of Bushmen, in an area larger than Ireland. It was so remote that most of it had never been explored and the Botswana government had not opened it for visitors. Consequently, no wildlife research had ever been done there. It was just what we had been looking for—if we could get there and solve the problems of surviving in such a remote and difficult environment.

After puzzling over the featureless map for some time, we finally devised a route into the Kalahari and, having done so, decided that we would go there without telling the Department of Wildlife. They probably would have refused us permission to work in such an isolated area, and they would learn about us soon enough, anyway.

The Grey Goose loaded with gasoline and other supplies, our red water drum lashed to the top, we set out for the Kalahari in search of Deception Valley. It was by then late April of 1974. Nine miles east of the village, we found a spoor running south to the Samadupe Drift on the Boteti River. There the water shallowed up, and a corduroy ford of logs was laid across the bottom. Tumbling over the logs and stones, the river fell away to easy swells and swirls between reed banks and a great avenue of giant fig trees. Cormorants dove, and trotters padded from one lily pad to another. Spurwing geese and egrets passed low above the water, their wings singing in the air.

We stopped on the ford for a last swim, and I cut off Delia's shoulder-length hair; it would take too much water to keep it clean in the desert. Her long locks fell to the water, eddied, and drifted away on the current.

For a moment I could see the reflection of her laughing face in the water—the way she looked the first time I saw her. I paused and held my hand to her cheek and then began snipping again.

After we had crossed the river and climbed a steep ridge of heavy sand, the track narrowed to two wheel marks bordered by thick acacia thornbush. For the rest of the day we slogged through heat, dust, and deep sand, on either side of us the dense scrub raking the sides of the Land Rover with a screeching that set our teeth on edge. In the late afternoon the spoor dead-ended. We found ourselves in a small dusty clearing where tumbleweeds blew past a crumbling mud hut and a tin watering trough for cattle. We sat wondering where we had gone wrong.

A gnarled, knobby old man—all elbows, knees, and knuckles—with a gnarled, knobby walking stick, appeared from the bushes. His wife and four spindly boys, dressed in little more than leather sashes, led a line of bony cattle through the blowing dust toward the watering trough.

I waved. "Hello!"

"Hello!" one of the boys shouted back. They all laughed.

"Ah, they can speak English," I thought.

"Could you help us? We're lost." I got out of the truck and began unfolding our map.

"Hello," said the boy again. They all crowded around. "Hello-hello-hello—"

I put away the map and took another tack.

"Ma-kal-a-ma-bedi?" I asked, holding my palms out and up, hoping they could understand the name of the fence line that would point us into the Kalahari. The skinniest and most garrulous boy scrambled onto the hood of the Land Rover and pointed back up the spoor; the three others joined him. We drove up the track, all of us laughing. The boys bounced on the hood, their twitching fingers showing us the way.

A few minutes later they all began pounding on the truck simultaneously. I stopped. They jumped off and pointed east through the bush. At first we did not understand. Then, standing next to them, we could see a faint line leading away through the savanna, an old survey cut-line running east. It was our only option. We were determined not to go back to Maun without having found Deception Valley.

We thanked the boys, gave them a paper bag of sugar, and set off.

"Hello-hello-hello!" They shouted and waved as we disappeared into the bush.

Early the next morning we came to the fence—weathered posts and five strands of wire running straight across our path as far north and south as we could see. We turned south, and hours later the barrier was still beside us, a great scar across the savanna. It was irritating to us then, but someday it would give us cause to hate the very sight of it.

We slept along the fence that night. The next morning, with the truck churning on through the sand, our backs became sweaty against the seat, and we were covered with a layer of dust and grass seed. Suddenly, the fence ended: There was nothing left but sand, thornscrub, grass, and heat. Two wheel tracks continued on through the grass, becoming fainter... and fainter... until, like a distant memory, they disappeared. Now we were driving over mostly flat grass savanna and occasional low sand ridges covered with lush green bushes and stands of trees. Was this the Kalahari Desert? Where were the great shifting sand dunes?

There was no way to be certain of our position. We consulted the map and calculated the number of miles we must have come south from Maun. Then we turned west. We would drive twenty more miles. If we hadn't found Deception Valley by then, we would have to find our way back to Maun.

Eighteen... nineteen... nineteen point six... and just as we were about to give up all hope, we crested the top of a large dune. Below us lay the gentle slopes and open plain of Deception Valley, an ancient fossilized river channel meandering through forested sand dunes. Herds of springbok, gemsbok, and hartebeest grazed peacefully on the old grass-covered riverbed, where water used to flow. The blue sky was stacked high with white puffs of cloud. Deception was incredibly serene and all we had hoped it would be. It was May 2, 1974, almost five months since we had left the United States, and we had found our place in Africa. Home, as it would turn out, for the next seven years.

The gentle dune face led us into the valley. We crossed the dry riverbed, and the springbok hardly bothered to lift their heads from the grass as we passed. On the western edge, we found a solitary island of acacia trees that would provide shelter and give a panoramic view. It would be a good campsite.

On the move for months, lugging our shelter with us wherever we went, we had begun to feel like a turtle with a steel shell. Already it felt good to be putting down roots.

It didn't take long to set up our first base camp: We tied our cloth sacks of mealie-meal and flour in an acacia tree to keep them safe from rodents, stacked our few tinned foods at the base of the tree, and arranged the pots and pans along a limb. Then we gathered firewood. With no shelter other than our tiny pack tent, we would sleep in the Grey Goose for the rest of the year.

Delia made a fire and brewed some tea while I unloaded our old red drum and rolled it beneath the acacia tree. It held the only water for thousands of square miles.

2

Water

Mark

> ... if one advances confidently in the direction of his dreams, and endeavors to live the life which he has imagined, he will meet with a success unexpected in common hours ... If you have built castles in the air, your work need not be lost; that is where they should be. Now put the foundations under them.
>
> —*Henry David Thoreau*

Squeezed by pressure from above, hour by hour, molecules of water sweated through the flakes of rust. Outside they coalesced: A drop grew. Swollen and heavy, the droplet ran along the battered rim. Finally losing its grip, it splattered quietly into a furrow of thirsty sand and disappeared. Above, on the rim, another drop had already taken its place.

Days passed. The drops continued their march from the rust, to the rim, to the sand. The drum's wound opened still farther ... the drops came more quickly, spat-spat-spatting into the dark stain hidden from the sun.

A near total silence crept in on me when I opened my eyes and gazed at the Land Rover ceiling. A moment's confusion; where was I? I turned to the window. A gnarled acacia tree loomed outside, its limbs held up in silhouette against the greying sky. Beyond the tree, in soft, easy lines, the wooded sand dunes descended to the riverbed. Morning, our first in Deception Valley, grew in the sky far beyond the dunes.

Delia stirred. We listened to Africa waking around us: A dove cooed from the acacia, a jackal* wailed with a quavering voice, and from far away to the north the bellow of a lion rolled in, heavy and insistent. A lone kestrel hovered, its wings fluttering against a sky turning fiery orange.

Grunts and snorts sounded from outside—very close. Quietly, slowly, Delia and I sat up and peered through the window. Just outside camp was a herd of at least 3000 springbok, small gazelles with horns a foot long turned inward over their heads. Their faces were boldly painted with white and black bars running from their eyes along their muzzles. They looked theatrical, like marionettes, as they grazed the dew-sodden grasses, some of them only fifteen yards from us. A few young females stared at us with deep, liquid eyes while quietly munching stems of grass. But most of the herd grazed, their stomachs rumbling and tails flicking, without looking our way. Easing ourselves up against the back of the front seat, we sat in our bed and watched two yearling bucks lock horns in a sparring match.

Though they hardly appeared to be moving, within twenty minutes the antelope had drifted more than 100 yards away. I started to speak, to try to express what I was feeling, when Delia pointed to the east. A black-backed jackal, first cousin to the American coyote, but smaller and with a sly, foxy face and a saddle of black hair over his back, trotted into our tree island and began sniffing around last night's campfire. Considered vermin and shot on sight in most of Africa, jackals usually run at the first sign of man. This one walked up to a tin coffee mug left near the coals, clamped the rim in his teeth, and inverted the cup over his nose. Looking right and left before ambling calmly out of camp, he surveyed our few belongings, and then shot us a glance, as if to say, "I'll be back for more later."

It's difficult to describe the excitement and joy we felt. We had found our Eden. Yet we were very anxious not to disturb the intricate patterns of life that were going on around us. Here was a place where creatures did not know of man's crimes against nature. Perhaps, if we were sensitive enough to the freedom of these animals, we could slip unnoticed into this ancient river valley and carefully study its treasures without damaging it. We were determined to protect one of the last untouched corners of earth from ourselves.

*Appendix D is a list of the Latin names for the mammals, birds, and snakes mentioned in the text.

Hoofbeats, thousands of them—the air shuddered. The springbok herd was charging south along the riverbed. I grabbed the field glasses, and we kicked out of our sleeping bags and jumped from the Land Rover into the tall, wet grass. Eight wild dogs bounded down the valley after the antelope. When they were abreast of camp, two of the predators veered straight toward us.

Delia quickly reopened the back door of the truck, but by then the dogs, their gold-and-black patchwork coats wet with dew, stood no more than five yards away. Their bold, dark eyes looked us up and down. We stayed still; several seconds passed while they leaned toward us, their noses twitching, their ragged tails raised. Then, with dark muzzles held high, they began to come closer, putting one paw carefully in front of the other. Delia edged toward the door. I squeezed her hand—it was not a time to move. The dogs stood hardly more than an arm's length away, staring as though they had never seen anything quite like us before.

A growl rose deep from the chest of the one with a swatch of golden fur dangling from his neck; his body trembled and his black nostrils flared. Both of them spun around and, rearing up, placed their forepaws on each other's shoulders, as if dancing a jig. Then they loped away, following the rest of the pack.

We pulled on our clothes, started the truck, and followed. Working as a team, the pack split the herd into three smaller groups and began to run each group, alternately, around the riverbed. The lead dog spotted a yearling that apparently seemed vulnerable. After being chased nearly a mile, wild-eyed and breathing heavily, the springbok began to zigzag sharply. The dog seized his prey high on its hind leg and dragged down the ninety-pound buck. Eight minutes later it had been consumed, and the dogs trotted to the shade of a tree island, where they would rest for the day. It was not our last encounter with "Bandit" and his pack.

Back in camp, we rolled up our sleeping bags, dug some powdered milk and raw oatmeal from the food box beneath, and washed it down with swigs from the canteen. After breakfast we set out to explore the dry riverbed as a study site.

The springbok had quieted down after the hunt and were again grazing in a line stretched across our path. Moving slowly and stopping when any of the animals began to show alarm, I eased the truck gingerly through the herd. We would have driven around them, but they were everywhere, so we took great care not to drive more than about three miles per hour or to make any sudden movements or noises that might frighten them. They did not yet have a negative impression of man or his vehicles, and we took every precaution to avoid giving them one.

Deception Valley is the remains of an ancient river that last flowed through the Kalahari about 16,000 years ago, at a time when rainfall was much more generous than it is today. But the land and its weather have always been fickle, and as it had done at least three times before, the climate turned arid, leaving the body of the river mummified in sand. The ancient riverbed remains in remarkable detail, a narrow ribbon of grassland wandering through dunes. It is so well preserved that when we drove along it we could easily imagine water flowing where grasses now wave in the wind.

Because it often receives somewhat more than ten inches of rainfall, the Central Kalahari is not a true desert. It has none of the naked, shifting sand dunes that typify the Sahara and other great deserts of the world. In some years the rains may exceed twenty—once even forty—inches, awakening a magic green paradise.

On the other hand, as we would learn later, all moisture received is soon either lost by evaporation, absorbed by the sands, or transpired by the vegetation. More dramatically, sometimes it may hardly rain at all for several years. So there is seldom a surplus of moisture: no secret springs, no lakes of standing water, no streams. The Kalahari is unique in this respect, a land of great contrasts, a semidesert with no oasis. It has no seasons as we know them. Instead, there are three distinct phases: the rains, which may begin anytime from November to January and last through March, April, or May; a cold-dry spell from June through August; and the hot-dry season, from September through December, or until the rains come again. We had arrived in Deception Valley after the rains and before the cold-dry season.

The sandy slopes, covered with grasses and thornbushes, rose from the old riverbanks to the dune crests, more than a mile away on both sides. The dune tops were capped with woodlands of *Combretum*, *Terminalia*, and *Acacia*, which, together with the mixed bush and grass communities, reached deep into the sand and prevented it from shifting.

Different zones of vegetation lay like tiers of a cake between the riverbed grasslands and the dune crest woodlands, and each community had something special to offer the various birds and animals there: Various species of plains antelope, mostly springbok and gemsbok, grazed short, nutritious grasses on the riverbed. Steenbok, duiker, hartebeest, and eland fed on taller, more fibrous grasses and leaves along the duneslope. Farther upslope, near the dune top, giraffe and greater kudu browsed on the leaves and fruits of the woodlands. Surely the concentration of antelope in our small area would attract predators such as lions, leopards, cheetahs, jackals, and spotted hyenas.

On our first drive, we began to name some of the landmarks that would help us pinpoint important observations and determine the ranges of the animals we would be studying. Clumps of acacia and ziziphus trees looked like small, round islands in the river of grass, and soon we knew them by such names as Eagle Island, Tree Island, Bush Island, and Lion Island. A bush-covered sand tongue protruding into the riverbed became Acacia Point; a bush where a family of bat-eared foxes slept became Bat Bush. Eventually each promiment feature had a name, for orientation and for easy reference.

Deception Valley seemed the perfect place to launch our predator research. Unlike the Makgadikgadi, the fossil river habitat provided a specific focus for the antelope prey populations, enabling us to locate our predator subjects consistently for observation.

The difficulties and dangers of operating in such an isolated area were obvious. Unlike research projects in most other parts of Africa, there was no nearby place to get water and food, and there were no dwellings, no contact with other humans, and no one to rescue us in an emergency. In fact, if we died, it was unlikely that anyone would realize it for months. Although we did not consider this remoteness a disadvantage, we would have to deal with some serious logistical problems: We faced an expensive 140-mile round trip to the Boteti River when the water in our drum ran out. Despite our efforts to ration ourselves to a gallon each a day since leaving Maun, we had finished half of the water in the Land Rover's inboard tank and much of that in our jerricans. I was glad we had another full drum. Especially after our Makgadikgadi experiences, we were very aware that the two absolute essentials for survival in the Kalahari were water and the truck.

In spite of these difficulties, we were certain that our predator research, along with an ecological analysis of soils, plant communities, and seasonal rainfall and humidity patterns, would reveal the dynamic workings of the entire fossil river system. Such a broad approach was necessary because no one had ever done research in this area and there was no background information available. We felt privileged to be breaking this new ground, but it would involve a lot of hard work apart from watching predators.

Considering our critical shortage of operating money, our primary subject would have to be a species that was fairly easy to observe, so we wouldn't have to go chasing all over the countryside, burning up precious gasoline to find it. It should also be an animal about which little was known, which would help to make our research more attractive to potential sponsors.

For days, in the mornings and afternoons, we sat on top of the Land Rover watching the antelope herds at various points on the riverbed, waiting for signs of a predator. Though we saw lions, jackals, cheetahs, and wild dogs, for one reason or another none of these would do. Since they all had been studied in other parts of Africa, we worried that we would be unable to attract a grant by researching them. Both wild dogs and cheetahs were rare and highly mobile in the Kalahari; they would be difficult to find and observe regularly. Furthermore, the cheetahs we saw were very wary—apparently with good reason. We heard later that Bushmen often chase them off their kills and appropriate the carcasses for themselves.

To help us decide which predator we should study, we took notes on any that we could find. In the process, we came to realize something that set the direction of our research for years to come: Night belongs to the carnivores of the Kalahari.

* * *

Purple-black and darker than the night, the supple dunes slept beside the ancient river. The sky sparkled with points of starlight and meteors streaked through the atmosphere. Below, the grasses, dry and tan before the dry season, reflected the celestial light, as if the river moved again.

I switched off the motor and the spotlight stabbed into the darkness. Eyes, thousands of them, shone like globes of phosphor. Behind the eyes the springbok herd rested, the vague curves of their horns and the bold white stripes on their faces showing above the grass. Some began to stand, nervously raising and lowering their heads. I swung the light away to a tree. Another eye, a larger one, stared down like a shiny marble from the treetop. A giraffe was browsing on acacia leaves.

We soon learned to recognize the various animals at night by the color and movements of their eye reflections, and by their height above the grass. A jackal's reflected yellow and jogged along just above the grass-heads. A lion's eyes were also yellow, but larger and higher above the ground, and they swung from side to side slightly as the animal walked.

We were driving back from making observations one night, watching along the spotlight's beam and trying to make out the dim forms of our camp trees. Suddenly, eyes that we had never before seen were reflected in the light; they were emerald-green and wide-set. A dark, bearlike form covered with long, flowing hair moved through the outer reaches of the light. It stood quite tall at the shoulder and had a large, squarish head, but its hindquarters were dwarfed, as if stunted, and it had a long bushy tail. It was walking quickly away from us. I eased my foot down on the accelerator pedal, and we strained through the cracked and yellowed windshield to hold it in sight. Moving faster, it seemed to glide across the savanna like some dark, shaggy ghost. Then it was gone.

Back at camp, we thumbed through our guidebook to the larger animals of Africa. Aardwolf? Spotted hyena? Aardvark? It certainly hadn't been a cat. None of the descriptions or pictures seemed to fit. We hadn't had a good view of it, but whatever the animal was, it was not common. Sitting cross-legged on our bedrolls in the back of the Land Rover, we paged through the book and back again, a flickering kerosene lantern hanging between us. Smaller than a spotted hyena, larger than an aardwolf, the wrong range for a striped hyena—but from its proportions, it definitely was a hyena. We finally decided it could only have been *Hyaena brunnea*, a brown hyena, one of the rarest and least-known large carnivores on earth.

What a stroke of luck! Here was an endangered species that had never before been studied in the wild and about which practically nothing was known. Anything we learned would be a contribution to science and important in the conservation of rare and endangered species. It seemed the perfect animal on which to focus our research.

Though they were entirely nocturnal, and secretive, we continued to see the brown hyenas, if only for fleeting seconds, when we jolted along over the riverbed. Their habits would make them difficult to study, but we grew more and more curious about them. Every night, beginning at dusk, we combed the riverbed with the truck and spotlight, looking for them. Left—right, right—left, I swung the light for hours as we drove slowly along. It was a frustrating business. Jackals, bat-eared foxes, korhaans, plovers, and wild cats were everywhere in the thick grass. Occasionally we did pick up those wide-set emerald eyes, but they were always at the outer limits of the spotlight, moving quickly away into the darkness.

* * *

Early one morning near the end of May, after a long disappointing night searching for hyenas, we reached camp stiff and sore, aching for sleep. Next to the fireplace stood a jackal, his feet planted solidly apart, his muzzle buried deep in our black iron stewing pot. Daring yellow eyes peered over the rim at us; gravy dripped from his whiskers. He finished licking the pot clean, cocked his leg, peed on it, and trotted casually out of camp. As he disappeared into the night, we recognized, from his black, anchor-shaped tail patch, the jackal we had named "Captain," a big, broad-chested male whom we saw often. He had a saddle of jet-black hair spiked with silver and a full, bushy tail.

Several nights later we sat watching a gemsbok carcass that had been abandoned by lions after they had eaten their fill. We were hoping a brown hyena would come by to scavenge. By 3:30 A.M., no matter how hard I tried, I couldn't stay awake. Leaving Delia to watch for hyenas, I quietly unrolled my sleeping bag on the ground beside the Land Rover. After setting my shoes in the grass next to me, I slipped into the bag and bunched my shirt up to form a pillow.

I had just dropped into a sound sleep when my head suddenly bounced on the hard ground. I sat up and fumbled for my flashlight. Five yards away a jackal was in high-speed reverse, dragging away the shirt he had yanked from beneath my head. "Hey! Drop that!" I was half amused, half annoyed, and still half asleep. I struggled out of my sleeping bag, scolding myself for having raised my voice; I might have frightened off a hyena. Then I began looking in the grass for my shoes. They, too, were gone.

This was more serious, because I didn't have another pair. I hobbled after the jackal, the sharp stubble spiking my bare feet. In the beam of my flashlight I could see his beady eyes fixed on me as he hauled my shirt away through the grass. My feet nicked and stinging, I finally gave up the chase and huddled in the Land Rover until dawn, when I recovered the slobbered toe of one shoe and the tattered remains of my shirt. Captain, the pirate jackal, had struck again. Later that day

I spent several hours sewing a pair of moccasins from two pieces of faded canvas.

At breakfast that morning the same thought struck Delia and me at the same time. While driving around the riverbed for hours each night, waiting for these timid brown hyenas to get used to us, why not find out what we could about jackals? They had never been studied in an area like the Kalahari, so anything we learned about them would be new.

Every sunset, we began parking the truck on Cheetah Hill, a bush-covered bulge of sand that intruded onto the riverbed north of camp. With field glasses, notebooks, and a tin of corned beef, we would sit, each cradled in a spare tire atop the roofrack, watching the nightlife begin in Deception Valley.

Sometime before dusk Captain would usually stand from his favorite resting place near North Tree, point his muzzle to the sky, and call to his jackal neighbors. Then, his ears cocked, he would listen to the high-pitched wavering cries that answered from up and down the valley. He would scratch and shake his thick coat, the silver hairs along his black saddle shimmering in the fading twilight. After a deep stretch, he would be off, his keen muzzle spearing through the grasses as he jogged along hunting for mice. From Cheetah Hill we would note his direction, then move to intercept and follow him.

Steering and changing gears with my left hand, holding the light out the window with my right, I would try to keep pace and contact with Captain, staying from fifteen to twenty-five yards behind him. If we followed any closer, he would look back at us, obviously disturbed; any farther away and we would lose him in the grasses. Meanwhile, Delia, holding a flashlight over a notebook and compass on her lap, made notes on his behavior, the directions in which he traveled, the distances, and habitat types. The binoculars lay on the seat between us so that either of us could grab them and describe what was happening. With some practice, our technique worked very well. We could see the species of bird, and often the kind of rat or mouse, that Captain caught before it had been chomped down. And by driving to the spot in the grass where he had been nosing about, we usually discovered a line of frenzied termites or ants he had just lapped with his tongue.

One night in early June, soon after the theft of my shoes, we were following Captain when, without warning and with incredible speed, he took off after a steenbok fawn. I accelerated, and we managed to keep him in sight during a long chase that involved several complete circles, before he disappeared. But after that, no matter which direction we took, we could not spot the lantern we had hung high on a limb in camp to guide us back after dark. Captain had led us out of the stretch of riverbed that was familiar to us, and he had changed directions so frequently that he had scrambled our mileage and compass readings. We could not backtrack with any certainty. We were lost.

With less than a quart of water on board the Land Rover, we could not risk driving farther from camp. So we stopped for the night. From the roofrack the next morning, we could see North Tree on the riverbed about a mile away; our camp was about the same distance south from there. Heading back, I decided that I would tap the red water drum that day and fill a jerrican, and from then on always keep it with us in the truck. There had been no rain for weeks. Each day was cloudless, the savanna drier than the day before. If we got lost again without water, it might be more serious than having to spend one night away from the shelter of our tree island.

Back in camp, while Delia began to make our breakfast, I took a wrench from the toolbox and carried one of our empty jerricans and a length of siphon hose to the drum. I laid the wrench in the bung to unscrew it. A hollow, empty sound rang from deep inside.

It just couldn't be . . . I dropped the wrench and pushed the drum. It toppled over and rolled aside—empty. All that was left of our water was a patch of dampness in the sand.

"Delia! There's no water in this blasted drum!" I stooped to look at the rusted bottom, and then I kicked the damned thing. Delia was as shocked as I was. In a small voice, she asked, "Mark, what are we going to do? Can we make it to the river?"

The Boteti River was nearly a full day's drive away through the heat, sand, and thornscrub. We had less than a quart of water in the truck, and we needed much more than that just to keep the motor cool. If it ran dry and seized up, we would be in a lot worse trouble. How could I have been so stupid! Each day I had measured the level of gasoline in the large inboard tank in the Land Rover to make sure we had enough to get to Maun. I thought we had plenty of water—but I should have *looked*! We stared at the damp spot as if to will the water out of the ground. I fought off a growing uneasiness. This was just the type of situation we should have avoided.

"We'll have to go tonight when the air is cool, so we won't have to use so much water in the radiator," I said, putting my arms around Delia. There was nothing else to do.

That afternoon we climbed into the Land Rover to leave for the river. I fumbled with the ignition key, switching it over and over. "Come *on*, you son of a bitch!" My throat was tight with anger and rising fear. There was nothing but a deadpan click. I jumped out, ran to the front, and threw up the hood. "Try it again!" I called to Delia, then listened to the motor, trying to find out what was wrong.

From the time we had driven out of Gaborone on our way north to Maun, what I had feared most was being stranded somewhere far away from help with a broken-down Land Rover, which I could not fix because I lacked the talent, tools, and spare parts. Up to this point we had had continual minor problems with the worn-out vehicle: corroded battery cables, a discharging generator, punctured tires, and broken exhaust lines. I had always been able to make these relatively minor repairs. But now, as I peered under the hood and Delia worked the ignition switch, the tension settled heavy in my chest. The click that comes from a dead battery now had become a deeper, more ominous clunk, a sign that something much more serious had gone wrong.

I kept my worst fears to myself and went to work. It was dark by the time I discovered that the starter had come apart. Its ring gear had fallen into the flywheel housing and had jammed the motor, so hand-cranking was going to get us nowhere.

I found a piece of heavy wire and bent the end into a hook. We crawled under the truck. Delia held the flashlight for me as I slid the long wire into the housing, trying to feel my way past the flywheel. But through the wire everything felt the same; I could only guess where the engine was jammed.

About midnight we came out from under the truck. My knuckles and forehead were bleeding and smeared with grass chaff, oil, grease, and dirt. It seemed hopeless. I could not be certain that I had even touched the ring gear. I heaved on the crank. The motor turned slightly, and then stopped solidly.

We put some wood on the fire, and while we warmed ourselves and rested, I tried to think through our predicament. If we were going to survive this, the starter gear had to come out. We were both thirsty, but neither of us would drink. I looked at Delia, sitting beside the fire, her head on her arms. I felt utterly frustrated. I couldn't think of anything else to try, and time was running out. Only a quart of water was left for the two of us.

Back at the truck I moved the crank counterclockwise until it stopped, then clockwise just slightly. I was sure the wire was long enough and must be touching the gear. For the rest of the night I bent the end into hooks of different shapes and inserted it at different angles, poking and probing into the housing while Delia held the light. When I could feel nothing move, I repositioned the engine and probed some more.

It was sometime after sunrise when I heard a clank. I hurried to the crank and turned the motor—it was free! We would rest through the day and set off at dusk.

This predicament made us realize that staying in an area as remote as Deception Valley was out of the question. Assuming that we were able to get to the river and return, how long before another crisis? And how many such crises would there be before a real disaster? The hard truth was that we just did not have enough money to do research in such a place. What little we had left would soon be consumed in trips to Maun for supplies, especially since we had no way to haul and store adequate quantities of water and gasoline. We would have to find a less remote place to work, a place less wild... and less free. It was a bitter realization. Two years of planning and working to save enough money for the expedition, five months of reconnaissance and study in Africa, all seemed to have drained away with our water into the sand. Though we had been in the Kalahari for little more than a month, we had already developed a deep attachment to this old riverbed and its animals, especially the ones, like Captain, whom we recognized.

We picked through a depressing breakfast of beans, a meal we had had three times a day for the last sixteen days, and then began loading the truck with our few belongings. The droning of an engine abruptly roused us from our apathy. A stubby green-and-white Land Rover bounced down the duneslope east of the riverbed, a long tail of dust rising behind it. We stood and watched it approach, completely amazed that there was another truck in the area. Before it had rolled to a stop a freckled, ruddy-faced man in baggy shorts, knee socks, and a knit shirt stretched over his round belly launched himself from the driver's seat. His thin, greying hair was slicked straight back over his sunburned head, and his eyes crinkled with a smile. Kalahari sun, wind, and sand had etched his face deeply.

"Hello! Name's Berghoffer, Bergie Berghoffer. You can call me Bergie. Someone in Maun told me that you two were out here somewhere, and when I crossed some truck spoor miles east of here, I figured it was you." Rummaging in the back of his Land Rover, he called over his shoulder, "I reckon by now you might be needing some of this." He set out some brown paper packets of goat meat, a bucket of mealie-meal with eggs buried inside—to keep them cool and protect them from breaking—potatoes, and coffee. While we were thanking him for about the twelfth time, he finally put up his hands and said with a wink, "It's only a pleasure . . . I'm half Yank myself, you know."

We were to learn later that Bergie had roamed the Kalahari for twenty-three years, living in bush camps while drilling mineral test holes for the Botswana Department of Surveys and Lands. He lived a nomadic existence, moving his camp from one area to another, usually far outside the game reserve. "I'd much rather never find anything out here except the animals—not sure I'd tell anyone if I did." He said wryly. "I'm bloody glad someone is finally here to study the wildlife. No one ever has, you know. The Kalahari needs someone to be her champion."

Bergie had a special affection for "Yanks" because his father was an American who had traveled to the Republic of South Africa with the Bill Cody Wild West Show. There he had met and married a woman of British extraction and had settled in the republic. Bergie reckoned it was his father's yearning to travel that coursed through his own veins and kept him on the move and in the bush for most of his life.

"I'm sorry . . . wish we could offer you some tea or coffee," I apologized. "But we've got a problem." I showed him the empty drum.

"Well, a bit of bad luck, that." He frowned, rubbing his chin. "Not to worry about the coffee, but what are you chaps going to do for water?"

I explained that we would be heading for the river, then Maun, and that we wouldn't be able to come back to Deception. "Oh . . . I *am* sorry about that . . . that really is a bit of a bugger." Looking out over the riverbed, he sighed.

"Tell you what." He brightened. "You take this, just to be sure you get there." He hefted a jerrican of water from the back of his Land Rover. "Now I'll have that cup of coffee, if you don't mind, missus."

Despite our protests, Bergie would take none of the water with him to insure his safe return to his own camp. He had scarcely finished his coffee when he held his hand out to me.

"Okay, Mark, okay, Delia, I must be on my way—I'll be seeing you." Then he was gone, his Land Rover disappearing over the eastern dune.

Blind luck and Bergie's generosity had provided us with more than enough water to get to the river—or to Maun, for that matter. We decided to spend one more night in Deception Valley. We hated to leave it, and besides, we were exhausted from the trials of the previous night.

Not an hour before we were to leave Deception Valley for good the next morning, Bergie was back, this time with a large flatbed truck and his drilling crew of eight natives. They unloaded a folding wooden table, two chairs, a heavy iron fire grate, a gas burner complete with cylinder, a small cooking tent with a big fly sheet, four drums of water, and some gasoline. Bergie was like a genie. He waved his arms and shouted orders to his crew, and as if by magic, a small camp appeared.

Almost before we had realized what was happening, he was gone, a wisp of dust vanishing across the dunes again. We stood in the middle of our instant camp staring after this whirling dervish of the Kalahari. In one swift gesture of unbelievable kindness, Bergie had made it possible for us to stay in Deception Valley, at least for a time, while we fought to get more research data and a grant.

We resumed our research, but it was not easy to observe and follow animals without a starter on the truck. Every day near dusk, when we found a jackal sleeping in the grass on the riverbed, we would park nearby, switch off the motor, and wait for it to get up and begin foraging. As soon as it stood and began to stretch, I would sneak to the front of the truck and crank the engine while Delia tried to keep her eye on the jackal moving away through the tall grass. The hand-cranking created such a terrific racket that it drew the attention of every creature for half a mile around. And whenever we were sitting with lions at night, it was a little disconcerting for me to turn my back on them in the dark, knowing that they were watching as I heaved on the crank.

Two weeks after Bergie had given us our camp, he was back with more water. While Delia was making coffee, he quietly took me by the arm and led me to his truck. "Now listen lad, if you expect to keep Delia in the Kalahari, you must spoil her a little. Every woman needs a hot bath!" He turned and pulled a tin tub from the back of his truck. "And does she have a looking glass?" Reaching through the window, he brought out a mirror. From the expression on Delia's face when she saw these gifts, I knew Bergie had been right.

His camp was so far away that we only saw him rarely, but he had an uncanny sense of timing. Weeks would pass, and just when we were getting low on water, he would appear, always with more gifts of goat or wildebeest meat, eggs, potatoes, brawn—a meat gelatin, or headcheese—and other luxury items that he brought either from his camp or from Gaborone. Even if we had had a way of getting these things, we could never have afforded to buy them.

One day he took us much farther south along Deception Valley than we had explored. After an hour of riding in his Land Rover, with its stiff, super-reinforced leaf springs—he was very proud of them—our kidneys ached and our necks were stiff from the pounding. We finally stopped on a dune overlooking a large, perfectly round clay pan. Because of the slate-grey soil in its bottom, it looked as if it were covered with water, an illusion so complete that in later years we saw migratory water birds, once even a pelican, drawn to its surface during drought. Bergie told us the Bushmen had named the valley after this pan, with a word in their language meaning "deception," and also because when traveling along the riverbed, one is deceived into believing every bend is the last. Below us, the old river channel continued winding away into the Kalahari beyond this Real Deception Pan, as we often called it.

"I've been this far and no farther," Bergie said. "Beyond here no man knows." None of us spoke for a long time. We listened to the wind singing in the grasses and looked over the great expanse of wilderness stretching for hundreds of miles beyond. "You know," Bergie said, "there's only one thing that really frightens me out here, and that's fire."

3

Fire

Mark

> Voices of jackals calling
> And, loud in the hush between,
> A morsel of dry earth falling
> From the flanks of the scarred ravine.
> —*Rudyard Kipling*

THE RAINS of 1974, which flooded many parts of the country, had been the heaviest ever recorded in Botswana. They had ended in May, but in their wake, the grasses of the savanna stood taller than a Bushman's head, like a field of golden wheat hundreds of miles across, bowing in the wind. By July, when we had been in Deception for three months, the dry-season sun had turned the wheat to straw, the straw to tinder. Some said the sun's rays passing through a dew drop could set it off.

"Grass number 27: base, 9.2 centimeters; dry canopy, 57.2; green canopy, 14.3..." We had been at it all morning, measuring the basal areas, canopies, and species composition of the grass and herb communities along our vegetation sample lines from riverbed to dune top.

I stood up to rest my cramped knees and noticed a curious grey cloud rising from the eastern horizon. Billowing thousands of feet into the higher atmosphere, its top was sheared off by winds into a vaporous tail that slowly drifted south. Far away—how far we could not tell—the Kalahari was burning.

As we stood watching the ominous cloud, a strong wind, gusting to thirty miles per hour, struck us full in the face, tugging at our clothes and bringing tears to our eyes. Only miles of dry grass stood between us and the fire.

We continued to follow Captain and the other jackals every night, always conscious of the eerie glow on the eastern horizon. There was still so much savanna between the fire and our camp that it would take several weeks to reach us. Before then we would have to develop some plan to protect ourselves, the Land Rover, and camp.

The July nights were bitterly cold. We had not expected temperatures that dropped from a daytime of seventy degrees to fourteen above zero just before dawn. We had no winter clothes—there had been no room for them in our packs when we left home. Following the jackals, we could hardly bear the frigid air, and after holding the spotlight out of the window for just a few minutes, my arm and shoulder would be numb. The truck had no heater, so I cut holes in the sides of a coffee can, turned it over a candle, and set it on the floor. We put socks on our hands, sleeping bags across our laps, and ate cans of stew heated on the exhaust manifold. Still we cramped with the cold and could stand no more than three or four hours in the Land Rover before heading back to the campfire.

At first most of the jackals looked alike, especially at night, so we decided to immobilize and collar some for easier identification. On our first supply trip to Maun, when I had fixed the starter on the truck, Norbert Drager, a German vet in the village, had given us some buffalo-collaring material and a carbon dioxide darting rifle full of leaks and covered with rust. I sealed the rifle with tire patches so that it would hold a charge and, using the buffalo material, made some lightweight collars that fastened with small bolts.

One very cold night in mid-July, we managed to immobilize a jackal near camp. Animals sometimes develop hypothermia when drugged in such weather, so when we had the collar in place, we gently carried our subject into camp, where he could recover near the warmth of the campfire. Then we kept watch from the Land Rover to protect him from larger predators until he fully regained his coordination.

Hours passed, the night grew colder, and our coffee-can heater could not keep us warm. By 1:00 A.M., Delia had had enough. Casting a dim yellow light ahead of her with our weak flashlight, she dragged her sleeping bag and our flimsy foam mattress into the small mess tent. On the riverbed there was a rodent boom—so many furry creatures that for several weeks we had had to eat supper with our feet on tin cans to keep them from crawling up our legs. In spite of the occasional rat or mouse that would scurry over her, Delia was determined to be warm and get some sleep.

I sat in the truck, now and then turning the spotlight on the jackal, who was beginning to flop around, trying to stand up. The light warmed my hands and I wanted to leave it on, but I didn't want to run down the battery. So I sat with my binoculars resting over the steering wheel, shivering in the dark and studying the distant glow of the grass fire, wondering how far away it was.

Two weeks had gone by since we first noticed it. Since then it had broadened and intensified into an orange-red corona stretching across the entire horizon from north to south. Now, in the quiet of night, with the air still and moist, the vivid colors had nearly faded from the sky. The fire seemed to have gone to sleep. But I knew that in the morning, the heavy winds would return and send an immense curtain of grey smoke into the atmosphere.

The little camp Bergie had given us wasn't worth much materially, but it was all we had in the world, and we could never have afforded to replace it. If the fire destroyed it, we would be wiped out financially and our research would be finished. Furthermore, the roots we had put down in that tree island were already something very vital. In the short time we had been there, Deception Valley had become our home.

We worried, too, about Captain and the other animals. Surely some of them would die in the fire. And the sample plots along our vegetation transect lines would be incinerated. After the burn there might be little left to study.

Now, sudden fountains of color surged into the night sky, and then, mysteriously, drained away to a small, dim smudge, only to flare up again minutes later: The fire was dune-walking. Each time it descended into the shelter of an interdunal valley where there was less tinder, its intensity diminished, but as it crept back to the wooded crests, added fuel and wind renewed it. With growing concern, I began to realize what a giant it really was. The Kalahari was burning along a front more than fifty miles long from north to south.

I hung the spotlight outside on the mirror bracket of the truck, and turned it on. It was about 3:30 A.M. and the jackal was recovering nicely. After switching off the light, I sat blowing through my hands to warm them. But then something urged me to have another look. I flipped the switch again and saw *seven lions standing over the jackal.*

Startled by the light, the two females and five subadults jumped back and turned away. But seconds later they were back, eyes fixed on their prey. I hit the starter and drove past the tent, where Delia was sleeping soundly. Ignoring the noise of the truck, the lionesses refused to leave the jackal. Their surprise and confusion gone, they stalked toward him, their heads low, their tails flicking from side to side.

I drove quickly by the jackal, getting between him and the lions. They turned to avoid the truck, and I nudged one of them gently in the rear with the bumper. The lioness grunted once and then wheeled and spat at the headlight. They tried to move around the truck, but I blocked their way, turning them around and heading them at a walking pace into West Prairie, the grassland off the riverbed beyond camp. By cutting the steering wheel left and right and holding the bumper close behind them, I kept them moving away. I didn't like manipulating the lionesses in this way, but my major concern at the moment had to be the jackal, because we had rendered him temporarily helpless.

I was about 400 yards west of camp when, through the rearview mirror, I noticed a weak glow winking on and off somewhere behind the truck. It took some seconds before I realized that it was coming from the mess tent.

Delia had been unaware of the lions. Awakened by the truck, she thought I was following the jackal from camp to make sure he had completely recovered. The Land Rover hadn't been gone long when she heard the padding of heavy feet on the ground outside the tent. The canvas walls shook once. Then a heavy rush of air sounded at her feet. She slowly raised her head. Framed in the doorway—there were no zippers left on the tent flaps—and just visible in the starlight, were the massive heads of two male lions looming over her toes.

She held her breath as the lions smelled the floor of the tent, puffs of air blowing from their nostrils, their whiskers skimming the nylon of her sleeping bag.

She moved her feet. The lions froze, looking straight into the tent. She could hear the Land Rover moving farther away. She slowly reached for the flashlight on the floor beside her. The lions were standing dead still; they seemed to have stopped breathing. She began to raise the flashlight to the screen window above her head. The lion on the left moved against the tent, and the walls trembled again. With the flashlight held to the window, Delia hesitated to thumb the switch, afraid of the noise it would make. Finally she nudged it once—in the silence, the click was like a shot.

The lions didn't budge. On-off, on-off, on-off, she signaled again and again. Moments later she let out a long, slow breath when she heard the Land Rover's engine racing and the peculiar squeak in its bumper as it rattled toward camp.

As I neared our tree island, I swung the spotlight back and forth. Everything looked normal. Still, the dim flashlight continued to blink on and off. I rounded the tent and then jammed on the brakes, gripping the steering wheel hard: Two black-maned lions stood shoulder to shoulder, their heads buried in the doorway. Delia was trapped like a mouse in a shoebox.

I had to do something to distract the lions without jeopardizing her by intimidating them in the wrong way. An inept move would increase the danger. A story had been circulating in Maun when we were last there about a woman being dragged from her sleeping bag by lions in Chobe, a park in northeast Botswana. For once I wished I had a firearm of some sort. At least I might have frightened the lions away from the tent by firing it in the air.

Maybe I could use the Land Rover to herd the males, as I had the females. Slowly, I drove toward the lions. Standing firmly in front of the tent's flap, they both looked at the truck, their eyes round, ears perked, tails twitching. At least their attention was focused on me now, not Delia. As I drew nearer they seemed to grow, until they stood as tall as the truck's hood, their shoulder muscles bunched and tense. They held their ground. I stopped.

After a few more seconds, the males began to blink their eyes. They settled back on their haunches and turned back to Delia. I let out the clutch and drove forward again, this time with my head out the window and slapping the side of the Rover to keep their attention on the truck. When I was very close, they finally turned away. Laying their ears back as if annoyed, they put their noses to the ground and walked off in the direction of the females. Just beyond camp they began to bellow, their crescendos rolling up and down the valley, and the lionesses answered from the bush savanna farther west. The jackal had escaped during all the commotion.

I quickly slipped into the tent to lie next to Delia. Half frightened and half excited, she chattered for a while and then buried her head in my chest. Soon we were sound asleep. I woke once, when a rat dropped onto my forehead. I slapped it against the wall of the tent and shivered, and after a while fell back to sleep.

Some nights later, we were following one of our collared jackals when the eastern sky flushed angry red. "Mark, the fire's almost here!

We've got to get back to camp and get ready!" I felt sure it was still quite far away and that it would be a waste of time to tear down camp so soon. But Delia insisted, and I finally succumbed to her pleas and turned the truck around.

Before I had even brought the Rover to a full stop, Delia leaped from her seat. She began collecting pots, pans, and bags of flour and mealie-meal, hauling everything she could drag or carry toward the truck. I tried to reason with her. "Look, Boo, it's not going to come tearing over the dunes within the next few minutes, or even before morning."

"How do you know!" She snapped, as she struggled with a heavy bag of onions. "You've never seen a range fire in the Kalahari—or anywhere else."

"We'll be able to hear the fire way off, you'll see the flames in the grass—there'll be sparks. Where are we going to eat, sleep, and work if we pack up before the fire's even here?"

But it was no use trying to stop her. I half expected her to smother me with a wet blanket at any moment. Now she was staggering toward the truck with another armload of boxes, some clothing, and a jerrican. The pile in the back of the Land Rover was growing by the minute. I began to sneak things out the side door as she piled them in through the back. "Now look, dammit! When the fire gets here we'll know it. Get hold of yourself!"

"I'm not taking any chances!" She shouted back.

I had just managed to hang the onions back in a tree on the dark side of the truck when one side of the mess tent collapsed. Delia was hauling up tent stakes like a gopher in a turnip patch.

"What are you doing?" I begged.

"I'm putting the tent in the Land Rover."

I stomped over to the truck and shoved all the stuff out the back onto the ground. "Stop!" I yelled, standing between her and the pile. "If it'll make you feel better, we'll do something constructive—like make a firebreak around camp."

I tied a fallen tree to the back of the Land Rover with a heavy piece of old cotton rope. A few circles around camp and I had flattened a swath through the tall grass.

When I had finished I began making up our bed in the back of the truck. By now it was long past midnight.

"What are you doing?" Delia was standing behind me.

"I'm going to sleep. I know we're perfectly safe. Anyway, you're so damned stubborn . . . no matter what, you'll watch that fire all night."

Much later, cold, stiff, and contrite, she crawled into her sleeping bag and huddled against me. I put my arms around her and drifted back to sleep.

About midmorning, Bergie's flatbed came churning over East Dune and into camp. Laughing, he slid from the driver's seat. "What's all this?" he asked, as he eyed our disheveled camp.

We asked him about the approaching fire.

"Well, I guess you'll likely survive for a while yet." He chuckled. "That fire's still thirty miles east of here—passed my camp day before yesterday."

Delia glanced at me and smiled faintly.

Then Bergie frowned. "Make no mistake, though, its bloody-minded. Even with a tractor to make a break and my crew to fight it, we had a time. Take care when it gets this side—it's no small fry."

"How did it get started?" I asked.

"Mon, the bloody Bushmen set these fires every year, you know. They can hunt—track—better with the thick grass burned away. And it's easier for them to collect bauhinia nuts, one of their staple foods. I suppose you can't blame 'em too much, but the fire sure raises Cain with the trees in the woodlands. Dries out the lower leaves the animals need for browse in the dry times. And the Bushmen aren't the only ones to blame. The safari hunters set the veld alight, too, though you'll never hear 'em admit it."

He turned to the back of his truck. "Had a few things extra around camp I thought you could use." He set a gunny sack full of goat meat, eggs, and mealie-meal in the grass next to the mess tent. Our near-empty water drums boomed as we filled them from the drums on his truck. Delia brewed some coffee.

With a last sip from his cup he was on his feet and saying goodbye. "I've got three weeks' leave due me. I reckon I'll go to Johannesburg for a spell to visit my daughter and her family. But you can bet I won't be able to stand the city life for long—I'll be back in ten days or so. Probably beat the fire here; it dies down a lot each night so it's still a couple of weeks away from Deception."

We begged him to spend a few days with us on his return, so that we could show him some of the things we had learned. "All right, all right—I'll pop over directly when I get back. Okay Mark, okay Delia—I'll be seeing you."

Two weeks went by, but still Bergie had not come back. Day after day we listened against the wind, imagining dozens of times that we could hear his truck approaching. Maybe it was a tent line humming in the wind, or our ears buzzing from the silence, that fooled us again and again. It's like that in the bush, when you've waited a long time for a friend.

Was he ill? Had his truck turned over somewhere along the spoor east of Deception? Worried, we finally drove along the track he took to our camp, but we found nothing. We decided he must have stayed longer than he had expected in Johannesburg.

A few days later, on a frosty morning in early August, I opened the back door of the Land Rover and crawled from bed. The sickly sun cast a frail, sallow half-light over the old riverbed. The birds were silent. Hordes of insects—ones that usually came out only at night—swarmed in the air or crawled through the trees and over the ground in the eerie quiet. The ashen skeleton of a grass leaf, incinerated by intense heat, settled on the back of my hand. I looked up, and the air was full of them, floating in, softly covering everything, like black snow. From north to south, the veil of smoke in the eastern sky boiled skyward for thousands of feet. The fire was almost on us. I felt small and threatened. It looked larger, more powerful than I had imagined. I knew we probably should have packed up camp days before and gone to Maun.

I hurriedly piled into the Land Rover pots, pans, bags of flour, mealie-meal, and everything else that would fit, and Delia flattened the mess tent and its fly sheet to the ground. But if the flames hit the valley in midafternoon, with the humidity at rock bottom and the winds blowing easterly at thirty to forty miles an hour, it would be almost impossible to keep the camp from burning. Aside from our personal safety and that of the animals, we were most concerned about our data books—the record of our research—and about the Land Rover. Tying the dead tree to the truck again, I dragged it around camp to broaden our firebreak. With a spade and axe, we cleared away as much grass and dead wood as we could. Delia set pans of water near the mess tent, and I cut branches for beating at the flames. There was little more we could do.

The morning wore on, the winds blew harder, and the roar from the fire grew louder. More and more ash rained into camp and swirled across the ground in the churning air. By midafternoon, driven by the heavy desert winds, the first flame reached the top of East Dune. It paused for a moment, licking at the tall grasses and lower branches of a tree, then leaped quickly to the top, turning the tree into a thirty-foot torch. Another flame crested the dune, then another. A line of fire invaded the woodlands, and whole trees exploded like flares.

The intense heat created its own wind, a wind that fed oxygen to the flames and spurred them down the duneslopes toward the riverbed at an incredible speed, sweeping them through grass and bush as far north and south as we could see. Nothing could have prepared us for that sight.

"Our break will never stop it!" I yelled above the roar. I dropped the branch in my hand and ran to the Land Rover, tied the fallen tree to the hitch again, and dragged it round and round camp to widen the firebreak.

When the flames reached the riverbed, 1000 yards from camp, they dropped and spread out in the grasses. An immense cloud of seething white smoke erupted from the savanna, and the fire, with flames eight to ten feet high, swept down the valley. I had hoped that our truck spoor across the riverbed, 400 yards from camp, would slow the advance, but the fire only paused for a moment and then surged toward us again. I could see immediately that the break around camp was still far too narrow.

Once again I dragged the tree, this time in large figure eights. When the flames were about 200 yards away, I ran to the edge of our break and knelt to set a backfire. My hands fumbled with the matches, trying to get one lit. It was impossible in that wind; I turned my body to form a shield and felt heat on the back of my neck. I fought off an urge to stand up and run. Finally I touched off the whole box and stuffed it into the grass.

But it was too late—the backfire could not burn fast enough against the strong wind. I sprinted to the truck and drove along just ahead of the fire line, pulling the dead tree. If I could break the fire's momentum, we could beat it out around camp when it reached our backfire and break.

I made several passes just ahead of the flames. But they were still moving much too quickly toward Delia and camp. At a spot where the fire had slowed down a little in the flattened grass, I drove directly into the flames, straddling the fire line with the truck and driving as fast as I could while dragging the tree. After about fifty yards, I turned out of the fire and looked back. It was working. There were gaps in the fire line, and it had been slowed. Before it could rebuild momentum, I swung around and made another pass, and then another.

On the third sweep, the smoke from smoldering grass was so thick that I could hardly see. Suddenly Delia appeared in front of the truck, beating at the flames, her branch above her head. I slammed on the brakes and missed her by a foot. She jumped back and I sped away.

When I was turning for another pass at the fire, she came running toward the Land Rover, screaming and waving, her face white.

"Mark! My God, you're on fire! The truck's on fire! Jump! Get out before it explodes!" I looked back. The tree, the cotton rope, and the undercarriage of the Rover were in flames.

A fifty-gallon tank of slopping gasoline was riding against the back of my seat; its overflow pipe ran through the floor of the truck and came out ahead of the right rear wheel. Stamping on the brake and turning off the motor, I lunged from the door as flames leaped up around both sides of the Land Rover. Then I ran the thirty yards to where Delia was standing. Together we waited for the explosion.

"All our data books, our cameras, *everything* is inside!" she cried.

Then I remembered the old fire extinguisher clipped to the ceiling over the front seat. I got back inside the burning truck, but the trigger of the extinguisher was frozen with rust. I threw it out the window, started the motor, and jammed the truck into gear. Holding the accelerator flat to the floor, with the engine racing, I slid my foot off the clutch pedal. The Land Rover lurched forward with a shudder that shook every part of it. The flaming rope and tree broke free and, miraculously, most of the burning grass dropped from beneath. I stopped the truck over a small patch of bare calcrete rock and threw sand into the undercarriage to put out the rest of the flames.

We poured pots of water over the mess tent and flailed with branches and tire innertubes while the fire continued to burn around the edge of camp. Flames crawled over the ground we had cleared, working their way across the break along single stems of grass. One of the guy ropes to the tent fly sheet was on fire; I cut it free. We dragged a plastic jerrican of gasoline and a box of Land Rover parts farther into camp. Sparks showered over us. Beating at the flames, we struggled to breathe, choking and gasping in the acrid smoke and hot, deoxygenated air. Time and the fire seemed to be standing still. We barely had the strength to raise our branches for another feeble swat at the flames.

In minutes, or seconds—I don't really know how long—the main fire had passed. We had slowed it just enough to divert it around camp. After mopping up some of the remaining small pockets of flame, we were finally safe.

We sank to our knees, coughing and heaving in exhaustion, our lungs burning. When we were able to look up, we watched in a stupor as, one by one, the other tree islands along the valley became torches of orange flame. North Tree and Eagle Island were burning wildly.

Our lips, foreheads, and hands were blistered, our eyebrows and lashes singed. We would be coughing up ash and soot for days after, and the charcoal had invaded the pores of our skin so deeply that it was impossible to wash it away. For weeks, wherever we drove or walked, a grey cloud would envelop us. On windy nights, the Land Rover would be filled with a gritty haze that dimmed the light of our kerosene lantern to a murky yellow glow. We slept with bandanas tied across our faces.

After the fire passed us it marched on across the dune tops into the Kalahari, lighting the night sky like a spectacular sunset. Behind it, the cool pink glow of burned-out trees and logs remained, until the fire's crimson was lost in the blush of dawn.

At sunrise the next morning we sat staring over the blackened Kalahari. Tendrils of white smoke crept from burned-out stumps. Fragile tufts of grey ash—all that remained of grasses along the dunes and riverbed—would soon crumble to a powder before the winds. Whole trees, big ones, had been completely consumed, leaving an embroidery of white ash against the blackened sands. We felt as though we were the only inhabitants on a volcanic island that had formed in the night. Lava and ash had not yet cooled, and flares from within the earth still flickered through the molten surface. Our research had been incinerated.

Around noon Bergie's big white truck came growling over the blackened face of East Dune and lumbered toward camp. Delia quickly began stoking the campfire for coffee.

The four-ton Bedford rolled to a stop, and the Africans who worked with Bergie climbed down and stood in a ragged line.

"*Dumella*!" I greeted them.

"*Ee*," came their hushed reply.

"Where is Mr. Bergie? How is he?" Delia asked. They all looked at the ground, coughing and scuffing their shoes in the dust.

"Khaopheli," I asked the foreman, "what's the matter? Where is Mr. Berghoffer?" They hung their heads in embarrassed silence.

"Mr. Bergie no coming back," Khaopheli said softly, still looking at his feet.

"Why not? You mean he's still in Johannesburg?"

"Mr. Bergie dead." I could scarcely hear him.

"Dead! What do you mean—that's impossible!"

He lifted his face, patted his chest, and muttered, "*Pilo*—heart."

I sat down on the bumper of the truck, my head in my hands. Though we had known him only a short time, he had been like a father to us. I kept shaking my head, still trying not to believe it.

"We take camp... Mr. Bergie's things," Khaopheli mumbled. I nodded and turned to stare over the Kalahari that Bergie had loved so much. The crew immediately began loading their truck with our only table, the two chairs, the tent, and other pieces of equipment.

"But Mr. Bergie would have wanted us to have these things," I protested. Khaopheli insisted that the government would have to decide what to do with them. When they began rolling the water drums toward their truck I flatly refused to give them up, explaining that I would contact the Department of Surveys and Lands for them to be formally loaned to us. They finally relented and drove away. The few trees we had saved from the fire, the Land Rover, the drums, a sack of mealie-meal, and other foodstuffs were all that was left.

We had never felt such utter despair. We couldn't even tell Bergie's family how much he had meant to us; we didn't know his daughter's name. A book we had planned to give him lay on the ground next to where the tent had stood, its pages fluttering, gathering ash in the wind.

After a while we drove across the charred riverbed. Dense clouds of soot and ash swirled about us, filling our eyes, noses, and throats. Everything was black. At the top of West Dune we stood on the roof of the Land Rover: Complete destruction ranged as far as we could see in every direction.

A month or so earlier, we had gambled our return airfares to the United States on more supplies for the project, trying to keep our research alive while waiting for word of a grant. None had come, and now we had less than $200 left. Our research was finished. Somehow we would have to earn the money to get home.

We stood staring despondently over miles of blackened dunes. Delia, with tears rising in her eyes, put her head on my shoulder and said, "Whatever brought us to this place?"

4

The Cry of the Kalahari

Mark

The earth never tires,
The earth is rude, silent, incomprehensible at first,
Nature is rude and incomprehensible at first,
Be not discouraged, keep on, there are divine things well envelop'd,
I swear to you there are divine things more beautiful than words can tell.

—*Walt Whitman*

THE SANDS were laid bare by the harsh, persistent winds. An ashen debris of cremated leaves tumbled over the dunes before the gale—a black wind howling over the Kalahari.

The fire had burned away the privacy of steenbok, korhaans, jackals, and others who lived in the grasses. Bat-eared foxes skulked nervously about, or tried to hide behind stubble an inch or two high, their big ears drooping sadly. There was no refuge.

But there was warmth and darkness not far below the blackened surface, and hidden in the soil, left by the heavy rains of months before, there was moisture, the universal ingredient of all life. Long chains of water molecules, linked through capillarity, were being drawn from deep beneath the dunes by the hot, thirsty winds above.

A tiny grass seed lay waiting in its moist, subterranean bed. Bursting with life, it finally split. A pale sprout emerged from within, and then, turning and shouldering its way between sand grains, it grew toward the surface. When, straining with turgor, it shoved aside a cinder and reached toward the sky, the sprout was not alone. It stood with millions of others, a hint of green on the sands.

Within three weeks after the fire, luxurious shocks of short grass blades had flushed from the blackened bases. Herds of springbok and gemsbok ambled over the faces of dunes near the riverbed, cropping away at the succulent greenery.

* * *

We stood together for long minutes on the dune, after Bergie's crew had left, and then drove silently back to camp. We had been living on nervous energy, not thinking about the reality of our situation. There were certain facts we had to face: Our money was gone and there was little chance for a job in Maun, because the safari hunting companies hired mostly native laborers, for only two or three dollars a day. Prospects in South Africa weren't much better. It would take us months to make enough to get home, find jobs with higher wages, and earn enough to come back again.

We still had several weeks of food and fuel stocks left in camp, and if we stayed longer in Deception Valley perhaps we could find out if a brown hyena study was really possible. By rationing our food and water, we could keep making research observations until we had just enough of everything to get us back to Maun. Foolish as it may seem, we decided to do it.

The day after the fire had passed our camp, curious about the animals' reaction to the fire, we drove west to the fire line to watch them. Few antelope or birds showed alarm: A small herd of gemsbok galloped onto a stony area, which had only a little grass, and let the flames pass by. A group of springbok milled about, pronking—leaping stiff-legged—high into the air 100 yards from the fire. Plovers and pheasantlike korhaans flushed ahead of the burning grasses, squawking.

Most of the animals stayed surprisingly calm. A family of five bat-eared foxes slept in the grass until the flames were several hundred yards away, and then they roused themselves, evidently not because of the approaching danger but because of the thousands of insects flying and crawling for safety. They stood, yawned, and stretched as usual, then began foraging through the grass, eating one large grasshopper after another. There were always a few bare spots or areas of short, sparse grass on pans and fossil riverbeds. When the fire burned too close, lions, springbok, gemsbok, and hartebeest strolled through these avenues of escape to places that had already burned. Many creatures, including squirrels, foxes, meerkats, mongooses, snakes, and even leopards, took refuge in underground burrows and waited for the fire to pass. Since the fire line moved so fast, there was little danger of asphyxiation inside the dens. The only victims of the fire were some rodents and insects and a few reptiles.

Captain, the black-backed jackal, wasted no time in taking advantage of the situation. At his usual fast trot, he bounded over the incinerated dunes, crunching up dead grasshoppers, beetles, mice, and snakes. He also fed on unfortunate insects and rodents who had lost their cover and were scurrying about fully exposed on the barren sands.

Our fears that our research would be ruined by the fire proved groundless. In fact, the burn opened interesting new lines of investigation and made it easier to observe and follow animals. We tried to measure how quickly the grasses were growing back and how the diets and movements of the jackals, bat-eared foxes, and antelope were changed. Like the other animals, we tried to take advantage of the situation. There was a great deal to learn about jackals, and a great deal to learn *from* them.

Our decision to stay in Deception until our supplies ran out did not come easily. For many weeks, even before the fire, we had been living mostly on mealie-meal, oatmeal, and pablum mixed with powdered milk. I had lost nearly thirty-five pounds and Delia had lost fifteen. We were persistently weak and lethargic, and I was sure Delia was anemic.

In late July, some days before the fire hit camp, I had been awakened by the sound of the truck's back door opening. I found Delia outside on the ground, doubled over with severe stomach pains. Though this had been happening for several weeks, she had managed to keep it from me. I was sure that her sickness was due not only to our lack of a proper diet but also to the stress of not having the funds either to continue our research or to go home. I lay awake that night trying to think of some way I could get something more substantial for her to eat.

The next night we were following a jackal through the sandveld, when a steenbok suddenly appeared in the spotlight. Quite naturally, with no second thoughts or feelings of guilt, I drew my large hunting knife from its scabbard, slipped off my shoes, and slid quietly from the Land Rover, ignoring Delia's whispered protests. Taking care not to get between the steenbok and the spotlight, I stalked toward the twenty-five-pound antelope. Its large emerald eyes glowed in the light, its nose twitching, trying to take my scent, and the veins stood out on the inside of its big ears, perked to catch the slightest sound. I felt a heightened sense of awareness, the sand cool on my bare feet as I stepped quietly around the grass stubble, my eyes locked on the animal. At the same time, I stood apart from myself, watching with interest this unfamiliar part of my nature that had so long lain dormant.

Finally, trembling and sweating heavily, I crouched no more than five feet from the steenbok, the knife raised in my right hand. Gathering myself, I sprang forward, driving the blade toward a spot just behind its shoulder. But it had sensed me, and at the last second it dodged me and ran away. I sprawled in the sand, pricking my arms, legs, and belly on devil's keys—sharp, three-cornered thorns. Stinging all over and feeling foolish, I walked back to the truck empty-handed.

There were other similar attempts to get protein for us, none of them successful, and we continued to subsist mostly on cereal. Delia's condition did not improve.

* * *

Studying the jackals through July and early August, we realized that we could identify them by the distinctive black tail patch each carried midway down its tail. There was no need to risk injuring or alienating them with the immobilization rifle. Since both they and the brown hyenas scavenged, we guessed that the jackals must compete with browns for carrion. If we followed them often enough, surely they would lead us to the reclusive hyenas.

Each evening all along the valley, the jackals called to one another in a type of reveille before beginning their night's hunt. Unlike black-back jackals in the Serengeti (also called silverbacks there), where mated pairs stay together year round, Kalahari jackals often foraged alone in the dry season. We took compass bearings on their cries to help us locate individuals to follow. Captain's hoarse voice, which sounded as though he had chronic laryngitis, made him easy to identify.

In the three months since we first set up camp in Deception Valley, there had been no rainfall, and there was no drinking water in the entire Central Kalahari. Captain and the other jackals survived on the moisture in the rodents and birds they killed, on maretwa (*Grewia* spp.) berries they picked with their teeth, and on wild melons they found scattered over the duneslopes.

Like an American coyote, Captain was a superior hunter and an opportunist par excellence. In the cool of the evenings, just after sunset, he often trotted along the riverbed below Cheetah Hill, pausing now and then to lap up termites from a column hauling grass stems toward its colony. A dive into a green clump of grass usually paid off with a large, horny grasshopper, a spider, or a beetle, which he quickly chopped up and swallowed. Then he would rush forward with his nose to the ground, curling his lips up tightly, and showing his front teeth as he deftly nipped at a scorpion. Snorting, shaking his head, and grinning widely—lest it sting him on the nose—Captain would toss the arachnid into the air. On the third try he'd bite it in two and swallow the brittle prey. As he trotted along, he often dodged this way and that, hopping off his back feet to snatch large sausage flies and flying termites from the air, crunching them up like appetizers.

By about eight-thirty or nine o'clock, when colder air rolled off the backs of the dunes into the valley, the insects stopped moving. Now Captain turned to the more rewarding task of catching mice. Trotting from one clump to the next, he would wade into the grass, holding his head high and cocking his ears forward. After smelling out a mouse's exact location, he would rear to full height on his hind legs, his paws drawn together against his chest. Then, launching his feet like javelins into the grass, he'd pin the rodent to the ground and seize it from under his paw. If he missed, his prey would sometimes jump straight up, only to be snatched in midair—three or four quick chomps and it was down. He might kill as many as thirty or forty mice in a three-hour hunting period, catching one in every four attempts. Even when his sides were bulging, like garbage bags, he still went on hunting, catching mice and rats in small holes that he dug in the sand with his forepaws and covered over with a quick push of his snout.

Captain was having his usual round of successes one night, trotting across North Pan, killing and burying one rodent after another. Now he was prancing around another patch of belly-high grass, sticking his nose in one side, then the other. He was just about to rear for the strike when he looked back along his line of caches. What he saw made him bristle: Another jackal was trotting from one cache to the next, uncovering and gobbling up his rats. She stood in full view, pilfering the stores of the male who was dominant in this part of the valley.

Captain rushed at the little thief, but she held her ground, her sleek head lifted high, her blonde neck and rufous shoulders standing proud. He was almost upon her when his charge fizzled. Somewhere inside him a circuit had shorted, he was powerless to attack her. It was as though she stood behind an invisible shield.

Instead of routing her as he normally would have, he began trying to impress her: His neck arched, his chest swelled, his ears perked forward, and his nose twitched. He strutted toward the slender female until they stood face to face. Slowly, gently, he touched his muzzle to hers. She stood stiff and tense. Captain's nose roamed from her nose to her cheek, up the side of her face to her ear, along her neck, then light as a whisper over her shoulder. Suddenly he flung his body around and bumped her hindquarters. She stumbled sideways, regained her balance, and froze under his roving nose. Then she abruptly sidestepped him and trotted off, coyly depositing her scent on an herb upwind from him. He smelled her mark for long moments as he watched her disappear into the bush of Cheetah Hill. Then he followed after her.

An indelible impression had been made, and Captain met the female again the next night. After a ritual greeting of nose-sniffing and gentle hip-nudging, the two stood, their necks crossed, sealing the bond. They hunted together, with Mate—as we called her—in the lead. She often paused to mark territory by cocking her leg against a shrub, or to advertise her femininity by squatting to scent-mark. Captain followed in her steps, and, watching her attentively, covered her every mark with his own, telling the other jackals that this female belonged to him.

While the night was still warm, together they plundered the insect population on the flat riverbed. Then, as the evening cooled, they took to mousing at a rodent colony in the sands of Cheetah Hill, poking their noses into one warren after another, snorting and snuffling, trying to find the most likely place to begin excavating. Captain suddenly began to dig excitedly, his front feet churning the sand like a waterwheel, spraying it through his spraddled hind legs, his tail waving like a flag as he tore at the burrow. Mate watched him for a while, and then trotted to another colony nearby, where she began her own dig.

Burrowing frenetically and biting big chunks of sod and sand away, Captain was getting close to his quarry. But the excavation had become too deep for him to keep a proper check on the warren's other exits.

He began digging in short bursts, then quickly backing out of the hole and looking from one escape route to another, intending to catch the rat either in the burrow or when it ran into the grass above ground.

After eons of predation, rats apparently have figured out such strategies, and this one wouldn't leave the warren until the last moment. Now the hole was so deep that precious seconds were lost to Captain each time he backed out to check the other exits. It was at this point that he displayed a touch of jackal genius and showed us a behavior pattern that, to our knowledge, has never been seen before in mammals.

Faced with the problem of digging underground and keeping watch at the same time, Captain stood on his hind legs, his head outside the hole, and began drumming with his forepaws on the ground near the entrance, snatching quick glances at one exit after another. After a short pause, it was back underground for another burst of four or five strokes of actual excavation. Then he stood and began "sham digging" again. From the vibration, the rat must have thought the jackal was getting very close, for it scurried from one of the exits. Captain leapt from the hole, snatched the rodent in his jaws, and ate it, his eyes closed and ears twigging sweetly.

By 10:30 P.M. it had become quite chilly and the rodent population had holed up for the night; bird hunting would be more profitable for the jackal pair. Abruptly they quit hopscotching from one grass clump to another in search of rats and mice. Now they headed back to the riverbed, where they began jogging much faster, circling and zigzagging, their noses glued to scent trails on the ground.

Near Acacia Point, Mate stopped, her front paw held to her chest, her tail rising. She stalked forward, step by step, her nose pointing straight ahead, ears perked, toward a kori bustard not fifteen yards ahead. At twenty-five pounds, with a twelve-foot wingspread, a male kori bustard is one of the heaviest flying birds in the world. In the Kalahari, lone jackals usually didn't tackle such large prey, but with Captain to back her up, the odds were better for Mate.

The big turkeylike bird flared its wings and its neck and tail feathers and made a short, threatening dash toward her. The cock outweighed her by about ten pounds, but without hesitation Mate charged him. The bird bluffed her once and then took to the air, his enormous wings whipping up swirls of dust. He was straining to gain height when Mate leaped more than six feet up and caught him by the thigh. Both were suspended in the air for an instant, the jackal clamped beneath the kori, the broad wings beating against their combined weights. Then, in a tumble of feathers, they crashed to the ground. While Mate fought to hold on, Captain sped in and crushed the kori's head in his jaws.

Both jackals began feeding furiously. Their tails wagged aggressively, and they glared at each other with blazing eyes, their faces smeared with blood and feathers. They had been feeding for two or three minutes when a brown hyena began circling at a distance, obviously wanting to challenge the jackals for their kill, but wary, as always, with us sitting nearby.

The hyena moved closer. We sat perfectly still, not making a sound. We could just make out a blaze of white on her forehead and hear her feet stir the grass. Then she charged. Captain and Mate scattered. The hyena seized the bird, hoisted it off the ground, and began moving quickly into the bush of West Prairie. We tried to follow, but she loped away and disappeared.

Captain and Mate had lost their meal, but they would easily find enough to eat among the insects, mice, birds, and snakes in the grass of the riverbed, and there was always the chance of scavenging something from a larger predator. Unlike the Serengeti jackals, which sometimes kill prey as large as gazelles, Captain and Mate, even hunting as a team, would not be likely to tackle anything larger than the kori they had just killed. When we would next see them hunting together, however, their intended prey would be much more dangerous than the kori had been.

To conserve our dwindling supply of gasoline, we often followed Captain and Mate on foot, just after dawn, before they lay up to rest for the day. One morning early in September, Delia was taking notes while I described the pair's lazy journey back to Cheetah Hill. We were picking our way carefully through thornbushes along the riverbed, when the droning of a small aircraft engine sounded from over the dunes. It was the first plane we had heard since arriving in Deception. The area was so remote that the Botswana Department of Civil Aviation restricted pilots from flying over it. We were sure the aircraft would be coming to our camp because we were the only people for thousands of square miles. Excited by the prospect of seeing other people, we raced onto the riverbed, waving wildly at the little blue-and-white Cessna zooming by just above us. I stripped off my shirt and held it up so the pilot could see the wind direction.

The plane circled, lost height, bounced across the riverbed once, twice, a third time—then took off again. As it flashed by I could see

Norbert Drager, the German vet from Maun, his tense face bent over the control wheel. He circled low over the dunes, made another approach, bounced a few more times, and took to the air again. It was his first cross-country flight as a student pilot, and he was trying to land in a gusty crosswind. As he passed us the third time we could see his wife, Kate, beside him and their daughter, Loni, in the back. On his fourth try he came in much too fast, and the plane hit the ground hard, just missing a fox's den. Then it swerved toward a stand of brush. With its wheels sliding, and leaning down hard on its nose wheel, it managed to stop just a few yards shy of it.

"You get more out of a single landing than any pilot I've ever seen," I kidded him. Norbert was a slight, blond Bavarian with a broad grin who was in Africa with German Technical Aid.

"I've just about had it with flying," he grumbled, switching off the plane's systems. "It's ninety-nine percent boring and one percent sheer terror."

Kate climbed out with a large wicker picnic basket filled with homemade bread, small meat pies, fresh fish, cheese (all the way from Rhodesia), salad, and cake. Red napkins and a checkered tablecloth were neatly folded over the food. We must have looked like two vultures eyeing this feast. We thanked them profusely for this kindness, one of many yet to come from Maun people.

We ate the banquet under the old acacia tree. Delia and I, not having seen anyone since Bergie's crew had come with the news of his death, rattled on like ticker-tape machines about the fire and everything we had learned about jackals. When we had finally run down, Kate asked, "By the way, did you know your country has a new president?"

"No—why, what happened?" I asked.

"Nixon resigned because of Watergate about a month ago, and someone named Ford has taken his place." We had not read a newspaper or listened to a radio for more than six months.

Norbert, who was worried about the trip back to Maun, herded his family to the plane after only an hour. They all waved from the windows as the aircraft roared down the riverbed and lifted into the sky, leaving a tunnel of dust behind. When they were out of sight we walked quietly back to camp. Their brief visit had reminded us of our isolation, and now we felt a loneliness that had not been there before. The bundle of letters they had brought was not likely to offer any consolation. This was it: We had to hear soon about a grant or pack up and go home.

The mail lay on the butt of a fallen tree, daring us to open it. Delia picked it up, removed the string and began shuffling through the letters. "Here's something from National Geographic." Her voice was tense.

"Well, go ahead and open it—we may as well get it over with," I said glumly. We had been disappointed so many times, and this was our last hope. Delia tore off the end of the envelope and took out the letter.

"Mark! It's a grant! They've given us a grant!" She jumped around, waving the papers and cheering. At last someone believed in us—at least in the amount of $3800. We were a bona fide research team.

After a trip to Maun for supplies, we set about our studies with renewed confidence and determination: Sooner or later the brown hyenas would get used to us and, in the meantime, we would follow jackals until they did. Delia's stomach ailment immediately disappeared.

* * *

In September the hot-dry season came to the Kalahari. We were as unprepared for it as we had been for winter in July. Almost overnight, midday temperatures climbed above 110 degrees—then up to 116, in the shade of the fallen tree where we had posted our thermometer. The ground outside of camp was too hot for our thermometer, but it must have been over 140 degrees.

We withered, like the new tender grass, in the strong easterly winds that swept hot and dry across the valley. In the late afternoons, when the winds had quit for the day, our ears rang from the silence. Barren trees, a brown monotony of dead grass and bush, with a bleary simmering sky above: It was a different Kalahari from the one we had known. Moisture escaped our bodies so quickly that our skin stayed dry of perspiration. Our eyes felt scratchy; they seemed to shrink into our skulls, away from the heat.

We rationed ourselves to seven gallons of water each per week, for bathing, cooking, and drinking. The water from the drums tasted like hot metallic tea, and to cool it for drinking, we filled tin dinner plates and set them in the shade of the acacia. But if we didn't watch it closely, the water would quickly evaporate or collect bees, twigs, and soil. After washing the dishes, we took sponge baths in the dishwater, then strained the coffee-colored liquid through a cloth into the truck's radiator. A jerrican stored any excess for later use. We always shared a few cupfuls of fresh water a day with the birds, who flocked to our camp for shade, bread crumbs, and mealie-meal.

Our skin chapped and flaked, our fingers and toes split and bled. Day after day it was the same: the same T-shirt, ragged cut-offs, and holey tennis shoes, the same grey calcareous dust over everything, the same heat that sapped our strength away. We tried to sleep by lying in the back of the Land Rover with wet towels spread over us, but within fifteen minutes we were covered by a carpet of honeybees attracted to the moisture.

The grasses of the riverbed, duneslopes, and savannas had become dry and lifeless; the waterholes were dusty. There was no water left to drink anywhere in the Kalahari. Without sufficient moisture in their forage, the antelope herds had broken into smaller groups of fifteen or so and nearly all had left the fossil river, dispersing over thousands of square miles of range. By spreading out into the sandveld to browse from trees and shrubs, and to dig up fleshy roots and succulent tubers with their hooves, most of the antelope had survived the dry months without drinking. Soon after their departure from the riverbed, the lions, leopards, and other large predators had followed.

By October it had been more than six months since we had seen rain, or even a cloud. Then one afternoon we noticed furry cat paws of vapor tracking into the eastern sky. The hot wind died and a curious quiet fell over the valley. Worn out from heat and night work, we dragged ourselves from camp and stood in the open, watching the billowing vapor above. A lone springbok faced the tentative clouds, his head raised in the sweltering heat waves, as though praying for relief. But the white ghosts vanished before the sun.

Each afternoon they came back, but they only dissolved in the heavy heat that ran like molten glass over the bleary image of the dunes. We were constantly dizzy and could not concentrate enough to read, repair the truck, or perform even the simplest of tasks. We were irritable and our arms and legs seemed too heavy to drag around. At night we followed jackals anyway, always hoping to see a brown hyena. Each hot, sleepless day began at dawn, before the heat, when we worked on our soil sampling, grass transects, and fecal analysis. Three weeks of this were about all we could take, then we would collapse for a cool night of deep sleep.

Most of the jackals along the valley had paired, each pair having established a territory of about one square mile, including a portion of prime riverbed habitat and an adjoining section of duneslope bush savanna. Captain and Mate held Cheetah Hill, Bonnie and Clyde defended an area near "Last Stop," Gimpy and Whinnie roamed east of North Tree, Sundance and Skinny Tail owned North Bay Hill, and so on. They called every sunset and periodically throughout the night, and we could recognize each of the seven pairs by their voices or by their location in relation to camp.

Their thick, black saddles of long hair insulated them against the sun to a great degree. All Captain and Mate seemed to need for shelter was the patchy shade of a small leafless bush on Cheetah Hill, where they slept through the scorching days. Even the early mornings and late afternoons were hot now, and they hunted only at night, when it was cool. They had had no water to drink for months, and we often saw them fighting other pairs of jackals for the moisture in a single wild melon.

November clouds tantalized us: Their filmy curtains of rain smelled incredibly sweet and fresh—but always fell somewhere far away in the desert. None of the clouds was dark and heavy enough to challenge the great convective barrier of heat that rose from the baking riverbed.

One day the morning winds did not come; the air was utterly still, as though waiting. At midmorning clouds began building beyond West Prairie. Hour by hour they grew until they stood shoulder to shoulder, towering columns of water vapor too big for the sky. By midafternoon the purple-black sky was boiling with vapor. Daggers of lightning slashed across the clouds and thunder boomed through the valley.

After weeks of disappointment we were sure the storm would probably pass us by. But then an avalanche of black cloud tumbled over the shoulder of West Dune, sucking up a yellow blizzard of sand as it rolled toward camp. The stagnant air began stirring around us. We ran to the truck and backed it out from under the trees.

Thirty yards from camp I turned the rear of the truck to the coming storm. Seconds later, the sand and wind slammed into us. We pressed our shirts to our faces, trying to breathe in the grey air while the Land Rover rocked and creaked, the keys jingling in the ignition. Hail drummed on the truck's metal roof, and through the windshield we could see boxes, sacks, pots, pans, and other bits of camp rising into the air. The acacia tree was reeling like a crazed animal clawing at itself.

At last it was raining. Water was streaming through gaps in the window frames and trickling into our laps. "Smell it! Smell it! God, how wonderful! How beautiful!" we shouted over and over.

The storm came in surges, craggy fingers of lightning skittering over the low, black clouds, causing a ghostly blue glow to reflect off the rain and sand in the air. Much later that night, we finally drifted off to sleep between gusts of wind that shook the truck.

The valley was bright with sunshine when we opened our eyes the next morning. But it was not the same malevolent sun that had scorched the Kalahari for months. Soft, mellow rays caressed the backs of several hundred springbok, nibbling grass bases succulent with glittering droplets. The storm was only a smudge on the distant horizon. From camp we could see Captain and Mate and a pair of bat-eared foxes drinking from puddles on the spongy desert floor.

Our clothes, pans, papers, and other belongings were scattered over the riverbed. Delia recovered a pot fifty yards from camp and cooked a porridge of oats mixed with sorghum and *samp*—cracked corn. After breakfast we began picking up the pieces. The gasoline drum had been rolled halfway across the valley.

The storm painted the desert green again, and within a week the valley was full of antelope herds dropping their scrawny, floppy-eared fawns into the new sprouts of velvet. Flying termites swarmed after their queens. Bat-eared foxes scurried here and there with their fluffy kits, fattening themselves on the hordes of insects hopping, flying, and crawling everywhere. Everyone was gearing up to have their young and get them reared during this short and fickle period of abundance. Everywhere there was a sense of life renewed, of rebirth after long trials of heat and fire. Other storms soon followed, and with the beginning of the rainy season, daytime temperatures dipped to the mid-seventies and eighties and blue skies were filled with balmy breezes and brilliant white clouds.

Perhaps best of all, the same pride of lions that had trapped Delia in the mess tent months before returned to the valley. Their roars in the night and early morning, together with the calls of the jackals, brought the fossil riverbed to life again. We talked of coming back to the Kalahari one day to make a complete study of lions. But first there were the jackals and brown hyenas to reckon with.

At sunset several days after that first storm of the rainy season, we were having a hurried meal at the campfire before going out to find Captain and Mate. One of the other jackal pairs, Gimpy and Whinnie, began calling east of the Twin Acacias, their strident, quavering, and strangely melodic cries ringing through the valley. We fell silent, moved, as always, by the mournful sound. It seemed to come from the very heart of the desert—the cry of the Kalahari. The others began to join the chorus: Bonnie and Clyde, Sundance and Skinny Tail, and finally, Captain's deep, hoarse voice, together with Mate's clear song, from Cheetah Hill.

"Wait a minute . . . what's that?" Delia asked. High-pitched breathless squeals tried earnestly to mimic Captain and Mate.

"Pups!" We jumped into the Land Rover and drove toward the calls. After parking some distance away from the jackals, we peered this way and that, trying to see through the cover of bush. Then Mate appeared at the den opening and lowered her head. When she stepped aside, two powder puffs of fur with wriggling tails, short, fuzzy faces, and stubby black noses waddled into view.

Mate began licking the faces, backs, and bellies of "Hansel" and "Gretel," rolling each one over and over in the sand while the other stumbled beneath her on stumpy, uncertain legs. Captain lay nearby, his head on his paws. Then Bonnie and Clyde began to call from the north again. Before the calls had died away, they began to answer, Hansel and Gretel standing beside Captain and Mate, their tiny muzzles straining toward the sky.

Both parents participated in raising their pups, but they had no "helpers," as have black-backed jackals in other areas of Africa. Dr. Patricia Moehlman[1] found that some jackal subadults on the Serengeti Plains remain with their parents to assist in providing for the next litter. They help by regurgitating food to their mother and to their younger brothers and sisters, and by guarding the den. Although we did not see this among the jackals we knew, some other Kalahari pairs may have had helpers. This behavior is often difficult to observe and may not be detected until a species has been studied for perhaps several years.

In the early weeks, either Captain or Mate was always at the den to guard the pups from predators. After sunset each evening, Captain would walk over to Mate, Hansel and Gretel romping around his feet, biting his ears, legs, and the tip of his tail, and he would touch her nose with his. Then, lifting his feet high and stepping over the tumbling pups, he would trot away to hunt, leaving Mate to tend the litter. Once their father was out of the way, Hansel and Gretel would immediately begin pestering their mother, chewing her ears, rolling over her face, tumbling across her back, and pouncing on her tail. Mate was tolerant, but seldom took an active part in the play.

From the very beginning, adult behavior patterns were apparent in the pups' activities. They repeatedly practiced the holds, stalks, pounces, and killing bites that would make them successful hunters as adults. If their mother wouldn't cooperate, they attacked each other, or else the grass clumps and sticks within a few feet of the den.

The pups were about three weeks old when Captain began bringing them raw meat to eat. Wagging their tails, the youngsters would burst from the entrance and rush to their father, licking his lips hungrily, begging for food. He would open his jaws wide and regurgitate a slimy mass of partially digested mice and birds on the ground before them. As Hansel and Gretel gobbled up the steaming hash, Captain would settle under a nearby bush to rest and babysit while Mate trotted off to hunt.

As soon as the pups had been partially weaned on fresh meat, their parents began taking them for short excursions away from the den. The adults strolled along while the youngsters romped and played, smelling bushes, grasses, antelope droppings—everything they could get their noses on. They were learning more and more about their fossil river environment. One of the most valuable lessons for the pups on these early morning forays was how to kill and eat insects. This was an important predatory skill, for it allowed them to supplement their diet of milk and regurgitated meat while Mate was weaning them.

Now that Hansel and Gretel were better able to look after themselves, Captain and Mate began to hunt together again, leaving the pups to forage for insects near the den. One night the parents hunted an area that included the riverbed east of the Cheetah Hill sand tongue, the hill itself, and a slip of bush and woodland behind it. They moved along, each pausing frequently to cock a hind leg and scent-mark a low shrub or woody herb along the boundary of their territory.

They had just entered the duneslope woodlands when Mate began dancing around something on the ground ahead, her tail waving in the air. Captain rushed to her and found a nine-foot black mamba, one of Africa's most poisonous snakes, its body reared three feet off the ground and ready to strike. The mamba's tongue flicked in and out, its sinister coffin-shaped head drawn back like a crossbow ready to fire.

Captain feinted this way and that, trying to get past the snake's defenses. But the beady eyes tracked him like a missile. Wherever he moved, the mamba adjusted itself, waiting.

Mate moved around until she was opposite Captain, with the snake between them. She darted toward it, and for an instant it was distracted. With a motion too quick to follow, Captain lunged for the mamba, but it had recovered its attention and it struck. Several feet of its long ropy body sprang off the ground as Captain dodged away in a shower of sand, the lethal head barely missing his shoulder.

Instantly he was back on the attack, pouncing again and again, and each time the mamba struck, he jumped away. He would not let up; after each strike, the snake was taking a little longer to rear and prepare for another attack.

It was when the mamba was trying to recover after a miss that Captain managed to nip it hard on the back. Tired and injured, it tried to crawl away. But Mate blocked the retreat, and it raised itself and made another thrust, just missing Captain when he charged forward. Before it could escape, he bit it hard about three feet back from the head, and then again. It was writhing now. Finally, after several more bites, he held it for a split second and shook it violently, its coils squirming about his legs. Then he dropped it, and grabbing the dangerous head, crushed it in his jaws.

At that point the perilous hunt became a comedy. As soon as Captain seized the mamba's head, Mate grabbed its tail. In contrast to their supreme cooperation of just seconds before, they now began yanking at either end of the snake in a tug of war, each trying to run off with the prize. They glared, eyes blazing and ears laid back, along several feet of reptile. Their hackles bristled and their tails slashed as they seesawed back and forth, until finally the snake was yanked into two equal lengths of stringy white meat. Each began feeding feverishly; it took them nearly ten minutes to finish. Then they rolled in the grass, sniffed noses, rubbed faces, and trotted off together on a border patrol of their territory, their bellies round and bouncing.

* * *

Before we thought to tape a tiny calendar inside the cover of one of our field journals, we had lost track of the date. Judging from the time of our last supply trip to Maun, we guessed that Christmas 1974 must be near. Without the money or time to go to the village for the holiday, we picked a day and began preparations for celebrating it at camp.

One morning, after great deliberation, we selected and cut a half-dead broad-leafed *Lonchocarpus nelsii* tree from the dune woodlands and hauled it back to camp on top of the Land Rover. We decorated the tree with the thermometer, some red collaring material, a few syringes, and the dissection scalpels, scissors, and forceps, adding the hand scales, a lantern, a springbok jawbone, the defective fire extinguisher, and various paraphernalia from around camp. Once we had tied these onto the branches of the tree, we began to plan our Christmas dinner.

A flock of thirteen guinea fowl had found camp at the beginning of the rainy season. At least once, often twice, a day they took a stroll along our kitchen counter, which consisted of boards laid across the tops of water drums. They raked their horny feet through our tin dinner plates, scattered knives, forks, and spoons onto the ground, flipped the lids off the cooking pots, and devoured any leftovers lying about. And when they found a loaf of freshly baked bread, pieces flew off it as if it were being shot to bits by a Gatling gun. At first we thought they were cute, but the noise they made early in the morning, after a long night of following jackals, was difficult to tolerate, and they hogged all the mealie-meal we scattered on the ground for the other birds.

I finally decided to discourage the guinea fowl flock from coming into camp. That I reached this decision near Christmas, when we had gone for nearly four months without fresh meat, was perhaps no coincidence.

Early one morning, I propped a box up with a stick, weighted it with a stone, and sprinkled some mealie-meal under it. I tied a nylon fishing line to the prop and strung it along the ground to the opposite side of the Land Rover, where I hid behind the wheel. Not long after sunrise the guinea flock arrived with its piping gabble, raising the dust as it scratched and pecked its way into camp. Almost immediately one of the cocks spied the trail of mealie-meal leading beneath the box and, without hesitation, began his rapid-fire pecking along it, leading his entire flock toward the trap. I could already taste freshly roasted guinea.

Four plump hens and the cock crowded beneath the box, gobbling up mealie-meal as fast as they could. I flicked the fishing line. The box plopped to the ground in a cloud of dust and flapping wings. The guineas railed loudly. I jumped from behind the truck and hurried forward while the birds eyed me suspiciously.

The trap lay perfectly still, not a peep from inside. I looked around: *Thirteen* pairs of guinea eyes glared at me. I was dumbfounded. What had gone wrong? They couldn't be all that quick and crafty; after all, they were little more than a bunch of barnyard chickens. I'd get one the next time. I reset the boxtrap and ambled discreetly toward the Land Rover. By this time Delia was sitting up in bed grinning.

The guineas pecked their way back to the trap. This time only two ventured beneath it. I yanked the line and the box hit the ground. I quickly counted heads again. "One, two, three, four, five—Damn!" Thirteen squawking guineas and one snickering wife. On the third try the birds only pecked to the edges of the box—not one would go under it.

On our self-appointed Christmas morning, the guineas were back as usual, scattering our pots, pans, and dishes about with a loud clatter. We ignored each other as I sifted the weevils from some flour and baked a loaf of caraway bread in the bucket oven. Delia made a meat pie with the last of the rock-hard biltong Bergie had left us. Our Christmas dessert was another pie made with maretwa berries we had picked from the bushes of West Prairie.

Christmas was a hot day and, despite efforts to cheer ourselves, without family or gifts we were short on holiday spirit. We sang a few carols, and then, feeling somewhat lonely and let-down, we drove to the den and spent the afternoon with the jackals.

Hansel and Gretel, now about seven weeks old and three-quarters as tall as their parents, scampered out to us as we were parking the truck. Their saddles were beginning to gain definition, changing from a soft grey to a bold black. They had gained much skill at catching insects and even took a mouse occasionally, displaying fairly sophisticated hunting behavior. Captain and Mate roamed farther from the den now and brought back much less food.

That Christmas night, before Captain and Mate left to hunt, a strange type of jackal call rang out from the North Tree area. The jackals immediately jumped to their feet. With Hansel and Gretel trailing their parents at a distance, the whole family hurried toward the unusual nasal *weeuugh*! . . . *weeuugh*! . . . *weeuugh*! that echoed urgently over and over again.

By the time Captain and Mate arrived at the scene, six jackals had already surrounded a patch of tall grass, all of them voicing that strange call as they sprang up and down on their stiffened legs. Again and again they bounced into the grass and back out again, a split second later. Captain and Mate joined the ritual while Hansel and Gretel sat on their haunches, watching.

After about fifteen minutes of this, a leopard came slinking out of the thicket. His face and chest covered in blood, and still surrounded by springing jackals, he laid back his ears and walked away. The jackals followed for forty yards, calling, darting, and bouncing all around him. Then they trotted back to the grass patch to scavenge the springbok remains he had left behind.

Jackals are a favorite prey of leopards. The strange call and the associated jumping display probably allow them to keep an eye on the predator in tall, thick cover and to communicate the danger to other jackals. It serves the same purpose as the mobbing of a predatory snake by birds.

After a time, Hansel and Gretel entered the long grass area where their parents and other jackals were squabbling over the springbok carcass. Captain and Mate had been unable to hold off the invasion of Bonnie and Clyde, Gimpy and Whinnie, and two other pairs from outlying territories. Intense bickering around this large food resource enforced the strict social hierarchy that existed among members of the population throughout the year.

When Hansel and Gretel tried to join in the feeding, both of their parents turned on them, snarling aggressively, their mouths pursed in threat and their tails lashing. Apparently surprised and intimidated, the youngsters retreated a short distance. These were not the tolerant parents they had known. Both Captain and Mate had been testy of late and had rebuffed their attempts at play, but these serious threats were something new. They were being treated as competitors, and Captain directed most of his aggression toward Hansel. Gretel tucked her tail and sat on it, opened her mouth wide, and raised her front paw in submission. She would have to wait her turn to feed.

Hansel's saddle was black and becoming more and more distinct, and silver hairs were beginning to show through. He was close to adulthood in size and markings. He persistently moved in on the carcass, only to be rebuffed by Captain. Finally he had had enough. The two males faced each other snarling, hackles stiff as wire. Captain charged and hit Hansel with his shoulder. The youngster took the blow and delivered a hip slam in return. For a second they were a mass of boiling fur. When it was over, Hansel advanced boldly and fed next to his father. He had developed the competitive spirit essential for winning a place in the adult social hierarchy, where a jackal with higher status gains longer feeding time at carcasses, as well as superior mates and better breeding territories.

The encounter between Captain, Mate, Hansel, and Gretel was typical of the "parent-offspring conflict"[2] that occurs in many animal species, including humans, and is perhaps most visible at weaning. Anyone who has ever heard the screams of a young baboon when first turned out of its mother's nest, or seen the facial expression of a kitten spat at by its parent after weeks of being cuddled, fed, and groomed knows that such conflicts can be severe. The classical explanation for this behavior is that the parent is still caring for the juvenile by forcing it to become independent, which is necessary for its survival. A more recent theory argues that there is a time, after the young are weaned and have become larger and more demanding, when it becomes too costly for the mother to provide food, energy for defense, and other resources for her subadult young. Instinct advises her to devote the same efforts toward the production of new offspring. She is also encouraging her young to begin breeding themselves. This is a genetic benefit to her because her own genes will be passed on by the young she has just alienated, as well as by herself.

In each Kalahari dry season, probably because of low prey densities, jackal pairs break up and their breeding territories completely disintegrate. In the next mating season, near the beginning of the rains, different pairs establish new territories along the riverbed. As stated earlier, we saw no evidence that families stay together, with adolescents helping to rear the new litter, though this may occur when several good consecutive rainy seasons occur. But paired or not, the jackals in Deception Valley maintained a strict social hierarchy from year to year.

On this Christmas evening, all of the jackals eating at the springbok carcass suddenly paused, looking into the darkness to the east. Then they began feeding faster, almost frantically, seizing meat on the neck and along the spine and lunging backward to tear it free. I lifted the spotlight and swung it eastward. The large, wide-set emerald eyes of a brown hyena were watching from 125 yards away. Apparently she had heard the mobbing call of the jackals and knew a leopard was in the area and that there was a possibility of a kill. We sat unmoving, hoping, as we had so often before, that she would come to feed despite our presence.

The hyena circled the truck several times and stood watching for a long while. Finally, with her hackles standing up along her shoulders and back, she walked toward the carcass. From her udders we could see that it was a female. The jackals gobbled the meat even faster until, at the last moment, they leaped over the dead antelope and dashed out of the hyena's reach. The brown turned and looked at the Land Rover for several seconds before beginning to feed. Then, puffing and straining, she started shattering bones and ripping the flesh from the skeleton. The circle of displaced jackals pulled in around her, but whenever they tried to snatch a bite, she went thundering after them with gaping jaws.

After a time, most of the jackals moved off a few yards and lay down, except for Captain, who circled around and came slowly, almost nonchalantly in behind the feeding brown. The hyena freed a length of springbok leg, laid it at her feet, and continued to feed on the softer parts near the ribs. Lowering himself on wiry legs, Captain crept closer and closer to the unsuspecting brown hyena, until he was crouched with his nose to her rear. Still she continued to feed, unaware. Slowly he raised his muzzle to the base of the brown's flicking tail; he held it there for several seconds. Then, as the tail moved aside, he bit the hyena on the backside. She whirled to her left and Captain dashed to the right, seizing the springbok leg and a large swatch of dangling skin. It was almost more than he could carry, but by holding his nose high in the air he could run—and run he did.

Hair streaming, her jaws open wide near the tip of Captain's tail, the hyena chased him in great circles across the riverbed. Whenever it seemed he was about to be swallowed up, Captain would make a turn too sudden for the lumbering hyena to follow. On he ran, his muzzle sagging lower and lower with his heavy loot, until finally he dropped it. Panting heavily, he watched the hyena carry it back to the carcass. Once again the brown laid the leg at her feet and began to feed.

Little more than two minutes later, Captain was back, sneaking up on the hyena again. It looked like an instant replay: Captain chomped the brown in the rear, stole the springbok leg and fled, his tail flying, with the hyena in hot pursuit. But this time he escaped into the bush at the edge of the riverbed. The hyena sloped back to the carcass, licking her chops, ears laid back in evident disgust. Eventually she lifted all that remained of the carcass and walked with it into the thick bush of North Dune.

It was after midnight when we turned into camp. The headlights swung among the trees and fell on another brown hyena—standing near the water drums, not fifteen yards away! Unconcerned with us, she continued smelling her way through camp. Eyeing our bag of onions hanging from a tree, she stood on her hind legs, grabbed the net sack by the corner, and pulled. When a cascade of bulbs thumped over her nose and onto the ground in a shower of papery skins, she jumped back. After smelling one carefully and biting into it, she shook her head and sneezed. At the fire grate (the coals had died hours before) she took the water kettle by its handle and strutted from camp. Putting it down a few yards away, she jarred the lid off with her nose and lapped up the water from inside. Then she raised her tail and began to walk away, but before she disappeared she stopped and looked directly at us for several seconds. There was a small white star on her forehead.

5

Star

Delia

How I wonder what you are . . .
—*Ann Taylor*

WE HAD had a Kalahari Christmas after all: The brown hyenas had accepted us at last. We woke up early the next morning full of kick and ready to go, in spite of the late night's work. Sipping from enamel cups of steaming tea and talking over the experiences of the previous night, we strolled from camp north toward Acacia Point, as we often did on cool mornings.

"I don't believe it, look over there." Mark pointed to the edge of the heavy bushes on North Bay Hill about 300 yards away. A brown hyena was walking directly toward our truck spoor on a course that would intercept ours. She had apparently not seen us and was moving quite fast through the belly-high grass, apparently in a hurry to reach her bed before the sun rose any higher.

We stood perfectly still, not knowing quite what to do. If we started back to camp, our movements might frighten her. It was one thing for the hyenas—or any of the other animals—to accept us in the truck, but they were generally much more intimidated by the sight of us on foot. Very slowly we each sat down in a tire rut, expecting her to run away at any moment. When she reached the track, fifty yards away, she turned south and came directly toward us, the small white blaze on her broad forehead bobbing up and down. It was the same hyena who had taken the water kettle.

Without hesitating once, she steadily closed the distance between us, finally stopping just five yards away. We were exactly at her eye level. Her dark eyes were moist, perhaps because of the unfriendly sun. The sides of her face were battle-scarred, and a cape of fine blonde hair lay over her shoulders. Her long slender forelegs were boldly striped black and grey, ending with large, round feet. Her square jaws, capable of crushing or carrying away a fifty-pound gemsbok leg, were slightly parted.

Slowly putting one padded foot before the other, she reached her nose toward me, taking gentle wisps of my scent, her long whiskers twitching. Finally her face was no more than eighteen inches from mine. We stared into each other's eyes.

Courses in animal behavior teach that carnivores communicate fear and aggression through the postures of their ears, eyes, and mouth. Star had no expression on her face, and that in itself conveyed the strongest message of all. We had seen peaceful interactions between different species in the desert on many occasions: a ground squirrel smelling the nose of a mongoose; cape foxes actually denning in the same complex of burrows with a colony of meerkats; four tiny bat-eared foxes playfully chasing a small herd of hartebeest. And now, Star was communicating, through her curiosity and lack of fear, an acceptance of us into her natural world.

She stepped still closer, lifting her nose slightly and sniffing the edge of my hair. Then she sidestepped rather clumsily over her front feet and smelled Mark's beard. After that, she turned and walked on at the same even pace toward West Dune.

Star was enterprising and spunky, always ready to rally. Now and then, padding along the riverbed, she would dance a curious jig, leaping off her hind legs, tossing her head, and turning a half circle in the air. It was Star, mostly, who taught us the secrets of brown hyena society, and eventually some secrets about ourselves.

She and several of the other hyenas allowed us to follow them in the truck, as we had done with the jackals. But four or five hours, at the most, was as long as we could keep her in sight. As soon as she left the riverbed, tall grass and thick bush would close over her. Since we could never keep up with the hyenas all night, we still had no idea where they slept in the daytime. In the evenings we often searched the dark riverbed for hours before finding one to follow. Our entire study of brown hyenas was restricted to chance meetings with them on a narrow ribbon of riverbed grassland no more than 1000 yards across.

One night in January, a large pair of eyes was reflected in the spotlight, and trailing behind them was a long line of smaller eyes, all bouncing up and down. At first glance it looked like a female carnivore leading her cubs through the grass. But it was Star and, trotting single file behind her, five young jackals, including Hansel and Gretel, all apparently playing follow-the-leader. When Star stopped, they stopped; when she zigzagged, they zigzagged. From time to time she would wheel around, as if annoyed by her shadows and hoping to shake them off. When she reached Eagle Island, on the edge of the open riverbed, and lay down for a rest in the grass, the young jackals arranged themselves in a circle around her. Because brown hyenas and jackals are keen competitors, they always check on each other when meeting and often discover that the other has food. These inexperienced youngsters were apparently hoping Star would lead them to an easy meal.

A few minutes later, Hansel walked up to Star and put his small black nose up to her large muzzle, in what looked like a warm greeting between friends. In fact, he may have been assessing whether or not she had recently fed. Apparently Hansel found nothing interesting on Star's chops because he trotted away, as did the other jackals, each in a separate direction.

After resting for twenty minutes at Eagle Island, Star began to follow a zag-stitch course along the moonlit riverbed, walking at about three miles per hour. Now and then she would stop to lap up a few termites or leap into the air for a flying grasshopper. Suddenly she pivoted to the west and raised her nose high, analyzing the odors on the night air. Then she sprang forward and loped through the taller grasses of West Prairie, dodging around bushes and termite mounds and pausing only to retest the breeze. The scent led her for over two miles to the edge of the dune woodlands, where she stopped abruptly, peering into a dense thicket.

Two feeding lionesses and their cubs—low, dark forms in the grass—lay around the remains of a gemsbok, its belly torn open and flanks smeared red. The night air was heavy with the pungent odor of the gemsbok's rumen, which was probably how Star had smelled it two miles away. She circled widely around the area, then stood downwind. The kill was very fresh, not more than half an hour old, and the lions would not leave it tonight. She walked away north into the trees. For a scavenger, patience is the key to the pantry.

Early the next evening, we found Star headed straight for the lions' gemsbok kill, which was by now reduced to a rubble of white bones, strips of tattered red meat, and folds of skin. The lions were still there, sleeping on their backs, their legs sticking up from bloated bellies. Star flopped down beneath a bush to sleep, and to wait.

These were the same lions Mark had pushed away from the drugged jackal with the Land Rover; we had seen them quite often and believed they were permanent residents in our area. Tonight it was around eleven when they finally roused themselves and walked single file through the woodland of West Dune.

Star must have heard them leave. She stood up and circled the kill site three times, smelling and staring from different positions. This is one of the most dangerous situations brown hyenas ever face. They depend heavily on the leftovers from lions, and on finding such carrion before it is gobbled up by jackals or other brown hyenas, or by the vultures that arrive at dawn. But without being able to actually see the gemsbok carcass in the tall grass, Star had to rely primarily on her sense of smell to tell her whether all the lions had gone. It must have been difficult, in the confusion of odors from gemsbok remains and those of lion dung and urine. She took several tentative steps forward, then stood still, her nose raised, her ears perked to pick up any clue that might help her avoid walking into a lion. Fifteen minutes later, she had worked her way to within twenty-five yards of the gemsbok. After another long wait, she finally went to the carcass and began to feed.

After nibbling at morsels of stringy meat, tendons, and sinew, she opened her jaws wide and began to crush leg bones as thick as baseball bats and to swallow splinters at least three inches long. (We measured these later, by fecal analysis.) A brown hyena's teeth are veritable hammers specialized for processing bone: The premolars are flattened and enlarged, unlike the sharp, scissorlike cutting blades of other predators. Tilting her head to one side, Star wedged her teeth between the ball and socket of a hind leg until it tore free. Carrying it by the knee, she walked into the thick bush of the duneslope, where she tucked the leg under an acacia bush about 100 yards from the riverbed.

Star was uncanny in her ability to locate lion kills and to know when the remains—the most important part of a brown hyena's wet-season diet—would be abandoned. However, she also spent many long, lonely nights walking for miles and finding nothing to eat but a mouse or an old bone.

* * *

The few scanty reports on brown hyenas described them as solitary scavengers, real loners that ate only carrion or occasionally hunted small mammals. At first we thought this description was probably accurate: Star followed that feeding pattern and was always alone. But soon we began seeing some extraordinary behavior that made us question whether browns were indeed solitary creatures.

Any information about how many of them live in a group, whether or not they defend a communal territory, and why they associate together is important for the conservation of hyenas. But there is another reason to investigate their social life: Man is also a social carnivore, and by understanding the evolution and nature of societies of other predators, we can better understand our own sense of territoriality, our need for identity as part of a group, and our aggressive tendencies as competitors.

Later that night, following Star when she left the carcass, we noticed that she did not wander aimlessly over the range, but traveled on the distinct pathways she had used on previous nights. Some of these joined or crossed well-used game trails, such as Leopard Trail, a major route for gemsbok, kudu, giraffe, jackals, and leopards moving north-south along a string of temporary water holes at the foot of West Dune. Usually, however, the hyenas' paths were visible only as faintly divided grass or lightly compacted sand.

Star paused at a grass clump, smelling a small, dark blob at nose level on one of the stems. Then, in a most bizarre display, she stepped over the grass, raised her tail, and everted a special rectal pouch. By swiveling her hindquarters to feel for the stalk, she directed the two-lobed pouch to the stem and "pasted" a drop of white substance that looked remarkably like Elmer's Glue. After she had lowered her tail, she retracted the pouch and walked on. We took a sniff of the paste; it had a pungent, musty odor. Just above the white drop, a smaller rust-colored secretion was also smeared on the grass.

During the following weeks we saw other hyenas traveling the same trails that Star used, always alone, and often stopping to smell the paste that Star and others had left on the grass-stalks. Before moving on, they would add their own chemical signature to the stem, so that, in spots where paths crossed, a grass clump could have as many as thirteen scent marks, very much like a sign post at a highway intersection.

Late one night we were following a very timid female, about Star's size, that we had named Shadow. She was walking south along the riverbed on one of the hyena paths and pausing every hundred yards or so to smell a scent mark and then paste over it. She crossed South Pan through Tree Island and entered the thick bush, where we lost her. It was one o'clock in the morning, so we stopped for coffee on the edge of the riverbed before looking for another hyena. We were sitting on top of the Land Rover in the moonlight sipping from our Thermos cups, when Star came along. She crossed the first hyena's path and stood smelling Shadow's fresh paste mark for nearly a minute, her long hairs bristling. Then she changed course and followed quickly after her.

We managed to keep Star in sight until we could see Shadow walking back toward Star in the moonlight, the two dark forms moving silently through the tall, silvery grass. We stopped, Mark flicked on the spotlight, and the most unusual behavior we had ever seen between two animals began to unfold.

Star approached and Shadow crouched down until her belly was flat to the ground. She drew her lips up tightly and opened her mouth wide, showing her teeth in an exaggerated grin. Her long ears stuck out from her head like a floppy hat, and her tail curled tightly over her back. Squealing like a rusty gate hinge, she began crawling around Star, who also turned, but in the opposite direction. Each time Shadow passed beneath Star's nose, she paused to let her smell the scent glands beneath her tail. The hyenas pirouetted around and around, like ballerinas on a dimly lit stage.

The strange greeting continued for several minutes, even after Star tried to walk on down the trail. Each time she began to move away, Shadow hurried to lie in front of her, inviting Star to take another sniff under her tail. Like an aristocratic lady dismissing her attendant, Star finally stood with her nose held high, refusing to further indulge Shadow. Eventually she walked away, and Shadow departed in a different direction.

Several nights later we found Star again, but she was not alone. Tagging along behind her were two smaller hyenas who were only three-quarters her size and had finer, darker hair. We named them Pogo and Hawkins. They were romping behind Star along the riverbed near Cheetah Hill, playfully biting each other's ears, face, and neck. Whenever Star found a bit of carrion, they rushed to her, "grinning," squealing, and crawling back and forth under her nose, begging for food. In response to this performance, Star shared her find with them, and we naturally assumed that they were her cubs. But the next night we found Pogo and Hawkins with Patches, an adult female with tattered ears. If they were Star's cubs, why would they follow Patches?

By April we could recognize seven different brown hyenas in the immediate area. A large male we called Ivey had immigrated into the area quite a few months before. There were four adult females—Patches, Lucky, Star, and Shadow—and the youngsters, Pogo and Hawkins. But it was often difficult to identify the dark, shaggy creatures at night, and since brown hyenas are notoriously difficult to sex under the best of conditions, there were many times when we were unsure of both the sex and the identity of the hyena we were following.

Reluctantly, we came to the conclusion that we would have to immobilize and eartag as many of the browns as possible. This was a dismaying prospect, for it had taken many months to habituate the seven hyenas to our presence. If the darting alienated any of them, it could jeopardize our entire research program. Yet, unless we marked them, we could make mistakes in our observations of their social behavior.

Mark used a silencer for the darting rifle made by modifying a Volkswagen muffler, and we waited for an opportunity to dart Star, Pogo, and Hawkins. It came one night when the youngsters were following the older female to the remains of a gemsbok carcass. The cubs soon lost interest in the wrinkled skin, and in the bones that were probably too large for them to break, and wandered off, leaving Star to feed alone. By inching the truck slowly forward and stopping each time Star looked up, we moved to within twenty yards of her. Working slowly, with quiet movements, Mark estimated the dosage, prepared the dart, and slid it into the rifle. Star was very nervous, perhaps because of the odor of lions in the area. At the click of the rifle bolt she looked up into the spotlight and then dashed off a few yards. But after staring at the truck for a minute, she licked her chops and returned slowly to feed, her tail flicking—a sign that she had relaxed again.

Mark put his cheek to the rifle stock and took aim at her dark form. I gripped my notebook hard and looked away, afraid of what was about to happen and certain that she would dash off and we would never see her again. Months of hard work—everything, it seemed—were riding on this one shot. Mark brought his arm slowly up under the gun, but at the mere rustling of his nylon jacket, Star ran off again. This time she stared at the Land Rover for several minutes, and then began walking away.

We didn't move—not a muscle—for the next hour. Star was still in sight, lying down with her head on her paws, watching. After a while my back began to ache and my hips and legs to numb. I couldn't imagine how Mark must be feeling, one elbow on the steering wheel, the other on the door frame, and his cheek on the stock as he hunched forward over the gunsights.

Star knew something wasn't right with that carcass. When she stood again we could almost see her trying to decide whether to leave or come back to feed. Finally she lowered her head and plodded slowly toward the carcass.

Mark gently squeezed the trigger. There was a muffled pop, and we could actually see the dart fly from the barrel of the rifle. It slapped Star in the shoulder. She jumped back, whirling, twisting, and biting at the missile. Then she ran. Swearing under his breath, Mark quietly swung the spotlight after her. Otherwise, we did not move.

Star loped to the very limit of the light, where we could barely see her. There she stopped and looked around in the darkness, staring and listening, as if trying to figure out what had stung her in the shoulder. I was sure we had blown it and that she would never trust us again. But then her tail began flicking, and, unbelievably, she walked directly back to the carcass and started feeding again, without even giving us a glance.

Minutes later she slumped to the ground, and we let out deep sighs of relief. Pogo and Hawkins, who were much less wary than adult browns, came back to the carcass, and having briefly smelled Star, began to gnaw on the bones. Mark darted them, and within fifteen minutes the three hyenas were lying peacefully in the grass. Carrying our equipment box, we eased quietly from the truck, stretched our numb limbs, and began ear-tagging and measuring them.

"This *is* a female, isn't it?" Mark whispered, kneeling beside Star.

"I'm not sure. Are those things real?" I poked at two fleshy lobes that looked like testicles.

There we were—two students of zoology, with thirteen years of university between us—poking and prodding the confusing array of sexual and pseudosexual organs carried by this odd beast. Although female brown hyenas lack the enlarged pseudopenis (actually the clitoris) of spotted hyena females, they are equipped with fatty lobes or nodules located where the testicles would be if they were males. After a considerable period of investigation and consultation, we were still not sure if Star was male or female. Fortunately, Hawkins was well equipped with genuine testicles, which resolved our confusion: Star and Pogo were definitely female.

Star wasn't the least bit wary of us, several nights later, when she passed within fifteen yards of the truck, wearing her blue plastic ear tag. We followed her to a hartebeest carcass left by lions near the base of Acacia Point, where she began to feed. Fifteen minutes later Pogo and Hawkins joined her.

They had fed only briefly when all three raised their heads and stared into the darkness. Patches, holding her head high, was walking directly toward them in the spotlight. Pogo and Hawkins fed, but the two adult females glared at each other. Star lowered her head and ears, and every hair on her body stood straight out. Suddenly Patches rushed in and seized her by the neck, biting and shaking her violently. Star shrieked when Patches' teeth cut through her skin and the blood spread through her blonde neck hair. The two hyenas turned and stumbled through the dry grass, Star throwing her muzzle up and back, trying to break the grip. A cloud of dust shrouded the fighting pair.

Patches held on for almost ten minutes, flinging her adversary back and forth with such fury that Star's front feet were lifted from the ground. Blood dripped onto the sand. Between rasping breaths and screams came the sound of teeth grating through thick skin. Patches released Star briefly, found another grip near her ear, and held on. Inches away, Star's unprotected jugular surged with life. Again and again Patches changed her hold on Star's neck, raking her through the sand as if she were a rag doll. It was like watching someone being murdered in the street.

After twenty grueling minutes Patches suddenly released her. I was sickened by the sight of Star's neck, minced and shredded, with open penny-sized holes in her skin. For a moment I thought she would stumble to her forelegs, never to rise again. But then, as if she had been through little more than a mild scrap, she shook her long hair, flicked her tail, and side by side with Patches, walked over to the carcass. The two cubs had paid no attention to the ruckus; now all four fed close together, their muzzles almost touching. Even though there were no further signs of aggression, after five minutes Star walked away from the carcass and went to sleep nearby. She did not return to feed until Patches had left. Such neck-biting behavior had never before been reported, and it was one of the most intense and stirring encounters between animals that we would witness in the Kalahari.

For weeks we had seen hyenas, who were supposedly solitary, traveling and scent-marking the same trails and greeting each other with a bizarre crawling ceremony. We had seen Pogo and Hawkins foraging with two different adult females. And now, although the two females had just engaged in a pitched battle, we saw them feeding together at the same carcass. What a hodgepodge of signals they were giving us! This was most definitely *not* the behavior of a solitary species, in which males and females tolerate each other only long enough for courtship and mating. We became more and more sure that brown hyenas had some sort of unusual social system.

A few nights later, while looking for a hyena to follow, we found the resident pride of lions feeding on a gemsbok they had killed near Eagle Island, a group of trees north of the Mid Pan water hole. By 11:00 P.M. they had abandoned the carcass and were walking south along the riverbed. Within an hour Ivey, Patches, Star, Shadow, Pogo, and Hawkins were all either at or near the carcass.

During the rest of that night we saw more instances of their peculiar greeting and neck biting, sometimes preceded by a bout of muzzle-wrestling, when two hyenas would stand side by side, throwing their muzzles up high and hard against each other, each trying to get a grip on the other's neck.

But on the whole, the gathering at the carcass was very peaceful, as well as being organized. Usually one hyena—and never more than three—fed while the others slept, groomed, or socialized nearby. They alternated at the carcass; while one was carrying a leg off into the bush, another began to feed. Tonight it was six hours before the last hyena walked off into the bush, leaving only jawbone and scattered rumen content behind. This was leisurely feeding compared to the "scramble competition" between spotted hyenas in the Serengeti of East Africa. The spotteds crowd around a kill in a seething mass of bodies, competing with their fellows by eating as fast as possible. Dr. Hans Kruuk,[1] who studied them in the Serengeti, once saw a clan of twenty-one spotted hyenas consume in thirteen minutes a yearling wildebeest weighing about 220 pounds.

Unfortunately, we found the browns feeding together on a large carcass only once or twice a week during the rains. But after several months, a sketchy picture of their social organization began to emerge. We were sure that the seven hyenas in the area were not solitary animals but members of a clan.[2] Through muzzle-wrestling and neck-biting contests, each had gained a particular rank in the social hierarchy, which was displayed and reinforced in greeting. Ivey, the only adult male in the group, was dominant. The social order among the females ran from Patches at the top, down through Star, Lucky, and Shadow, to Pogo. Hawkins, the young male, was on the same social level as Pogo.

Usually when two brown hyenas met on a path, they would confirm their status through greeting, and then separate. Neck-biting followed only when the status was not well established, or when a hyena tried to rise through the ranks. Star seemed especially keen on social climbing; some nights she would arrive at a kill site and never feed. Her long hair on end, she would spend the entire time picking on lower-ranking females or challenging Patches.

One of the benefits of high status was obvious when several hyenas were feeding on a large carcass: If Ivey approached Shadow, they would usually eat together for only two or three minutes, after which Shadow would walk off and rest nearby until Ivey had left. Quite often there would be no obvious aggression on the part of the dominant hyena; it was as if the subordinate simply did not feel comfortable feeding with its superior and preferred to wait until later. As a result, dominants usually held priority at food sources.

At large carcasses, such as a gemsbok, even the low-ranking Shadow had a chance to feed. But at smaller ones, a steenbok or springbok, the competition was much more intense: The hyenas would feed faster, and only the first one or two arrivals would get anything to eat. When the carcass had been reduced to less than forty or fifty pounds, a dominant would often tuck all the ragged bits and pieces into a bundle and, tripping over dangling flaps of skin, carry it off, a trail of jackals tagging behind.

Lions, wolves, and other social carnivores usually sleep, hunt, and feed with at least some members of their group. But though the browns lived in a clan, they usually foraged and slept alone, only meeting other group members occasionally, while traveling along common pathways or at a kill. They have a limited repertoire of vocal signals, and none with which to communicate over large distances, as do the spotted hyenas. This may be because the dry Kalahari air does not carry sound very far, or perhaps because their territories are too large for clan members to transmit and receive even loud calls effectively. For whatever reason, brown hyenas do not attempt to communicate vocally over distances of more than a few feet, and they do not have the loud *whoo-oop*, or even the "laugh," of their spotted cousins.

This lack of a loud voice might seem to present a problem for animals who roam separately in a jointly owned territory as large as 400 square miles but must also maintain contact with other group members. However, the hyenas' well-developed system of chemical communication through scent-marking—*pasting*, as it is termed—probably takes the place of loud vocalizations. Spotted hyenas also paste, but not quite as extensively as browns, who use it as the most important means of transmitting information among individuals. Clan members appear to recognize the sex, social status, and identity of one another by the paste. For a social animal who must spend long hours alone searching for scattered bits of food, it is an ideal way for group members to stay in touch by "phoning long distance." The hyenas of the Deception Pan Clan also pasted extensively to demarcate their territorial boundaries.

So, the brown hyenas were a curious blend of social and solitary: They foraged and slept alone; they fed together on large carcasses, but carried away the remains for themselves at the first opportunity; they did not use loud vocalizations to communicate with each other, but did leave chemical messages. And, at least for a while, the females allowed the youngsters to follow them when they searched for food.

But when Pogo and Hawkins reached adult stature, at about thirty months of age, Patches, Star, Lucky, and Shadow no longer tolerated their tagging along on foraging expeditions. The subadults were forced to find food on their own. In order to secure a position in the pecking order, Pogo had to compete with the other females, and Star never let the young female forget for a minute who was boss.

On one unforgettable occasion we watched Star neck-biting Pogo for over two hours, chewing and shaking her by the neck for more than a quarter of an hour at a time. The youngster made loud humanlike screams, and it was difficult for us not to interfere. After Star had emphatically made her point, Pogo accepted her status and began displaying the deferential crawl of the subordinate in their greetings.

Hawkins had a different fate. Early one morning, while feeding on the remains of a lion kill, he looked up to see Ivey coming from the north. Hawkins walked slowly toward the dominant male, and he had begun to submit, when Ivey lunged forward, seized him by the neck, and shook him vigorously. Hawkins shrieked and struggled to free himself. Ivey chewed the youngster's ear, the side of his face, and his neck until blood ran through his blond neck hair. When Ivey tried to change his grip, Hawkins broke free. But he did not actually run away; instead, he loped in a large circle around the carcass until the dominant male easily overtook him. They faced each other, clopping their powerful muzzles together, each wrestling for a grip on the other's neck.

Ivey succeeded in again seizing the young hyena by the neck. This time he shook him violently and threw him to the ground.

Hawkins managed to get away, but again he made little real effort to escape, as though inviting another chance to challenge the other male. The stakes were high: The opportunity to remain in his natal clan and its familiar territory hung in the balance. Ivey soon caught him again. The contest continued for over two hours, with Hawkins taking all the abuse.

Finally, Ivey released the younger male. He walked to the water hole to have a drink and, panting heavily, lay down. Having followed him, Hawkins began to saunter back and forth in front of the older male, as if daring him to attack again. When Ivey ignored the challenge, Hawkins carried a stick to within eight yards of the old champion and made an obvious, if not terribly impressive, display of mutilating it. When that brought no response from Ivey, he began pacing back and forth in front of him again, drawing nearer and nearer, until he was within five yards. After resting, Ivey charged once more, and again began mauling Hawkins, who took several more minutes of this punishment before he finally broke free and started walking slowly toward the East Dune woodland. Ivey did not follow him.

Over the following weeks, Hawkins found it more and more difficult to forage and feed in the clan's home range without being harassed by Ivey. He took to roaming in the outskirts of the territory, and finally he disappeared. If he survived on his own as a nomad, someday he would challenge the dominant of another clan and perhaps become its only breeding male. Should he be unsuccessful in his bid for females and a territory, he would remain a solitary outcast, eking a living from marginal habitats away from the prime river valleys. His only chance to breed would be to mate with the occasional nomadic female or to sneak a copulation with a clan female.

Despite the fact that they always foraged alone, brown hyenas, we now knew, were social—and quite social, at that. But animals associate for some adaptive purpose, not because they enjoy being together. Lions, wild dogs, wolves, primitive men, and spotted hyenas hunting in a group are able to kill larger prey than can a single individual. Brown hyenas were scavengers, for the most part, and they rarely hunted. But since they did not hunt together, why did they live in a clan and share large kills left by lions? Why did they need each other? Why did they bother to socialize at all? There was a single answer for all these questions, as we were to discover.

6

Camp

Delia

I love not Man the less, but Nature more.
—Lord Byron

SHORTLY AFTER the fire, we found our original campsite too exposed to the persistent winds, so we had literally molded a new one into the interior of a tree island, cutting two or three dead branches to make room for the faded tent given to us by a friend in Maun.

Our island was thick with ziziphus and acacia trees standing in long grass and tangled undergrowth. The ziziphus had multiple trunks that splayed, at about fifteen feet above ground, into hundreds of smaller, thorny branches, which fell back toward the ground in a snarled tumble. The flat-topped acacias and the drooping ziziphus interlaced, forming a roof over our heads so dense and green that in the rainy season we could barely see the sky. Camp was surrounded by the open plains of the ancient riverbed, which stretched to the northern and southern horizons. On the east and west, duneslopes crept gently to their wooded crests.

Because we hated to disturb the small mammals and birds in the island, we had left the dead wood, "sticky grass," and undershrubs in place. Only narrow footpaths led from the kitchen, in an open alcove at one end of the grove, to the tent. For the first year the island was so overgrown after the heavy rains, and our camp so well hidden, that now and then a giraffe's head would suddenly appear in the canopy above us. After stripping some leaves from a thorny branch, he would discover us and our few belongings tucked away below. Curling his tail over his rump, the giraffe would clomp over the riverbed for a way, and then look back as if he had imagined the whole thing.

And sometimes, during the rainy season of 1975, as many as 3000 springbok grazed so close that we could hear their stomachs rumbling.

Because this was a desert, every living plant was important to some creature. We became obsessed with saving the leafy branches and wilting grass, even to the point of always asking our rare human visitors to stay on the footpaths. I once became very annoyed when some visiting scientists cleared a large area in the center of camp for their sleeping bags. For months after they had gone, until the rains came again, their bivouac was the dusty "vacuum which nature abhors." Our behavior was perhaps a desperate attempt to fit in, to slip back into the natural world without being offensive or noticed. We felt as if we were guests who had been away for a long, long time.

* * *

I stood on the woodpile and watched until the heat waves swallowed the bleary image of the truck. It was early in the rainy season of 1975, and Mark was driving into Maun for supplies. Because he would be gone for three or four days, he had not liked leaving me alone in camp, but I had insisted that I remain at Deception to catch up on paper work. The drone of the engine faded from the dunes, making me one of the most remote people on earth. I stayed behind not only to transcribe notes, but also to experience the sensation of total isolation. Looking over the riverbed for a while, I let the feeling settle over me. It was comfortable.

But total solitude takes some getting used to. Although I was the only person for thousands of square miles, it took a while to shake the feeling that I was being watched. While making tea I talked to myself openly, but with the urge to look over my shoulder to make sure no one was listening. It never was being alone that bothered me, but rather the feeling that I might *not* be alone when I was supposed to be.

I walked to the kitchen, poked some life into the grey coals and moved the old enamel kettle over the fire for tea. It was coated in flaky layers of black—the history of a thousand campfires—and its worried old handle wore the tooth marks of the brown hyenas who had often stolen it from its perch. The kettle was our only source of hot water, and whether we wanted a sponge bath or a cup of coffee, it was always ready.

I made a simple bean stew for myself, and soon the pot was bubbling on the heavy iron fire grate that Bergie had given us. Then I kneaded bread dough, put it in the black three-legged mealie pot, and set it in the sun to rise. Later I turned a five-gallon pail on its side and set two dough-filled bread pans inside. Using the spade, I sprinkled glowing red coals beneath and on top of the bucket oven. In the midday temperature, with the wind blowing steadily, the bread would bake in seventeen minutes. It took as long as twenty-five minutes to cook if there wasn't any wind, and during the calm, cool, and more humid night, an hour.

Our food supply was limited by what was available in Maun, what we could afford to buy, and what would survive the long haul to camp in the heat. Sometimes even staples like flour, mealie-meal, sugar, lard, and salt could not be found in the general stores.

We had no refrigerator, so we could not store perishables of any kind for very long. Onions kept for several months if left hanging in the dry air, and the carrots, beets, and turnips that we bought occasionally from the gardens in Maun lasted for two weeks if buried under the sand and sprinkled with waste water, and if moved from time to time to fool the termites. Oranges or grapefruits stayed edible for up to two and a half months in the dry season, the rind gradually turning to a tough shell that protected the succulent pulp from dehydration. Nothing rotted in the dry months.

In 1975 we were given permission by the Department of Wildlife to shoot an occasional antelope, in order to analyse its rumen contents. We hated to do this, but it was important for the conservation of the animals to know which grasses or leaves they ate from season to season. Mark always took many hours to hunt, carefully stalking an individual separate from the others, to keep from disturbing and alienating the herd. These precautions paid off, for during our entire stay in Deception the springbok and gemsbok showed no more fear of us than when we had first arrived.

We learned how to make *biltong*—jerky—out of the antelope meat by soaking raw slices overnight in the washtub, in a concoction of salt, pepper, and vinegar and then hanging them up to dry on wire hooks. They dried in three days and could be kept for several months. Often our only source of protein were these biltong sticks, dipped in hot mustard, which were quite tasty. But we soon tired of this stringy meal, so I tried to prepare the meat in more creative ways. One recipe we devised was Biltong Fritters:

INGREDIENTS:

Two slabs of very dry biltong
desert-dried green pepper
desert-dried onion
short pastry

Pulverize the biltong in the bathtub with a five-pound hammer and a trailer hitch, then soak in water with onions and peppers for some time. Drain well and fry briefly in hot oil. Cut pastry into triangles, place one tablespoon of biltong hash on each and roll up. Fry fritters until crisp and golden brown.

Biltong also tasted good with Camp Cornbread (eggless), one of our standbys:

1/3 cup tinned margarine
1/3 cup brown sugar
1 cup flour
3 teaspoons baking powder
4 tablespoons powdered milk
1 cup water
1 cup mealie-meal (cornmeal)
salt to taste

Cream the margarine and sugar together. Mix in the powdered milk and water. Add the flour, mealie-meal, baking powder, and salt and mix well. Place in a greased pan and cook in bucket oven with moderate coals for 25 minutes (15 if the wind is blowing steadily).

When we didn't have meat, we ate various stews made of dried beans, corn, sorghum, and mealie-meal. Their insipid taste could be improved a bit with onions, curries, chile, and Mexican-style pastries, but it was often a matter of swallowing the food as quickly as possible and following it with a can of sweet fruit cocktail, if one was left in the tea-crate larder.

In September and October, before the rains begin, a female ostrich lays up to twenty large ivory-colored eggs, each about seven inches long and fifteen inches around, roughly equivalent to two dozen chicken eggs. Although we never robbed an undisturbed nest, we sometimes found an egg that had been abandoned after a predator had chased the parent birds away. Had we guessed then how highly prized such eggs would have been for a brown hyena, who had no water stored in drums or cans of fruit cocktail stashed away, we wouldn't have taken them.

With a hand drill, Mark would bore a quarter-inch hole in one end of an egg. Then, holding it between his knees, he would insert an L-shaped wire—first sterilized over the fire—through the hole and roll it back and forth between his palms, scrambling the white and yolk. I would shake enough for one meal into the frying pan, and then seal the hole with a Band-Aid before burying the egg under a shady tree. As long as the contents did not get contaminated, we could have scrambled eggs or an omelette every morning for the next twelve days or so.

The only danger in eating ostrich eggs was that we could not be certain how fresh one was until the drill bit actually broke through the thick shell. Unless Mark was very careful, the stinking juices from a very bad egg would erupt and squirt him in the face. Whenever he opened one, I left the kitchen, but his language left no doubt about whether or not it was rotten.

* * *

The morning Mark left for Maun slipped away before I could even start on the mountain of paper work stacked on the table beneath the ziziphus tree. We always had tapes to be transcribed onto data sheets and letters to write. Before leaving the kitchen I automatically moved the kettle to the edge of the fire grate to keep it from boiling dry. Conserving water had become second nature; if it hadn't, we would have spent much of our time and money trying to keep it in stock.

Whenever low grey-black clouds rolled in over the dunes, Mark and I would rush around placing pots and pans around the tent to catch the rain. Then we would zip the tent, topple gasoline drums onto their sides, stuff cloth bags of flour and all our data books into the front of the truck, cover the food shelf with canvas, set the equipment boxes up on blocks, and cover the fire with the half drum. Finally, after checking the tie-downs on the tents, camp would be secure.

As soon as the downpour eased, we would grab the pots and pans and pour the fresh rainwater into drums. Then we would scoop up as many as eighty gallons of the coffee-colored water that stood ankle deep in camp.

Later, when the mud had settled a bit, we would drive to the water hole on Mid Pan and, using pots and funnels made from plastic bottles, spend hours collecting more water. It was impossible to avoid including some of the springbok and gemsbok droppings that bobbed on the surface, but they would settle out in the drum and they did no real harm because we boiled all our drinking water. We hadn't always taken this precaution.

One month in the dry season of 1975 we both came down with

severe intestinal cramps, diarrhea, and lethargy that persisted for days. We kept getting weaker and had no idea what was causing the trouble. Our water supply was nearly finished, and I worried that if our illness worsened, we wouldn't be strong enough to make the trip for more. Without a radio, there would be no way for us to get help.

Mark dragged himself from the tent, and pausing frequently to rest, he consolidated into a bucket the last gallon or two from all the drums. As he tipped up the last one, feathers swirled into the pail, followed by the ripe ooze of a putrified bird, which had apparently drowned in the drum weeks before. From then on we boiled every drop that we drank, no matter how clean it looked, and kept the bungs plugged with rags.

Lionel Palmer, the hunter who had suggested that we work in the Kalahari, had recently loaned us a small trailer and had assured us that we could use it to haul water. The morning after we had found the decomposed bird, we pulled the trailer to the cattle post, where we now got our water, and loaded one drum inside the Grey Goose, one on the roofrack, and three in the bed of the trailer. A single drum filled with fifty gallons of water weighs nearly 500 pounds, so Mark chopped some log wedges and drove them beneath the spring blades of the Land Rover to help support the load.

On our return to camp, we were no more than a mile from the borehole when a tremendous screeching came from behind the truck. The Grey Goose lurched forward and slid to a stop. One of the drums had fallen through the floor of the trailer, wedging itself against the wheel. We heaved it up, placed bits of spare planking over the holes in the trailer bed, and roped the barrel in position before setting off again.

Two miles farther down the track, the second drum broke through. We blocked and secured it as best we could with fragments of the frayed rope and slogged on, now at a snail's pace.

We had gone perhaps another four or five miles when the truck staggered to one side, drums clamoring from behind. We ran to the trailer and found its tow-bar bent into an S shape. It had dropped to the ground and plowed a furrow through the sand when all three drums had tumbled forward.

Covered with dust, grass seed, and sweat, we had taken four hours to cover eight miles in the 120-degree heat. Exhausted and weakened from our illness, we sank to the sand in the shade of the boiling truck, our throbbing heads resting on our knees. I didn't see how we could go on. His jaw rigid, Mark stared silently across the savanna. The Kalahari would not give an inch—she never let anything come easily.

After a few moments, Mark pulled himself up and gave me a hand. Placing the highlift jack under the arms of the tow-bar, and with the trailer still hooked to the Land Rover, he jacked them until they were nearly straight. Then he fashioned a splint for the broken hitch with the Land Rover crank handle and small logs cut from a nearby stand of trees. We reorganized the drums and started off again.

At the end of nearly every mile, we had to stop and cool the Goose. While Mark poured water over the top of the radiator, I used a hairbrush to clean away the thick carpet of grass seed that blocked the air flow. By removing a spark plug, putting a hose to the opened cylinder, and racing the engine, we blew out the clogged grill. Before starting up again, Mark crawled under the Land Rover and, using a long screwdriver, cleaned away the charred straw that was smoldering on the undercarriage. Trucks in the bush often burn up when grass on the exhaust ignites.

Creeping along again, we suddenly smelled smoke. Mark slammed on the brakes and we jumped out. It was impossible to keep the overheated exhaust pipe clean for long, and now it had caught fire. Thick white smoke was pouring from underneath the truck. Mark grabbed the hose and a wrench, vaulted into the back of the Land Rover, and quickly opened a drum. Flames began to sneak through, showing orange against the billowing white. He sucked on the end of the hose, got the siphon going, and sprayed water onto the undercarriage. The smoke turned black, and a roil of steam and ash hissed back at him as the fire died.

Five hours and three flat tires later, we staggered into camp and collapsed onto our foam rubber pads under the stars.

The next day a freak storm appeared from nowhere and rained buckets of water all around us. We didn't even have an extra canteen to fill, and the Kalahari drank it all.

* * *

Though I was completely isolated from humans those four days Mark was in Maun, I was by no means alone. Late on the first afternoon, I put away our field notes, cut myself a slice of freshly baked caraway bread, and sat in our tea room, the alcove under the weeping branches of the ziziphus tree. In an instant, flocks of chippering birds crowded around. "Chief," a yellow-billed hornbill with a mischievous eye, watched from the acacia tree across the path. Then he fell from his perch, spread his wings, and swooped to a landing on my head, his wings fluttering around my ears. Two others sat on my shoulders, and the four in my lap pecked at my hands and nibbled my fingers. Another hovered in midair until he managed to bite off a chunk of crust. I divided the rest of the bread among them.

One of the first things we had done in our tree island camp was put out bread scraps and a small dish of water. Soon scores of birds—violet-eared waxbills, scaly-feathered finches, crimson-breasted shrikes, tit-babblers, Marico flycatchers—were twittering and preening in the trees. In the early morning, striped mice, shrews, and ground squirrels scurried around our feet to compete with the birds for food. But the hornbills were always our favorites.

The yellow-billed hornbill is an odd assemblage of parts: a hooked yellow bill that seems too large for his scrawny black-and-white body, a long black tail that looks like an afterthought, and seductive eyelashes that flutter over foxy eyes—a most beguiling companion. We could recognize forty of them by their natural markings or by dabs of black paint I applied to their bills while they were taking bread from my fingers.

Whenever I cooked, the "billies" crowded around the kitchen, perching on my head and shoulders, and even on the frying pan, picking up first one foot, then the other, fixing me with rude glares, as though they somehow knew it was my fault the pan was getting too hot. They found our leftover oatmeal and rice, stored in pots, by prying off the lids with their crescent bills. And when we sat down to eat under the ziziphus tree, we guarded our plates carefully lest our food disappear in a cloud of feathers. They also spoiled many a cup of tea by dropping their whitewash with uncanny aim from overhead branches.

One day while we sat writing under the trees, a small pearl-spotted owl dove from his perch and captured a scaly-feathered finch, a tiny bird with a distinctive black goatee. All the birds in camp, not just the finches, immediately rushed to the scene, bobbing up and down on the outer branches, giving their alarm calls. The captive finch screeched and flapped its wings wildly as it struggled in the clutches of the owl. Then one of the hornbills, hopping onto a branch just under the owl, reached up and snatched away the finch, who escaped to safety. It is impossible to say whether the hornbill was attempting to rescue the finch or to get an easy meal for himself; I prefer the former but believe the latter.

Another permanent companion in camp was Laramie the lizard, who nested every night in an empty Di-Gel box on the orange crate–bedside table. He was especially welcome because of his voracious appetite for the flies that invaded our tent. With never-ending patience and acute skill he tracked them down one by one, smacking loudly as he chewed them up. But termites were Laramie's favorite food, and I often fed them to him with a pair of forceps while he perched on the old tin clothes trunk next to our bed.

Since zippers on tents are notoriously short-lived, we rarely had a tent in which the doors and windows closed securely. Thus, mice were common visitors to our bedroom at night, and they often found their way into bed with us, especially in the cold-dry season. Feeling a slight pressure roaming between the blankets, we would bolt out of bed and trip around in the dark, waving dim flashlights and shaking out the blankets. When the mouse finally shot out from between the bed covers, we would throw shoes, flashlights, and books in every direction until he escaped.

We were quite accustomed to these intrusions, but one dawn I was half awakened by a very heavy pressure moving around over my legs. I imagined the world's largest rat crawling on our bed, and I began kicking with a frenzy. I sat up just in time to see a slender mongoose leap for the tent door. He paused for a few seconds, looking back, and we stared into each other's startled eyes. That was our introduction to "Moose."

Moose became the camp clown. He always remained aloof, maybe because I'd kicked him out of my bed. He would never accept a handout, but he was not above stealing everything in sight. One morning when we sat drinking tea under the ziziphus tree, Moose came sidling down the footpath, our pot of leftover oatmeal clattering behind him. Without so much as a glance in our direction, his head high and the handle in his mouth, he scraped his pot of porridge past us and straight out of camp, where he ate his breakfast in the morning sun.

Because the ever-present mice were always chewing their way into our food containers, we set traps in the kitchen area nightly. We did this reluctantly because there was always the possibility of killing some creature other than a mouse. Sure enough, when Mark and I neared the kitchen one dawn, I heard a loud snap and looked up to see a Marico flycatcher flopping about with the trap closed on his skull. Mark immediately freed the small bird, who stumbled about in ever-widening circles. I suggested that we should put him out of his misery, but Mark insisted that we wait to see what happened.

The flycatcher eventually stopped walking in circles and flew to a rather clumsy landing on a low acacia branch. From that moment on, Marique continued the normal life of a Marico flycatcher, except for three things: He was blind in the left eye, he lost all fear of human beings, and he took up the habit of "begging" from us by flapping his wings like a fledgling. Tamer than most parakeets, Marique would land on our heads, our plates, our books. He would stand on the path in front of us and shake his wings vigorously to demand food; we could almost imagine his hands on his hips and his little foot stomping. Probably because of our guilt over the accident, we always fed him, even if it meant dropping whatever we were doing to make a special trip to the kitchen.

When Marique took a mate, she also became very tame, though she did not beg. But when they reared their second brood (the first was lost in a storm), the babes soon picked up their father's habit of begging from us. And so the behavior was passed on, and for the rest of our years in the Kalahari, Marico flycatchers in camp would land at our feet and shake their wings for food. We could never refuse them.

Having wild creatures around us was one of our greatest pleasures, yet at times it was a mixed blessing. Early one morning, still groggy from sleep, I threw back the cover from the dilapidated tea crate. When I reached inside, looking for a tin of oatmeal, my breath caught. The long grey body of a banded cobra was coiled on the cans, inches from my hand. I'm not usually intimidated by snakes, but this time I snatched my hand back and let out a respectable howl. Fortunately, the cobra must have been as intimidated as I was because he did not strike, but instead slithered down among the tins. Mark appeared an instant later with the .410 shotgun. So far we had killed only a few of the most poisonous snakes that had visited us and those only because they insisted on living in camp. This one would be a real danger if allowed to stay. Mark aimed the gun into the box, and I imagined losing a month's supply of food along with the snake. But when we turned the crate on its side to remove the dead cobra, we found only one irreparably damaged tin—unfortunately, it was fruit cocktail.

Boomslangs, puff adders, black mambas, and other poisonous snakes frequently appeared in camp. That we had not been bitten was due mostly to our own private warning system. Whenever the birds spotted a snake they all landed on the branches above it, chirping, clucking, and twittering in loud alarm. Since there were sometimes as many as 200 birds in camp, the racket they made always tipped us off that a snake was on the prowl. The only problem was that they also mobbed owls, mongooses, and hawks, and once even a homing pigeon, complete with leg band, who had miraculously found his way to our camp. Sometimes they would keep it up for hours, or for several days, as in the case of the pigeon, and we would begin to prefer the quiet snakes to the noisy birds.

Small animals were not the only ones who made themselves at home in camp. Walking down the path to the kitchen at dawn, we often surprised two or three jackals who had slipped under the flap into the little mess tent. On hearing our footsteps they would ricochet around inside, searching for a way out, the tent walls billowing, until suddenly they would squirt out from under the tent door, ears back and tails bouncing.

Lions, leopards, brown hyenas, or jackals would wander into camp almost every night of the rainy season. After we bought a small mess tent, we tried to protect it, and the kitchen, with a barricade made of drums, thorn branches, spare tires, and the fire grate. Even so, we often got up several times a night to usher animals out of camp. Walking slowly toward them while talking to them quietly always worked with the hyenas and jackals, but sometimes the lions and leopards were less willing to leave.

One night we drove into camp and a leopard stepped out of the shadows in front of our headlights. Mark jammed on the brakes just as the cat gracefully sidestepped the truck. Totally unperturbed, he sauntered to the middle of camp and, with a single silent motion, jumped onto the water drums. He walked from one to the other, smelling the water inside until, apparently convinced that he could not get to it, he jumped down. Next he climbed swiftly up the acacia tree that slanted against the flimsy reed structure we had made for dry-season shade. There, as he slowly stepped onto the roof, his front paw caved through the reeds with a loud splintering noise. Lifting his feet high, as if walking in tar, and with his tail lashing about for balance, he continued across, stabbing through the ceiling with every step. Finally, gripping the tree with his hind feet, he managed to extricate his legs from the now sagging and tattered roof. He then jumped from the tree and walked to our tent, and after a good look around inside, climbed to a limb that hung over the door and settled comfortably in its crook. He closed his eyes and began casually licking his forepaw with a long pink tongue; obviously he intended to stay awhile. All of this was very entertaining, but it was now 2:45 A.M. and we needed to get to bed. Mark drove the Land Rover a bit closer, thinking that the leopard would leave, but he just peered down at us benignly, his tail and legs dangling down from his perch over the door.

We didn't want to frighten him away, and we couldn't quite bring ourselves to walk directly under him to get into the tent, so, leaning sleepily against the truck, we watched for about fifty minutes while he napped. Eventually he yawned, stretched, climbed down, and padded out of camp, his long tail trailing easily behind him. Stiff and tired, we began brushing our teeth next to the tent.

"Look who's back," Mark whispered several minutes later. I whirled around to see the leopard standing at the back of the Land Rover, his muzzle raised and his amber eyes staring. He apparently meant us no harm, so we finished brushing our teeth while he sat fifteen feet away, his head cocked to one side. We went into the tent, closed the flap as well as we could, and crawled into our bed on the floor. A few minutes later we could hear the soft top-top-top of leopard pads on the plastic ground sheet, and then a sigh as he settled down for a cat nap, just outside the door.

* * *

I was always very conscious of the fact that besides being a coworker, I was also a wife. In spite of all the dirt and grime and my ragged cut-off jeans, I tried to stay as feminine as possible. I usually put on a little make-up every day, and on our nights off, when we relaxed by the fire, I wore a blouse and a skirt of African printed cotton. On one occasion Mark had gone by himself to collect firewood, and since we did not plan to follow hyenas that night, I decided to fix myself up. I dug bright yellow curlers from the bottom of my trunk, washed my hair, and put it up in rollers.

As I walked through camp toward the kitchen, the hornbills swooped down into the branches just above my head, clucking loudly. I recognized it as their alarm call, and stopping short, I began to look around me. But I couldn't find a snake or anything else that could have alarmed the billies. I walked warily back to the tent to get the shotgun, and as soon as I was inside, the mobbing stopped. When I stepped out again, the racket began once more, as if on cue. While I searched for the snake, gun in hand, the hornbills repeatedly dive-bombed my head. With a pang of humiliation I suddenly realized the problem. I never did understand why, but from then on, whenever I curled my hair, I would either have to stay inside the tent or put up with the noisy objections of the hornbills.

* * *

Just before sunset on my first day alone in Deception, I filled a bowl with bean stew and sat down on the flat riverbed outside camp to eat my supper. The hornbills sailed over my head on their way to roost for the night in the dune woodlands. Soon afterward two nightjars flitted across the fading day and landed a few feet away. They waddled about, making low purring sounds as they searched for insects. The sky deepened. I lay back in the straw-colored grass, and pressing my fingers into the rough surface of the riverbed, as I had so many times before, I wondered how long the Kalahari would belong to the wild.

I sat up. Thirty springbok had wandered to within fifty yards of me while I was hidden in the grass. The male whistled alarm, and they all looked at me with tails twitching and necks stiffly arched. I stood, and they relaxed when the odd, hunched shape in the grass, which could have been a predator, turned into my familiar form. They resumed their grazing, but drifted away from me at an almost imperceptible pace, just the same. They could not know that I was here for them, and they disappeared over the dune.

I walked down the track from camp speaking softly to myself as the last traces of that day vanished altogether. There may not be a fine line between dusk and darkness to the eye, but there is to the mind. When I was half a mile from camp, I felt the night settling on my shoulders and along my spine. I began snatching quick glances behind me, and, like any good primate, I returned to my trees.

* * *

Over the next three days, while Mark was in Maun, I finished our backlog of paper work and fed nearly half of the bread to the hornbills.

I was still enjoying being alone in the wilderness, but more and more often I stopped my work and ran out of the tent, thinking that I had heard the truck. I stood listening for the distant drone of the engine over the eastern dunes, but there was only the wind. Mark would probably be back soon, so I baked him a lop-sided, eggless spice cake in the bucket oven.

The notes all neatly transcribed, I spent the fourth day cleaning camp. But I was losing interest in really accomplishing anything, and I sat with the hornbills for a long time, talked to myself a lot, and walked from camp again and again to listen for the truck. Maybe Mark would bring me something special—some chocolate from Riley's perhaps, or the mail, with a package from my mother. When he wasn't back by 5 P.M., I felt very let down.

In the early evening I was stirring my supper over the fire when seven lions came padding directly toward camp. My heart began doing flip-flops, and I quickly put the pot of stew on top of the hyena table and hurried deeper into the tree island. Peering through the branches, I could see the long, low forms gliding silently toward me, just 100 yards away. It was the same lionesses and their adolescent young we had often seen. But on the other occasions when they had visited camp, the truck had always been nearby; now I felt as vulnerable as a turtle without a shell. I tried to reason with myself: What difference would the truck or Mark have made, the lions weren't likely to do anything, anyway. Still, I felt trapped. Crouching low, I crept inside the tent and peeped through the window.

When they reached the edge of camp the lions began to play like giant kittens, romping and chasing one another over the woodpile and through the kitchen. Even when they were behind the bushes, I could tell by their sounds what they were doing. Then a pot hit the ground, and everything went quiet. They had probably found my stew.

It soon grew dark and for a while I could neither see nor hear them. *Where were they? What were they up to?* Suddenly their heavy thuds sounded on the ground just outside the tent. I sat back onto our bed, my thoughts racing. When we had last been in Maun one of the hunters had told of Kalahari lions flattening three of his tents one night while he and his clients huddled in the truck. I had thought the story an exaggeration; now I was sure that it was true.

I had to make a plan. My eye caught the tin clothes trunk. Moving very quietly, I opened it and piled its contents on the bed. If the lions began playing with the tent, I would get inside and close the lid. I sat in total darkness on the edge of the bed, one hand on the open trunk, and listened to the slaps, grunts, and pounding feet outside. Suddenly there was utter silence again. For minutes not a sound came from outside. They *had* to be there. I would have heard them move away. Huddled on the bed beside the trunk, I visualized all seven of them lying in a semicircle around the tent door.

Ages passed and still no sounds. Could they smell me? Should I get into the trunk or sit still? A twig snapped. The side of the tent began to balloon slightly. Then a rope sang out with a twang. Through the window I could see one of the lionesses pulling a guy line with her teeth. Soft footsteps in the leaves and loud sniffing noises: They were smelling along the base of the tent only inches from where I knelt.

Then there was a deep droning far away. The truck? God, let it be the truck! On quiet, damp nights I could sometimes hear it for three-quarters of an hour before it reached camp; then there would be long silences as it descended between dunes.

Once more all was quiet. Maybe I had imagined the sound. Soft footfalls moved along the side of the tent toward the door. I wondered what would happen if I stood up and screamed "Shoo—get out!" But I didn't budge. I was so much more brave when Mark was around.

Again the motor sounded from the distance—it had to be Mark. After an eternity the pitch changed completely, and the truck turned onto the riverbed and headed directly toward camp.

A noise just outside made me jump—a long brushing motion against the canvas side.

As Mark rounded Acacia Point he was surprised to see that no fire was blazing, no lanterns were lit; camp was completely dark. He switched on the spotlight and immediately saw the seven lions prowling around the tent. He drove quickly into camp, switched off the truck, and called out the window, "Delia . . . Delia, you okay!?"

"Yeah—yeah—I'm—I'm all right," I stammered. "Thank God you're back."

Mark's arrival having spoiled their fun, the lions left camp and filed slowly southward down the riverbed. I jumped up to give Mark a grand welcome, but then I remembered the pile of clothes on the bed, so I stopped to stuff them into the trunk. After all, there was no reason to tell him of my plan, which now seemed rather ridiculous.

"Are you sure you're all right?" Mark met me on the tent stoop and hugged me.

"Yes—now that you're here. And what about you? You must be starving."

We unloaded the truck and cooked a feast with the supplies he had brought from Maun. We ate goat meat, fried potatoes, and onions, and I chattered nonstop about the previous four days. Mark patiently let me talk myself out, and then he told me all the news from Maun as we snuggled by the firelight. A long while later, when we went to bed, I found a bar of chocolate under my pillow.

7

Maun: The African Frontier

Mark

Quick, ere the gift escape us!
Out of the darkness reach
For a handful of week-old papers
And a mouthful of human speech.
—*Rudyard Kipling*

THE SUN was high over the river when the truck crossed the last sand ridge. Grey with dust and fatigue, we drove into the Boteti, opened the doors, and fell sizzling into the cool water. It was as if a fever had broken. Though we had been cautioned about big crocodiles and bilharzia, a debilitating parasitic disease picked up from infested rivers or lakes, nothing could have kept us from the water after the Kalahari heat. We lay with only our heads bobbing above the surface, letting the current rush over us, but we kept looking from one bank to the other for the telltale ripples of a croc.

It was March 1975, three months since my trip alone to Maun, and low on supplies again, we had set off for the village at dawn the day before. Besides restocking, we wanted to find an assistant, someone to take care of the dozens of camp chores that were eroding our research time. While trying to keep up with our expanding research project, it had become more and more difficult to cope with vegetation transects, scat collection and analysis, cartography, truck maintenance, hauling water and firewood, boiling drinking water, cooking, mending tents, and the myriad of other tasks associated with living in such a remote area. There just wasn't enough time or energy left for following hyenas each night, or enough hours left in the day to sleep.

But finding a native African who would live isolated in the Kalahari with very little water, no comforts, and lions roaming the valley would not be easy, especially considering the embarrassing wage we could afford to offer him. Only a very special person would do.

Now Maun was only thirty minutes away. We lay in the cool river, chatting about seeing friends in the village. Skeins of pygmy geese, ducks, and snow-white egrets passed low over our heads. After scrubbing our clothes and hanging them on thornbushes along the bank, we soaked in the river again, the minnows nibbling at our toes. A grey-haired old man with a poncho of tattered goatskin thrown over his shoulders walked his donkey to the water. He gave us a wide, dusty smile and then waved and shouted to us in Setswana, the local language. We shouted and waved back with such bonhomie that he must have thought he'd done us some favor. This was the first human, other than me, that Delia had seen in more than six months.

Our clothes stiff and dry, we drove on to the village and straight for Riley's, two buildings of concrete stucco, with scuffed white paint and green corrugated tin roofs, standing on a sand patch next to the river. Behind the hotel, bar, and bottle store, a long veranda with a red waxed floor was dwarfed by tall, spreading fig trees and the broad Thamalakane River drifting by.

Riley's was the first hotel on the frontier of Northern Botswana. Built as a trading post by settlers who arrived in ox wagons about the turn of the century, for decades it has been a staging point for expeditions north to the Zambesi River, west to Ghanzi, or back to Francistown, more than 300 miles east. Today it is still a popular meeting place, one of three or four in the entire territory of Ngamiland. Riley's has cold beer, meat pies on Saturday mornings—and ice. It was the best place to start looking for an assistant and to visit with friends.

After several months alone in the desert, we had begun to notice subtle signs that told us we needed to see other people, to be part of a social group again. It had become more and more difficult to concentrate on our research without wondering what Lionel and Phyllis were doing or thinking how nice it would be to have a cold beer with someone.

Already smiling with anticipation, we pulled up at Riley's and parked next to a line of trucks, all with rumpled fenders, long bush scratches down the sides, and oil dripping beneath. Behind the low block wall of the veranda, safari hunters in denims and khaki tilted their chairs back from wire tables, each man facing a row of empty beer cans. Weathered ranchers with bushy eyebrows leaned their beefy brown arms on the tables, their dusty, sweat-stained hats perched on the wall beside them. A Botawana tribesman in a red-and-black tunic, wearing a tasseled hat, hurried back and forth with mugs of Lion and Castle beer.

Dolene Paul, an attractive young woman with chopped blonde hair whom we had met on a previous trip, waved to us across the veranda. Born and raised near Maun, she was married to Simon, an Englishman recently trained as a professional hunter. As we moved toward her table, friendly jeers rose from the safari crowd: "Oh Chrrrist! Watch your beer, here come the bloody ecologists!"

Shaking hands, I found myself holding on too long, grasping a friend's hand or lower arm with my left while pumping away with my right. We smiled so much our cheeks ached, and greeted everyone over and over again, repeating their first names several times. Then, suddenly feeling foolish, I quickly sat down at a table and ordered a beer.

It was early afternoon, but no one seemed to have anywhere to go, so we all sipped cold beer and listened to hunting stories. Too anxious to join in, Delia and I made comments that seemed to bring conversation to a temporary halt, and we caught ourselves rambling on, talking much too loudly, and for too long, about subjects that must have bored everyone else. Socially, we were out of practice.

Occasionally the conversation turned to Simon's truck, which needed a new clutch bearing, and how sometime that afternoon they'd have to fix it. Then somebody bought another round of beer.

Since Dolene knew most of the local Africans, we asked if she had heard of anyone who was a good worker and in need of a job, one who might be willing to live with us in Deception Valley. "Can't think of anyone right offhand," she said. "It'll be tough to find a bloke who'll stay in the bush for a long time without other Africans around. You must come round to Dad's *braii* tonight. Maybe one of the other hunters or ranchers will know of someone." A braii—or *braiivlace*—is a southern African barbecue, and though we'd heard of Maun's version, we had never been to one.

Several hours later everyone began to stand and stretch and to talk of driving on over to Dad's. The afternoon was slipping away and nothing more was said about fixing Simon's truck; apparently it could wait until the next day.

Driving over to Dad's, we analyzed the reception we had got. "How do you think Larry acted toward us? Do you think Willy was really glad to see us?" Delia even coached me: "Try not to act so excited when we see everyone at Dad's place."

Dolene's father, "Dad" Riggs, was one of the first white settlers in the area and had for years been a shopkeeper in Sehithwa, a village near Lake Ngami, before moving his family to Maun. Dolene and her brothers spoke Setswana long before they learned English at boarding school in the Republic of South Africa. In later years, Dad had been a stock-taker for the Ngamiland Trading Center, a general store and trading company in Maun.

Dad's place, a pale yellow adobe with a corrugated tin roof, flaking foundation, and sagging screen porch, was hidden behind the trading store. A tack shed, with saddles, blankets, and bridles thrown over a hitching rail, stood near the front corner of the house. Chickens, horses, and goats cropped the sparse grass in the sandy yard while several black children tended the stock. A splintered reed fence enclosed the yard where four or five hunters, ranchers, and their wives lounged next to the front porch on stained mattresses with stuffing peeking through. Dad Riggs strode across the yard to meet us, his weathered face creased with a grin. His wiry blond hair, flecked with grey, curled like wood shavings, and a clipped moustache was crimped over the firm line of his mouth. When Dolene introduced us, he lay a heavy arm around Delia's shoulder and wagged the stump of an index finger, lopped to keep the venom of a snakebite from spreading. "Make no mistake," he said, "*anybody* who lives in the Kalahari is always welcome at my place. Make *no* mistake."

Dad drew us into his circle of friends, and before we could take our places on one of the mattresses, Cecil, his son, a hard-riding, hard-drinking cowboy, pressed cold beer into our hands. Delia sat stroking a goat with long white hair and nervous yellow eyes that was tethered to a water spigot. We listened to more stories of lion, elephant, and buffalo hunts; of clients who'd never held a rifle before coming on safari, about the wounded buffalo that had gored Tony, about the biggest lion, the biggest elephant, and the biggest rifle, the four-five-eight. There was talk of cattle buying and cattle selling, the Rhodesian war, and how Roger had clobbered Richard with a Mopane pole for fooling around with his wife . . . gales of laughter and more beer. Donkeys brayed, dogs barked, and gumba music played from the native huts in the village beyond.

The rusty wire gate squawked and Lionel Palmer and Eustice Wright, magistrate-cum-rancher, strutted into the yard. Eustice's corpulent belly strained at a gap where buttons were missing on his shirt, and he wore great baggy shorts that waddled above legs like knotted walking sticks. His face florid from heat and exertion, he flopped onto a mattress next to Lionel, lit a cigarette and inhaled deeply. "I knew you bloody bastards would be drinking a peasant's brew," he croaked, pouring himself half a water glass of Bell's Scotch whisky from a bottle tucked under his arm. He couldn't understand why he had consented to join such riffraff . . . "the bloody flotsam and jetsam of Maun!" He downed a generous gulp of whisky, then belched, "Chrrrist! What the bloody hell am *I* doing here anyway!" Everyone cheered.

Lionel and Eustice, the top two social figures in the village, triggered stories of old Maun. "Were you here, Simon, when Lionel and Kenny, here, stole the cash register from Riley's? Yessus, but Ronnie wasn't happy *that* week."

It was Maun's very first cash register and Ronnie Kays, the bartender at Riley's, was very proud of it. While his brother Kenny chatted him up one day, Lionel, Cecil, and Dougie Wright, all professional hunters, grabbed the register, ran to Lionel's truck, threw it in the back and drove away. Ronnie was not amused; when it was finally returned he bolted it to the bar top. Several days later, Lionel and the others walked calmly into Riley's with a winch cable hidden behind them. When Ronnie's back was turned, they threw a loop around the cash register and signaled to someone waiting in the truck beyond the veranda. The cable snapped tight, and the register leaped from the bar top and bounced out the door. It was considered very poor sportmanship when Ronnie reported the theft to the district commissioner of police.

"I remember one night when Dad got pissed as a lord at Palmer's," Simon led in with his clipped British accent.

"Nothing unusual about that," Cecil laughed.

"Except we took him home and put him to bed with a donkey foal we picked up in front of the butchery."

"He thought it was bloody Christine!" Everybody roared, and slapped Dad on the back.

When I could get Eustice aside, I asked him if he knew of anyone who might work for us. "Who the bloody hell would want to stay in the middle of the bloody Kalahari?" he laughed. "He'd have to be bloody bonkers."

"What about it? Can you help us find someone?" I asked.

"'ell, Mark, that's a tough order. These blokes don't like to be by themselves, you know, and especially not when there are lions crawling about." He took a heavy drag on his cigarette. "Wait a minute, there's a bloke everybody calls Mox—I practically raised him; worked for me for bloody years. A quiet sort, unless he's drinking. Then he terrorizes the whole village. Chr-r-i-i-ist! The guy's a regular Attila the Hun, a real piss-cat. He's got a hell of a reputation with the women . . . they aren't safe from the bugger when he's on a toot. Started getting pissed on *buljalwa* every day, so I sent him to the cattle post to work with Willy. He might go with you, and out there where he couldn't get ahold of any booze he might work out all right. Stop by my place noonish tomorrow, I'll send for him and you can see if you want to take him with . . . and if he'll go."

Dad pushed himself to his feet and announced, to no one in particular, that it was time to get on with the business of the braii. He grabbed the goat by its horns, dragged it to the center of the yard, and slit its throat with a sweep of his knife. It gave a short bleat and sank to its knees spewing blood. I swallowed hard, and glanced at Delia's startled face.

Using a block and tackle hanging from a tree limb, Dad and the Africans hauled the carcass up by its feet, and put half a truck tire beneath its head to catch the drizzling blood. "*Gotsa molelo!*" Dad bellowed, as he knelt rinsing his knife and hands under the faucet. The Africans lit a large pile of mopane logs. The men all gathered round, sawing at the carcass with knives until the goat was quickly reduced to a pile of meat, its skinned head with its bulging eyes perched on top.

Evening shadows grew as tall as the tales, and beer after beer followed yarn after yarn around the bonfire. Daisy, Eustice's Botswana wife, raked coals out of the fire and set a heavy iron pot of water on them. Orange sparks showered into the night. When the water was boiling she stirred in handfuls of mealie-meal with a large wooden spoon. Meanwhile Dad and Cecil shoveled out more coals and laid a big square rack of goat meat over them. By the time the mealie-meal had cooked down to a thick paste, called "pop," the meat was brown and sizzling. We gathered around to eat. Everyone gnawed on goat chops in the firelight, and the grease ran down chins and dripped from glistening fingers.

We were reliving an important part of our evolutionary history as social carnivores. The hunting stories, the fire, the drink, the camaraderie—all a legacy from the first frail prehominids who descended from the trees, leaving behind their herbivorous existence in the forests of Africa to venture onto the savannas. Ill-equipped as they were for stalking and killing dangerous game, there was a great advantage to hunting cooperatively, both for the sharing of meat and for the development of language skills for communicating the details of the stalk and kill. Sharing food while verbally reviewing their techniques reinforced the essential cooperation between hunters, as well as encouraging and teaching the young. Powerful social bonding, together with the evolution of superior intelligence, made human beings the most successful carnivores the earth had ever known. As I took part in this primitive ritual I was reminded that this part of our fundamental nature hasn't really changed that much in thousands of years.

* * *

After the braii, Dolene and Simon invited us to sleep at Buffalo Cottage. Their bungalow, set on a bulge in the river, was smothered in flowering bougainvillea, and the head of a cape buffalo glared from over the door. Our bedroom had a sweeping view of the water, and clean sheets and towels had been laid out for us on a kaross of jackal pelts. Before we went to sleep, I ran my fingers through the silky black and silver hair of the kaross. It had taken thirty Captains to make it.

Next morning we were awakened by the smell of tea and spice cookies, as the bare feet of a small native boy padded off down the hallway. Later we shared a breakfast of toast, orange marmalade, and more tea with Simon and Dolene, on the veranda overlooking the river. Several other hunters, bleary-eyed and thick-tongued from the night before, arrived, and Simon called for another pot of tea.

They all asked us to go fishing the next day, but we felt pressed to get back to the Kalahari and regretfully declined. "Right then—piss off to the bloody Kalahari," someone said in jest. Though we knew it hadn't been a serious jibe, it still hurt, and we worried that perhaps we were being antisocial. The talk ran to Dad's braii and plans for the fishing trip and now and then someone mentioned the job to be done on Simon's truck. We excused ourselves and began shopping for supplies.

The stores in Maun are low concrete block buildings with tin roofs set along the footpaths and major tracks that run through the village.

We usually had to visit every one in order to find all the food staples and bits of hardware needed for another few months in the Kalahari. Items as basic as truck tire tubes and patches were often unavailable, and we had to arrange with one of the transport drivers to purchase them in Francistown and bring them back with his supplies for the village. Sometimes, when the gravel road was bad, we waited for days to get gasoline and other essentials. Only recently have such perishables as cheese, bread, eggs, and milk become available, with the arrival of the first refrigerators in one or two of the shops.

We made our way from one store to the next along deep sand ruts, jamming on the brakes, banging the sides of the Land Rover, and whistling away the donkeys, dogs, goats, cattle, and children, who sometimes dared us to run over them by dashing in front of the truck. At Maun Wholesalers, also known locally as Spiro's (for the Greek who owned it), a horse was tethered to a rail. A goatskin saddle, a bedroll of plaid wool blankets, and a skin sack of goat-milk curds were tied over its back with rawhide strips. The shop was a single large room lined with shelves of rough-cut lumber; a heavy wooden counter ran nearly all the way around it. One end was stacked to the ceiling with canned foods, bars of Sunlight soap, boxes of Tiger oats, Lion matches, packets of lard, tins of Nespray powdered milk, and other grocery items. There were shirts, pants, cheap tennis shoes, and yards of colorful fabric. Metal bins of bulk flour, mealie-meal, *samp*, and sorghum stood along the front of the shop, and an iron scale with a copper pan and sliding weights sat on the wooden counter above. Saddles, bridles, hosepiping, chains, and kerosene lanterns hung from the rafters.

Two tall, somber-faced Herero women swayed into the shop. In spite of the heat, they were dressed in brightly colored flowing dresses, purple shawls, and red turbans. Puffing on their pipes, each filled a Coke bottle from the spigot of a kerosene drum; a tin bathtub caught the spills. The shop was crowded with men, women, and children lying across the counter, holding out money and shouting their orders to the shop assistants.

Delia began taking cans from the shelves. A young black girl, her dress hanging off one shoulder, tore a strip from a brown paper bag, brushed away the mealie dust on the counter, and began to tally with a pencil stub. I found a hefty axe handle in a tumble of three-legged pots, kettles, tin bathtubs, shovels, and picks leaning against the wall.

Later, when we unloaded in camp, we found that our three months' supply of flour and sugar had been stolen from the truck, along with some other grocery items. We were furious. On our limited budget, there was no going back to Maun until our next regularly scheduled trip, so for three months we were without bread, an important part of our diet. Since most of the door and window locks on the old Land Rover were broken, there seemed to be no defense against being robbed, other than for one of us to watch our goods every minute while in the village. But on our next supply trip, I solved the problem for good.

When we were getting ready to go, the birds in camp suddenly burst into a cacaphony of chirring, twittering alarm calls. We soon spotted two ten-foot mambas winding their way into the trees above our dining tent, apparently intending to have a couple of our feathered friends for lunch. The black mamba is so poisonous that the natives use a term for it that literally means "two step"; according to them, two steps is as far as you ever get if you're bitten by one.

I shot the snakes, took them to Maun with us, and coiled them over the pile of fresh supplies in the back of the Land Rover. It didn't matter that they were dead. The first curious young lad who strolled past our truck, trailing his fingers along the side of the window, suddenly leaped back with a yell and disappeared through the village. The word soon got around that the Grey Goose was not to be molested.

* * *

There were two butcheries in Maun, both owned and operated by Greek merchants: the "Maun Butchery" and "Dirty George's," the latter known for its flies, general lack of sanitation, and cheaper meat.

We always shopped at the Maun Butchery, though there was actually little difference between it and Dirty George's. These two places were the only sources of fresh meat for villagers who had once lived by hunting large herds of antelope, most of which have now been displaced around Maun by monocultures of cattle, goats, and sheep. Two towering tribesmen in blood-smeared boots and aprons heaved slabs of stringy, tough meat from blocks to scales to counter, slicing off portions as demanded by customers. I often wondered if the poor quality of the meat was due to the reverence that native ranchers had for cattle on the hoof. A cow is worth much more to them as a display of wealth when it is alive. Many Maun people believed that only the oldest and most infirm and scrawny beasts found their way to the butchers.

When we had finished buying supplies, we drove north on the track to Eustice's small farm at a bend in the Thamalakane. The small frame house stood high above a broad sweep of the river. Behind the house a big yard with tall trees and a vegetable garden fell gently to the water and reed banks below.

As we drove up the long, sandy driveway, Eustice appeared from a side door near the garden. A slender black man in his mid twenties, medium in height and wearing a floppy hat, stood under a jacaranda tree next to his canvas tote-bag. I shook his hand, noticing that he had strong arms and shoulders, but that his legs were those of a gazelle, long and slender.

While Eustice interpreted, I explained that we lived in a camp far away in the Kalahari beyond the Boteti River, and that if he came to work with us, the life would be hard: There was very little water; he would not see other people for months; there would be lions in camp some nights; and we could afford to pay him very little other than his food. The only shelter we could offer was what we could make from a ten-by-twelve tarp. He would be expected to patch tires and generally help maintain the truck. He would help keep camp clean, assist me in hauling water and firewood, and lend a hand with the research when we needed it.

Throughout our one-sided conversation I could see that Mox was extraordinarily shy. He stared at the ground, unmoving, with his hands hanging awkwardly at his sides. Now and then when Eustice asked him something he would utter, "*Ee*"—little more than a whispered assent.

"What does he know how to do?" I asked Eustice. "Can he patch a truck tire or cook?"

"He says he doesn't know how to patch tires, but I taught him to cook a little. He'll try to learn anything you want to teach him."

"Can he spoor—track animals?"

"No, but . . . 'ell, Mark, any of these blokes can pick that up, but quick."

"Does he speak any English?"

"No."

I glanced at Delia. We were both skeptical. How could we possibly work with someone this shy, who was too embarrassed even to look at us, and who had no skills and was unable to speak our language? According to Eustice, Mox had spent most of his twenty-six years tending cattle for thirty cents a day. He lived with his mother, to whom he gave everything he earned. His father was a skinner for Safari South.

Without skills or the ability to communicate with us, we didn't see how Mox could be of much assistance. If he did agree to come to the Kalahari with us, I felt sure he wouldn't last for more than one three-month stint. But we needed help badly, and for what we could afford to pay, we wouldn't be able to hire a skilled worker.

"Ask Mox if he'll come to the Kalahari for fifty cents a day and food—that's twenty cents more than he's getting now. If he learns well, and if we get another grant, we'll give him a raise."

Eustice rattled off more Setswana, and Mox raised his eyes to me for the first time. They were bloodshot from native beer. Through a ragged cough he whispered, "*Ee*," and we arranged to meet him at Safari South the next morning.

We had finished packing the Land Rover by the time the sun rose over the river. While we were thanking Dolene and Simon for their hospitality, the others in the fishing party arrived—fishing rods, shotguns, folding chairs, old mattresses, and cases of cold beer in the back of their trucks. Simon insisted that they should all have tea and biscuits before leaving. We said our goodbyes, and they all settled down around the table. Someone said that if they got back before sunset, they might work on Simon's truck.

We found Mox sitting next to the sandy track on a small bundle of blankets. Inside the bundle was an enamel bowl, a knife, a piece of hardwood for sharpening the knife, a piece of broken comb, a wooden spoon, a splinter of mirror, and a small cloth sack of Springbok tobacco; it was all he owned in the world. Wearing holey blue shorts, an open shirt, and shoes without laces, their tongues hanging out, he climbed to the roofrack and sat on the spare tire.

It was about 9 A.M. when we passed Buffalo Cottage on our way out of Maun. The hunters were still drinking tea on the veranda, and, jacked up on blocks, Simon's truck stood beside the house.

That night we spread our sleeping bags and set our chuck box on the ground near the edge of the Central Kalahari Game Reserve. Mox built a fire, and Delia made a supper of goat meat, mealie-pop, and tea. We sat eating quietly, happy to be back in the bush, yet both of us feeling somehow lonely, missing the warm afterglow that usually follows a visit with good friends. "I feel let down . . . as though we don't really belong anywhere but Deception Valley," Delia said sadly.

We had gone to Maun not only to get supplies, but also to socialize. Yet, in spite of the generosity of the people in the village, we had come away disappointed and unfulfilled, still feeling that we weren't really a part of any group. We were both overly friendly after long stretches alone in the Kalahari. Our Maun friends did not respond to us with the same *exaggerated* enthusiasm. In contrast to us, they were casual, and we misinterpreted this to mean that we weren't really accepted by them. And since there was no other social circle, it was important that we be accepted. This anxiety grew over the years, and we gradually turned more and more exclusively to each other.

* * *

It felt strange to have someone else around the campfire. Mox was silent, totally unobtrusive, yet we felt his presence, as though the shadow of a person was with us but not the person himself. We tried to communicate with him, using what little Setswana we had learned, aided by a phrasebook published by Catholic missionaries. He never spoke unless a question was addressed to him, and then very softly, hardly daring to glance at us. His answers were mostly, "*ee*," and "*nnya*." Still, we were able to understand some of what he knew about the world.

Though he had lived all his life on the edge of the Okavango River Delta and the Kalahari, he had only been into the delta during a few hunting trips with Eustice, and he knew little about the Kalahari. Using a stick to draw a picture of the globe in the sand, we tried to explain that the earth was round and we were from America, across the ocean on the other side of the world. But he half smiled and shook his head, his brow furrowed in embarrassed confusion. He didn't know what "world" or "ocean" meant, in his language or any other. He had never even seen a lake, much less an ocean, and his world consisted of little more than what he could see.

Much later, when the fire had died to embers, I lay on my back looking up at the blue-black star-filled sky. Had we made a mistake? Had Mox? Why had he left the security of the village and his family—his social group—for the unknown of the Kalahari Desert? I turned the question back on myself. Far away to the south, somewhere near Deception, a lion roared.

8

Bones

Mark

A king of shreds and patches
—*William Shakespeare*

SWAYING and ducking tree limbs, his wiry black hair plastered with grass seed and straw, Mox rode on top of the Grey Goose through the woodland of East Dune and into Deception Valley. At the edge of the riverbed, still half a mile from camp, we could see that something was wrong. We raced toward our tree island, the truck shaking and rattling over grass clumps, and found pots, pans, bits of clothing, pieces of hose, sacks, and boxes scattered for hundreds of yards around. Camp was a shambles.

A big dust devil? A heavy storm? What or who could have made such a mess? I began picking through the rubble and found one of our heavy aluminum pots with a large hole, the size of a fifty calibre bullet, in the bottom. Just as I realized the pot had been punctured by a big tooth, nine furry heads emerged to peer at us from a thorny hedge west of camp. We were still standing next to the Land Rover when the lions started strolling toward us in a long single file. Two large lionesses led the way, their bodies swaying with easy power, and five slightly smaller subadult females strode confidently after them. Two yearling male cubs, biting at each other's ears and tail, brought up the rear. This was the same pride I had herded into West Prairie with the Land Rover the night Delia had been trapped in the tent. We had seen them many times since then in this part of the valley, and apparently they were the ones who had raided us.

Like justices arriving in court, they slowly took their places side by side in a half-circle on the perimeter of camp, not more than twelve or fifteen yards away. Licking their paws and washing their faces, the lionesses watched us with idle curiosity and without apparent fear or aggression. Besides the excitement and mild apprehension we felt with them so near, there was also the sad feeling that it would end all too soon, whenever they chose to go away.

Mox felt otherwise. While Delia made a fire and put on a pot of soup, he and I began, with slow, cautious movements, picking up the pieces of camp. But he kept the Land Rover between himself and the lions, and he never really took his eyes off them.

Later, we drove Mox to another stand of trees, 150 yards south of our own, to help him rig a tarp shelter beneath a spreading acacia tree. We lashed together deadwood poles for a frame, and with the canvas fastened over it, a crude but snug hut took shape. To "lion-proof" the camp according to Mox's native custom, we cut wait-a-bit bushes, a shrub with wicked clawlike thorns that snare the flesh and clothing of those passing by, forcing them to "wait a bit" while they unhook the needle-sharp spines. We piled the thornbush in a tight *boma*—a circular enclosure—leaving an entrance for Mox that he could close with a single large bush. When he seemed satisfied with the comfort and security of his quarters, Delia and I went back to our camp, leaving him to make his bed and arrange his belongings.

The lions stood up as we drove in, but then lay down again. Around sunset Delia served up steaming potato soup, and while mealie cakes sizzled in the black skillet, the lions watched everything we did, seldom moving, except to yawn or lick a forepaw.

This was a valuable experience for us, and we took careful note of the way they reacted to what we did: Their widened eyes and tense shoulder muscles expressed fear if we walked too quickly or too directly toward them. Their chins lifted, their ears perked, and their tails twitched with curiosity when I dragged a branch toward the fire. Each posture and expression told us more about how to avoid inciting fear, aggression, or undue curiosity in them.

The cool evening air began to settle from the sandslopes into the valley, and the last colors of sunset were draining from the sky behind West Dune. The forms of the big cats grew dim, lost focus, and finally faded. As it grew dark, more primitive, less scientific feelings settled in on us, and I switched on the light to check the positions of the lions. To our surprise only one large lioness and the two yearling males were left; the others had quietly disappeared. Despite the protection his thornbush boma provided Mox, we had to make sure that he was safely in his shelter.

When I swung the spotlight around, pairs of glowing amber eyes leaped into view—the lions were roaming all around Mox's camp! We jumped into the truck, but by the time we got there, three females had already picked their way across the boma and had their noses to the canvas. Two others were on the opposite side of the tree, and the last, and largest, sat on her haunches near the entrance to the circle of thornbush.

I stopped the Land Rover behind the shelter and put the spotlight on it. "Mox, are you all right?" I whispered as loudly as I could. No answer.

"Mox!" I called again, louder. "Are you okay?"

"Ra?" But his voice didn't come from inside the canvas.

"Mox, where are you?" Then I noticed the large lioness near the boma staring into the tree above her. I followed her gaze with the spotlight until I found Mox, grinning nervously, perched naked on a branch not ten feet above the big cat!

I eased the truck between the base of the tree and lioness. She gave way without a grumble and then came and sat next to my door, peering at me through the open window. In one smooth motion, as though the trunk of the tree were greased, Mox slid down, grabbed his shorts, put them on, and shot safely into the Land Rover.

"*Tau*—huh-uh." He shook his head, shivering. He mumbled something about Maun as we drove slowly away. We stayed in the truck until the lions lost interest and moved north up the valley.

In the morning the sweet smell of woodsmoke was drifting through camp when I opened my eyes. Delia was still asleep beside me. The muffled clatter of Mox busy with dishes in the kitchen was pleasant, and it stirred memories of mornings on the farm, my brother, sisters, and I waking to the smell and sounds of Mother making breakfast downstairs. It was still early, and Mox's apparent eagerness to get busy with the details of his new job temporarily eased my doubts about whether he would last in the Kalahari. I pulled on my cut-offs and sandals and stepped outside. Clucking hornbills and fluttering flycatchers landed on the branches along the path, begging for their morning's ration of mealie-meal.

At the kitchen I found Mox sitting on the ground among pieces of litter and garbage scattered about by the hyenas during the night. Carefully picking his way through the mess, he had done the dishes and stacked them neatly away on the table. Now he was innocently cleaning his toenails with the point of our best kitchen knife.

* * *

During breakfast, lions began roaring in the valley to the north. It was now early May 1975, and although the Kalahari was still receiving scattered rain showers, the dry season would soon be upon us. Within a month or six weeks the lions would be gone, traveling through lands unknown. No one knew how far, or in which direction they migrated, and we wondered if they would return to Deception. If so, would they defend a part of the old river valley as their territory? How could we recognize them if they did come back, especially after such a long time away and at night, when we would be most likely to encounter them?

We had come to realize that at least during the rainy season these predators were the hyenas' chief source of carrion, influencing the diet and range movements of the scavengers to a great degree. If the brown hyenas depended on them for food, it was important to know more about the lions in Deception Valley. Though we still continued our night observations on the brown hyenas, we decided to begin watching local prides more often, to learn what we could about their habits and their ecological relationships to the hyenas.

The best way to be certain of their identities, if and when they came back, was to mark them with ear tags. Perhaps if any of them were shot, the colored plastic discs would be taken to the Department of Wildlife, or they might turn up on some Bushman's necklace. At least it would be a chance to learn how far from the riverbed the prides traveled during the dry-season migration, and how many were killed by man and who was responsible. Finding out which individuals stayed together would reveal something about Kalahari lion social organization, which had never before been studied or described in detail. The immediate problem was to ear-tag as many as possible before they left the riverbed, probably within a night or two, and to keep from alienating them in the process. Above all, we didn't want to permanently alter their natural behavior.

While we were getting our darting equipment ready, we agreed on some ground rules that we hoped would minimize trauma to the lions during immobilization. Whenever possible, we would dart only at night to avoid exposing them, in their unconscious state, to the extreme heat of day. We would tranquilize them only while they were preoccupied with feeding on a kill, and only after we had sat with them long enough to insure their complete habituation to us. We would never chase them with the truck or manipulate them with cowboy tactics (which often result in a great deal of stress, alienation, and even death). A minimal drug dosage would be used, and we would work as quietly and quickly as possible to avoid stressing them unnecessarily. As with the hyenas, our criterion for complete success was an ear-tagged lion who showed no more fear of us or the Land Rover than it had before the procedure.

Time was short, so we would dart as many as possible in one session and Mox would hold the spotlight while we tagged them. But we could cope with no more than three to five in various stages of unconsciousness and recovery at one time, and meanwhile, the others would be roaming about in the darkness nearby. We had never darted lions before, and didn't know how they would react.

Together with Mox, we found the pride lying in Leopard Island, a clump of acacia and ziziphus trees on the west edge of North Pan near Cheetah Hill. Approaching them in a half-circle with the truck, we slowly worked closer until, at about fifteen yards away, they lifted their heads and began to look nervously about for an avenue of escape. Lions and other wild animals are generally much less disturbed if they have the initiative, as when the pride had strolled into our camp. Now, as we moved in on them, they began to feel a bit threatened. I switched off the engine. They immediately relaxed, blinking their eyes and yawning. For the next several hours we sat quietly, letting them get more used to us and hoping that they would make a kill.

We had seen these lions many times and had given each of them a name. The two older females were Blue and Chary. Blue was always preoccupied with chewing the tires of the truck; fortunately they were of a heavy ply and she never punctured one. Chary, a big lioness with a sagging back, was the oldest female in the pride, and for some reason a little wary of us. Even when she put her head on her paws to rest, she never completely closed her eyes.

Of the five subadult females, Sassy was the most bold and curious. She had a broad chest and large frame that promised someday she would fill out to be a very large lioness. She often stalked the truck as if it were prey, creeping slowly up to its rear, ready to spring if it tried to get away. But if our departure didn't happen to coincide with her game-plan, she would find herself jaw to bumper with an animal she didn't know how to tackle. Then she would stand up from her stalk and pat a tire with her paw once or twice or chew on a fender or taillight. Once I forgot that she was still involved with her game and started the motor. Taking a shot of exhaust in the face, she leaped back and then hissed and spat at the tail pipe. She was fascinated with the rotation of the wheels and invariably, when we drove slowly away after watching the pride, she would hurry to the side of the Land Rover and watch them go round and round, her eyes rolling and her chin bobbing in time with each revolution. After that she would trot along behind us, crouching as if looking for a place to deliver a killing bite. Sassy was a favorite with us.

Gypsy could never sit still, and whenever the pride visited camp, she would roam its perimeter or leave to be by herself for a time. Spicy, who once mock-charged me, was the color of cinnamon, and she was pugnacious. Spooky had great round eyes, and Liesa was small, neat, and pretty. The two yearling males, Rascal and Hombre, were constantly irritating one of the adults and getting slapped across the nose.

When we were sitting with the lions that evening, Chary seemed to sense something was being planned, and she moved a few yards farther away to lie under a small bush. While the others slept, she watched us.

Around nine o'clock she lifted her head and began staring alertly into the distance, the muscles of her shoulders tensing. The other lions were immediately still and attentive, looking in the same direction. I raised the spotlight and saw an ostrich picking its way carefully through the bush at the base of North Dune. I doused the light. Chary rose slowly to her feet and began stalking toward the big bird. Gliding like a serpent through the grass, she disappeared into the night. One by one the other females followed; Delia and I were left sitting alone in the moonlight. We didn't want to follow the lions or use the spotlight, for fear of influencing the hunt by confusing them or their prey. The minutes dragged... we were anxious to know how the chase was going.

About three-quarters of an hour after they had left us, snarls and throaty rumbles carried from the bushes on the duneslope. The lions were still quarreling over the ostrich when we parked the truck close to where they were feeding in a circle around the carcass. They turned to glare at us, and Chary and Spicy rose to a crouch and laid their ears back, obviously resenting the intrusion. Their muzzles were plastered with blood and feathers and their broad paws were clamped possessively over the bird as they tore out big chunks of red meat. I reached slowly for the ignition key and switched off the truck. They turned back to their kill and settled down on their bellies to feed. We were within fifteen yards of them, so there would be little chance of missing with the old dart gun.

Delia held the spotlight while I fumbled with equipment boxes, syringes, and the bottles containing the drug, trying as best I could to be quiet as I filled the darts. I was all thumbs, and the steering wheel and gear shift kept getting in the way. I felt as if the lions were watching over my shoulder through the low half door beside me; I had taken out the window and frame so that I could swing the rifle around if one of the targets moved past the truck.

Chary's dart was finally filled with its mixture of phencyclidine hydrochloride and xylizene. As she was the most wary, it was important to put her down first so that she couldn't alert the others. Several minutes went by while I sighted down the barrel of the rifle, holding on the line of Chary's back. But she was lying on the opposite side of the carcass behind Hombre, and I couldn't get a clear shot. My hands were sweaty on the gunstock, and it all seemed so unreal, poking a 350-pound lion in the shoulder with a needle from a few yards away.

The lions spat and swiped at each other. Then Chary abruptly rose, looking huge in the spotlight, and turned to step over Blue, who was feeding on her right. I strained to see the sights, lined them up, and squeezed the trigger.

The gun popped and the dart hit the lioness in the shoulder. There was an eruption of snarls and growls. Dust and feathers flew as the pride leaped into the air and across the carcass, their tails lashing like whips. For a tense moment, we froze, half expecting one or more of them to charge the truck. They were milling about, looking from truck to carcass, then off into the night and at each other, trying to place the cause of the disturbance. Suddenly Chary slapped Blue across the nose; a score was settled, the tension broke, and the lions resumed feeding. We settled back in our seats to wait.

Ten minutes after the shot, Chary's eyes began to widen and her pupils enlarged. She left the kill and staggered off to a spot in the thick bush, where we could barely see her. Mox, who seemed to have the eyes of a cat himself, kept watch on her while we darted Blue, Gypsy, and Liesa in succession, allowing time after each shot for the others to relax and resume feeding. Before long, four darted lionesses were lying scattered within a fifty-yard radius of the kill; the other five, young females and cubs, kept feeding.

By now it was almost forty minutes since Chary had gone down. She and the others would begin to recover within an hour after being darted. We quickly drove to the place where Mox had last spotted Chary, and after several minutes of shining the spotlight from the top of the truck, we found her near a stand of bushes; her beautiful amber eyes wide-open. Her ears twitched to the sound of the approaching truck, and she raised her head slightly.

I parked the Land Rover about ten yards behind her, switched off the engine, and stepped out, all the while wondering if I was doing the right thing. Since I wasn't sure how immobilized Chary was, I wasn't keen on walking up to her. My feet rustled the dry grass, and she jerked her head. If she could hear, some of her other faculties must still be functioning, so I clapped my hands twice to test her reflexes. She didn't respond. Stalking carefully up to her, I finally crouched beside her tail, still ready for a flat-out retreat to the Land Rover, and gently nudged her big rump with my toe; she seemed to take little notice.

I signaled okay to Delia, who handed the spotlight to Mox in the back of the Land Rover, and got out to take the equipment to me. The lioness at our feet was the color of dry-season grass, sleek and powerful, her body as solid as the trunk of an oak. We regretted taking advantage of her like this, after having gained her trust. While Delia felt inside her upper foreleg for a pulse, I hurried to squirt salve into her eyes in order to keep the corneas from drying out. Chary was lying on the dart, so, holding her broad paws and using her legs as levers, we rolled her over. Delia dressed the small wound with salve, and I clipped a tag in her ear.

By the time we finished with Blue and Gypsy, more than an hour and a half had passed since we'd begun to dart. Chary and the others were regaining coordination. Furthermore, the undarted lions had sated themselves on the ostrich kill, and they were getting more interested in us, and in what was happening to their pride-mates. There were big cats prowling everywhere, and Liesa still had to be tagged.

When we found her, Liesa was supporting herself unsteadily on her

Moffet has just finished eating a porcupine, a staple food for desert lions in the dry season. Many of the lions had never seen humans before, and after they got used to us, we could often sit close to them with little danger.

Top: *Our camp within a "tree island." There were no other people for thousands of square miles*. Bottom: *Mark enjoys a rare bath in a gallon of water. Except during the short rainy season, we had to haul all of our water in drums from a cattle post fifty miles from camp.*

Top: *Mark bores a hole in the shell of an ostrich egg, then shakes out some for breakfast. By taping over the hole and burying the egg to keep it cool and fresh, we could enjoy the egg for as long as ten days or two weeks. One ostrich egg is the equivalent of two dozen chicken eggs.* Bottom: *Pepper, a brown hyena cub, visits Delia in camp on one of the cub's first trips away from her clan's communal den.*

Top: *Hansel and Gretel, two jackal pups, play-fight on the grass of the fossil riverbed in their first rainy season.* Bottom: *Gretel begs from Mate, her mother, who then regurgitates food for her. Carrying food in her stomach is a safe way for Mate to get food to her young without its being stolen by a brown hyena or another jackal.*

Top: *Captain, Mate's mate, fights for a share of a gemsbok carcass abandoned by the Blue Pride lions*. Bottom: *Captain fights off vultures to protect a scrap of food*.

Hansel gets soaked by a heavy rain while he sleeps on the riverbed, and then shakes off the cold water.

Top: *Still soaked, Hansel gives us a forlorn look before beginning the night's hunt.* Bottom: *Camp after a storm.* Overleaf: *Chary's and Sassy's cubs have one of their first drinks of water ever. During the drought, for more than nine months, the lions' only liquid came from the fluids of their prey.*

Mark stalks a half-drugged lion with a syringe.

Top: *Mark treats Chary of the Blue Pride after immobilizing her. We usually darted lions and hyenas at night to avoid subjecting them to the severe heat and light of the desert day.* Bottom: *Bones, still weak from the surgery on his broken leg, struggles to drag the gemsbok we gave him into the shade.*

Bones mates with Blue.

Top: *Bimbo nibbles at Blue's chin while Sandy rests on her back*. Bottom: *Bimbo and Sandy play-fight next to Blue*.

Bones charges Blue as she tries to get a share of a kill she made herself.

Top: *Sassy bites at Spooky's belly in play.* Bottom: *Spicy and Spooky rest after playing.*

Satan and a lioness of the Springbok Pan Pride.

forelegs; she could almost stand up. We would never be able to tag her without first injecting a supplemental dose of tranquilizer. But we didn't want to subject her to the trauma of the darting rifle a second time, especially with all the other lions watching. I went back to the truck and prepared a syringe. *"Go leba de tau, sintle*—watch the lions closely," I said to Mox, and I slipped off my shoes, opened the door, and began crawling toward Liesa.

Both Delia and I knew that this was probably not wise, but we were afraid that if we tried to drive the truck toward the half-drugged lioness, the sound of the engine might terrify her. And if she began charging around the area, we might alienate the entire pride.

Take your time, and don't make any noise. Watch where you put your hands and knees! I thought as I crawled away from the Land Rover, my shadow stretching in front of me, almost to the big swaying form of the lioness, who was sitting on her haunches, looking away. I felt my way quietly through dry leaves and grass tussocks, and twigs that would snap like cap pistols if I put my weight on one. The farther I got from the truck, the more I knew that this was foolish. I was tempted to turn back, but I convinced myself that the lioness, partially drugged as she was, would probably not even feel the injection. I was depending on Mox and Delia to warn me if any of her pride-mates became a more immediate threat. I would bolt for the Land Rover at the first sign of trouble.

When I was about five yards from her my knee crushed some dry leaves with a loud crackle. Liesa swung around and looked directly at me. I froze, waiting for her to turn away, but she held me with her yellow eyes, her ears perked, weaving unsteadily, saliva dripping from her chin whiskers. I was afraid to make even the slightest move; her eyes seemed to narrow as they tried to focus.

"Tau, Morena!" Mox whispered urgently from the Land Rover, warning me of the approach of another lion.

To my right, about twenty yards away, one of the undarted lionesses was stalking me through the bush, crouching, head low and tail twitching. I flattened my belly into the sharp bristles of a grass clump and pressed my cheek to the sand, trying to get out of sight. My pulse hammered in my ears.

It was too far to the Land Rover to run for it; the undarted lioness was too close. I put my arm over the back of my neck and closed my eyes, trying not to breathe, but inhaling sand and ash up my nose. I could see the crooked arms of two hunter friends in Maun who had been foolish with lions, and the broad platter of lumpy scar tissue, from hip to breast, in the side of a little Bushman who had been dragged from his hut. I hugged the ground and waited.

"Mox! Hold the light in her eyes!" I could hear Delia's insistent whisper in the silence. Though he spoke almost no English, Mox understood what to do. He turned the spotlight and fixed it full in the eyes of the stalking lioness. She stopped, half stood up from her crouch, and squinted into the beam.

Liesa must have heard her pride-mate, for she looked in that direction. Seeing a chance, I got slowly to my knees and began backing toward the truck, trying to be quiet in the dry grass. The undarted lioness was raising and lowering her head, still trying to see me through the bright light. She started forward. I flattened myself again. Mox kept the spot on her until she stopped, blinking her eyes, not more than ten yards from me. Feeling like a mouse under the nose of a house cat, I raised my belly from the ground and began crawling in reverse, my arms rubbery with fear. Then the front bumper of the truck was beside me. I lunged through the door and sank back in the seat. I wiped the grit and sweat from my face with a shaking hand.

The stalking lioness finally lost interest and moved back to the ostrich carcass. After what I had just been through, I was somewhat less concerned about frightening Liesa. I drove the truck forward and stopped next to her rump, slipped my arm out the door, and injected her with more drug. About ten minutes later we tagged her. We waited near the ostrich carcass until all the lions had recovered from being immobilized and then went back to camp to get some sleep.

The next evening, the entire pride, except for Chary, came into camp and circled the Land Rover, smelling its tires, bumpers, and grill. They seemed unaware of their blue plastic ear tags, each with a different number. They were the Blue Pride.

* * *

As much as we hated darting, on one occasion, at least, it allowed us to learn something about the strength of the social bond between male lions. Having grown up with each other, Pappy and Brother had traveled large expanses of the Kalahari together as nomads, without having found a pride of their own to rule. Young males, often brothers, frequently stay together as adults, and these two seemed inseparable.

Immobilizing Pappy was a routine operation. After the shot he sagged to the ground and went to sleep on his side, the dart dangling from its needle just behind the shoulder. Brother, his head raised and his eyes wide, had watched intently as his partner had lost coordination and then consciousness. He looked from Pappy to us, and back to Pappy again, as if trying to understand. Then, ignoring the truck parked just eight yards away, he walked to the downed lion and sniffed along his body until he found the dart. Clamping it between his front teeth, he backed up and pulled. A cone of Pappy's skin clung to the needle and then finally popped free. After chewing the dart up and spitting out the pieces, he walked to his companion's side and licked the small wound made by the needle. He rubbed his head against Pappy's, cooing softly. Then, lowering himself on his forequarters, he took Pappy's neck gently in his mouth and began to lift. But the other's bulk was too unmanageable. After struggling in this way for more than a minute, Brother put his jaws over Pappy's rump and did the same thing; then under his neck again, while cooing. For fifteen minutes he went first to one end, then the other, trying to lift him with his mouth.

Was he trying to stand his companion back on his feet? It certainly looked like it, though we can't be sure. We know that elephants occasionally attempt to lift a fallen family member, and it does not seem unreasonable to suppose that lions might try to do the same thing.

We were greatly moved by this, but Brother was so persistent that we worried that his canines might injure Pappy's neck. I eased the Land Rover to Brother's side and maneuvered him far enough away so that we could ear-tag, weigh, and measure Pappy. Then we rolled the immobile lion onto a tarp, lashed the corners to the back of the truck, and dragged him to a shade tree, where he would be cool during his recovery. Brother followed and lay nearby until Pappy regained consciousness. Then he eagerly rubbed his head and muzzle all over his fallen comrade.

* * *

"Tau, Morena!" It was early morning, only a few days after we had darted the Blue Pride. We had followed hyenas late into the night before and were asleep on the tent floor when Mox roused us. He stood in a patch of sunlight just beyond the flap, pointing to a lion 300 yards east of camp. Through the tent door we could see the male's tottering figure, hunkered over the months-old remains of a gemsbok,

as he tugged at the few bones and the brittle skin. Normally, a lion would hardly have noticed such useless carrion—so parched and tough it could not be eaten. But this male was struggling urgently to get the wizened carcass to the shade of Topless Trio, a clump of trees opposite camp on the riverbed. Through field binoculars we could see that he was terribly emaciated and very weak. The gemsbok carcass must have weighed no more than thirty pounds, yet the lion could not move it more than a few feet at a time before stopping to rest, panting heavily. He would straddle the carcass again and again, trying to drag it forward, without much success. Then he would turn, take the paper-dry skin in his mouth, and pull in reverse, with the same result. Each attempt left him weaker, until he finally collapsed, clearly near death from starvation.

We pulled on our clothes, jumped into the truck, and drove slowly toward him. When we got closer, he stared blankly, hardly noticing us. We were appalled by his condition. There was nothing but the shell of a once proud lion. His ribs stuck out sharply, his skin hung in great folds, and I could have encircled his midriff with my two hands. He must have been suffering for weeks, with virtually nothing to eat.

With an enormous effort he stood up and began staggering toward the Topless Trio, and it was then we noticed a dozen or more porcupine quills deeply embedded in his neck, shoulders, and flanks. While trying to get food in his weakened state, he had probably botched a hunt. He made his way to the shade of the tree island, where he slumped to the ground as though his large, bony head and tattered mane were too heavy for him.

We left him there but returned with the darting equipment in the late afternoon. We wanted to examine the lion more closely and to determine his age and his chances for survival. When the dart struck him he didn't even flinch, and he quickly sagged to the ground. We began removing the festering quills, some of them lodged more than six inches deep.

There was one quill that Delia could not pull out. It was sticking out from the inside of the upper right foreleg, and since the lion lay on his side, the left leg kept getting in the way. Mox was watching from a distance, his hand on the fender of the Land Rover. "Mox, *tla kwano*—come hold this," she called, straining to push the heavy leg aside. Mox shuffled over hesitantly, his eyes shifting nervously. We didn't know it at the time, but as a child he had apparently been taught by his tribesmen that if he touched a lion, his arm would rot off. He believed in this taboo, yet he still came forward.

Noticing his halting, tentative movements with the lion, Delia tried to reassure him. "It's *go siami*, Mox—*go siami*; it's okay." She smiled. Mox took hold of the great furry leg as if it would spring to life at any moment and gently pulled it back. After Delia had removed the quill, Mox, still holding the lion paw, spread his palm and fingers against the great calloused pad. He held it there for several seconds and then looked up, the glimmer of a smile in his eyes.

Dusk had fallen. We had nearly finished taking out the quills and treating the wounds with ointment. I was having problems with a broken quill lodged in cartilage just below the knee of the right hind leg. It would not budge, so I got some pliers from the Land Rover, seized it, and yanked several times. No matter how hard I pulled, the pliers just slipped off. It was getting dark, so I asked Mox to switch on the spotlight. When I could see better, I discovered I had not been pulling on a quill, but on the broken end of the lion's tibia. He had a severe compound fracture.

We were faced with a dilemma: According to the dictates of objective scientific research, we should simply allow the lion to die. Even if we tried to help him, neither of us had been trained to deal with such a wound and, furthermore, our efforts would be hampered by darkness. Yet we had already anesthetized him, and we knew from the small amount of wear on his teeth that he was in his prime, no more than five or six years old. So, although he would probably not survive, we decided to do what we could.

The lion would never tolerate a splint. Our only hope would be to open the leg at the fracture, saw off the splintered end of the bone, sew up the torn muscle, and then disinfect and close the wound. If we could somehow entice him to stay off his feet for a few days, the bone might begin to knit.

We drove to camp and assembled some makeshift surgical tools: a broken hacksaw blade, a razor blade for a scalpel, a dish-scrubbing brush to clean out the wound, and ordinary needle and thread for suturing.

It was dark when we got back. Mox held the spotlight while we opened the wound further, scrubbed and disinfected it, and sawed about three-quarters of an inch off the splintered bone. We stitched the muscle and skin back into place and injected a large dose of antibiotic, then clipped an orange ear tag, numbered 001, into his left ear. We stood back and looked at this pitiful wreck of a lion. If he lived, we would call him "Bones."

He would need moisture and food immediately if he was to survive, but he couldn't hunt without stressing his injured leg. Using an old poacher's rifle loaned to us by the Department of Wildlife, I shot a steenbok, and while Bones was still sedated, we placed the twenty-five-pound antelope under his head, where it would be safe from jackals and hyenas until he regained consciousness. Several hours later Bones began to feed on the meat, slowly at first, then gulping down large red chunks. By dawn he had consumed the entire carcass, and he was sleeping deeply when the sun crept over East Dune.

Bones would soon need much more to eat, and he would try to hunt unless we gave him another antelope. Early that same morning I shot a 530-pound gemsbok and pulled it to him at the end of a thirty-foot chain attached to the truck. Lions—Kalahari lions in particular—are prone to drag their kills to the nearest shade. If I unhooked the carcass too far from Bones he would get up and try to move it, perhaps permanently crippling his leg. The problem was how to get his food supply practically up to his nose without frightening him away or provoking a charge. He was fully alert now and, in his weakened and vulnerable condition, undoubtedly more nervous than he would ordinarily have been.

I had the gemsbok no closer than about twenty yards from him when he began to tense. So I slipped out of the Land Rover, loosened the chain, and drove away. Bones got to his feet and limped over to the heavy carcass. He straddled it and, taking the neck in his jaws, began to drag it, putting full weight on his broken leg. The stitches began to separate and blood poured from the wound. The pain must have been intense.

For an hour and a half he struggled to get the gemsbok into the shade, moving it only a very small distance at a time, then pausing, heaving from exhaustion. He managed to drag it only ten yards before his strength finally failed him. He staggered to his shade tree and collapsed, totally drained. It had been a magnificent, though grueling, performance, one we knew he would repeat unless we could get the carcass closer to him.

Over the next hour I inched the Land Rover back to the gemsbok and rechained it to the ball hitch. Slowly we worked it closer to Bones, switching off the motor when he showed alarm, moving in an arc around the tree, until finally the carcass was within four yards of him. He grew more and more agitated as I backed the Land Rover up to the gemsbok, slid out my door, and crept to the rear of the truck. I slowly reached from behind the protection of the rear wheel and began fumbling with the knotted chain, sweat streaming down my face. Meanwhile, Bones, his shoulder muscles tensed and twitching, his eyes wide with fear and aggression, sat watching my nervous movements. I tried not to meet his piercing stare or do anything sudden that might bring on a charge. The chain finally came free, and I scrambled into the Land Rover and drove away.

We watched from a distance as Bones, still not satisfied with the positioning of his carcass, and oblivious to the pain, dragged it safely to the trunk of his tree.

From camp we could see him lying at Topless Trio, and each morning and evening we sat near him in the truck, watching as he gained weight and recovered lost strength. Daily he became more and more accustomed to us, and our hopes grew that somehow he would live. He was treating his leg better now, only getting to his feet to feed on the gemsbok, or to shift position under the tree. But we could not justify shooting more antelope for him to eat, and we believed that, once he had to hunt again, the stress of the chase would surely snap the weakened leg. He would never be able to survive alone.

On the ninth night after his surgery, we were awakened by his bellows flooding through the valley as he moved south down the old riverbed. We doubted that we would ever see him again.

* * *

Bones had been gone for ten days. We had seen no sign of him. Early one morning Mox and I were spooring a hyena we had lost in thick bush the night before. While we two tracked, Delia kept pace with us in the Land Rover, taking notes on the brown's route of travel and foraging habits, all encoded in its footprints in the sand. It was slow, tedious work in the heat and thornscrub, and we were depressed by how far we had to go for each bit of information. But it was the only way to learn how far the hyenas roamed from the riverbed and what their activities were in the sandveld, where the bush and grass were too thick for us to keep up with them at night. Mox and I stalked along side by side, stopping often to discuss a spot where the hyena had rested, fed, and socialized with another, or chased a springhare. If we lost the trail for some reason, we often backtracked to learn more information. We weren't trying to find the animal, so it made no difference to Delia and me which direction we went, as long as we learned where it had been and what it had been doing. But when we tried to follow the tracks in reverse, Mox was hopeless; he lost all interest. We often noticed him, standing with his hands clasped behind him, gazing absent-mindedly into the veld. No matter how we tried to inspire him, he could see no sense to "tracking backward." He thought we were a funny lot for trying to spoor hyenas in the first place. To many Africans, and to many other people, hyenas are the scourge of the earth. Why anyone would want to follow their footprints for hours on end was incomprehensible to Mox.

On this particular morning, we spoored the hyena to Leopard Trail. It had been tough going; we were often on our hands and knees, straining to find a single claw mark in the hard-packed soil. The tracks led us northwest into the soft sand of the duneslope, where, near the top, the hyena's spoor cut the fresh tracks of a large male lion. We had had little contact with males in the area, and we were anxious to meet those of the Blue Pride.

Following the lion now, we slowly moved off through the woodlands and into a complex of springhare burrows. Mox and I were abreast, casting around for tracks, when my eye caught the flattened, wedge-shaped head of a very large puff adder. The snake was coiled tightly, and Mox's foot was descending toward it. With no time to warn him, I swung my left arm across his chest, knocking him off balance and backward. In the same instant, the adder hissed loudly and I jumped back. Mox gave me a peculiar grin, but his eyes were wide as we skirted the snake and walked on.

Just beyond the adder, the lion's tracks deepened—he had chased a porcupine. Rain began falling lightly while we spoored ahead, reading the story of the hunt in the sand: The porcupine had run over a low, worn termite mound and made a sharp turn south. Skidding clumsily, the pursuing lion had lost his footing on the greasy clay surface and had fallen. But he must have recovered quickly, for 200 yards beyond we found a pile of quills and a smear of blood.

I felt Mox's hand on my shoulder. *"Tau, kwa!"* he whispered.

Under an acacia bush 100 yards ahead, a big male lion sat looking through the veil of rain into the open woodland and the valley beyond—it was a timeless picture of Africa.

Mox and I joined Delia in the Land Rover. We drove toward the lion and he turned to watch us. Then we saw the orange tag, number 001, in his left ear. It was Bones. He had gained a lot of weight, and though his leg was not completely healed, the wound was scabbed over and obviously on the mend. Of course he was full of porcupine quills; we wondered if his lameness was keeping him from tackling larger prey.

We sat with him for a long while, glad that this once we had interfered with the ways of nature. Finally he stood, stretched, and began to walk away, the only sign of his past ordeal a trace of stiffness that interrupted the rhythmic roll of his gait. Studying his spoor more closely, I noticed a slight twist in the track made by the right hind paw, a trademark that would follow Bones throughout his life. We would know his spoor anywhere.

* * *

While counting antelope on the riverbed one morning, we rounded Acacia Point and discovered Bones on a young bull gemsbok he had just killed. It had been three weeks since we had seen him in the rain, and he had filled out remarkably. We were amazed that he had successfully tackled such a powerful and formidable prey little more than a month after we had taken three-quarters of an inch of shattered bone from his leg. As the sun rose higher, he began eyeing the shade of our camp, about 400 yards away. Panting from the heat, he dragged the carcass toward the trees, while kamakaze jackals circled around him, snatching meat from his kill. Though he rested every thirty yards or so, he hadn't the trace of a limp, and we now believed he would survive. Killing the gemsbok had been the ultimate test, and a testimony to the remarkable recuperative powers of a Kalahari lion.

Bones spent the following two days under a tree twenty yards outside of camp, feasting on his kill. In the evenings, we sat in the truck on the riverbed nearby, watching him feed and laughing when he rolled onto his back and pawed at the sky.

* * *

We were following Star, our favorite brown hyena, across the riverbed one night when she suddenly stopped and began to bristle, every hair standing out from her body. Suddenly she bolted westward: The Blue Pride was on the prowl. Sassy and Blue trotted to the truck and stood peering over the half door at us. At times this made us a little uneasy, wondering if their mood might suddenly become dangerous. But no matter how close they came, they were always playful.

After their initial investigation, Sassy and Blue apparently tired of trying to spook us. Without warning, they launched a mock attack on Spicy, bowling her over and then chasing her in circles around the Land Rover, their big feet drumming on the ground. Their mood was infectious, and the two male cubs, Rascal and Hombre, joined in the fun, all the lions romping in the bright moonlight, except for Chary, who remained aloof as usual.

Abruptly the nine lions stopped their play and lined up shoulder to shoulder, looking north. I swung the spotlight and saw Bones charge into the beam with a powerful stiff-legged trot, his massive head and mane swinging side to side. He strutted to the waiting pride and stood there while each female greeted him in a fluid fusion of her body with his, beginning cheek to cheek, then rubbing along his length until she sidled off his ropey, tufted tail. After their exuberant greetings, the pride lay together quietly, Bones a few yards away. The master of the Blue Pride had come home.

Bones's arrival seemed to have changed the mood of the females. Their playfulness had given way to a calm sense of business as they stared intently into the night, hunting even as they lay there. Sometime later Chary stood and moved off silently, followed soon by the two youngsters, Spicy and Sassy. Then Blue and Gypsy were gone, and finally the entire pride had slipped away into the growing darkness, a long procession, with Rascal, Hombre, and Bones bringing up the rear. The moon was setting toward West Dune.

The pride moved along the riverbed to Last Stop, a small group of trees on the edge of North Pan, where they often scent-marked and rested before leaving the valley. In the early light of dawn they walked slowly toward a herd of seven red hartebeest browsing on silvery catophractes bushes on the west slope of North Dune. An old bull, the tips of his horns worn to shiny nubs, stood a little apart, licking the mineral from a termite mound. Lowering themselves for the stalk, the lionesses fanned out toward the herd, gliding through the brush, ears drawn down beside their heads. Nearly an hour later they were moving abreast, in a line about 100 yards long, still seventy or eighty yards from the hartebeest but moving toward them. Rascal and Hombre stayed far to the rear with Bones. But while the lionesses were stalking north, the hartebeest had turned east; they would miss their chance unless adjustments were made. Chary and Sassy pulled from the line, and slipping behind their pride-mates, they disappeared in the grass to position themselves in front of the antelope. Liesa, Blue, and Gypsy began stalking slowly forward.

Waiting . . . then moving from bush to grass clump to hedge . . . then waiting some more, the pride worked its way toward its target. The hartebeest sensed something. Staring back at the lions, they began prancing and blowing their alarm calls. Then the herd cantered away.

The old bull was in the lead. As he dodged an acacia bush, Chary's thick arm flashed out and hooked over his shoulder. He disappeared into the cover, groaning harshly, his feet flailing wildly. The other hartebeest dashed to the top of the dune and stood looking down, snorting and flicking their tails. Within seconds all the lions were tumbling toward the kill. We could hear their throaty rumblings and the tearing of flesh.

Bones heard the commotion too, and trotted past us on his way to join the others, Rascal and Hombre scampering through the tall grass behind him. At the carcass he rushed forward, snarling and scattering the lionesses, and clamping his wide paws over the hartebeest, he began to feed alone. The females, with Rascal and Hombre, watched him from ten yards away.

But Blue began to edge closer, watching Bones and sinking to the ground whenever he shot a glance at her. At about eight yards, she made a slow arc toward the carcass. Bones stopped feeding. A deep rumble grew in his throat and his lips rose to expose his three-inch canines. Blue spat at him. He roared across the carcass, shoveling sand as he charged, and clubbed her across the nose with his paw. The lioness bellowed, her ears pressed to her head as she flattened to the ground again. Bones went back to the carcass, and twenty minutes later the females, followed by Rascal and Hombre, slowly walked away. That night, while their male was occupied with his hartebeest, the lionesses killed and consumed an eighty-pound springbok on South Pan.

* * *

It was the end of May 1975 and almost a month since the last rain shower. The skies were pale and cloudless, the cool nights perfumed with the sweet musk of golden grasses, and the morning wind had a cutting edge. All spoke of the coming winter. The heavy clay soil of the riverbed had lost most of its moisture, and the gemsbok and hartebeest herds had fragmented and moved away.

We saw the lions less and less frequently; finally they were gone. We missed the sound of their bellows rolling through the valley on the night wind and wondered where their migration had taken them, and whether we would ever see Bones and the Blue Pride again. We knew it would probably be more than eight months before the rains brought the flush of new grasses and the larger antelope back to the fossil river, late in 1975 or early in 1976. The lions would not be back before then. We began concentrating on our study of brown hyenas, learning as much as we could about every facet of their existence.

9

The Carnivore Rivalry

Mark

Nor heed the rumble of a distant drum.
—*Edward FitzGerald,*
The Rubaiyat of Omar Khayyam

DELIA elbowed me in the ribs. "Did you hear it?" she asked.

"Did I hear what?" I groaned, lifting my sleepy head.

"The drums!"

"Drums?"

"Quick, we've got to answer them!" It was a bright and frosty dawn. She wormed out of her sleeping bag and, clad in nothing but panties, pushed back the flap and hurried outside. Her breath coming in clouds of steam, she huddled against the cold, listening.

"Maybe you've been in the bush too long," I teased her. Then I heard them too. Tum, tum, tum-tum-tumtum—a very low-pitched sound, like someone beating a large bass drum.

"What can I use to answer them?" she asked, searching the kitchen area. I suggested—not seriously—the five-gallon pail we used for our oven and a tent stake. Holding the pail under her arm, she began clobbering the bottom, mimicking the cadence of the drums. After each series, she listened for an answer. But the drums had gone silent. She whacked the pail again and again, and I buried my head inside my sleeping bag to shut out the racket. Finally she gave up and scrambled shivering and subdued back into bed.

For days, at sunrise and sunset, we heard the drums. It must be a Bushman hunting party, we reasoned, since we first heard them south of camp, but later in the west and north. They seemed to be moving up and down the valley but avoiding the part of the riverbed where we could have seen them. Delia kept her pail and tent stake handy. But each time she answered the drums, they fell silent.

Thinking that Delia's clatter had been frightening the hunters, instead of answering one evening when we heard them, we dropped everything and jumped into the Land Rover. Safari hunters had told us that the few truly wild Bushmen left were shy people who avoided contact with modern man. We would probably be lucky even to see them before they ran away.

We drove slowly toward the drums, craning out the windows of the truck and taking a compass bearing each time we heard them. Tense with anticipation, we imagined that at any moment we would round a hedge and see little black men in animal skins, with bows and arrows slung over their backs, gathered around a small campfire, roasting a steenbok for their supper. Or maybe one of the hunters would be beating a drum while the others danced around in a circle. We wondered what they would do when they saw us, and if we should have brought sugar or tobacco to offer them.

We were almost on top of the sound and I was easing the truck around a large clump of bushes, when I stopped abruptly. A few yards ahead of us was a large male kori bustard, feathers puffed out from his swollen neck, strutting through the grass, his beady eyes fixed on us: *Whum, whum, whum-wumwum! Whum, whum, whum-wumwum!* It was his mating call.

We left the kori to his dance and turned toward camp, promising each other that we would never tell another soul about this.

* * *

During the nights of the dry season of 1975, we followed Star, Patches, Shadow, or any brown hyena we were lucky enough to find on the open riverbed. If we missed a single night of observation, we felt compelled, no matter what the reason, to enter it in our journal: "Alternator on truck broken, severe wind and sand storm; impossible to follow hyenas tonight," or "had to haul water today; got back too late to look for hyenas." We had to learn as much as we could, and as fast as we could, about brown hyenas, not only for their conservation but also for our own. We still had to prove ourselves as field biologists if we wanted to stay in Deception Valley.

We were especially fascinated with the brown hyenas' relationship to other carnivores, on whom they relied heavily for food. We hadn't yet learned which species they could dominate successfully enough to steal their kills. Leftovers from lions made up the major portion of their diet during the rainy season, but it would be a short-lived brown hyena that tried to take a kill from them. They could only wait until the cats abandoned their carcass. And though the hyenas often appropriated kills from jackals, their interactions with leopards, wild dogs, spotted hyenas, and cheetahs were completely unknown. We planned to investigate these fundamental relationships during the dry season, while the lions were away.

We had been censusing antelope one evening, and it was almost dark when we stopped the truck in camp. Mox's fire glowed weakly from beneath a big, brooding acacia tree. I switched on the spotlight. If we were lucky, one of the hyenas we wanted to follow would be walking by, saving us hours of searching. When I played the light along the riverbed, large yellow eyes winked from the branches of a tree between Mox's camp and ours. The leopard, whom we had named the Pink Panther, was draped over a limb about ten feet above the ground, his tail hanging straight down. He paid no attention to us, apparently absorbed in watching something north toward Cheetah Hill.

I turned the light in that direction, and the shaggy form of a brown hyena came into view. It was Star, moving slowly in our direction, following a zigzag course, with her nose to the ground. In seconds she would be directly below the Pink Panther.

"Mark, he's going to attack her!" Delia whispered. Since one of our objectives was to learn the relationship between brown hyenas and leopards, I didn't think we should interfere. Delia leaned forward in her seat, her hands clenched around the covers of the field journal in her lap. If the leopard did attack Star, I was sure—having seen browns lug off the heavy parts from gemsbok carcasses—that we would see a hell of a scrap. Still, I thought the hyena would surely smell or see the cat and avoid the tree. I was wrong.

Star moved directly under the Pink Panther. Peering down at her, the tip of his tail twitching, the cat carefully drew himself into a crouch. Star began walking circles around the base of the tree, still smelling the ground. The leopard did not move. Half a minute passed. At any moment the attack would come and Star would be torn apart before she could even look up.

When she walked out from under the tree and started south toward Eagle Island, Delia let out a long sigh and settled back in her seat. Star was about 200 yards away when the Pink Panther climbed down and began walking west. The hyena swung to pick up a scent and saw him. Her hackles rose like spikes along her back; she lowered her head and charged. When she was nearly on him, the leopard launched himself toward the acacia tree that he had just left. By the time he was at full pace, his body stretching into another stride, Star's open jaws were inches from the end of his streaming tail. He hit the acacia at full speed, and chips of bark flew from his claws as his momentum swung him around the trunk. Spitting and growling, he reached the safety of the limb just as Star made a last lunge for his tail. Her front paws against the tree, she howl-barked at the leopard again and again as if frustrated, while he glared down at her from his perch. Finally she walked off. The Pink Panther watched until she was at a safe distance. Then he hurried down and slunk into the tall grass of West Prairie.

It must have been a fluke, we told ourselves, a mishap. Surely sawed-off brown hyenas did not usually dominate leopards single-handedly. But the Pink Panther's rivalry with brown hyenas was not over.

Several weeks later, while we sat at the campfire eating supper, a groaning death rattle rose from the darkness just beyond our tree island; a springbok had just been killed. We had started for the truck to go to investigate when the Pink Panther trotted into camp, his muzzle and chest smeared with blood. He stopped within three yards of us, looking quickly over his shoulder, and then hurried up a nearby tree. He had apparently just killed the antelope. But why had he left it?

On the opposite side of camp we found Shadow, the most subordinate brown hyena in the clan, chewing at the belly of the springbok. We waited, and after about twenty minutes, the Pink Panther reappeared from the island, working his way toward her. She paid little attention and continued gnawing on the antelope she had taken from him. He lay in the grass watching her devour his kill, his ears turned back, his tail twitching. Then, as if he could stand it no longer, he jumped up, curled his tail over his back, and took three pounces toward Shadow.

Without hesitation, the chunky hyena launched herself over the carcass directly at him, her hackles bristling and jaws open wide. Again the Pink Panther turned tail, and the two now stormed into camp, where the cat streaked up the tree next to our kitchen boma. Shadow sat below for a few minutes, watching him lick his paws, and then she walked back to the carcass. Ivey, the clan's dominant male, joined her, and the two of them finished off the springbok. The Pink Panther slipped quietly away.

Apart from our having learned a great deal from this interaction, we were gratified to know that neither Shadow nor the Pink Panther had the slightest hesitation about using our camp as a battleground. We had wanted to blend into the Deception Valley scene. This was testimony that we had succeeded.

We had gained a new respect for the brown hyenas. Scavengers they are, but they don't just wait passively for a handout from the predator community. They often steal from quite formidable competitors. Apparently it is too risky for a leopard to fight a brown hyena, whose massive shoulders and neck could absorb many bites and slashes, whereas a single crushing bite from the hyena could break the cat's leg, or even kill it. As for the Pink Panther, losing a carcass was less costly then losing a leg.

The browns are as skillful as they are bold. During the rains, they key on lions to such an extent that the clan's territory almost perfectly overlaps that of the Blue Pride, boundary for boundary. They know the pathways and lying-up places habitually used by lions and leopards, and they keep close tabs on their activities by coming downwind from them once or twice a night to smell if they have made a kill. They even use flocks of circling vultures to help them find carcasses in the early mornings or evenings, and, as we had seen, they find other kills by following the strident calls jackals make when mobbing leopards. If a leopard has not already stashed its carcass safely in a tree by the time a hyena arrives, it soon loses its meal to a brown.

We learned that hyenas not only dominate leopards, but they also chase cheetahs from their kills. Cheetahs are less powerfully built than leopards, and much more timid. In the Kalahari, as distinct from their behavior in East Africa, cheetahs often hunt at night, when the browns are busy foraging. Spotted hyenas, on the other hand, will displace brown hyenas at carcasses, though they wander into Deception Valley so seldom that they rarely compete with their smaller brown cousins.

A pack of wild dogs is apparently too much for one brown hyena. Star appropriated a springbok kill from a cheetah near Acacia Point one night. While she was busy trying to free a leg to cache, the wild dog, Bandit, and two others of his pack rushed to the carcass and chased her off. Two minutes later Star was back, pulling at the leg while the dogs fed at the other end. Without warning, Bandit bounded over the dead springbok and bit Star on the rump. She yelped and galloped away just as the rest of Bandit's pack arrived on the scene. In seven minutes, the wild dogs completely devoured the ninety-pound springbok, except for the horns, skull, spine, and jawbone. Star did not get one more bite of meat and could only finish off the bones after the dogs had left.

Practically speaking, brown hyenas are near the top of the hierarchy in their ability to displace other carnivores at carcasses. The order descends from lions to spotted hyenas, to wild dogs, brown hyenas, leopards, cheetahs, and jackals (the last two about equal in this regard). But since lions are absent during the entire Kalahari dry season, and wild dogs and spotted hyenas are seldom present in any season, brown hyenas are often the most dominant carnivores around. They are not the shy, skulking creatures many people think them to be.

* * *

It was late when we swung into camp after our night's observations. Some jumping jacks helped to shake the kinks out of our cramped legs. We then tipped some water from a jerrican into the washbasin, splashed it onto our faces, and headed for the tent to sleep. I was a little indignant when Delia suggested that I leave my shoes outside.

My tennis shoes were more holes than canvas, but they'd carried me a long way in a country where even the best footwear doesn't last long. Each step had widened the holes a little, improving the ventilation and making them more comfortable. But for the sake of domestic harmony—and a fresher atmosphere—I put them on the flysheet over the tent, where the jackals couldn't carry them off, before slipping into bed.

When I got up around dawn, Mox was already on his hands and knees, blowing life into a reluctant fire. Springbok herds were stirring restlessly near camp, whizzing their nasal alarm calls; there was a predator on the riverbed. I parted the flap, slipped into my cold, ragged tennis shoes, and stepped into the frosty morning.

The sun was creeping toward East Dune, the air dead still, crisp, and fresh, one of those special mornings when you have to get moving.

I stuffed some leathery strips of biltong into my pocket and headed for the truck. We had lost track of Bandit and his pack in the bush of North Bay Hill the night before, but maybe now they had come back to hunt the springbok grazing on Mid Pan.

Delia had to transcribe some notes in camp, so I asked Mox to join me; it might be a welcome break from his camp chores. Silent as always, he climbed into the Land Rover beside me, his hands folded on his lap. As we drove along, his sharp eyes missed nothing on the old riverbed before us, but his face was expressionless.

We drifted through the springbok, who were nibbling the drying grasses. It was June, the cold-dry season in the Kalahari. Gemsbok, hartebeest, and herds of other broad-muzzled, nonselective grazers—those that crop away the overburden of straw—had left the valley for the season. It had become more and more difficult for the springbok to find the few remaining green stems. Like the other antelope, they, too, had adjusted their feeding strategies by moving into the sandveld in the evenings. There they grazed greener grasses and browsed leaves, some of which absorbed up to forty percent of their weight in moisture from the humid night air. At dawn they moved back to the open riverbed, where they rested and socialized until evening.

Later, in the hot-dry season, when the relative humidity is at its lowest, fires would sweep the desert again, burning the last moisture from the leaves. To survive, the scattered bands of antelope would eat acacia flowers and wild melons—if there were any—or dig fleshy roots from deep in the sand with their hoofs. There is something pathetic about a handsome bull gemsbok on his knees, his head and shoulders pushing deep into a hole, chewing off woody fiber to get the moisture and nutrients he needs to stay alive. The antelope are remarkably well adapted to this whimsical land. Living and reproducing in large herds during times of plenty, they eke out a near solitary existence by grubbing roots from the barren soil in the severe dry season and drought.

When we were driving through the springbok herd early that morning, something suddenly galvanized their attention. Like iron filings drawn by a magnet, they all turned to the north. I raised my binoculars and saw Bandit and his pack shagging along in rough file, headed toward the dry water hole about a mile away. We caught up with the pack as the dogs wandered over the dried and crusted surface, searching eagerly for water, sniffing with their noses at the clods and cracks in the clay. But it would be more than eight months before the rains would come and they could drink again. Until then, like the other predators, they would subsist only on the moisture found in the fluids of their prey.

Bandit stood on the calcrete rim of the water hole and eyed the herd of springbok across the valley. Then he turned and rushed to the other dogs, touching noses with them, his tail raised with excitement as he incited the hunting mood. The pack crowded into a huddle, pushing muzzle to muzzle, their tails waving like tassels as they welded themselves into a coordinated hunting machine. Bandit raced away, leading the others toward the herd.

Minutes later they had pulled down a springbok, and when Mox and I arrived, it had already been quartered and torn to pieces. Bandit and the other adults stepped back from the kill to let the yearlings feed first, as is the habit of wild dogs. After the young had fed alone for about five minutes, the older dogs rejoined them and finished off the carcass. Then they all pushed their crimson-stained muzzles through the grass and rolled over and over on their backs to clean themselves.

A game of tag began, with several dogs racing around the Land Rover, using a springbok leg for a baton. Mox and I watched the circus: dancing, high-spirited gypsy dogs with rag-tag coats, tattered ears, and broom-sedge tails. Finally the sun grew hotter, and three of the dogs settled into the shade of the truck.

The lower jaw bone of the springbok they had killed was lying about fifteen yards away in the short grass, and if I could get it, we could determine its age. I would have to collect it immediately, however, or one of the dogs would certainly carry it off. Cape hunting dogs had never been known to attack a person on foot, so, gathering up my camera, I eased open the door and stepped out. Mox was shaking his head and muttering, "Uh-uh, uh-uh," while I crept slowly to the front of the truck, ready to retreat if necessary.

I moved ahead several yards, and two dogs raced between me and the Land Rover, one chomping on the ear of the other. Three more streaked in front of me, one of them carrying the springbok's leg jutting at right angles from its jaws. With the pack dancing and dodging around me, I felt a rush of exhilaration, a sense of freedom, almost as if I were one of them.

I began to snap pictures as fast as I could. The wild dogs were running, jumping, and wheeling in hyperanimation, their golden-and-black coats a kaleidoscope in the soft morning light. They seemed totally unconcerned with me. But when I squatted to pick up the springbok jaw bone, the mood of the pack suddenly changed. A young dog turned toward me, first raising his head very high, then lowering it, as if seeing me for the first time. He stalked toward me until he was only ten feet away, his eyes, like black opals, staring me in the face. A loud *Hurraagh!* came from deep in his chest, and immediately the rest of the pack turned on me. In a second they had formed a tight semicircle around me, and shoulder to shoulder, tails raised above their backs, they continued growling as they pressed in on me. Beads of sweat broke out on my face. I had gone too far. A dash for the truck was out of the question; yet unless I did something immediately, they might attack.

I stood up. The effect was immediate and striking: The entire pack suddenly relaxed as if tranquilized. Dropping their tails, looking away, they broke their formation and began wandering about, some returning to play. A couple of them gave me wry looks, as if to say, "Now why did you pull a stunt like that?"

I looked back at Mox in the truck. Poor guy, he'd been treed twice by lions and once by a gemsbok since coming to work for us. He just couldn't understand why anyone would be so foolish as to walk among wild dogs.

I had learned to manipulate the pack. By squatting or sitting I could draw immediate threat; several dogs would dart forward and nip at the camera tripod before springing back. If I thought they were getting too agitated, I stood, and they would back up and relax. After several minutes of this experiment, some of the threat seemed tempered by curiosity. I was interested in their responses to my positions, so I decided to try lying down.

I sank slowly to a sitting position, and again the same young dog gave the alarm. Six of the pack members strutted toward me, tails over their backs, growling and bristling with threat. They were little more than a yard or two away when I stretched out on my back, with the camera on my belly. Strangely enough this posture stimulated more curiosity than threat, and two dogs moved cautiously toward my head, noses near the ground; two others moved in on my feet. The ones on my left seemed content to threaten the tripod. They all smelled rather high, like Limburger cheese.

I didn't worry too much about the dogs at my feet, but it was hard to observe the two coming at my head. Suddenly all four of them began rushing in for quick sniffs of my hair and feet before dancing away. I found that if I wiggled my feet and my head now and then, they were more cautious, content to just stalk in for a whiff and then dart away.

I was waggling my shoes and shaking my head to keep the pack off while I photographed them, and I had taken some great shots of my foot just under the chin of one particular dog. Everything was fine until he touched my toe with his nose a couple of times. He cocked his head, and his face assumed a peculiar look, as if he'd been stunned. Then he turned completely around and began kicking sand over my foot, trying to bury my tennis shoes.

10

Lions in the Rain

Mark

Deception Valley
January 1976

Dear Mother & Dad,

We could not have known what the Kalahari had in store for us. All through September, October, November, and December the rains did not come, and at the beginning of January there was not a cloud in the sky. The temperatures soared past 120 degrees in the shade, and the wind blew hot as a blast furnace across the dry, dusty valley. As in the previous dry season, for weeks we were able to do nothing but lie on our cots, dizzy from the heat and covered in wet towels. We tried to conserve our energy so that we could work at night, but by sundown we were always weak from heat fatigue. We ate salt tablets like candy, and our joints ached continuously. We just existed. The sun and wind seemed determined to sear and strip the last vestige of life from the dry Kalahari.

But if the heat was bad for us, it was much worse for the animals. There were no antelope on the old riverbed, and only a few ground squirrels and birds scratched around for food. In the sandveld, gemsbok pawed deep holes in the ground, searching for the fleshy, succulent roots and tubers from which they could get enough moisture and nourishment to stay alive. Giraffe stood spraddle-legged in dry water holes, dragging their heads through the dust in the shimmering heat. The nights were deathly quiet, empty of all sound except the occasional squawk of a korhaan or the cry of a lonely jackal.

Then in mid-January, puffs of snow-white cumulus clouds began to appear each day, softening the harsh glare of the desert sky. But, like apparitions, they disappeared into the great void of heat that gripped the Kalahari. Again and again the clouds challenged the inert high-pressure system that locked the land in drought. Each day they grew, until they stood like great cathedrals with massive columns in the sky. As if in anticipation, small herds of springbok began appearing on the riverbed, their bodies a misshapen illusion in the silent waves of midday heat. They seemed to understand the language of the distant, rumbling clouds. The sky beneath was streaked with rain; we could smell it. Standing at the edge of camp, we willed the storms toward us, but they would not come. And we knew it might not rain at all.

Then, late one afternoon the clouds were back, stacked closely, dark mountains of vapor growing over the valley. A black squall line dropped low and rolled toward the riverbed. The trees seemed to quiver, and we could feel the thunder deep in our chests. Lightning cut across the sky, swirling clouds swept over the dunes, and fingers of sand raced down the slopes with the rushing wind. The sweet fragrance of rain was everywhere, and like an avalanche, the storm broke over the parched desert. We could not contain ourselves. Laughing and singing, we ran from the camp to meet the stinging wall of wind and rain. We danced around, and even rolled in the mud. The storm meant the rebirth of our spirits and new life for the Kalahari. It rained and rained, and that storm ushered in the Kalahari wet season. No wonder that *pula* is the most important word in Setswana. It means "rain" and is both a greeting and the name for a unit of Botswana's currency.

It must truly be one of the wonders of the world to see the Kalahari change from a bleak desert to a verdant paradise. Through eons of time, all the life in the desert has adapted to these extreme conditions and dramatic changes. Animals and plants alike wasted no time getting reproduction into full swing to take advantage of the short and unreliable rainy season. Every living thing from grasshoppers to giraffe, jackals, and gemsbok quickly give birth to their young before the dry season begins all over again. It would be a major challenge for an animal behaviorist to describe the facial expression of a male springbok, who, after standing alone for months on his dusty midden, suddenly looks up to see 2000 females prancing into his territory.

Before dawn one morning another heavy storm charged into the valley. Howling winds drove sheets of rain through camp, and lightning cast the shadows of frenzied trees on the billowing wall of our tent. Before long the legs of our cots stood eight inches deep in water, and we lay listening to the symphony of the thunder accompanied by the wind and rain on canvas. When the storm had passed, the Kalahari stood in soggy silence, as though holding its breath while drinking the life-giving moisture. The only sound was the pok-pok-pok of water dripping on the tent from the trees overhead. Then the deep roar of a lion, the first of the season, rolled through the valley on the still dawn air.

We slogged over to the truck through ankle-deep mud and water and headed north along the riverbed in the direction of the call. North Pan was wreathed in a thin layer of ground fog, and just as the sun appeared over East Dune, a big male lion stepped through a golden curtain of swirling mist. We stopped some distance away, in case he was a stranger and not used to us. Lifting his head, his sides heaving, he came toward us, his bellows punctuated with puffs of vapor. At the truck he stood five feet away, listening for an answer to his calls. And then we saw it—the orange tag, number 001, clipped in his ear. It was Bones!

You cannot know the feeling, and we cannot explain it. He looked at us for several long moments, and then he walked south along the valley, roaring. We wondered where he had been since June, eight months earlier; how far he had traveled, and in which direction. Was he looking for his Blue Pride females? So far we have not seen them, but we hope to anytime now. We followed him to camp, where he sunned himself while we ate breakfast.

Our research is going well, and we are both in good health. Will mail this in a few weeks when we go to Maun for supplies, and we hope to hear from all of you then. We miss you all very much.

Love,

Delia and Mark

* * *

A crash, then the sound of splintering wood brought my head up sharply from the pillow. Through the gauze of the tent I could see the full moon settling low above the dunes west of the valley . . . must be near morning. I looked over at Delia, still sound asleep. We had already gotten up three times to coax the brown hyenas from camp. Now they were back again, obviously tearing something apart. Groggy from lack of sleep and thoroughly irritated, I jumped up and, without bothering to dress or light the gas lamp, I stomped down the narrow path in the darkness. This time I was going to make sure they got the message.

I could see a dark form ahead and hear teeth grating on the screen frame I had made for drying lion and hyena scats. Swinging my arms and swearing in a low voice, I strode to within four or five feet of the intruder, stamped my foot, and barked, "Go on now, dammit! Get the hell out of—" I bit off my words as I suddenly realized this was much too large for a brown hyena. With a growl tearing from her throat, the lioness spun around and crouched in front of me, the screen clamped defiantly in her jaws, her ropy tail lashing from side to side.

We had vowed never to put lions in a compromising position, never to threaten them. Half asleep, I had broken our cardinal rule. Bolts of nervous energy shot up my spine as we stared at each other through the darkness. I began to sweat in the chilly night air. It was dead quiet, except for her breathing and the swish of her tail in the grass. We were so close I could have reached out and put my hand on her head; yet I had no idea who this was. "Sassy, you devil, is that you?" I whispered.

The lioness didn't move, and my words fell away in the darkness. Somewhere on the riverbed a plover screamed. I tried not to breathe. Unable to see the lion's face, I wasn't getting any clues. Her only vocalization had been one of surprise and threat when she had crouched down over her hindquarters. She could very well lash out and lay me open from shoulder to waist or send me sprawling like a rag doll into the thorns. If I moved, she might spring at me; if I stood still, she might just turn and walk away.

Delia's voice from the tent behind me sounded small and far away. "Mark, is everything all right?"

Too frightened to answer, I slowly put one foot behind me and began a retreat. With a loud, straining grunt, the lioness leaped into the air, whirled around, and hoisting the screen frame high, she romped out of camp. As I made my way back toward the tent, the drumming of heavy feet and more grunts sounded in the dark around me.

I knelt to light the gas lamp. Delia raised up on her elbow. "Mark, what are you going to do?"

"I can't let them tear up camp."

"Please be careful," she urged, as I started back along the footpath toward the kitchen. I held the lamp low and shielded my eyes with my hand so I could see ahead. The lions seemed to be gone, or perhaps their sounds were being covered by the hissing of the lantern. I moved past our dining tent and stepped around the row of water drums. Three lionesses of the Blue Pride were stalking toward me from only ten yards away; Sassy, as usual, was in the lead. To my right, three others were invading camp along the footpath to the kitchen, and Rascal and Hombre were pushing through the bushes behind the water drums.

There is a great difference in the posture and expressions of mildly curious lions and those bent on destruction. The Blue Pride was keyed up, their ears perked forward, bodies held low, tails thrashing. I had seldom seen them in such a mood—a mixture of curiosity and playful rambunctiousness, with perhaps more than a dash of predatory urge thrown in. They had probably come from hunting along the riverbed.

They had visited us on numerous other occasions in the previous rainy season, and each time had grown less and less afraid of us and the camp's surroundings. Each time it had become more difficult to convince them to leave without damaging anything important. The first time or two I had only to start the truck's motor, raise my voice, or wave my arms slowly to start them moving away. But since then, progressively stronger action had been required.

Now they stared directly at me as they came. It would take more than the usual amount of persuasion to turn them out of camp before they began to ransack it. If they discovered how flimsy the tents were and how much fun to bat around, they might break them down and shred them to pieces.

Sassy, Spicy, and Gypsy were about six feet away. "Okay, that's far enough!" I said in a loud, shaky voice. At the same time I stepped forward and swung the lantern within a foot of their noses. I had used this deterrence successfully before, but this time they quickly dropped to a crouch, their tails whipping up puffs of dust in the path. The other two groups were advancing from each side of me and were now less than twelve feet away.

Unnerved, I took a few steps backward. Then I noticed an aluminum tent pole propped against a tree next to one of the water drums. Confident that this would do the trick, I swung it hard against the empty drum. Wang! Once again they all just crouched.

When they started toward me again, I grabbed a stick of heavy firewood lying near the footpath. Against my better judgment, but seeing no other option, I drew back and threw the block of wood toward Sassy, ten feet in front of me. Turning once in the air before it reached her, it would have struck her cleanly across the snout had it not been for the big paw she raised like a catcher's mitt at the last instant. With astonishing speed she deftly blocked the missile with the flat of her pad and grounded it at her feet. She then looked at me for a second before seizing the chunk of wood in her jaws and strutting out of camp. It was as if my rash action had broken the tension; the rest of the lions sprinted after her.

Swinging the lantern from side to side, trying to see in the underbrush along the path, I made my way quickly back to the tent, where Delia was waiting anxiously. As I pulled back the flap to step inside, the lantern reflected the amber eyes of lions standing all around the Land Rover, which was parked just off the back corner of the tent.

"These lions are in a hell of a funny mood," I whispered. "We'd better get into the truck. I don't know exactly how we're going to do it, though."

Delia pulled on jeans and a shirt while I watched the big cats playing around the Land Rover. One was chewing a tire. Bones stood near the left front fender, his head taller than the hood, and as he turned to the side, I could see the heavy scar over his right hind knee.

We waited, crouching near the corner of the tent; some of the lions were now lying around the truck. Meanwhile, one of the others stole the spade from near the campfire, and another romped out of the reed kitchen with a large tin of powdered milk.

About half an hour later, Bones began roaring, and the entire pride joined in the chorus. Continuing to bellow, the two near the door on the driver's side of the truck moved to the rear. We crawled along the wall of the tent and slipped quietly into the cab.

When the morning sun crested East Dune, I sat dozing with my forehead against the steering wheel and Delia was slumped against my side, her coat pulled up snug around her neck. The dull thonk of rubber in trouble and a movement of the steering wheel brought my head up sharply. I leaned out the window to see Sassy lying on her side next to the front wheel, her long canines poking into the tire. Having spent themselves during the raid on camp, Gypsy, Liesa, Spicy, Spooky, Blue, Chary, Rascal, Hombre, and Bones lay sprawled in the pool of warm sun around our truck. The Blue Pride had come back to Deception Valley.

Rascal and Hombre had grown up considerably, despite the rigors of the long dry season, and each sported a fringe of patchy, untidy mane. The young females had lost most of their adolescent spots and their forelegs, chests, and necks had thickened. They were adults now, but obviously still youngsters at heart.

* * *

It was urgent that we learn as much about the Blue Pride as we could during the short rainy season: the size of their territory; what prey they ate, how much, and how often; how their kills influenced the movements and feeding habits of the brown hyenas. We were also interested in finding out how their social system compared with that of lions in the more moderate climate of the Serengeti Plains. Within two to four months, depending on how long the rains lasted and how late the large antelope prey stayed in the valley, the lions would migrate away again.

But even when the lions were near Deception Valley, they spent most of their time in duneslope woodlands and bush habitats, where it was very hard to follow and observe them, especially at night, when they were most active. Unless we stumbled onto them while following brown hyenas, homing on their roars was our only way of finding them.

Typically, we would have just gone to sleep after hours of night work, and then hearing a lion's bellow, we would jump out of bed swearing and fumbling for the flashlight. Whoever found it first dashed for the truck to take a compass bearing on the sound. We had no more than about forty seconds before the first series of roars died away. If we didn't get a fix then, invariably, it seemed, the lion would not call again. We would be left standing nude in the dark, often with skinned or rope-burned shins and toes from running the gauntlet of thorns, sharp tent stakes, and tie-down lines that lay along the path out of the trees to the truck. As soon as we would crawl back under the covers, another bellow would echo through the valley.

If we managed to get a bearing, we would pull on our clothes and climb into the truck. Then Delia would hold the compass on her lap, directing me as we drove along. We were able to find the lion about half the time, unless it was moving when it bellowed, as lions often do. Crude as this technique was, we began to get good rainy-season information on the Blue Pride's movements in the valley and what antelope they were eating.

Nearly even evening, the roars of the Blue Pride were answered by lions farther south in Deception Valley. We grew more and more curious about these neighbors, especially since observations on only one pride would never give us a reliable picture of Kalahari lion ecology. We would have to head south to locate and observe as many of the other valley prides as we could.

The idea was a little intimidating at first, since it was an expedition that we had never made and for which we were not equipped. We would have to find our way deeper into the Kalahari along the shallow, meandering riverbed, which would be totally obliterated in places, blocked with sand dunes. Alone in our battered old truck, without a back-up vehicle or any radio communication, and with only the food and water we could carry, we might lose the river course and wander around for days trying to find our camp again.

Nevertheless, we decided to do it. We packed the Land Rover with water, cooking pots, fuel, spare parts, and essential food and bedding. I wrapped our only tube of tire patch solution in a piece of plastic fertilizer bag to keep it from evaporating and from being punctured in the toolbox. The thornbush would be heavy in places and a flat tire or two was inevitable. The plastic fertilizer bag would seal small leaks in the radiator if stuffed into the grill and then set alight—according to an old Bushman tracker who didn't know much except how to come back from the Kalahari.

Early one morning, we set off south along the riverbed. We left Mox standing at the edge of camp, a piece of paper in his hand. Our note read:

To Whom It May Concern:

On April 6, 1976, we left camp to explore Deception Valley south from this point. If it has been more than two weeks since our departure when you read this, please go to Maun and ask someone to send a search plane out to fly along the valley.

Thank you,
Mark and Delia Owens

It was highly unlikely that anyone other than Mox would ever see our scrawl, but we felt better having left it just the same. Mox had instructions to walk along our truck spoor, east out of the reserve, to a cattle post if we were not back after the sun had risen and set fourteen times.

As we drove south, the familiar line of West Dune with its picturesque acacia woodlands followed us for a mile, and then fell easily behind. A stranger took its place: The riverbed grew narrow and tentative, less distinct. Soon all that was familiar about the Kalahari disappeared, and we were headed toward a flat horizon of thornscrub, grass, and sand.

Several miles later a bottleneck in the riverbed spilled out into a generous open plain, or pan, where hundreds of gemsbok and hartebeest and thousands of springbok grazed on lush grasses. "Springbok Pan," we wrote in our log for the first time. Other antelope sipped at shallow water holes a few feet across, where hottentot teals dabbled in the mud. White storks, migrants from chimneys in Europe, and their white-bellied cousins from North Africa strolled along picking up grasshoppers. Black-shouldered and yellow-billed kites, tawny eagles, lappet-faced vultures, and kestrels hovered and turned through the sky, while jackals and bat-eared foxes trotted over the savanna pouncing on mice and snatching grasshoppers from grass stems.

We drove slowly through the herds and across the pans, then found our way back into the narrow part of the rivercourse. Giraffes craned their necks curiously at us from low, shrub-covered dunes, close along either side. Never had we seen so many antelope—herd after herd cantered aside as we passed.

Later we rounded a bend, and a large conical sand dune with a lopsided cap of woodland loomed ahead, blocking the river channel; there seemed no way around. We drove straight up the side to the top and stood there in the wind, feeling minute against the endless savanna. The river channel beyond splayed in several directions, like the unbraided ends of a rope; it was not altogether obvious which tributary we should take.

From the truck's storage box I pulled out a tattered photograph, a composite of tiny aerial pictures taken by the British Royal Air Force years ago. In printing this collage of photos, the geographic features along the edges of the smaller prints had not been carefully matched up by technicians in the Department of Surveys and Lands: they were scattered about like the pieces of a jigsaw puzzle. As a navigational tool, this enlarged mosaic was fuzzy and inaccurate, but it was all we had. From the picture it looked as if the middle fork was the channel most likely to be the continuation of Deception Valley, so we set course along that one, stopping to look for lion tracks in the mud at water holes, to collect scats from tree islands, and to study old kill sites.

We tried to keep track of our position, but in many places the old channel was shallow and covered with the same vegetation found in the bordering sandveld. Every now and then we would stop, worried because we had lost touch with Deception. Then, by standing on top of the Land Rover to get above the flat terrain, we would find the narrow trough again, faintly visible as it wandered away to the north or south of us through the waving grass-heads. At each temporary campsite I took star shots with an old Royal Air Force bubble sextant from a World War II bomber. But it wasn't much help without an accurate map.

Looking back, those nights far from base camp seem as if they were of another world. We lay on our backs beneath stars and planets set like diamonds in the inky black of space and undimmed by any lights of human civilization. Meteors left blue-white trails across the sky, and manmade satellites hurried along on their journeys through space. No one on earth knew where we were; we barely knew ourselves.

* * *

The roll of RAF photographs fluttered in the wind as I tried to flatten them on the hood of the truck. Squinting in the bright sun, Delia and I studied a large lightly shaded area that appeared to be about fifteen miles south of our position.

"It's huge! It must be several miles across." In the aerial photo the pans looked much larger than any others we had seen in the Kalahari.

"There must be stacks of game there." Delia added. "Hyenas, too—and lions."

Because of our limited food, water, and gasoline, we were hesitant to leave the riverbed in search of the pans; it was our only landmark and navigational aid. But we needed to know to what extent the wildlife was using the pans, and if we drove due south and recorded mileage readings from the odometer as we went, it should be easy to find our way back—especially since we could follow our truck tracks through the grass. After double-checking our supplies, we turned straight south, toward the center of the big circular depressions we had seen on the map.

It was slow going. The ground was studded with grass clumps, pocked with holes, and spiked with dry bushes. Pitching and rolling in the truck, we could manage only two to three miles per hour. Every few hundred yards I stood in front of the truck and sighted along the compass to pick a tree, dune, or some other feature in the distance to aim for as we drove. We slowly made headway, but, battling the soft sand and tough thornscrub, the Rover had begun to use much more gasoline. Travel on the hard-packed soil and through the shorter grasses of the riverbed had been much faster. Even more worrisome was our water consumption; we had to stop every quarter of a mile or so to clean grass seed out of the radiator and pour several cups of water over it to cool the motor. As we churned along I was hoping that the pans would be where they were shown on the aerial photo. I was beginning to have doubts about having left the river channel.

Hours later, we stopped—hot, irritable, itching from the grass seed and dust. The spot where the large pan should have been had come and gone. After another look at the photos we drove farther south, then east, then west, getting more and more confused about where we were, relative to the pans. And by now we had lost our north-south spoor from the riverbed. I clawed my way to the top of a thorn tree; swaying in the wind and straining through the binoculars, I could see nothing but rolling sandveld in every direction. Every ridge, every stand of trees or clump of bushes, looked bewilderingly familiar and unfamiliar at the same time.

I climbed down, my legs and arms scratched and bleeding, my clothes torn. We glared once more at the RAF photographs, and I finally noticed that the edges of the pan were fuzzy and unclear, unlike the sharply defined features of those familiar to us near camp. I tried to think what had gone wrong.

"Unbelievable . . . *Unbelievable*!" I moaned. "You know what this is? It's a piece of dust! We've been driving for hours toward a piece of damned dust!"

Decades before, an RAF aerial reconnaissance crew had become careless, and a fleck of dust, charged with static electricity, had invaded their camera and left an impression of itself on the film. Enlargement had made the impression much bigger, so that it looked almost identical to the images of Kalahari pans. We had been searching for a phantom.

Going back was not just a simple matter of heading north for the riverbed. The valley was so indistinct in many places that, unless we found our tire tracks, we could easily drive right across Deception without ever knowing it. During all the driving, we had stopped keeping notes on mileages and directions; neither of us could remember whether we had last driven east of our spoor or west. In fact, we had not seen our north-south tracks in the four- or five-square mile area we had searched.

With Delia perched on the hood of the truck, I began driving slowly west, searching for the tire tracks that would take us safely back to Deception Valley. But after a few minutes of staring at the sea of waving grasses, our vision began to swim so much that we probably wouldn't have seen the spoor to the north if we had parked right across it. Forty minutes and two miles later, we turned back east, still looking. But it was hopeless and we were using too much precious gasoline and water. We turned and headed north toward Deception Valley.

Delia rode in the spare tire on the roof, where she should be able to see the channel of the riverbed. She *had* to see it. Bits of chaff, grass straw, and grasshoppers drifted into my lap from the windows and vents. My mouth was dry from the heat of the motor and the desert. I reached around behind the seat, had a swig of hot water from the plastic bottle, and passed it up to Delia.

I couldn't help wondering just how far a person could walk from where we were—wherever that was. Lionel Palmer had been hunting lions near the border of the game reserve one day when he and his native tracker saw ahead of them what appeared to be a man's head set down upon the sand. What they found was a fourteen-year-old native boy near death. After they had revived him with water, they learned that it was the morning of the third day since he had set off on foot from one cattle post to another. He had lost his way and had soon drunk all the water he carried in his goatskin. He walked only at night, covering himself with sand during the day in order to stay cool and help his body hold moisture. After two nights he had buried himself for what would have been the last time had Lionel not come along. I doubted that we could last for more than two days, either.

We passed through several shallow depressions ringed with catophractes, the brittle silver-leafed bush that fringes Kalahari pans and fossil rivercourses. We hoped the shrub was a sign that we had found the channel. I stopped and we both got up on the roof. Shielding our eyes from the glare, we tried to follow the nuances of the slopes around the shallow bowl; but none of them ran into the flat, open channel of the wandering riverbed.

The longer I drove, the more convinced I became that we had crossed Deception at one of its indistinct points and were driving to nowhere. We stopped, talked it over, and decided to go only three more miles. If we still hadn't found the river valley, we would turn back at an angle and shoot for another intercept, hoping to hit a spot where the old channel might be deeper and better defined.

Hunched forward over the steering wheel, my shoulders tight with fatigue and tension, I looked back at our last half-empty jerrican of water. Suddenly Delia shouted and banged on the roof. "Mark, I see our spoor! Off to the left!" Her eye had caught the faint line of tire tracks running through the shorter grasses of a small pan. I grabbed the water bottle and passed it up to her for a well-deserved drink. We were so relieved at the sight of those two arrows pointing the way back to the riverbed that we camped right there. The next morning we followed our tracks to the valley.

We had been gone from camp for only five days, but we had used a lot of water looking for the nonexistent pan. Logically, we should have headed straight back to camp and at least made it to the water hole on Springbok Pan. But there was still more of this end of the valley to see, and so we drove on, looking for a place to top up the jerricans. There had been no rain in this area for quite some time, and the several pans we found were filled only with mud and animal tracks. The Kalahari was drying up.

By noon the following day, the riverbed had become shallow, intermittently obscured by ridges of bush-covered sand, and more and more difficult to follow. We came to a grove of trees at a calcrete pan. Less than an inch of water covered the grey, muddy bottom, and antelope droppings floated on the surface. Never mind all that—it looked like an oasis to us. I shoveled out a deeper hole, and while we waited for the water to clear, we sat under a shade tree drinking tea and chewing strips of biltong. Later we scooped up water with pots and strained it through my shirt into our jerricans. When we had finished, I dug out another hole, and after stripping, we sat on the slimy bottom and bathed. After drying off in the wind, we smeared lard on our faces and arms to ease our burning skin.

The next day the ancient riverbed faded into the desert, so we turned back for home. Several days later we crossed the large conical dune at the turn in the valley and entered Springbok Pan. "Lions!" Delia pointed to an open stand of acacias: Two males and five lionesses were sleeping in the canopy of a fallen tree, beside a giraffe they had killed. The males, who had dark coats and thick, jet-black manes with halos of golden hair around their faces, raised their heads to look at us, yawning deeply.

We named the males Satan and Morena (which in Setswana means "a respected man"). The largest female we called Happy, and the others Dixie, Muzzy, Taco, and Sunny. Stonewall, a scraggly male adolescent, completed the pride. We set up our four-by-six nylon pack tent under the trees nearby, and early the following night we were able to ear-tag some of the lions. They all recovered well and, after sleeping off their hangovers, began to feed on their giraffe kill again. Later that night we scoured the riverbed for a couple of hours, searching for brown hyenas before heading back to the tent. I was tired from the darting, but Delia was determined to find a hyena, so she drove away to continue looking. I crawled into the pup tent for some sleep.

But I was too keyed up to doze off. I lit a lantern and set it just outside the gauze flap to keep the insects from crawling in, and propped up on one elbow, I began writing in my journal. Sometime later I heard a sound, rather like someone slapping his leg. It took a moment before I realized that it was a lion shaking his head. I slowly reached out and doused the lantern. I felt a little uneasy about my visitor, for we did not know these lions the way we did the Blue Pride. The moon was nearly full, but suddenly a great black shadow blocked it out. Satan stood within inches of where I lay.

At twelve feet four inches long and more than four feet tall, he could have squashed the tent like a bubble with just one paw. His shadow moved; a twang sounded and the tent sides shook. He had stumbled over a tie-down line.

Satan was very still for a few long moments, the shaggy silhouette of his mane against the side of the tent. His feet made a crisp rustle in the grass as he moved around the tent toward the flap. A second later he set one of his forepaws directly in front of me: I was looking right under his sagging belly at the riverbed. The belly tensed, he lifted his head, and his roar carried away into the valley. *Aaoouu-ah aaooouu-ah aaaooouuah-ah aaaoooouuah-huh-huh-huh-huh*. When he had finished he stood perfectly still, ears perked, listening to two lions answer from not far away. Then he walked over to them and joined their chorus of bellows, all three lying together in the moonlight.

In a few moments I heard the truck coming. "I came as soon as I heard them roaring," Delia said, unzipping the gauze and slipping in beside me. I was still stirred by my encounter with Satan.

"Incredible—*Incredible*!" was all I could say. It was not until after dawn that they moved away to the west, still bellowing at Bones and the Blue Pride, who answered from the valley six miles to the north.

* * *

We found the Springbok Pan and Blue prides as often as we could, knowing they would leave at the end of the rains. The Blue Pride was not difficult to observe, since our camp was a favorite point of interest along their route through the valley.

Our relationship with these lions had gradually changed. As we had learned to recognize facial expressions and postures that indicated their moods and intentions, and as they had become less curious about us, we found we had little to fear from them, as long as we did not create a setting that they might interpret as compromising or threatening. This is not to say that they had become house cats; we realized that they were still wild and potentially dangerous predators. Yet, even when we blundered into them during the many times they had come into camp, they had never done us any harm. We no longer hurried to the truck when they wandered into camp, but sat quietly under the ziziphus tree or at the fire while they moved around us. Because we no longer felt threatened, we could more fully appreciate and enjoy them in our close encounters. We were not just observing them, we were knowing them in a way that few people have ever known truly wild lions in their natural state, and this was a unique privilege.

When we began our research, most of the information about lions in the wild had come from studies by Dr. George Schaller on East African prides, particularly those in the Serengeti. Our observations were beginning to reveal that lions in different parts of Africa do not necessarily behave the same.

The portion of real estate used by a pride is termed its *area*, and it may overlap others.[1] The territory, a smaller portion within the area, is defended against intruders—lions from other prides and nomads. In the Serengeti, a pride may move its territory around within its area to take advantage of seasonal changes in the densities of prey. However, they still defend the territory against foreigners.

The rainy-season behavior and ecology of Kalahari lions was similar to the year-round behavior and ecology of the Serengeti populations. By spooring the Blue Pride, we had learned that during the rains their area is comparable in size to that of some Serengeti prides, roughly 130 square miles. However, because the prey communities are different, the diets of the two populations of lions are quite dissimilar: Serengeti lions feed mostly on wildebeest and zebra, whereas gemsbok, springbok, hartebeest, kudu, and giraffe make up most of a Kalahari lion's prey. Wildebeest are included when they are available.

Each East Aican lion pride has a nucleus of related adult females (grandmothers, mothers, sisters, and daughters), their young, and from one to three dominant males, who are unrelated to the older lionesses. The females usually remain in the same pride until they die, although a few may be forced to become nomadic if the pride gets too large. But when they are about three years old, young males are expelled by the dominant adult males. They become nomads, wandering widely and without territory, until they reach their full size and have well-developed manes, at five to six years of age. From two to five of these prime males form an alliance, or "coalition," which often includes brothers or half-brothers, and after collaborating in driving established older males from a pride area, they assume possession of its harem of resident females.

During the rainy season, Kalahari prides, too, are made up of several females who associate together. The difference—as we were to learn later—is that, unlike the lionesses of Serengeti social groups, they are often not closely related.

The behavior of the two groups is, however, very similar: In prides of both the Serengeti and the Kalahari there is a great deal of touching and camaraderie. While sleeping during the day, Sassy often rolled over and placed her paw on Blue's shoulder; Blue nuzzled Chary's flank; Chary's tail dropped over Spicy's ear; and so on throughout the pride. Everybody was in contact with someone else, except for Bones, who usually lay a few yards apart. The females hunted cooperatively, as well. In the evening and at sunrise, when they weren't sleeping, hunting, or feeding, they licked one another's faces and romped in play.

One of the most striking differences between Kalahari Desert lions and those in the Serengeti is related to the amount of rainfall in each area. Because the Serengeti normally receives more than twice as much rain, it has a greater number of large prey animals that are permanent residents. Furthermore, there are usually places for lions to get water year round. But in the Kalahari, as we have described, when antelope herds drift away from the fossil river valley, the lions disappear for months and stop defending their riverbed territories. The questions of how much their ranges expanded, what they ate, and where they found water to drink were intriguing. But we were especially curious about how their social behavior changed in response to diminished prey resources and other ecological constraints. It was our desire to answer these questions that eventually led us to new and exciting discoveries about desert lions, and lions in general.

* * *

In the meantime we began to study more about how lions communicate. When pride members are together at close range, they signal their moods and intentions with a combination of ear, eyebrow, lip, tail, and general body postures. Even the pupils of the eye have expressive value.

Blue was resting with the Blue Pride in Easter Island one morning when she noticed a lone gemsbok, an old bull, entering the riverbed at South Pan. Her ears cocked forward, her eyes widened, she lifted her head, and the tip of her tail began to twitch. Seconds later Sassy and Gypsy had picked up her cues and were looking in the same direction. Blue had as much as said to them, "I see something interesting over there."

After they had killed the gemsbok, Bones arrived, intending, as usual, to take the carcass from his females. Sassy faced him, her eyes little more than slits. With her mouth three-quarters open, she bared her teeth, wrinkled her nose, spat, and growled. She was expressing defensive threat, saying in effect, "I'm not going to attack you first, but you had better not try to take my carcass." Unfortunately for her, Bones took the carcass in spite of her threats.

After having snarled, growled, and cuffed one another during feeding, lions make up by engaging in an elaborate face-licking and head-rubbing ritual. By the time they have washed all the gore from one another's faces, peace has been restored to the group.

A lion often locates others and advertises its claim to a territory by roaring or bellowing. To roar, a lion draws air deep into its chest, tightens its abdomen with great force to compress the air, and then releases it through its vocal cords, the sound erupting from the throat with such energy that it carries great distances. Occasionally, when the Blue Pride assembled around the truck, roaring in unison, the metal floor buzzed in sympathetic resonance.

A lion's roar consists of three parts: The first one or two sounds are low moans; these build in volume and duration to a series of four to six full bellows, followed by a number of grunts. Both males and females usually roar while standing, their muzzles pointed forward, parallel to the ground, or slightly lifted. But they may also roar while lying on their sides or while trotting.

We noticed that Kalahari lions roared most often when the air was still, moist, and at its most efficient as a conductor of sound. They almost always roared after a rainstorm and during that part of the night when the relative humidity was highest, from about 4:00 A.M. to half an hour after sunrise. In the valley, and under the conditions described, the sound carries the farthest, up to eight miles, to our comparatively unspecialized human ear. Sometimes the Blue Pride also roared in apparent response to the morning or evening calls of jackals, who also vocalized soon after storms.

In the dry season, however, we could hear a lion no more than a mile and a half to two miles away. Actually, in fact, they rarely roared at that time of the year, possibly because large antelope prey were so scattered that it was not economical for them to spend the energy to advertise and defend territories; or perhaps it was a waste of energy to try to communicate through the dry air. It may also have been that subgroups of prides were so spread out, looking for food, that they would not likely have heard one another even if they had roared.

Whether or not pride-mates are successful at locating each other by roaring depends on whether the recipient of the call chooses to answer. Bones regularly became separated from his lionesses, especially if he had taken their kill from them. The females would move on until they made another one, often miles away from him. One, two, or three days later, when he had finished his carcass, Bones was faced with the problem of finding his pride. He would walk in the general direction they had taken, roaring as he went and listening for answers. In the rains, when the territory size was comparatively small, his roar carried the full length of his domain, and he could reach the females wherever they happened to be. Usually they answered him, and the pride would reunite.

But sometimes the lionesses seemed less than anxious to get in touch with Bones. On several occasions he walked down the riverbed roaring and passed within several hundred yards of where the females lay silently in the bushes. He called repeatedly, smelling the ground and looking in every direction as he continued on down the valley. But for some reason, perhaps to protect their kill, his pride would not answer him. When in estrus, however, it was often the females who first put out a call for Bones. With them it was, at times, a matter of "Don't call us; we'll call you."

Lions can also coo as gently as a baby. This *aaouu* sound is tossed softly back and forth among them when they are moving through thick cover. It apparently helps them keep track of each other, as well as providing mutual reassurance in uncertain situations. Sometimes at night we were able to find and follow a pride through the bush by stopping the truck and listening for this genial call. In the early years, before the Blue Pride lions felt completely at home in our camp, we were often awakened by their coos as they moved through our tree island investigating the tents, water drums, and other pieces of equipment that were strange to them.

A third way lions communicate is through olfaction—by scent-marking and smelling. The Blue Pride walked through the valley at night along scent-paths, often coincident with trails made by antelope or our truck. In most areas the trail was defined only by scent-marking; there was no visible path. Taking one of these routes, Bones would often stop at a bush or small tree, raise his head into the lower branches, close his eyes, and rub his face and mane against the leaves, as if reveling in the scent from a previous mark, and perhaps also applying it to himself. Then he would turn, raise his tail, and spray urine, mixed with secretions from two anal glands, into the branches. Certain bushes and small trees along his route were irresistible favorites, including the acacia bush next to the window of our tent. He would never pass by without giving it a squirt or two. To our unsophisticated noses his odor never lasted for more than several minutes after he had gone. The females also marked bushes, but only occasionally.

Sometimes these bushes became visual signposts as well. Bones never failed to spray a seven-foot albizzia tree on North Pan when he walked by. Its bark had been shredded by the Blue Pride lionesses in sharpening their claws, and its limbs had been twisted and broken because they couldn't resist playing in it—all of them at once. After three or four of the lionesses had managed to get into the canopy, another would try to climb up the trunk. One of them would end up hanging beneath a limb while the newcomer stood on top. Rumps and tails poked from every quarter of the poor tree, until the inevitable happened: A limb broke, dropping the lionesses to the ground. In the end, the albizzia was reduced to a tangle of woody rubble that Bones, nevertheless, continued to spray every time he passed.

A scrape mark is another type of olfactory and visual signpost used by male and female lions. The sign is made when the individual hunches its back, lowers its rump, and rakes its back feet over the ground, tearing up the turf with its claws while dribbling urine into the soil. Lions mark territory in this way, and scrapes are often made while roaring to foreign prides. Two young males who had recently taken over a new territory, scraped twenty-six times in three weeks along a 400-yard stretch of our truck spoor on the riverbed. By comparison, the older male they had replaced usually scraped once or twice along the same route in a similar period of time. The youngsters also jetted the same bushes he had marked. They were making sure that every lion in the valley knew they now owned this piece of real estate.

Besides marking territory, scent probably identifies the lion that left the mark and indicates how long ago it passed the spot. It also communicates the condition of females in estrus. George Schaller reported that Serengeti lions can locate each other with scent, and he observed one male track two others for a kilometer by smelling their trail. Kalahari lions appear to be less successful at this, especially in the dry season, possibly because the scent denatures more quickly in the arid desert heat. We once watched Bones circle, his nose to the ground like a bloodhound, searching for Sassy, who had left him only thirty minutes earlier for better shade; she was a mere 200 yards away. He kept losing her scent and circling back to their former resting place, but he could have seen her if he had only looked in the right direction. When he finally did stumble upon her, he turned back his ears, squinted, and looked away. If I hadn't known better, I could have sworn he was embarrassed.

Whenever he was smelling a female's scent, Bones would lift his head and raise his lips to expose his teeth. Then, as air passed through his pharynx, he would wrinkle his nose in a grimace. This behavior, termed *flehmen*, is a way of "tasting" the scent, or better discriminating its chemical message by passing it over a special pouch, filled with sensory cells, that is located in the roof of the mouth. A lion showing flehmen reminds me of a wine connoisseur who draws air into his mouth and breathes it out his nose to better experience the bouquet and flavor of his selection.

* * *

Lions generally kill large antelope by suffocation. First they knock or pull it down, and then seize and hold its throat, or occasionally clamp their jaws over its muzzle. I had always been curious about how they could accomplish this with a giraffe, who may weigh up to 2600 pounds and whose throat may be seventeen feet above the ground. Late one afternoon the Blue Pride showed us their giraffe-hunting technique. They had eaten little more than a gemsbok calf and a springbok fawn for several days—not much for over 3000 pounds of hungry lions. After spending the day in Tree Island on South Pan, they began to hunt through the open woodlands of West Dune. A light rain began to fall, and they lay down along either side of a heavy-game trail used by antelope to cross from the fossil river to the bush savanna. Their heads were raised and their ears were perked to catch any sound, each one of them looking in a slightly different direction. For nearly two hours they had scarcely moved, lying like statues. Instead of stalking, Kalahari lions often hunt by waiting along game trails, especially where there is little cover.

But now all the females drew themselves to their haunches, leaning forward, their muscles bunching. Near the foot of the dune a large bull giraffe walked into view, browsing the green leaves from the tops of the acacia trees. Chary and Sassy were closest to him; they slowly rose to a low crouch and each began a divergent course around the unsuspecting giraffe. Liesa, Gypsy, Spicy, Spooky, and Blue spread out in an arc across the trail. Over the next hour they stalked slowly toward their prey, using grass, bushes, and trees to cover their approach. At the same time, Chary and Sassy managed to skirt the giraffe and hide in the grass beyond it, along the same trail but farther west.

The five lionesses who were working together got to within thirty yards of the giraffe. Suddenly he wheeled and went thundering down the trail toward the dune, his tail curled tightly over his rump, flinging chunks of sod from platter-sized hooves. When it seemed they were about to be trampled by the 2000-pound bull, Chary and Sassy sprung the ambush. The giraffe dug in his feet, trying to stop and sidestep the lions charging from both front and rear. But his hooves failed him in the wet sand. Like a collapsing tower, he slewed forward out of control, right into Chary and Sassy. Instantly the other lions were at his flanks, raking and tearing at his belly and sides. The giraffe bolted forward again, trying to outrun the lions, but Blue locked her jaws around his right hind leg just above the hoof, set her own legs stiffly in reverse, and hung on.

For twenty-five yards the giraffe staggered forward, his eyes white and his breath ragged, dragging the lion clamped to his leg. Refusing to release her hold, Blue's claws plowed up clumps of grass and left deep furrows in the sand. The others ran along beside the bull, slashing at him until his entrails burst from his body. Finally he collapsed, flailing weakly at the gang of predators.

There was no way Bones could drive his hungry females from this mountain of meat; there were too many of them and too much of it. But during the week that the Blue Pride spent at this giraffe kill, we noticed that the relationship between Bones and the two young males, Rascal and Hombre, had changed dramatically. The youngsters were now nearly three years old, and shaggy ruffs showed where their manes were coming in. Their very presence seemed to incense Bones. At first he wouldn't let them feed at all, driving them off with snarls whenever they ventured too near him at the carcass. Only after he had sated himself did they manage to snatch a few bites.

By restricting their food supply Bones was forcing independence on Rascal and Hombre; before long they would leave the pride to become nomads. The next two or three years would be a critical period for them, without females to help them hunt. In the coming dry season, prey would be scarce and there would be little cover for hunting, and what was more serious, their predatory skills would still be dangerously underdeveloped. They could easily starve to death—many young inexperienced males do—before they were big enough and aggressive enough to acquire a pride of females and a territory. Somehow they had to survive together until the rains, when hunting would be easier.

In the Kalahari Desert it may be more important that young male lions learn how to hunt on their own than it is in a more moderate climate, such as that of East Africa. As adults they will be separated from their pride females more often, and for longer periods, than males in areas where prey is more readily available and lion pride territories are generally much smaller. When a Kalahari male appropriates a kill from his females and they move on, it frequently takes several days for him to find them again. During this time he may have to hunt alone, killing somewhat smaller prey like springbok, young gemsbok, and steenbok.

Rascal and Hombre were growing up fast, and as the weeks passed, they were less and less inclined to back down in confrontations with Bones. They would often seize pieces of carcass, snarling and threatening him—muzzle to muzzle—before he cuffed them into retreat. They were developing the aggression they would someday need to take over and hold a pride area and its females.

* * *

During these early years we learned a great deal about the wet-season diet of Kalahari lions by watching the Blue Pride and Springbok Pan Pride hunt. To supplement this information we collected, dried, crushed, screened, sorted, weighed, and identified bits of horns, hooves, bone chips, and hair in dozens of lion scats. One day I called Mox to join us at the edge of camp, where we sat with bandanas tied over our faces, a smelly cloud of white dust rising around us as we smashed lion feces with a hammer. He arrived just as I was pouring the powdered remains of a scat to be weighed into an extra dinner plate. When he saw what we were about, he clamped his hand over his mouth—"Ow!"—shaking his head and staring in slack-jawed disbelief.

But before long Mox—though a little reluctant at first—had disappeared in his own white cloud, hammering and grinding away at a pile of feces. A day or two later, however, I noticed that he was no longer bringing his enamel plate to our camp to be washed with our dishes.

11

The van der Westhuizen Story

Delia

It is not easy to remember
that in the fading light of day . . .
the shadows always point toward the dawn.
— *Winston O. Abbott*

WITH A LONG sweeping motion Mark stripped the silver-grey leaves from a thin catophractes branch. He dipped the stick very slowly into the drum of gasoline, pulled it out again, and pinched the spot where the coating of liquid ended. "This has to last us for eight more weeks."

It was May 1976, twenty-one months since we had received the $3800 grant from National Geographic. Once again our money was nearly gone. Without another grant very soon, we would have to abandon our research and earn the funds to get home. We also desperately needed money for radio-tracking the brown hyenas and lions, who were difficult to follow in the thick bush savanna, where they spent most of the dry season. In this habitat we could usually only follow the hyenas for an hour or so before losing them. And so far, we had no idea where the lions traveled in the hot months. We had done just about all the research on them we could do, without more sophisticated equipment.

A few days after Mark had checked our gasoline supply, a bush plane zoomed down the valley just above the treetops and buzzed camp, circling and dive-bombing the island like a mobbing bird. We ran out just in time to see a small bundle tumble out the window and the aircraft waggle its wings in salute and speed away. Our mail from Maun, tied up with string, lay in the grass. We never found out who had done us this favor.

We opened the package and found a handwritten message from Richard Flattery, Maun's new bank manager, telling us that a Mr. van der Westhuizen would be in the village soon with some money for our project. Van der Westhuizen was the name of the director of the South African Nature Foundation, to which we had applied for a $20,000 grant. Declaring the night a holiday, we celebrated with pancakes and homemade syrup.

Next day we packed the Land Rover and started for the village before the sun had reached East Dune. Night had fallen when we wound our way through the jumble of earthen huts, each softly lighted by a flickering cook fire and shrouded in a drifting haze of smoke. The Flattery's house was a flat-topped stucco standing opposite the reed fence of Dad Rigg's place. Through the screen door, patched and repatched with an assortment of mesh, we could see Richard cleaning fish over a bucket. His wife, Nellie, was frying fresh bream over a gas stove.

"Glad to meet you . . . heard all about you . . . yes, Mr. van der Westhuizen has money for you. We'll tell you all about it—stay and have some food and a cold beer."

We sat down to a meal of fried fish, potatoes, and fresh bread in a small raftered dining room that might have been in an English cottage, except for an active termite mound protruding through the floor.

As it turned out, Richard knew little about the grant—only that Mr. van der Westhuizen would be arriving in Maun the very next morning. Later on, after a pleasant evening, we asked Richard to invite our prospective sponsor to join us for lunch the following noon at the "Riviera," a ramshackle retreat set on the banks of the Thamalakane River.

The owner of the Riviera, an innkeeper from Selebi Phikwe, had given us permission to use the camp on our supply trips to Maun. The complex consisted of five dilapidated reed-and-straw huts that clung to the steep banks of the river like abandoned birds' nests. The largest hut, which we used, had a partially caved-in roof and leaned heavily toward the river, straining against guy wires that tied it to a massive fig tree. The shaggy encampment, a welcome refuge from the desert, was all but hidden in tall grass. We pulled two rusted camp beds from under the fallen section, swept off the spotted mattresses, and hung a mosquito net—more mends than mesh—from a rafter over our sleeping bags.

Mark Muller, a young bush pilot, also stayed at the camp, in one of the smaller thatched huts. The next morning we were awakened by a grinding clatter before dawn. Muller was starting his ancient Land Rover, a roofless relic resembling a World War II German staff car. He left it ticking over idly at the top of the bank while he went back to his hut for something. The next thing we knew, the nose of the truck crashed through the wall of our house with a splintering of reeds, stopping six feet from our bed. The hut swayed dramatically around us as thatch, reed, and poles rained down. We both jumped up, afraid the house might collapse any second, but it slowly steadied itself. Muller ran down the hill after his runaway truck, muttering incoherently to himself. "Sorry," he said and backed out of our bedroom and drove away.

We began immediately preparing a special lunch for our meeting with Mr. van der Westhuizen. Mark stoked up a rust-eaten pot-bellied wood stove that squatted beneath the fig tree, and, tears streaming down my face from the cloud of smoke that belched from the stovepipe, I baked a loaf of orange bread while Mark went for supplies. About noon we laid out a lunch of cold sliced mutton, fresh fruits, and hot bread—the most extravagant meal we had prepared since coming to Botswana.

Sitting on tin trunks on the reed house veranda, we ate our lunch with Mr. van der Westhuizen, a soft-spoken man with greying hair and a slight limp. In the wide, lazy river, a few feet away, coots splashed among the reeds, and on the opposite bank, a group of baboons moved toward the water's edge to drink.

As Mr. van der Westhuizen quizzed us about our research we grew more and more puzzled. He seemed to know almost nothing about us or the nature of our work.

Finally Mark asked, "Haven't you read our proposal?"

"Proposal?"

"The one we submitted to the South African Nature Foundation."

"I don't understand. Oh, . . . I'm afraid there has been some mistake. I'm not from the Nature Foundation." He went on to explain that he was an architect from Johannesburg who had heard about our research and wanted to donate $200 of his own money to our project.

Two hundred dollars would barely fill up our auxiliary gas tank and pay for the trip to Maun. We tried to conceal our dismay, saying, "We really do appreciate your contribution, it couldn't have come at a better time." But, it was no use. We heard little more of what he said, and after an eternity Mr. van der Westhuizen drove away in his shiny new truck. We stared silently at the river.

* * *

A vise crushed both sides of my head, and a sharp wedge pressed down from above, splitting my brain. The pain of resting my head on the pillow was unbearable. I tried to sit up, but a wave of nausea swept over me. Under the soft mesh of the mosquito net Mark slept restlessly beside me. Without moving my head I nudged him, "Mark . . . some pills . . . I must have malaria."

He felt my forehead, then eased from the bed, and brought me six bitter chloroquin tablets from our first-aid kit. I swallowed them with great difficulty. He carried me to a mattress on the floor of one of the smaller huts, which had no holes in its walls. There was no reason to take me to the mission clinic in Maun, which had nothing better for malaria than chloroquin and where there was a good chance of picking up tuberculosis or something worse. In the rainy season Maun was rife with malaria. According to the hunters, "You either take the pills, sweat out the fever, and get better, or you die."

The hut was dank, dark. I was buried under heavy blankets of scratchy wool, but I was still stone-cold, my skin clammy. Mark lay next to me, trying to keep me from shivering, but I could feel no warmth. The blood in my head pounded against my skull, and a brilliant light from one tiny window stabbed at my eyes.

Then my body began to burn. With all my strength I shoved Mark away and threw back the covers. The sheets were damp and a putrid odor smothered me. For a long time my mind floated in darkness, and then there was a kind of peace. I saw home, live oaks and Spanish moss, the red-brick house where I grew up, and Fort Log, built with pine logs as a fortress against some imaginary neighborhood Indians. But when my thoughts tried to focus, I thrashed in the bed and cried out. Home was far away. *Clickety-clack, clickety-clack, you can't get off and you'll never get back. Clickety-clack.*

After a long time, the light from the hut's window grew softer and my mind began to clear. Tap-tap-tap-tap. We would stay in Africa somehow, and make it work. Tap-tap-tap. Mark was working on a borrowed typewriter set up on a tin trunk near my mattress. He came over to me. Clean sheets and warmth, a snug fresh feeling caressed me. His familiar smile, a kiss, hot soup, and cold, cold water welcomed me back. I tried to get up, but a firm hand gripped my shoulder and pushed me back . . . rest.

During the days that I had been delirious with fever, Mark had stayed at my side, writing proposals to conservation organizations all over the world, describing our progress and needs. When I was much better he drove into Maun one morning to mail the stack of thick envelopes. I propped myself up on pillows and waited for him to come back. Though still a bit woozy, it felt good to sit up. I watched two scimitar-billed hoopoes flitting about in the fig trees just outside the window. An hour later I could hear the Land Rover growling its way back through the sand.

"Hi, Boo. Glad to see you sitting up," Mark said quietly. He sat on the edge of the bed. "Feeling better?"

"Yeah—I think we can get back to the desert soon." I smiled at him.

"Well, we can't rush it," he said. He walked to the small window.

"Didn't we get any mail, any news from home?" I asked.

"Uh . . . no." He went on staring blankly at the river beyond the trees.

"But isn't that a letter from Helen?" I had recognized one of my sister's personalized envelopes tucked in the back pocket of his cut-offs.

His hand shot to his hip. He turned and came to the bed, his face full of pain. "God, love, I didn't want to tell you until you were stronger. There's some bad news. It's your dad. He died of a heart attack about six weeks ago."

I sank numbly back in the bed. "My mother—what about my mother?" I heard myself ask. "And we don't even have the money to go home."

My father had been one of our staunchest supporters, writing letters of encouragement, sending addresses and reference books, not to mention the newspaper clippings about football games that piled up in our post box at Safari South over the months.

Mark lay down beside me. One of the hardest things to bear during our seven years in Africa was being away from home at such times. While we were gone, Mark's mother passed away, and his grandmother. And besides my father, I lost my grandmother. And I missed the marriage of my twin brother. We struggled with feelings of guilt because we were not at home to help our families through the difficult times, or to celebrate the good ones.

"If you want to go home, I'll get the money from somewhere, Boo," Mark told me.

"Let's make our project succeed, that's the best thing we can do." I whispered.

When I was finally strong enough to go into the village to see the doctor, he warned that I had not only malaria, but also hepatitis, mononucleosis, and anemia. "You must not try to go back to the Kalahari for at least a month," he said sternly in a thick Swedish accent, as he peered over his spectacles. "You must rest, or run the risk of a relapse. If that happened out there, you would be in serious trouble."

But I could rest in camp just as easily as in the dank hut at the river, and we had to do as much research as possible before our money was gone. So I didn't pass on the doctor's comments to Mark and, instead, pretended to be feeling better than I really did. Three days later we were ready to leave for Deception.

On our way out of the village, our friends at Safari South, always ready to help in one way or another, loaned us a high-frequency, long-range radio. This meant that at noon every day, at least during the safari season, we could be in contact with the hunters in the field, or with someone in their Maun office. For the first time since our project began, we would be able to reach the outside world. But unless we received a grant soon, this would be our last trip to the Kalahari.

Back at camp we rationed our gasoline, food, and water more strictly than ever. Using only one point three gallons of gas each time we followed hyenas at night, and one gallon of water per day, we could last three months. By then we should have received word from our new grant applications. In the meantime we would get some solid data on lions and brown hyenas. At first I was too weak to stand the pounding in the truck, so I rested in camp while Mark followed the hyenas or lions by himself. But I slowly recovered, and for eight exhausting weeks we worked with mad enthusiasm, knowing we would soon have to leave Deception Valley.

* * *

"Zero, zero, nine, do you read me?" came the garbled voice of Phyllis Palmer on the radio.

"Roger, Phyllis, go ahead."

"Delia, Hans Veit, the director of the Okavango Wildlife Society, is in Maun. He would like to meet with you to discuss a possible grant for your project. Can you come in? Over."

We looked at each other and rolled our eyes. It might turn out to be another van der Westhuizen story, but what choice did we have? "Roger, Phil. We'll be in touch as soon as we get in. Thanks."

In Maun, two days later, we were relieved to find that Hans Veit really was the director of the Okavango Wildlife Society and that a grant for our research was very likely. But we would have to go to Johannesburg for further discussions with the society's Research Committee before a final decision could be made.

Once in the city, we negotiated a grant with the society for two years of research in the Kalahari. The funds would allow us to get a better second-hand truck, a tent, and, most important, to make a round trip to the United States to see our families, consult with American researchers, and buy much-needed radio-tracking gear for the lions and brown hyenas. To be able to follow the predators consistently in the long dry season would mark a major turning point in our project.

But the first thing we did in Johannesburg was to walk to a bakery. Standing in front of glass cases filled with small pink and yellow iced cakes, chocolates bulging with nuts, cookies covered with cherries, and puffy cream pastries, Mark and I ordered two of everything in the shop. Carrying our stack of neat white boxes tied up with string, we walked to a green park and sat in the sun. After inhaling the sweet, warm aroma of the freshly baked goods, we took a bite from every one and finished off our favorites. Laughing and talking, our lips covered with powdered sugar, we lay on our backs to rest our aching stomachs.

12

Return to Deception

Mark

> Though the sky be dark, and the voyage be long,
> Yet we never can think we were rash or wrong,
> While round in our Sieve we spin.
> —*Edward Lear*

IN OCTOBER 1976, we flew back from New York to Johannesburg and found the city buzzing with ugly reports of the terrorist war in Rhodesia. The conflict was spilling across the Botswana border near Francistown. Farther south, along the only main road to the east and north, terrorists were beating and shooting travelers at roadblocks set up along the 500-mile route to Maun.

It had been four hectic weeks since we had left Deception Valley, and we were anxious to get back and to begin radio-tracking lions and hyenas. But it would be risky to try to enter Botswana at this time. The Soweto riots had still been smoldering when we had left Johannesburg for the United States, and now there was the threat of total anarchy to the north, perhaps all over southern Africa.

For some months Botswana had resisted getting embroiled in the conflicts on her borders. But now it was rumored that terrorist training camps had been established near Francistown and the village of Selebi Phikwe. In the past months, Angolan refugees had begun to appear in Maun, many of them suspected terrorists, and the mood of the native people in the village had begun to sour toward whites. On one tense occasion, Delia had been heckled by a group of men while shopping at the Ngamiland Trading Center. Such a thing would have been unheard of even two years before. An atmosphere of fear and suspicion had begun to drift through the settlement, like smoke from the evening cooking fires. Remote as it was, Maun had become tainted by world politics.

In response to the conceived threat from Rhodesia, Botswana had hurriedly formed the Botswana Defense Force, or BDF. Together with mobile police units, this ill-equipped instant army was to roam the countryside seeking out the insurgents who were supposedly infiltrating from Rhodesia and South Africa. We had heard a number of reports about innocent people having been injured or killed either by terrorists, the BDF, or the mobile police—no one seemed to know for sure who was responsible.

We had promised ourselves and our families that if the political turmoil became too threatening, we would delay our departure for the desert, or even leave the country altogether. But as we packed our gear, we rationalized that we might wait forever and never hear more than rumors, and that we would be safe once we got to our remote Kalahari camp. The worst terrorist incidents were mostly confined to Francistown, on the border with Rhodesia, but when we passed through there on our way north to Maun, we planned to make it during midday hours, when we thought it least likely there would be trouble. We bought a second-hand Toyota Land Cruiser, loaded it with a ton of supplies, and began the long trip north.

Early in the afternoon of the first day we reached the Botswana border, where the road abruptly changed from macadam to gravel, with the usual corrugations and deep ruts. Other traffic disappeared. We drove on alone, a dust trail rising behind us. Our tires crunching on loose stone, we hurried past meager mealie patches and occasional mud huts enclosed by bomas of thornbush. No one waved, and if they looked at us at all, they seemed to scowl.

On a lonely curve in the road, a wooden pole, freshly cut and still covered with bark, blocked the way. Ten or fifteen black men stood to one side—were these police, terrorists, or soldiers? No uniforms; but that didn't mean much. Several of them carried stubby olive-green submachine guns slung at waist level; others held rifles. My skin prickled with fear and my hands wrung the steering wheel. I wanted to keep going, but they strolled across the road and stood facing us, their weapons ready. We had no choice but to stop.

We locked the doors and I rolled down my window, leaving the Land Cruiser in gear, and its motor running, my feet poised on the clutch and accelerator. I would break through the roadblock if they ordered us to get out. A young black with blood-shot eyes strolled up unsteadily, his machine gun leveled at the door. He pushed his face to the open window, and I could smell *bujalwa*, the native beer, on his breath. The others peered into the back, lifting the canvas, pointing to the cases of canned food, the new tent, and the other supplies, while they chattered among themselves. The youth at my window began firing questions at me, his finger on the trigger: Who were we? Where were we going? Why? Whose truck was this? Why was it registered in South Africa? How could just the two of us need so many cans of powdered milk and so many bags of sugar?

After a while, the men at the back started conferring at the side of the road, talking quickly in a language we didn't understand, and the youth joined them. I stifled an urge to let out the clutch and make a run for it. They had no obvious vehicles and could not pursue us, but I was afraid they would open fire.

"Don't get out of the truck . . . Get down on the floor if I tell you to!" I whispered to Delia.

The men looked our way as the hard-eyed teen-ager strutted toward the truck, his gun still leveled at my door. He leaned through the window glaring at me, silent. My stomach turned over as I remembered one of the stories we had heard in Johannesburg. A young teacher from Europe, on his way to a school in northern Botswana, had been dragged from a bus and savagely beaten in the face with rifle butts—they hadn't liked his beard. Before we had left the city, Delia had pleaded with me to shave mine off. "They're just rumors," I had tried to console her. Now I wasn't so sure.

"You—go." The words came thick and slow. I wasn't sure I'd heard him right.

"*Go siami*—okay?" I asked. Saying nothing, he stood back from the truck. Without taking my eyes off him, I slowly let out the clutch. The other men stared at us as we began to pull away. I pushed the gas pedal flat to the floor, accelerating as fast as I could. In the rearview mirror I could see them watching us, and the skin on my back crawled. A young girl had been shot in the back just days before as she and her parents were driving away from a similar roadblock. "Keep down!" I shouted to Delia and hunched forward over the wheel, urging the truck toward a bend in the road.

Several miles later I pulled over and held Delia close for a moment.

We were both wrung out from the encounter. When we had regained some composure I unfolded a map of Botswana. "We've got to get off the main road as soon as we can," I said, looking at the great white void that was the Kalahari, in the middle of the chart. "There has to be another way to get there, even if we have to cut cross-country." But from that point it was more than 200 miles overland to Deception Valley. Even with the extra fifty gallons of fuel in our new reserve tank and the ten gallons of water in our jerricans, I didn't see how we could make it.

"Mark, what about the old spoor Bergie mentioned that time, the one that comes up from the southeast?"

"That's an idea... If we can find it, we'll take it."

We drove off the road and about 200 yards into the bushes, where we slept the night fitfully, rolled up in our new yellow tent, afraid it would be seen from the road if we set it up. The next day, in a small village on the edge of the Kalahari, we crossed a shoal of white calcrete and drove through a kraal and around the corner of a trading store. Suddenly we found ourselves heading into the desert on what looked like a cattle trail. It worried its way in several different directions around dry washouts and pans, but according to our compass, we were headed in the general direction of Deception Valley, still 190 miles away across the desert.

By nightfall we were miles from the last road, the last village, the last contact with humans. From here on we would reckon distance in time, and time by the positions of the sun, moon, and stars in the sky. I slipped off my watch and laid it in the ashtray; it spoke the language of another world.

No longer afraid to be seen, we built a fire that night and sat talking quietly about how good it was to be back. A lion roared from the west, close. Slowly the tightness drained from my chest, and I relaxed again for the first time in weeks. The trappings and anxieties of man's artificial world—the airport crowds, the city traffic, the wars and Watergates—were behind us. Primitive, unscarred Africa embraced us again. As we settled into our bedrolls, we wondered whether any rain had fallen in the valley, and how Mox had handled village life while we were gone.

Thick thornscrub, hot, heavy sand—the going was tough beneath a broiling midmorning sun the next day. We drove farther and farther into the desert, and the track began to lose itself in the grass and thornbush. Would it disappear altogether? Giddy from the 120-degree heat, we wiped our faces and necks with a damp rag whenever we stopped to cool the steaming radiator. Delia rode with her feet on a cardboard box; we could have fried a steak on the metal flooring.

"I smell gas!" I jammed on the brakes, but by the time we jumped out, gasoline was pouring into the sand from every corner of the truck bed. The big auxiliary tank had shifted, snapping off its out-flow line. The precious fuel that we needed to get us to camp was quickly running away.

"Hurry! Get something to catch it in!" We both ran to the back of the truck and began rummaging through the load. But nothing would hold more than a gallon. I dove under the Toyota and rammed my finger into the hole I had drilled to bring the fuel line through the truck bed. But the tank outlet had moved away from it and had come down flat against the steel; there was no way to reach the broken nipple to plug it.

I grabbed a packet of putty from the tool kit in the cab, and sprawling in the sand again, my shirt and shorts soaked with drizzling gasoline, I frantically tried to force a gob into the small space. But I couldn't get to the break, and the putty wouldn't have sealed it if I had—not with gasoline spraying out.

The tank was bolted to the bed of the truck, with the fuel line beneath; above were the truck's iron gate and a ton of supplies. In a fit of panic, we began throwing cases of tinned food, jerricans of water, tools, and other equipment from the back, while our gasoline continued to stream away. I grabbed a wrench from the toolbox, and while Delia hurled things off the truck, I sat astride the tank, working with clumsy, frenzied movements to unbolt the iron gate and steel straps that held it to the truck bed.

Minutes passed; the sound of the gasoline dripping into the sand was maddening. Working feverishly over the tank, I kept saying to myself, There must be something I've overlooked . . . *think*!

Finally the tank was free, but no matter how hard I strained, with my hands around its wet, slippery bottom, I could not lift it. I jammed the spade under it and tried to lever it upward—still it wouldn't budge. My tennis shoes were soaked with gasoline, and for the first time the thought of an explosion and fire shot through me.

I finally got control of myself, stopped fighting with the tank and began to think more clearly.

"Pour the water out of one of the jerricans—we'll have to fill it with gas!" I shouted.

I grabbed a roll of siphon hose from behind the front seat, rammed one end into the tank, and sucked on the other. Gasoline gushed into my mouth. Choking and spitting, I stuffed the hose into the jerrican. After we had filled the second can, I hopped into the truck, seized one end of the long tank, and heaved. Now that it was lighter, we finally managed to pick it up and stand it on end. The fuel ran away from the broken line and, after it had dried, we plugged the hole with putty. The rest of our gas was secure.

We sat on the truck bed sick with exhaustion, our mouths like cotton, and I was still trying to spit out the raw taste of gasoline. Then I noticed that the lids were off *both* jerricans. In the confusion to rescue our fuel, we had poured out all of our water.

Even so, I wasn't sure we had managed to save enough gas to take us to Deception Valley. We had no way of knowing how deep the sand ahead would be, no way to predict how fast the truck would use fuel. If we ran out of gasoline, we would have to walk, and even if we moved only at night, when it was cool, we wouldn't get much farther than about twenty miles on foot without water. I ran my hand up and down the side of the tank, trying to feel the coolness that would indicate the level of the liquid inside. If we could at least be sure we were on the right track . . .

We sat in the shade of the truck and pushed our bare feet deep into the cool sand below the surface. Our choice was to go ahead with no water and limited gasoline or to turn back and travel the main road through Francistown, risking confrontation with terrorists or the military. Suddenly Delia hurried over to the cab and tilted the front seat forward. She had filled an extra two-quart water bottle and put it there before leaving Johannesburg. Small consolation—except for a sip or two, it would have to be saved for the radiator.

While we were picking up our scattered tins of fruit, I thought of the syrup in the cans; we could drink it on our way to Deception Valley. So, having decided to go on, we tied the upended auxiliary tank onto the bed of the truck, reloaded our supplies, and sat in the shade waiting for nightfall and coolness. At sunset we stashed some cans of fruit behind the front seat, and I poked small holes in the tops of two others with my pocket knife. We set off through the desert evening, sipping the cloyingly sweet juice to quench our thirst.

For hours we followed the yellow patch of our headlights, mesmerized by the continuous sea of grass that swept toward us. Finally, nodding and too sleepy to go on, we stopped. We stood beside the track and breathed deeply of the cool night air. The sweet smell of the grasses and the bush was refreshing. Checking our course again and again with the compass, we drove until sunrise and then slept in the tire tracks beneath the truck, until the heat of the day grew intolerable.

The next night, each time we stopped to siphon more gasoline from the reserve tank to the main tank, I grew more worried. By morning its level was very low.

At sunrise we pushed on, and as I drove, I thought about trying to collect water that night by spreading our canvas on the ground to catch condensed moisture. If worse came to worse, we had a mirror to use for signaling an airplane—should one fly over—and food in the back of the Toyota. But the going was slower than ever, and without a detailed map, we could not be sure how much farther it was to Deception.

* * *

Midafternoon on a late November day, we finally sat on the crest of East Dune, shading our eyes against the sun and squinting down at Deception Valley. We should have been elated, but we had been through too much, and we were stunned by what we saw. Below us, shrouded in heat haze, the ancient river sprawled between the shimmering dunes. Not an ant, not a blade of grass, not a living thing graced its bleak and scorching surface—a slab of grey earth with bleached bones and bits of white calcrete scattered about.

We had somehow hoped that in Deception we would find relief from the heat, drought, and searing wind. Instead, it was more of the same. Neither of us spoke.

A dozen dust devils skipped across the parched plains, as if the ground was too hot to touch. Sunburned, with cracked lips and reddened eyes, we slowly crossed the riverbed and stopped at what was left of camp: A heap of twisted poles, some shredded, sun-bleached canvas, and a scattering of rusted tin cans all lay under a layer of broken twigs and sand. The hanging shelf dangled from its tree limb by a frayed length of rope, and the shelter we had built for shade had collapsed to a stack of reeds. Crescents of sand had climbed the windward sides of the water drums at the edge of camp. Except for the wind whistling through the trees, a ghostly silence greeted us.

We tried to come to grips with feelings of utter despair. Typically blithe and overoptimistic, we had hoped for rain. There had been none. There were no antelope, and no lions or hyenas. Only wind, thornscrub, sand, and heat. A tattered strip of canvas still holding to a corner of the buckled tent frame flapped harshly in the wind. We tied rags over our faces against the stinging sand carried by the gale and slowly picked up a pot here, a tin can there. What are we doing here . . . and why? we wondered silently.

Sunset . . . the heat broke and the wind fell. The desert stood in numbed silence. The red sun, looking bloated and lop-sided in the blowing dust and sand, sagged ponderously behind West Dune. From the woodlands in Captain's territory, the stirring cry of a jackal lifted across the valley. We knew why we had come back.

* * *

From here on, our entire study would depend on making the radio-tracking equipment work, but as had been the case with the darting, neither of us had had any previous experience with it. Radio telemetry was still in its infancy, and other field researchers had found the system temperamental and, in many cases, more trouble than it was worth.

"Test the equipment under conditions that resemble as closely as possible the actual field situation," read the instructions. Delia paced off 400 yards from camp, strapped on one of the radio collars, and began crawling on her hands and knees across the riverbed, simulating the movements of a foraging hyena. I was spinning dials and flicking switches on the new receiver, pointing the antenna in her direction, when I heard the soft scraping of Mox's feet behind me. We had driven to Maun and brought him back to camp several days after returning to Deception.

I turned to where he stood, broom in hand, about to sweep out the tent. A curious look came over his face as his sharp eyes focused first on Delia in the distance, and then at the receiver and antenna in my hands. I put one of the large collars around my neck, "Radio—wireless—for *peri*—hyena—inside here." I showed him the lump of pink dental acrylic that molded the transmitter to the heavy belting.

Mox looked from the collar to Delia, then back at me. "Wireless!" I said urgently, holding up the receiver and pulling the whip antenna out from the collar.

"Ow! Missus . . . *peri*? *Peri* . . . music?" he asked quietly. He shot another look at Delia, and his hand went to his throat. The corners of his mouth struggled against the faint beginnings of a smile; he sniffed and turned. Despite the times Mox must have wanted to laugh at us, he had always managed to control himself—afraid, I think, that we might take it as a sign of disrespect. "Huh," he sniffed again. Shaking his head, he walked into the tent. I was reminded of his views on backtracking hyenas.

No matter how I held the antenna or turned the receiver, at distances of more than 400 yards—far less than the mile-and-a-half range we had been led to expect by the manufacturer—I could not hear a sound from the transmitter on Delia's neck. We sat on the riverbed, our heads on our knees. This was a critical defeat for our research. Though it meant a special trip to Maun and months of delay, all we could do was send the radio equipment off for tuning and readjustment. We boxed it up and gave it to a bush pilot, who flew it to South Africa.

Meanwhile, we turned again to our old method of searching for brown hyenas. But knowing how limited our chances were of finding one that way, it wasn't easy to motivate ourselves for the long hours of driving over rough ground, watching the light sweep back and forth across an empty riverbed. We sang and recited poetry to stay awake.

* * *

The beginning of the rains in early 1977 brought welcome relief from the heat. The antelope herds filtered back to the valley, and our clucking flock of hornbills arrived from the West Dune woodland early one morning, landing on the tea table and begging for bread crumbs. Delia was out of her chair and getting a bowlful of yellow mealie-meal almost before they had landed.

A lion roar awakened us one morning, and from our bed we could see a large male sauntering down the riverbed toward camp. Propped up on our elbows, we watched, through the mesh window of the tent, a herd of 1500 springbok split neatly down the middle, the antelope ambling aside to let him pass. They knew he was not hunting.

When he was thirty yards from camp we could see the orange ear tag, number 001. Once more Bones had come back to Deception Valley after the dry season. Pausing at the acacia bush beside our window, he gave us a casual glance and, lifting his long tufted tail, shot urine and scent into its lower branches. He roared again, then listened—head high, ears perked—looking far up the valley to the north, where a chorus of lions answered. He walked quickly in that direction, and we followed in the truck.

At the water hole on Mid Pan he stood looking across the valley at the approach of a long single file of lions. Delia raised her field glasses. "Mark, it's the Blue Pride!" Bones walked a short distance toward them, before casually lying down. His pride trotted up, each rubbing cheek to cheek with him and then sliding along his body in greeting. Afterward Sassy, Spooky, Gypsy, Spicy, and Blue headed straight for the truck, and after smelling it thoroughly, they chewed on the tires until I bumped the starter to make them quit. Chary, her back sagging lower than ever, remained aloof from all this tomfoolery and watched from a safe distance.

We sat with the lions for a while, then headed back. When we pulled away from the pride, Sassy, still as fascinated with the turning of the wheels as she had been as a cub, trotted along with her nose close to the rear bumper, while the others followed in a long line behind us. Wearing one of his rare smiles, Mox came to the edge of camp and stood there drying a plate. We must have looked like Pied Pipers.

With Sassy leading, the lionesses invaded camp. Bones lay down near the fireplace. As always, Mox slipped out the back of the island, circled around, and joined us in the truck. By now he was quite used to these surprise visits by lions, leopards, and hyenas, and thoroughly enjoyed the Blue Pride's traveling circus. Sassy grabbed the hosepipe from the water drum. Holding her head high as if she had killed a prize snake, she pranced out of camp with her trophy. Grunting, sprinting, dodging, and turning, their claws tearing at the grass, the others gave chase in a great game of keep-away. Blue pounced on the trailing end but Sassy kept pulling, and the hose snapped in two. Spicy and Gypsy grabbed at one of the pieces and soon the thing was reduced to mere bits of green plastic. Leaving us to figure another way to conveniently get water from our drums, the lions marched off to sleep the day in "Lions' Rest," the bush hedge 200 yards to the west.

We observed the lions whenever we could find them near the riverbed, but early one morning in late May 1977, we followed the Blue Pride when they passed camp and went hunting, north up the valley. It was the last we saw of them that year, justifying our fears that they would leave the valley before our radio telemetry equipment came back. An entire season of lion research was lost.

* * *

When our radio equipment was returned for the third time, it worked no better than before. There was nothing to do but go ahead and improvise with it on the brown hyenas, since the lions were already gone. We had neither the money nor the time to purchase another system.

The only way to increase the range of the collar transmitters was to increase the height of the receiver's loop antenna. Holding it at arm's length from the window was not enough, so we tied it to a tent pole section, and by adding other lengths beneath, we could raise the antenna to twenty or twenty-five feet above the truck. Delia and I stood in the back of the Land Cruiser, developing and practicing a technique for getting the antenna up and down quickly in order to keep up with a moving hyena. Meanwhile, Mox noted every detail of the operation from wherever he happened to be working.

One night we immobilized Star, bolted a radio collar around her neck, and laid her gently beneath a ziziphus tree in Bush Island, a thick clump of bushes close to camp, where we could keep an eye on her recovery. We watched her until dawn, anxious for her to regain her senses and move off into the bush so that we could try out our radio-tracking technique.

After a quick bite to eat at camp, we went back to find that Star was gone from Bush Island. We didn't panic. She couldn't have gone far, and we should be able to find her easily with the radio collar. Delia climbed into the back of the truck, and began swinging the loop antenna, while I switched the receiver to Star's frequency. I immediately heard a beep-beep-beep in my earphones. "I've got a signal! Null—back left—now right—a little more—peak! That's it. Get a compass bearing and let's go."

We drove west into the thick bush of the sandveld, scanning ahead for any sign of Star. A couple of minutes later we still had not seen her, so I stopped and held up the loop antenna. "She must really be moving out. I can barely hear her signal now." I climbed into the back of the truck, stumbling over the clanking pile of tent poles, and began putting segments together. When the antenna was up about fifteen feet, the winds, which begin with clockwork regularity on dry-season mornings, suddenly sprang to life and set the antenna mast in dramatic motion, its middle bending and swaying. I struggled to hold it up while Delia, a tangle of guy ropes in her hands and her face red and rigid with determination, began running back and forth through the thorn bushes, shredding her clothes and scratching herself on the wicked briers as she tried to guess which way the pole would veer next.

A gust of wind set the rickety affair careering toward the west like a piece of spaghetti. "Get on this side—hurry, I can't hold it!" I growled.

"I am—I *AM*!"

"Hold it. Okay, I've got a fix. Let's go." We unhooked the bits and pieces of our jury-rigged antenna mast and drove through the bush in the direction of Star's radio signal. But after several hundred yards we could hear nothing but thick static on the receiver. "We've got to get this damned antenna higher." I began adding more poles to the mast while Delia tried to control the reeling head of the antenna with the guyropes. By now she was nearly in tears and I was mad as a snake—not at her, but from the frustration of it all.

The antenna was about twenty-five feet above the truck and barely under control, and the wind was getting stronger by the minute. Suddenly the worst happened. With an almighty wiggle, the mast crumpled and the antenna soared off into a thornbush. Delia stood holding the limp guy ropes, tears welling in her eyes, while I glared at the doubled-over, soda-straw mast.

"Let's get to the top of the dune!" I spat. "If we can't get her signal from there, we never will!" We threw the antenna pieces into the truck again. Bouncing and bashing through the bushes, we drove to the top of West Dune, more than 120 feet higher, and stuck the unbent sections of the antenna pole together. Still no signal. We were absolutely deflated. We had waited for this equipment for months, and it was useless.

A stony silence filled the cab as we drove toward the riverbed. When we neared camp, Mox was standing next to the tent, waving his arms and pointing east, an ill-concealed grin on his face. Not 100 yards away, Star was walking across the riverbed in full view, headed opposite the direction we had taken.

We gave up on raising the antenna. Instead I would hold it out of the truck's window and monitor the signal while trying to stay within range of the hyena's transmitter. Without any idea where Star slept during the day, we tried unsuccessfully to locate her with the radio gear, driving long grids for several miles east and west over the dunes from the river valley. When that didn't work, we went back to our old method of searching the riverbed for hours every night. Once we had found her with the spotlight, we were able to use the radio receiver to follow her through the sandveld bush savanna. So long as we stayed within 200 or 300 yards of her, we could hear her signal and, in spite of the limitations of the radio equipment, we were able to get some useful service from it.

The night after she was collared, we found Star on North Bay Hill. We were determined to stay with her wherever she went, though we had no idea how far she would take us from camp, or in which direction. We had packed the truck with extra food, water, and other camping gear. For all we knew, we might end up fifty miles from camp by morning.

She turned east and disappeared in the tall grass and bush of the sandveld. It was the last we saw of her for the next twelve hours. We followed her weak signal through a nightmare of thorn thickets and dense woodlands to East Dune, then north along its crest through heavy underbrush. We drove over logs, around stumps, and through walls of thornbush often ten feet high and so tough and impregnable that the front wheels of the truck were actually lifted off the ground at times. After two or three nights of this, the Toyota's electrical wiring, exhaust pipe, and brake lines were torn away. We drove without them for a week or two, until I found the time to encase them in heavy rubber hose and wire them solidly against the chassis. Twigs, bark, and whole branches would shower onto the hood when the brush screeched along the sides, clawing at the truck. Whenever I could, I held out the spotlight or the radio antenna, to see what was ahead or get a new fix on Star's signal. Delia took compass bearings, mileage readings, and notes on the habitat and behavior of the hyena. I never could understand how she handled the flashlight and compass and wrote legibly, all at the same time, in the pitching truck.

Since there were no lion kills to scavenge, Star sought out the thickest cover, where her chances of surprising a leopard, civet, serval, or jackal with a fresh kill were much better than in more open habitat. She never stopped to rest, so neither could we. The scratches and bruises from a night's follow would last for days after. But for the first time since our study had begun, more than three years earlier, we were getting the details of how a brown hyena lived away from the riverbed during the dry season.

It was just after dawn one morning that Star came out of a woodland and into an open glade of tall grass on a duneslope. We could see her from the crest above. She was smelling her way through the grass when two tall, thin forms loomed directly ahead, like lampposts rising out of the grass and scrub. Star froze, then lowered her head and stalked forward. The necks grew longer, until two ostriches stood up, ruffling their wings and peering around alertly. Suddenly the female dashed away, her feathers flickering. But the large black male fanned his wings and swept toward Star, his big horny feet clipping through the grass and stomping the ground. She bristled and rushed forward to meet him. When they were still a few yards apart, the ostrich broke to his left and, dropping his wing, dragged it along as if it had come adrift from his body. Then he fell in a tumble of black and white feathers. When Star didn't fall for the ruse, he stood up and started turning in circles, his "broken" wing hanging limp. It was a spectacular deception, but Star had been around too long; she wasn't fooled. She roamed over the area, her nose to the ground, until she finally found the nest. It was a brown hyena's dry season bonanza.

She stood among the eggs—cream-colored globes the size of summer melons—and opened her jaws wide, trying to get her mouth around one to pick it up. Her teeth lost their purchase on the smooth shell, and the egg popped out of her mouth, her jaws chopping together. She tried again, standing over her muzzle, driving her weight down upon her canines until the shell gave way and the succulent nutriment was released. She lapped up three eggs at the nest, and then carried off and cached eight others in separate hiding places for future meals.

The sun found us sitting on a dune top miles from camp, munching biltong rolls and sipping cold coffee—strained through a cloth to get out bits of our broken Thermos. I patched two flat tires while Delia reviewed her log of compass and odometer readings to work out a course to camp. Star had led us over a twenty-two mile zigzag trek. We had no idea how long it would take us to get home.

We learned so much from our first follows of Star that we soon put radio collars on Shadow, Patches, and Ivey. After each night's tracking, we would rest as best we could in the heat and then try it again the next night. Several days of this and we were ready to feed each other to the lions. Two nights of rest usually quelled these atavistic desires, but because the heat made sleep during the day impossible, we were constantly fatigued.

From the beginning, we had been fascinated by the many mysteries surrounding brown hyena ecology. The bits of information about their range movements, social behavior, and feeding habits that we had managed to get by following them with a spotlight during the rainy season had only raised new questions that whetted our appetites for more. Inadequate as it was, our radio equipment gave us an inside look at the dry-season world of the hyenas. By following their signals, we quickly gained a great admiration for the ways these tough, adaptable scavengers manage to grub out a living in such a harsh and unpredictable environment.

We were continually amazed at how Star survived the rigors of drought. Since carrion items are so widely scattered in the dry months, and since brown hyenas scavenge most of their food, they must expand their ranges to nearly twice their wet-season areas and walk formidable distances to find enough scraps to eat. Including the zigs and zags she made while foraging, many nights Star covered distances of more than thirty miles while searching for food. The energy she needed to push through thornscrub and to muddle through loose sand during these nocturnal marathons must have been considerable, yet she often ate very little or nothing at all. Some nights she fed on nothing more than a single horn, a hoof, a flap of parched skin, or a few sun-bleached splinters of bone—perhaps a pound or two of carrion—all from carcasses picked over and discarded months before by lions, jackals, vultures, and other hyenas.

Brown hyenas are also remarkable for their ability to go for months—even years, in times of drought—with nothing to drink. They actually kill little more than about sixteen percent of what they eat, but they do hunt occasional small prey in the dry season, digging springhares and other rodents from their burrows and occasionally stealing bird or antelope kills from jackals, leopards, or cheetahs. The tissues of such prey and carrion are needed as much for moisture as for food, for though a hyena can make a meal of bone, it provides little fluid, even if it is fresh. If the rains have been good enough to produce a crop of wild melons, the browns eat these for moisture.

At the same time that we were studying brown hyenas, Gus Mills was conducting a thorough study of the hyenas' foraging behavior in the southern Kalahari. But there were still many unanswered questions about this species: for example, the type of social organization they maintained. Mills and his colleagues were then describing the brown hyena as a solitary species,[2] but we often saw as many as five of them meet and socialize while scavenging on large kills left by lions. We knew that, at least during the rainy season, they lived in clans with a social hierarchy. Perhaps, after the lions and their large antelope prey had left the valley in the dry season, such group contact between the browns would dissolve, since there would be fewer large carcasses to bring them together; perhaps individuals would then have their own separate ranges.

By radio-tracking them, we did indeed learn that clan members met less frequently in the dry months and that individuals foraged alone. But though they were often separated by several miles, they stayed in touch with one another by leaving scent marks along common pathways over a shared range. Furthermore, the group maintained its social hierarchy throughout the long dry months. But we still did not know why the hyenas bothered with all these social conventions. Since they had to separate and travel all over the landscape to find enough to eat, why did they even try to keep contact with one another? The answer to this question continued to be one of the main objectives of our brown hyena research.

One day Ivey, the dominant male of the clan, was sloping through the bush and woodland along the crest of East Dune. The zigzag course he followed improved his chances of picking up the scent of a kill made by a predator. By a scavenger's standards it hadn't been a bad night; he'd already run a jackal off a freshly killed guinea fowl and fed on a kudu leg he had cached some days earlier. No longer hungry, he only had to scent-mark the eastern boundary of the clan's territory to finish his night's tour.

A stranger's scent suddenly filled his nostrils. He froze in mid stride, hackles bristling, as McDuff strode from a stand of acacia bushes not fifteen yards ahead. A large male with a cape of blond hair over his thick neck and broad shoulders, he carried his big, brutish head high. When he saw Ivey he seemed to grow even larger. Both males squared off, pawing the ground with their front feet. They measured each other for several seconds, and then Ivey lowered his head and attacked. McDuff stood fast, waiting. They went for each other's neck with unearthly barks and shrieks, shouldering each other and muzzle-wrestling through churning dust and splintering bushes. The stranger scored first. He knocked Ivey off balance and seized him by the side of his head, shaking him violently. Blood dripped from Ivey's face. He screamed and thrust back and upward, struggling to break the vise-grip, tearing his face as he tried to wrench free. Like a warder leading a prisoner, McDuff marched Ivey in circles, shaking him until he flung him to the ground.

McDuff tried to shift his grip, but suddenly Ivey spun around and grabbed his neck. Turning and stumbling like sumo wrestlers, they chewed at each other's neck and face, pausing only to catch their breath. Finally, in a great show of strength, McDuff turned around and stripped Ivey's teeth from his neck. Then he began to run, with Ivey charging at his hind legs and nipping at his heels. But instead of leaving the territory, McDuff circled back, and fighting on the run, the two males disappeared into the bush.

Several nights later we found Ivey again. His neck and face had been severely mauled. But the thickened skin on the neck of a brown hyena can take such punishment, and it would heal quickly. There were more battles between Ivey and McDuff, who usually won, and we saw Ivey less and less frequently; then not at all. McDuff seemed to be everywhere, feeding at kills with Patches and Star, and patrolling the clan's territory as he scent-marked up and down the valley. The Deception Clan had a new dominant male.

There was something about brown hyenas that greatly puzzled us: In nearly two and a half years of following individuals at night, we had learned very little about their reproduction and had not even seen any of their young. Where were they hiding them? We had seen several adult females with Pogo and Hawkins, but there was no way to tell who had been their mother. Our study would never be complete without knowing how often the hyenas bred, how many young survived, and how they were raised.

Shadow appeared at an oryx carcass one night in the dry season of 1977, and we noticed immediately, and with great excitement, that her udders were heavy with milk. It was our first opportunity to follow a hyena mother to her den. Carrying a leg from the carcass into the sandveld, she quickly disappeared into the brush while we followed close behind her. At the base of West Dune, near Leopard Trail, her signal changed pitch and then suddenly vanished. "She's gone into a den!" I said, thinking she must have moved underground, where her radio would not transmit well. Three hours later neither she nor her signal had reappeared. Confused by this development, and disappointed that we had not confirmed the location of a den, we strung some toilet paper in a bush to mark the spot and drove to camp.

At dawn we were back, listening to the radio and watching for some sign of Shadow. Just after sunrise her signal came on, getting closer and louder: She was coming to the den again. When it stopped moving we took bearings on it from three points around the area. Then, like a phantom, it was gone. Two hours later we had seen or heard nothing more of the hyena.

After two and a half years of waiting, we were determined to find this den. I drove slowly ahead through the bush while Delia observed from the roof, to make certain that we didn't get close enough to frighten the mother. When she tapped on the roof, I stopped. In front of us was the entrance to a small den dug from the center of a springhare colony. On the mound of earth were the tiny tracks of hyena cubs. I leaned out my window, hung more tissue on a bush, and backed quietly away.

We sat near the den for the next ten days, and as far as we could tell, Shadow never came back. We were mystified, and we wondered if she had eaten or abandoned her cubs. Perhaps we had stressed her too much in her nervous maternal state; or maybe our scent had driven her off.

David Macdonald[3] found that dominant female red foxes harass low-ranking females with cubs and cause them to abandon their litters. Shadow had the lowest status of any member of the Deception Pan Clan, and Patches or Star may have been intimidating her more than usual. For whatever reason, the chance to find a hyena den had slipped by us.

Months later we had an almost identical experience with Patches, the highest ranking female in the clan, who also led us to a den. But, just as Shadow had done, she, too, stopped coming to the area before we could get a glimpse of her young, leaving not a trace of them behind. We were baffled about what the female brown hyenas were doing with their cubs. We had no way of knowing then that the answer to this question was closely related to the mystery of why they are social.

13

Gone from the Valley

Mark

> I look down now. It is all changed.
> Whatever it was I lost, whatever I wept for
> Was a wild gentle thing, the small dark eyes
> Loving me in secret.
>
> —*James Wright*

IT MUST HAVE BEEN the rustle of his feet in the grass that awakened me. I opened my eyes to find Bones standing a few feet away, spraying his acacia tree beside the gauze window of the tent. "Good morning, Mr. Bones," I said. "Fine morning today. What are you doing here so late in the season?" He swung his face toward the window and watched us for a few seconds, his tail still snaked to the limbs. Then he padded down the footpath through camp. We followed in our bare feet as he smelled the flap of the dining tent and headed for the fireplace. Mox was washing dishes with his back to Bones when he strolled past the hyena table. Suddenly the lion's 450-pound bulk filled the kitchen.

I whistled softly. Mox looked over his shoulder, dropped a tin plate and towel back into the water, and shot around the reed wall into the bushes. A minute later he came up behind us. "*Tau*, huh-uh," he chuckled softly. He had grown to love the lions as much as we, and even reported their locations when he heard them roar in the night. "*Msadi* Blue—*huuooah*—*kwa, kgakala ya bosigo*," he would say in the morning, pointing to the dunes ("Last night Missus Blue roared that way, far away").

Bones went up to the utility table and took a large tin of powdered milk in his mouth. His canines punctured the can and a white plume shot past his nose. He sneezed, shook his head, and sneezed again. The water kettle was steaming on the fire grate, and when he touched the hot handle with his nose he jerked back. Then he walked down the path and into the reed bath boma. His tall backside filling the narrow entrance, he lifted his head to the wash table and found the pink plastic tub filled with the leftover water from my sponge-bath. My arms had been smeared with grease when I washed the night before, and it had taken lots of powdered detergent to get them clean. Bones began to drink the black, sudsy water, his muzzle filling the tub and his immense pink tongue lapping the water to a froth. The more he drank, the more the water foamed, until white suds covered his nose. When he finally finished, he looked up, gave a deep sigh, and belched, blowing a large bubble that hung on the end of his nose. He sneezed again, the bubble exploded, and he shook the suds from his muzzle.

With one end of the tub jutting from his mouth like a great pink bill, he strutted out of camp. Chewing on the tub, he walked north along the riverbed, dropping bits and pieces of pink plastic from his mouth as he went. A long trek to North Tree, then east over the dunes, and finally he lay in tall butter-colored grasses, warming himself in the autumn sun, his mane and the grass straw part of the same pattern.

Later he started walking eastward again. "Sure wish we knew where you were headed," I said. But this was in June 1977, before our radio gear had been returned, and since we could not collar him, there was no way to follow his migration. The dry season was well under way, and there was no water anywhere in the Kalahari. We wondered if he was headed for the Boteti River, and if he would join the rest of the Blue Pride there. It would be months before the rains and the shifting herds of antelope brought him home to Deception Valley again.

"Here's to you, my rambling boy," Delia said softly, as Bones turned and walked away through the savanna.

* * *

By September 1977 it was hot again and we were exhausted from several months of radio-tracking the brown hyenas. We had not seen the lions since Bones's last visit to camp in June, so we had not been able to collar them either. Short on supplies, we went to Maun to restock and rejuvenate ourselves. We were driving along the northeast corner of the reserve, on our way back to camp, when we met Lionel

Palmer and two of his hunting clients, a druggist and his wife, from Illinois. Hot and tired, we gladly accepted their invitation to stay the night in the safari camp, a mile east of the reserve boundary.

The camp was set in a clearing on the edge of a belt of acacia woodland that followed the Deception rivercourse for miles west into the Central Kalahari Reserve. Five large bedroom tents of heavy canvas sat beneath shade trees. Deck chairs and small cocktail tables were arranged around a campfire in the center of a sandy clearing. The mess tent stood a few yards away, trim and tight beneath a big acacia tree. Inside there was a long dining table, a gas-powered freezer, and a refrigerator.

In the kitchen area, surrounded by a reed windbreak, native Africans were busy cooking and baking bread in a large metal box half-buried in the ground and smothered in hot coals. One young man sat thumbing a hand piano, a palm-sized board with metal strips of different lengths, each producing a different pitch. Another was weaving a basket from strips of grass. The cupboards were filled with imported Swedish hams, American mayonnaise, and tinned seafood.

The skinning and salting of the trophies were done at the end of the encampment, 100 yards from the dining tent. There, dozens of hides were draped about, and vultures sat waiting eagerly in the trees. Piles of horned skulls were wired with metal tags, each with a hunting client's name and address.

As we rolled to a stop, several black waiters with red jackets and tasseled hats shouted, *"Dumella!"* and clapped their hands in greeting. One of them led us to our quarters, a twelve-by-fifteen, dark green manyara tent that had large mesh windows and a fly sheet for shade. At either end of the stoop was a canvas washstand, and in the middle, a table with a mirror, a can of insect spray, a flashlight, a new bar of soap, and a washcloth and towel, all neatly arranged in a row. Inside were two tall iron beds with thick mattresses made up with clean sheets and heavy blankets. Two chairs, another table with more insect spray, and a lantern stood at the far end.

Delia ran her hand wistfully along the sides of the tent. "Imagine having a camp like this in Deception."

"Umm. But I'll bet they've never had a lion spray the bushes right outside their window."

"Right," Delia replied, "and I wouldn't trade that for anything. Anyway, they've cut down all the bushes and cleared away the grass."

"Tisa de metse!" Lionel called from his tent to Syanda, a tall, laughing Kenyan with greying hair who was in charge of the service staff. Syanda relayed the order, and soon a young tribesman, treading on the cuffs of his baggy blue coveralls, carried two five-gallon pails of slopping hot water to a reed shower stall. An empty pail with a shower head welded to the bottom dangled from a tree limb. The bucket was lowered, filled with steaming water, and hoisted back over the stall, where there was a wooden slatboard to keep the sand off our feet while we washed.

Freshly dressed, we met the others at the fireplace. Rows of glasses, an ice bucket, and bottles of Chivas Regal whisky, South African wine, and soft drinks were neatly arranged on a cloth-draped table. Nandi, one of the camp attendants, crushed together the smoldering butts of three branches left from the morning's fire and the flames jumped to life.

Wes, the druggist, was a middle-aged man with a fleshy face, thick black hair streaked with grey, and delicate, almost feminine hands. His wife, Anne, a school teacher, was small, neat, and pleasant. They were a khaki couple: khaki jackets with dozens of pockets, khaki hats, khaki shirts, and pants, khaki cartridge belts, and boots. They had brought to the camp bags and suitcases full of insect spray, tubes of block-out, and bottles of lotion. Like most of the clients on a hunting safari they looked straight out of an L. L. Bean catalogue. But, they were friendly, and we genuinely liked them.

Syanda, a white linen cloth draped over his arm, brought a stainless-steel tray with smoked oysters, mussels poached in wine, and cubes of fried springbok liver. We drank, ate hors d'oeuvres, and dissected the day's hartebeest hunt. To the west, beyond the trees, a jackal called.

Sometime later, Syanda announced dinner. The chinaware and wine glasses on the long mess table reflected the yellow light of tall gas lamps. Two waiters, who had been standing smartly against the wall when we entered, passed a tureen of steaming gemsbok-tail soup. The main course was eland steaks, french fried onions, stuffed baked potatoes, asparagus, and freshly baked bread with butter, accompanied by glasses of clear, cold wine. Coffee, cheese, and gooseberry pudding completed the meal. With a little help from the rest of us, Lionel finished the store of expensive wines his clients had brought with them on safari.

The last flame had spent itself on the reddened embers of the fire when, prompted by Lionel, the woman asked us to tell the story of Bones, who had by this time become somewhat of a legend in northern Botswana.

Anne's face grew concerned when she heard about Bones's near death, filled with festering porcupine quills, the splintered shank of bone stabbing through the skin of his leg. She and Wes sat forward on their chairs, watching our faces closely across the fire. They were absorbed by the details of the surgery that cleaned the wound and removed the shattered bone, and of sewing the muscle and skin back into place. Bones's miraculous recovery and his return to dominate the Blue Pride, as well as his special relationship with us, made their eyes sparkle with tears. When we had finished there was a long silence, and then Anne said, "That's the most beautiful story I've ever heard. Thank you for telling us."

The sszzzz of the heavy zipper on the flap awakened us the next morning. "*Dumella!*" Nandi greeted us, setting a tray of tea with cream and sugar on the nightstand between the beds. We were sipping from our cups when another servant trudged to the stoop, filled the canvas washstands with piping hot water, and laid out towels and washcloths. Breakfast, served in the mess tent, was fresh fruit, sausage, bacon, eggs, toast, cheese, jam, and coffee. All this luxury in the bush costs clients from $750 to $1000 a day.

It was still early when we left the hunters on a track near the boundary of the game reserve. Wes was sitting on a special seat across the back of the truck, his rifle clipped at the ready in a rack in front of him. We waved goodbye and turned southeast into the game reserve toward camp.

Just before noon, a few minutes ahead of our scheduled radio contact with the Safari South Office in Maun, we crested East Dune above Deception Valley. In camp, I set the HF radio on the fender and clipped the wires to the battery terminals. It crackled to life, and Delia stood waiting for the call. I went to the dining tent and started transcribing field notes.

"Zero-zero-nine; zero-zero-nine, this is four-three-two, do you read, over?" It was Dougie Wright, another hunter, calling us from Lionel's camp, where he had just arrived with more clients.

"Four-three-two, this is zero-zero-nine. Good afternoon, Dougie. How are you? Over." Delia answered.

"I'm afraid I have a bit of bad news for you, Delia, over."

"Oh . . . Well, okay, Dougie . . . what is it? Over."

"Lionel and Wes shot one of your lions this morning."

". . . Oh . . . I see." I could barely hear Delia as she asked, "Do you know the color and number of the ear tag, Dougie?"

"Uh . . . he had an orange ear tag in his left ear . . . number zero-zero-one."

"Mark! My God! It's Bones—they've shot Bones!" She choked and dropped the microphone. I started from the dining tent, but when I got to the truck she was gone, running across the riverbed.

"No . . . no . . . no . . . no . . . no!" Her sobs drifted back to me on the wind.

14

The Trophy Shed

Mark

> When I look behind, as I am compelled to look before I can gather strength to proceed on my journey, I see the milestones dwindling toward the horizon and the slow fires trailing from the abandoned camp-sites, over which scavenger angels wheel on heavy wings.
>
> —*Stanley Kunitz*

THE SHED, old, dark, and musty, was filled with animal skins, stiff, salted skins with shrunken ears and hairy rawhide strips for tails. Each had a bullet hole, some several.

Against the bamboo walls, shelves held stacks of bleached white skulls: There were wildebeest, zebra, buffalo, impala, kudu, leopard, jackal, and dozens of others. And lions. Each had a red metal tag wired through a socket where once a clear, bright eye had been.

We found his skin in a bale of others. The orange tag, 001, was scarcely visible inside his wizened ear. Heartsick, I pried at the folds of cartilage with a screwdriver, but they would not give up the tag. Pebbles of rock salt showered our feet when we pulled his hide, flat and stiff, out of the bale, its hair like so much steel wool. The scar from his broken leg and our crude surgery was still there over his knee. We made some hurried, clumsy measurements for the sake of science, wrote them in a notebook, and walked outside into the bright sunlight. Tears were brimming in Delia's eyes, and it was some time before I could speak.

Bones was killed in the dry season, when there was no water in the

Kalahari. More than a thousand gemsbok had passed through the woodlands along the Deception rivercourse and east out of the reserve into the Safari South hunting concession area. He had apparently been following these antelope, for the Kalahari was ablaze with grass fires and prey was extremely scarce.

They had found him resting under a bush with Rascal and one of the Blue Pride lionesses, just a few yards outside the reserve boundary. When he heard the truck he raised his head from his paws. Wes and Lionel drove to within fifty yards, stopped, looked at him through binoculars, and shot him through the heart. If they had seen him sleeping next to our camp, they would have known that they could practically walk up to him and put the muzzle of the rifle against his head. Hadn't they seen the orange ear tag? It wouldn't have mattered if they had. Unfortunately, lions don't understand the laws of man; he and the others had become fair game when they left the game reserve to find food.

At the shot, the lioness dashed away into the bush, but Rascal stood at Bones's side, snarling defiantly and charging whenever the hunters tried to collect their trophy. They were able to frighten him away only by firing their rifles into the air and driving at him with their truck.

The news that Bones had been shot crushed us. We stood beneath the ziziphus tree, cursing and crying and holding each other as the hurt slowly seeped in and fed on his memory. For days we were swamped with depression. If they had seen his ear tag, it was incomprehensible to us how they could have shot him since, only hours before, they had been so touched by his story. Finally, there was despair: Bones had been the symbol of what we had hoped for, and believed could exist, between man and other animals. When he was shot, everything we had been trying to accomplish for the conservation of Kalahari wildlife seemed lost. He had first been our patient, then our friend and mascot. One friend had killed another.

As trained biologists, we knew that we could not fault anyone personally for the death of Bones. He had been a legal trophy, and it was not the hunters' fault that he had left the game reserve. Besides, carefully regulated hunting can be a useful tool in the conservation and management of some animal populations. Unfortunately, many governments insist that wildlife is worth conserving only if it can pay for itself through hunting, tourism, or some other means. Knowing this was true of Botswana, we tried to overrule our emotions and deal with Bones's death on a more rational level.

Though we had never objected to hunting per se, a few of the hunters we knew openly admitted that they were consistently disobeying Botswana's hunting regulations and other recognized sporting codes. They described chasing animals with their trucks, letting clients shoot several antelope until they got the trophy they wanted, setting grass fires to make tracking easier and to burn lions out of thickets, hunting inside game reserves, and shooting game in areas where the quotas had already been exhausted. We had no way of knowing whether they were exaggerating, but this began to strain our friendships.

Because of our responsibilities as ecologists, we encouraged better enforcement of hunting regulations by the Wildlife Department and objected strongly whenever we discovered that one of the hunters had shot animals inside the game reserve. We also recommended that desert lion quotas be reduced and that license fees be increased. These actions were difficult for some hunters to understand, and it was easy for them to believe we were working against their interests, especially since they had helped us so much through the years. But not all the hunters or clients shared these attitudes or participated in illegal practices, and some remained our good friends until the day we left Botswana.

Botswana's Department of Wildlife has next to the smallest budget of any of its government agencies. It is hopelessly understaffed and cannot hope to effectively patrol large, remote areas. Officials told us that in one year alone, more than 600 lions, most of them males, had been *legally* shot by ranchers, safari hunters, and tribal hunters. Additionally, a large, undetermined number, again mostly males, were shot by poachers for the black market trade in skins.

Unfortunately, the Botswana government has encouraged the eradication of all predators outside parks and reserves by enacting a sweeping predator control law. It permits the shooting of predators on ranchland if they are deemed a threat to livestock, crops, water installations, or fences, whether or not they have actually molested domestic animals. This is reason enough for native people to kill every predator they see outside game reserves and national parks. Another section of the new law permits a rancher to keep the skin of a predator that has killed his stock. A lion skin brought about three hundred pula (about $300) on the market in 1978. This law cites as predators two endangered species, cheetahs and brown hyenas, as well as lions, leopards, crocodiles, spotted hyenas, baboons, monkeys, and jackals.

Safari hunters told us that "shootable" lions—those with full manes—were quickly becoming scarce in most desert hunting areas and that they had been virtually eradicated from others. Some of their clients were shooting young males that had mere fringes for manes, simply because they had bought a license and could find no older lions.

This startled us. We were concerned about how long Kalahari lions could withstand such a high mortality rate, especially since it was primarily among the males. Surely the welfare of the population would be undermined. Studies of Serengeti lions, by Brian Bertram,[1] showed that the reproduction of pride females who have lost their males suffer from a reduced fecundity for a considerable period after new males join the pride. A strange lion may even kill cubs that are not his own, so that the females will come into estrus sooner and bear his cubs. If, whenever their males were shot, Kalahari pride lionesses experienced a reproductive depression similar to that found in Serengeti prides, the population might very well be threatened. We had to do something to find out.

Since no long-term wildlife studies had ever been conducted in the Central Kalahari before, the most fundamental knowledge of the lion population was totally lacking. No one, including the Wildlife Department, had even the vaguest idea how many lions there were. And though we had been studying them whenever we could, lions had only been on or near the riverbed, where we could find and observe them, for two or three months each year. In these brief periods, we had been able to learn very little that would benefit their conservation. Out of our feelings for Bones grew a compulsion—perhaps an obsession—to do more. We were determined to find out how many lions roamed the Central Kalahari, what they ate and whether there was enough of it, what habitats were needed by them and their prey, and what, if anything, was threatening the survival of the population. It was essential to know how many were being shot and trapped each year, how many were dying naturally, and how many cubs were surviving to offset this mortality rate.

Since the Kalahari is a desert, one of the most important and intriguing considerations was how lions, and other predators, were satisfying their need for moisture. Large as it is, the reserve contains no water except during the brief rains. But did lions *have* to drink? The longest anyone had seen wild lions go without drinking was nine days; perhaps they could survive even longer than that. But even if they could, presumably they would be forced to leave the protection of the reserve for months each year to find some place to get water. Maybe Bones had been traveling to the Boteti River when he was shot. If this was true, then, large as it was, the Central Kalahari reserve was too small to offer adequate habitat during dry seasons and drought.

Even if we could learn all these things about lions, in order for any of it to benefit the Kalahari population, we would have to sell the Botswana government on the idea that predators are a valuable resource, one that could bring in much more money if they were conserved. At the time the attitude of many officials was that since predators prey on cattle, they are vermin that must be eradicated.

A large scale study of lions in thousands of square miles of untracked wilderness would be impossible unless we could somehow maintain daily contact with our research animals year round. The use of an airplane and radio-tracking equipment was the only way this could be done. But the very idea that we could get a plane for our research seemed preposterous. Neither of us knew how to fly, and I had only been in a small plane a few times in my life. Furthermore, airplanes are exorbitantly expensive to own and operate in Africa. With just a Land Rover to keep going, we had practically starved while trying to keep our research funded. It was ludicrous to think we could raise enough money for an airplane. But we had to try.

15

Echo Whisky Golf

Mark

> Only when we pause to wonder
> do we go beyond the limits
> of our little lives.
> —*Rod McKuen*

ON A HOT AFTERNOON in late October 1977, we stood on a dusty track in Maun reading a letter from Dr. Richard Faust, director of the Frankfurt Zoological Society in West Germany. I was electrified by the news that the society was seriously reviewing our request for an airplane. But they wanted to know my pilot's license number and how many hours of flying experience I had. Somehow I would have to learn to fly before answering that letter.

Leaving Mox in the village, we raced back to camp, threw our best clothes into the truck, and set off for Johannesburg. At four o'clock in the morning several days later, covered with dust and grime, we quietly slipped inside the gate at Roy and Marianne Liebenberg's home in Benoni, a Johannesburg suburb. We had met Roy, a captain for South African Airways, in Maun about a year earlier, when he had flown some tourists to the Okavango River delta. He had been interested in our research and had offered to teach me how to fly if I ever needed to learn. Spreading our sleeping bags on the ground to get a little sleep before dawn, I hoped he would remember his offer.

At 5:30 A.M. the milkman stepped over us, carrying a wire basket of tinkling bottles, and a couple of hours later Roy and Marianne came to investigate the truck and the two lumps parked in their front yard. Captain Liebenberg, a middle-aged man, neat, soft-spoken, and precise, pulled at his sharp nose; a grin cut through the black stubble on his round face. Almost before we could get out of our sleeping bags, he offered us the use of their guest cottage while he taught me to fly.

Six weeks later, after numerous delays from bad weather, I had almost finished my training. We wrote Dr. Faust that I was about to get my license and that I had accumulated forty-one hours of flying experience. I assured him that Roy had given me adequate preparation for bush flying.

We could hardly believe it when the grant was approved and the money sent. That someone we had never met could have such faith in us and our abilities was very gratifying. After shopping around, we bought a ten-year-old blue-and-white Cessna tail-dragger with EWG—Echo Whisky Golf—painted under the wings.

Our first heady reactions quickly gave way to some serious contemplation. We had been so determined to get an airplane and learn to fly, that we had not given much thought to the next phase of the project: getting the plane to camp. With a mixture of anxiety and anticipation, I realized that soon I would have to fly into the Kalahari, an area so remote and featureless that Botswana law prohibited pilots with fewer than 500 hours of experience from flying over it. For the next year, until I could get the required hours, we would have to avoid flying near Gaborone. If civil aviation officials there learned that we were operating a plane in the desert, they would probably ground us, and that would be the end of our project at Deception Valley.

Other problems seemed even harder to solve: Once Echo Whisky Golf was at camp we would not only have to maintain her, but also find a way to haul the thousands of gallons of fuel needed to keep her running. Besides the logistical problems, just learning to fly around the desert without getting lost would be a major challenge.

At dawn the morning after I received my pilot's license, I got ready to take off on my first flight across the Kalahari. It was only my third solo cross-country, and Roy seemed more nervous than I. "Now don't forget, after crossing the Gaborone-Francistown road there will be no more landmarks to help you navigate. Make sure of your position at the railway line before going on." He double-checked the pencil I had tied around my neck and made sure that the black plastic sheet for making emergency water was stowed in the tail.

I kissed Delia goodbye and shook hands with Roy. They would drive the Land Cruiser and pull a trailer back to camp, leading a heavy truck from the Botswana Wildlife Department loaded with drums of aviation fuel. They watched anxiously as I climbed into Echo Whisky

Golf and taxied across the field to the grass airstrip. Then, when I turned and began revving the engine for takeoff, Roy came running toward me, waving his arms frantically and pointing toward the windsock. I was headed the wrong way. Waving back—and smiling sheepishly—I spun the plane around and accelerated down the runway. With a roar and a rush of cold air, I slipped into the smooth morning sky. The sense of freedom and the exhiliration were narcotic.

Euphoria didn't last long. At 300 feet the plane began to fly sideways—or so it seemed. I had climbed into a strong crosswind. I eyeballed a drift correction on the mountain peak ahead, then leveled off just below a layer of cloud at 1500 feet above the ground. On the radio, Jan Smuts International Airport advised that the stratus would be lifting and that the weather looked okay for a flight to Botswana. The charts showed the ground elevation dropping away from Johannesburg, and I relaxed a little, knowing that I would have more room between cloud and ground as I neared the Kalahari.

Half an hour out, the radio chatter died away and there was nothing but the droning engine and whistling wind. A gap between two peaks let me through the Waterberg Mountains, and soon the last traces of civilization faded as the Kalahari began to unfold below. Four hours from now, I would have to find a tiny tree island with two tents in the middle of this incredibly vast wilderness. Without navigational aids or any way to check my position on the featureless map, it would be a little like trying to push a piece of frayed thread through the eye of a needle. I could only hold my compass heading and hope that I had made an adequate correction for the crosswind that was trying to push me off course.

Instead of lifting, the clouds began to drop and rain began to fall. To stay beneath the clouds, I began a low descent. "Stay high so you can see Real Deception Pan," Roy had cautioned. "Remember, it's the only landmark you have to show you where the camp is." But the clouds forced me lower and lower until I could see grasses bending in the wind and rolling, bush-covered sand ridges flashing by a few feet below. Because I could not hold my altitude, I might fly past Deception Valley and never see it. Flying for hours with no way to fix my position, I felt suspended in time and motion—lost.

I had been in the air about three hours when av-gas fumes suddenly flooded the cabin. A thin stream of fuel was trailing along the underside of the port wing root and over the rear window. My stomach went hollow. The previous owner had agreed to replace the rotten rubber fuel bladders inside the wings, and I had foolishly accepted his word that this had been done.

The stream seemed to be growing now, spreading from just outside my window farther out along the wing, flowing over the flaps and spraying into the slipstream. The port-side fuel gauge was flickering lower. I fumbled for the fuel selector and switched it to left, hoping to burn as much of the escaping gasoline as I could before it was gone.

I didn't know if the fuel in the starboard wing would carry me to camp; I did know that the slightest static spark could turn EWG into a fireball. I opened the windows to let more air circulate through the cabin.

At the same instant the leaking fuel bladder split. Green gasoline gushed from the wing and ran along the fuselage and off the tail wheel. I quickly switched the fuel selector to the starboard tank and banked the plane right and left, looking for a place to land. There was nothing but thornbrush and small trees below. I tried to broadcast an emergency call on the radio, but all I heard was static. I was too low for my transmission to carry very far, and it was unlikely there was anyone within hundreds of miles to hear my call, anyway.

The fumes were getting stronger and my head had begun to ache. I trimmed the airplane for level flight and rummaged around inside, trying to see if fuel was leaking into the cabin. The carpet inside the rear cargo hatch was wet. High-octane gasoline was seeping through the hatch and into the *battery hold* behind the jump seat. Though I had already turned off the master switch, the risk of an explosion and fire were magnified. Worse, there was nothing more I could do about it.

I took the plane down to just above the savanna, so I would have a chance to crash-land and get out if a fire did occur—assuming EWG didn't just blow up. As the minutes passed, the fuel gauge needle for the damaged tank quickly dropped into the red, then finally came to rest against its peg. The stream of gasoline under the wing narrowed as the ruptured tank finished emptying its volatile load. With the danger of an explosion reduced, my main worry was whether the other tank had enough fuel to get to camp. I figured and refigured until my pencil lead was a nub. With almost half an hour to my estimated time of arrival (ETA), the gauge began to flicker just above EMPTY. Finally it settled onto the mark and stayed there. Each minute seemed like an hour, and I kept waggling my wings to see if there was enough fuel left sloshing in the tank to make the gauge flicker.

Make sure all electrical and fuel systems are switched off, unlatch the door, and attempt the landing with the control column all the way back... The procedures for an emergency landing kept running through my mind, over and over.

I gripped the control wheel hard. My neck was stiff from craning to recognize some feature in the flat, homogenous bush savanna below. A dozen times I imagined that the engine was changing pitch and that I could feel a strange vibration. There was still no good place to land if it quit.

Just before my ETA, I squinted past the whirling propeller. I was sure my imagination was playing tricks again—a round, slate-grey depression with a frazzle of white cloud hanging low above it, took form in the mist. It was just to the right of my course. I held my heading, afraid to make a mistake and waste precious fuel. But suddenly the shallow riverbed of Deception Valley flashed underneath.

I throttled back and sailed over the wet, waxy surface of Real Deception Pan. The fuel gauge was solid red. Let the engine quit—now I could land and walk to camp!

There had been a lot of rain, and several dozen giraffe stood in the pan, peering curiously at what must have looked to them like a huge bird sailing past. I drifted slowly up the valley above herds of springbok, gemsbok, and hartebeest grazing on the lush green grasses of the riverbed. Then I was over Cheetah Pan, the Midway Islands, Jackal Island, Tree Island, Bush Island, and finally camp. All the water holes along the riverbed were full, but the surface of the airstrip we had made—months before we even knew we were going to get a plane—seemed firm enough for a landing. The stall warning bawled, my wheels bumped, and I taxied to camp. Echo Whisky Golf was home in Deception.

The tents had been flattened by a heavy storm. Water and mud stood everywhere; I needed Mox. After propping up one end of the tent and chasing a six-foot banded cobra from under the bed, I took a short nap on the soggy mattress. Then I refueled the good tank from a drum of av-gas we had previously hauled to camp; I would fly on that one fuel bladder until I could replace the damaged one. Because I didn't know my way around the Kalahari from the air yet, I felt a bit uneasy about this, but I couldn't wait around for a new fuel tank to be ordered from the United States. I climbed back into the plane and flew to Maun.

While we were in Johannesburg, Mox had enjoyed village life to its fullest. I found him sitting beside his *rondavel*, his head sagging between his knees, trying to recover from his latest drinking bout. His eyes were bloodshot and bleary, and he had a bad cough from smoking the harsh stemmy tobacco he rolled in strips of brown paper bag. Walking on unsteady legs, he fetched his kit and threw it into the back of the truck I had borrowed.

When we arrived at the village airstrip, he must have realized he was about to be my first passenger, because he sobered up within seconds. He tried to explain that he had never been in a *fa-ly* before, and I tried not to understand, knowing that if he refused to go I would have no other way to get him to camp. He bumped his head on the wing, and before he could focus on what was happening, I had him belted in and we were taxiing for the takeoff. I shoved the throttle forward, and Echo Whisky Golf lunged ahead, gobbling up runway. No bush plane is quiet, especially not on takeoff, and this one roared like the very devil. Mox's eyes bugged out of his head and he clutched at the seat, the door, and the dash. I kept shouting, "It's *go siami! Go siami!*—It's okay! Okay!" and suddenly we were airborne and climbing away.

I throttled back to a cruise climb and banked to establish my heading. When Mox saw his village and the river quickly growing smaller, a wide grin broke across his face and he began pointing to the huts of friends along the water. I showed him the controls and demonstrated their effects, every movement of my hands and feet producing a different sensation. With each new maneuver, a laugh caught in Mox's throat. In fact, he took to flying so completely, and was so proud of the status it gave him among his tribesmen—all of whom depended on walking or donkeys—that some of the hunters nicknamed him "Neil Armstrong."

Mox and I spent the next three days cleaning camp. At 1:30 A.M. of the third night, I was awakened by the sound of the Land Cruiser's engine. By the time I had pulled on my clothes, Delia and Roy were coasting to a stop near the tent. At first I didn't recognize our truck—with its lumps of dried mud and grass, it looked like a poorly formed adobe brick.

Roy and Delia crawled slowly out of the cab and stood in the glare of the headlights, their hair matted with mud and grass-seed, eyes sunken with exhaustion. After our happy, if grubby, reunion, they explained that the four-ton fuel truck from the Wildlife Department was hopelessly bogged in mud sixty miles east. It would have to be dug out if we ever hoped to get all fifteen drums of fuel to camp. Furthermore, they had had to offload all of our groceries to lighten the Land Cruiser enough to get through the muck. They had left behind bags of flour, mealie-meal, and sugar, cases of canned food, and the new tents and the equipment for the plane, all of it stacked on the wet ground near the trailer they had been pulling.

For the next five days, dawn found Mox and me bouncing through tall grass and bush savanna, headed for the mired fuel truck. Together with the driver of the four-ton Bedford and his assistant, we shoveled tons of mud away from the undercarriage and hauled in rocks to put under the big wheels, but the soft ground swallowed up everything, and whenever we had the truck ready to back out, a rain shower made the ground like grease again. Each night we rolled a drum or two of fuel across the bog, loaded it into our Toyota, and headed back to camp. The drivers had made a camp near the truck, and we left extra food for them.

On the fifth day, we arrived at the marsh to find the fuel truck gone and most of our aviation fuel lying on the ground. We never saw the truck again, and that was the last time the Wildlife Department ever offered to help us transport av-gas to camp.

Trying to get the rest of the fuel to camp on one last trip, Mox and I loaded ten of the last eleven drums into the back of the Toyota and onto the trailer and chained the last one onto the front bumper. Then we set off for Deception Valley.

We had just crossed into the game reserve, twenty-eight miles from camp, when, with a shriek of tearing metal, the truck leaped into the air and began to roll onto its right side. Mox was thrown to the floor, and my head slammed against the roof as I fought to regain control. I managed to keep us upright, until the truck smashed through a grove of thick brush, slewed heavily around, and heeled over onto its left wheels. The fuel drums shifted at the same instant, and I thought we were going over. I cut the steering wheel hard left and jammed on the brakes. We came to a stop in a shower of sand, leaves, and broken branches.

Dazed and bruised, I stuck my head out the window. At the end of a long, deep furrow a mangled fuel drum spewed high-octane fumes and gasoline into the air. Muttering in Setswana, Mox pulled himself up from the floor. Eyes white and round, hands shaking, he reached for his pouch of Springbok tobacco and tore a strip from a brown paper bag. "*Nnya!* Petrol—*mellelo*—fire!" I shouted and grabbed his hand.

The drum on the front bumper had come unchained and we had run over it. Luckily it hadn't exploded. I slapped some putty into the fuming hole, rolled the drum off the spoor, and picked up the battered exhaust line that had been ripped off the Toyota. After straightening the truck's buckled shock spring with a sledgehammer, we limped off toward camp, Mox drawing deeply on a wrinkled fag.

I would have to fly Roy back to South Africa the next morning, so early that night, Delia and I collapsed onto our cots, and Roy bunked down on the dry spot he had been using on the floor of the supply tent. Mox had a brand-new tent of his own that we had brought from Johannesburg.

We were not quite asleep when lions began roaring from the airstrip. We jumped out of bed. Maybe it was the Blue Pride! But we had not seen them since Bones was shot, and since Rascal and one of the females had watched the shooting, we worried that they might no longer accept us.

At the airstrip, instead of the Blue Pride, two young males we had never seen before lay in the middle of the runway squinting at the spotlight, their blond, patchy manes like the peach-fuzz beard on a fifteen-year-old boy. They were carbon copies of each other, and we speculated that they were brothers. One had a distinct J-shaped scar on his right hip. Totally unconcerned with us, they began bellowing again, making quite a respectable racket.

We drove back to camp somewhat disappointed. As I flopped onto my cot I thought to myself, surely these two youngsters didn't intend to take over the Blue Pride territory. They could never take the place of Bones.

16

Kalahari Gypsies

Mark

Like the river, we were free to wander.
—*Aldo Leopold*

IT WAS one thing to write the proposal, but quite another to actually find lions, put collars on them, and then track them over tens of thousands of square miles of Kalahari wilderness. January 1978 had come and gone by the time we had the plane and its fuel in camp. We had no idea how long it would take us to collar the lions, but we were racing against the coming dry season, when they would disappear into the vast bush savanna away from the fossil rivercourses, for eight months or more. Major international conservation interests had invested in our project, and now it was up to us to demonstrate that what we had set out to do was, in fact, possible. If we failed, we were not likely to get more financing.

Our plan was to immobilize and radio-collar lions and brown hyenas along the full length of Deception Valley, as well as some lion prides in the Passarge and Hidden Valley fossil river systems to the north. The immediate problem was how to find these roving predators in such a remote area and then get to them on the ground for the collaring. Our only chance of spotting them would be to catch them on the open grasslands of the riverbeds in the early morning.

Each dawn for the next six weeks, we roused ourselves for a quick bowl of uncooked oatmeal and powdered milk. Then, our pockets stuffed with sticks of biltong, we hurried to Echo Whisky Golf, standing cold and wet with dew in the pale dawn.

"Switches on, master on, throttle set." Delia shivered behind the foggy windshield.

"Contact!" I spun the propeller and stepped back. A puff of white smoke, a sputter, and a roar—Echo Whisky Golf came to life.

Boeing, a springbok who used the airstrip as the center of his territory, pawed a spot on the ground, urinated on it to freshen his midden, and trotted casually to one side as we taxied into takeoff position. He had become so tame that we had to be careful not to run into him during takeoffs and landings.

On takeoff, camp flashed by and we could see Mox stoking the fire, smoke curling through the trees. We cruised slowly north above Deception Valley, our foreheads pressed against the side windows as we looked for lions on the fossil riverbed.

With Echo Whisky Golf, the days were gone when we groveled like turtles, slowly dragging the metal shell of our Land Cruiser laboratory and home wherever we went. Now that we could see beyond the next rise, our view of the Kalahari was no longer limited to a few square miles of savanna. We soared above the sinuous channel of the ancient river, casting our long shadow across the browns and greens of the sandveld at dawn and dusk. From the air we discovered and named new pans and oxbows—segments of fossil river channels cut off ages ago by ridges of shifting sands. Hidden Valley, Paradise Pan, Crocodile Pan—they had been there all along, lost beyond the dunes. Recently there had been heavy rains, and now the riverbed was dressed in green velvet, a sparkling necklace of water holes along her length.

From the beginning, Echo Whisky Golf made it plain that she did not like life in the bush. Her alternator burned out, and for more than two months, until we could get parts to fix it, I had to start the plane by hand. The engine would run on the current from its magnetos, but without electricity from the battery, we could not use the radio and our compass was out.

The Kalahari looked featureless and there was only one tiny area around camp we could recognize. We followed the fossil river valleys to keep from getting lost, but they were shallow and indistinct in places; at times dark cloud shadows, like inkblots, disguised them in the desert topography. As for the compass, we found out just how badly it was behaving on our first flight to Maun together: We arrived over Makalamabedi, instead, a village more than forty miles east of our course.

When flying far away from Deception, we always carried food and survival gear stowed in the plane's aft baggage compartment. We seldom knew which direction from camp we would be, at any particular time, or how long we would be gone, and there was no one, other than Mox, with whom we could leave a flight plan. I was irritable much of the time, in those early days with Echo Whisky Golf, but now I realize how much stress I felt from flying an aircraft with so many mechanical difficulties in such a remote area. If we had gone down somewhere, our chances of rescue would not have been very good. And there was always the danger of holes. We often had to land and take off in tall grass, where a badger's excavation, a fox's den, or a springhare's burrow could easily have broken off one of the plane's wheels. Later, however, I learned a technique for spotting holes, by flying low while running my wheels lightly over the ground—"feeling" the surface before landing.

* * *

"Lions—there, in that tree island!" Delia shouted above the engine. I banked the plane steeply and we swept low over the flat-topped trees. Below us a pride of lions was sprawled near a hartebeest carcass about half a mile off Tau Pan on Hidden Valley. I throttled back and pulled flap. We skimmed the top of a nearby tree, and after Delia had dropped some toilet paper into its branches to mark the spot, I took a compass bearing on a big forked acacia on the pan, and we set course for camp.

We packed the truck with camping gear, food, water, darting equipment, and cameras. Delia then drove off in the direction of the lions. I watched the truck until it was lost in the wavering heat mirage; it was the first time she had driven into the Kalahari alone.

Several hours later, when she should have reached the general area of the lions, I took off and flew along the course she had taken, searching the savanna for the white speck of the truck below. I finally spotted it, crawling like a beetle through the bush. Though she wasn't far from our rendezvous at the forked tree on the riverbed, Delia was off course. Unless she changed direction, she would miss the valley altogether. I dropped low and flew just above the truck, directly toward the tree. She stopped, took a compass bearing on the plane, changed course, and drove on. Satisfied she was going the right way, I flew to the trees where we had found the lions earlier that morning. The hartebeest remains were still there, but the lions had gone. I started making slow turns over the area, hoping to find the pride.

Delia arrived at the tree and began driving the truck back and forth along a relatively smooth section of the pan to make a landing strip. Then she walked up and down with a spade, filling in holes and knocking down the worst nodes of clay and the taller grass bases, which could damage the plane. When she was 300 yards from the truck and satisfied that the strip was safe, she turned to walk back to the Land Cruiser. Glancing up, she found the lions: They had moved from their carcass to the trees along the edge of the riverbed. She had been so busy filling in holes that she hadn't seen them coming. Now, strung out in a line, they were headed straight toward her, the nearest one not fifty yards away and moving between her and the truck. With no other cover for miles around, she stood rooted to the ground. We could usually trust the Blue Pride, but these were strange lions, and this was almost certainly their first encounter with a human.

The lionesses began to walk more slowly and deliberately toward Delia, staring intently, raising and lowering their heads, watching her every move. She could hear Echo Whisky Golf turning lazy circles in the sky not more than half a mile away, but she had no way to signal me.

Slowly she began to back away, trying to read the lions' expressions and postures. But suddenly she realized that, by retreating, she was inviting their pursuit, so she forced herself to stand still. The lions kept pressing forward, and when they closed to thirty yards, her fear reached a primal level. She raised the spade, wielding it like a club, and from deep inside her came a sound so primitive it could have come from a Neanderthal woman. "HAARRAUGGH!"

As if on command, the lions stopped and slowly sat down on their haunches in a long line, their heads and necks craned forward, watching the primate that stood before them brandishing her weapon.

Delia held her ground, terrified that if she moved, the lions would again follow. Yet she had to get past them to the safety of the truck. The longer she stayed where she was, the greater the chances that they would come for her. Slowly she took one step, then two, then began moving obliquely past the lionesses, holding her spade at waist level, her eyes fixed on the pride. They tracked her like radar, their heads slowly turning as she worked her way past them, waving her spade and beginning a long arc toward the truck.

She had flanked the pride and begun backing away when one of the lionesses abruptly stood up and stalked quickly toward her, her head low. Resisting an overpowering urge to run, she stomped the ground, screamed, and waved the spade high above her head. The lioness stopped, one forepaw poised above the ground. Delia stood still. The lioness sat down.

Again Delia backed toward the truck, and again the lioness followed. She yelled and slammed the spade on the ground, and the lioness sat. Once more the predator and her ape-prey played the game to the same conclusion. But now Delia was nearing the truck. When she was about ten yards away, she threw the spade toward the lioness and ran for the Land Cruiser. The lioness leaped for the spade and was sniffing it when Delia jerked open the door and scrambled to safety. For several minutes she lay on the seat, trembling.

The sound of the plane grew louder, and Echo Whisky Golf glided in for a landing, the lions watching it intently from nearby. I taxied next to the truck and cut the engine. "Great! You've found the lions," I said cheerfully. Then I noticed her face, pale and wide-eyed, her chin resting on the window frame. I jumped from the plane into the Land Cruiser and held her tight.

That evening we darted and collared three of the lions, naming the group the Tau Pride. The next day, flying low over our section of the valley, we spent several hours searching for the Blue Pride in all of their favorite lying-up places. We had not seen them since Bones had been shot, and we found no trace of them now. Perhaps, after their encounter with hunters, they would not come back to Deception Valley.

Instead, we found the Springbok Pan Pride, who held the territory south of camp. Early in the evening we put transmitter collars on Satan, the dominant male, and Happy, one of the females. While they were recovering, we set up a small camp under the wing of the plane, just 100 yards or so away from them. Delia hung a mosquito net from the wing strut and unrolled our bedding and I set out the jerrican of water and the chuck box and built a small campfire. Before long the kettle was steaming and rattling over the coals and a hash of dried meat, potatoes, and onions was sizzling in the skillet.

The fire died to red coals and the moon peered over the dunes, flooding the valley with silvery light. Sitting under Echo Whisky Golf's broad wing, we could see springbok herds grazing along the riverbed. The lions were beginning to roar when we slid into our bedrolls.

Sometime later I woke up. The moon had set and a layer of cirrus clouds obscured the stars. I fumbled for our flashlight. Its batteries were nearly spent, as usual, and the weak yellow light hardly penetrated the darkness. But as I brought the beam slowly around, I caught the faint glow of nine pairs of large eyes in an arc around the plane. The entire Springbok Pan Pride was peering at us from no more than twenty-five yards away.

Echo Whisky Golf was still an object of curiosity to the lions, and I had the feeling they would love to sink their teeth into her tail and tires. She must have looked to them like an enormous powdered milk can with wings. Delia and I sat up for an hour or so, talking quietly and occasionally switching on the flashlight to check where the lions were and what they were doing. Eventually, one by one, they slowly disappeared into the night.

Later, a large herd of springbok stampeded past us, grunting and "whizzing" their nasal alarm calls. Then a deep, rattling groan was followed by slurping, cracking, tearing sounds, and the throaty rumbles of feeding lions. With our flashlight, we could just make out the Springbok Pan Pride quarreling over the spoils of their kill, about thirty yards off the wingtip of the plane. We had trouble falling asleep until they had finished feeding.

The morning sun was streaming through the netting that hung from the wing above us when we were awakened by Satan's feet swishing through the wet grass nearby. His thick mane rolled over his massive shoulders as he sauntered along, his radio collar scarcely visible in the tumble of jet-black hair. He lay down under a small tree and watched sleepily while we brewed coffee and toasted slivers of biltong on the fire.

We spent the day lolling under the wing of the plane and watching the sleeping lions. They seemed totally unconcerned about their collars, wearing them like light necklaces. About four o'clock that afternoon we took off in the plane to check the operation of the transmitters from the air and to search for more lions farther south along the valley. We were delighted to find that even at a distance of forty miles, we could still pick up Satan's radio signal.

As we turned back toward Springbok Pan, I was alarmed by a wall of black clouds rolling in. We had been preoccupied with the radio equipment and hadn't noticed the storm gathering behind us. We had to get back on the ground and secure the plane before the squall line hit the valley, so I gave Echo Whisky Golf as much throttle as I dared and pushed her nose down in a race for the riverbed.

Suddenly we were bouncing and rolling violently in the severe drafts that ran before the gale. The winnowing grass below indicated a wind of at least forty miles per hour, and when we reached the valley it would be blowing directly across the narrow rivercourse. We would have to make a crosswind landing and keep the plane from weathercocking, ground-looping, and digging its wing into the ground. Little of my flying experience had prepared me for this, and I vaguely remembered the plane's flight manual warning against landing in crosswinds of more than twenty miles per hour.

We made the valley as the first raindrops splattered fat against the windshield. "Push your seat back, tighten your safety belt, and put your head on your lap," I shouted to Delia over the crackle of hail that pelted the fuselage. I could just make out the tire tracks that marked the hole-free landing zone on the riverbed. We banked at a dizzy angle and dropped toward it. I crabbed Echo Whisky Golf into the sheets of hail and rain blown by the incredibly strong wind. I held full left rudder and rolled the starboard wing hard down into the storm.

Finally we were on a semblance of a glide-slope toward our touchdown point. But it took a balancing act to keep the plane lined up in the gusts. First too little bank and not enough rudder, then too much—we were slewing away from our airstrip and the riverbed. I crabbed even more to hold us in line. It seemed as if we were landing sideways!

I would have to straighten the plane and drop the right wing heavily into the wind at the same instant the right wheel touched the ground. If I straightened out too soon the gale would blow us sideways, and either shear off the landing gear or flip us onto our backs. As soon as the left wheel hit the ground and we had slowed enough, I would stand on the brakes and turn into the wind.

We slid sideways over an island of acacia trees, the ground rushing toward us. When we were gliding just above the grass, I pulled back the throttle and tried to line up for the landing. The stall warning horn bawled. Then suddenly the wind held its breath; without its force, all my maneuvers were wrong. The right wheel slammed into the ground and there was a loud cracking sound. Before I could react, we bounced out of control.

I rammed the throttle to full power and tried to recover flying speed and gain some height. But a gust slapped a wing and the plane reeled across the riverbed toward the dunes. I held full throttle and at the last instant it recovered, turned, and climbed away. I glanced at Delia; her head was still resting on her knees.

A thunderstorm ends the hot, dry season and brings life-giving rain to Deception Valley. Occasionally these storms blew down our tents and wrecked our camp.

The Pink Panther often lay in the tree above our camp and once slept an arm's length from us near the open flap of our tent.

Top: *Delia puts a radio collar on the Pink Panther.* Bottom: *Chief, a hornbill, searches for a snack in one of our pots.*

Chief gets a handout from Delia.

Top: *Bandit and another wild dog play-fight after feeding*. Bottom: *A wild dog from Bandit's pack smells Mark's feet. Most of the animals in the Kalahari had never seen humans before.*

Top: *Captain, the jackal, narrowly escapes the jaws of the brown hyena Star.*
Bottom: *Brown hyenas dismember, carry off, and cache legs and other parts of carcasses for later meals.*

Top: *Brown hyenas like McDuff are among the rarest and least-known large carnivores on earth*. Bottom: *We carry Ivey into the shade to recover from immobilization*. (Photo: Bob Ivey)

Top: *Star picks up her cub Cocoa to carry him to the communal den over three miles away.*
Bottom: *As Star nurses her cubs, Pippin, her offspring from her previous litter, smells Cocoa, Pepper, and Toffee, his new half-brothers and half-sister.*

On her first foraging expedition away from the communal den, Pepper surprises Delia as she emerges from the bath hut.

Pepper ventures away from the protection of the communal den at sunset. At such times she became more vulnerable to predators such as leopards.

Top: *Pepper greets Delia during one of her observation periods*. Bottom: *Dusty and Sooty, brother and sister brown hyenas, greet each other at the clan's communal den*.

Top: *Springbok pronking in alarm at the approach of predators*. Bottom: *Starbuck, Happy, and Dixie of the Springbok Pan Pride teamed up with Spicy of the Blue Pride for a springbok hunt and share the kill*.

Top: *While searching the Kalahari's fossil riverbeds for lions, we often landed far from camp and spent the night under the wing of the plane.* Bottom: *Moffet made some unexpected visits to our toilet in the early morning.*

Top: *Muffin, Moffet, and the Blue Pride often rambled into camp to drink our dishwater and play with our gear.* Bottom: *Bimbo, now two years old, peers through the branches at Mark.*

Chary rests beneath a ziziphus tree in the rainy season.

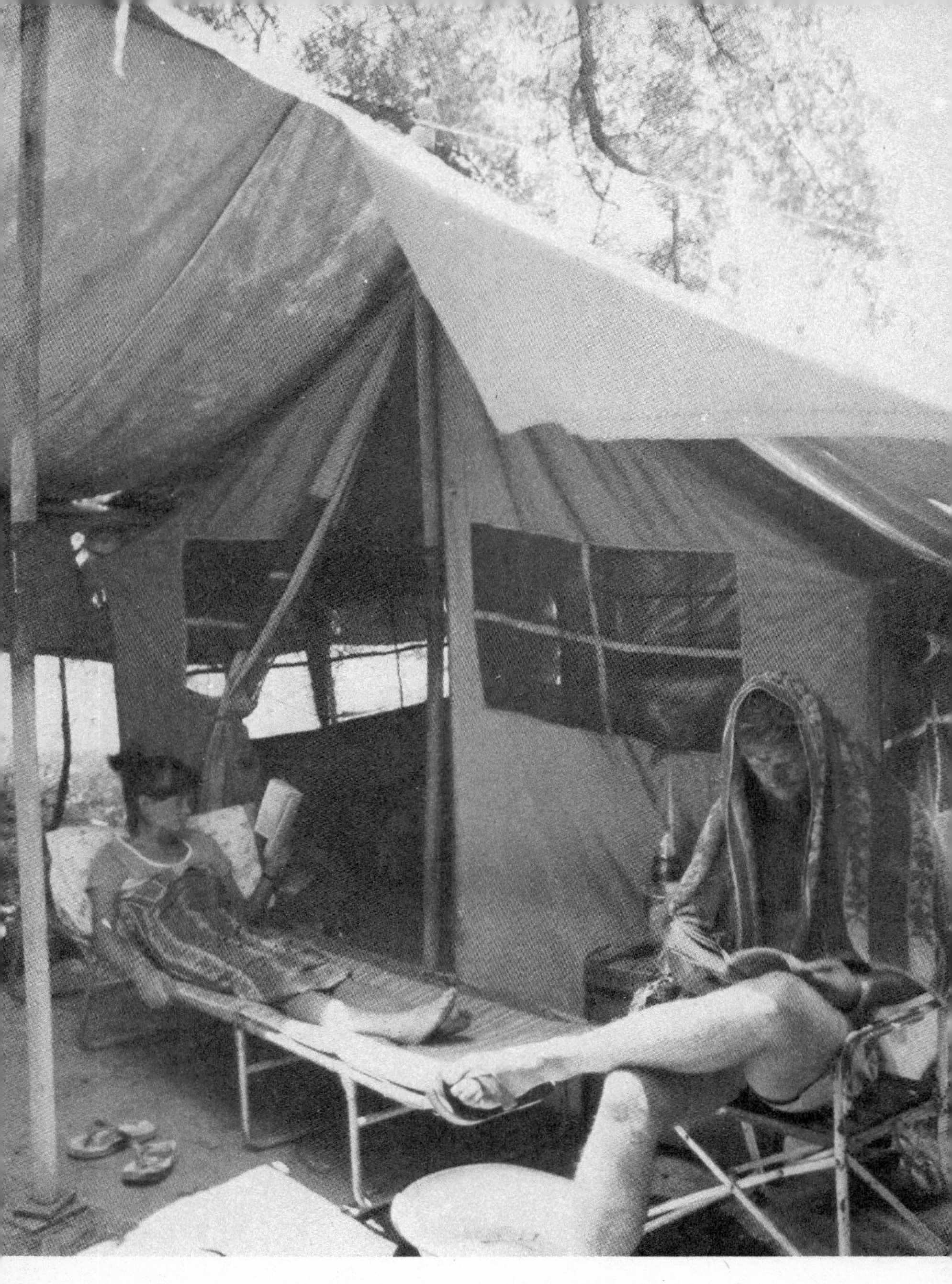

We survived the 120° heat of the drought by lying under wet towels. The moisture attracted hundreds of honeybees.

The wind was too strong. I would have to fly onto the ground with power on and the tail up. Once again I put the plane on the approach. I kept nursing the power, holding the aircraft in stable flight against the wind. Now we were just above the ground, but too far from the touchdown point. I eased on more power and we lifted slightly. The wind picked up—more bank. I thought we were on track, but the rain was pouring down so hard I couldn't see. I looked out my side window and found the faint line below. I bled off a little power, and the right wheel began to rumble. We were down! But the plane was trying to swing too soon, and neither the rudder nor the brake would stop it. We shot off the landing strip and through the grass toward the trees where the lions were lying. Leaning heavily on both brakes, sliding the main wheels, I prayed there were no holes. The outlines of trees loomed in the storm ahead. But the headwind helped to slow us. Finally we skidded to a stop.

Delia was out before me, dragging stakes and tie-down lines from the aft hatch. I cut the engine and jumped into the stinging rain. Together we secured Whisky Golf against the storm.

We pitched our billowing pup tent beneath the wing of the plane and heated steaming cups of tea and soup over a backpack burner. Wind and rain lashed the tent all night long, the plane rocked and creaked, but we were warm and content inside our sleeping bags.

During the following weeks we flew all over the Central Kalahari, collaring lions farther and farther from camp. Delia often drove for hours, on a compass bearing, to meet me on some distant pan or dry riverbed. When we couldn't find lions from the air, we landed Echo Whisky Golf near an antelope herd and spent the night camped under her wing, watching and listening for some pride on a hunt. And always, when we returned to our base camp area, we searched for the Blue Pride.

Time was running out. It was already nearing the end of March and the rainy season would only last another month or so. When the antelope began to leave the valley, we would be less and less likely to find these lions. They were our most important group because they were nearest camp and we knew them best, but we hadn't yet equipped them with radio transmitters. Maybe more of the pride had been killed by hunters or ranchers. Whenever we came back to camp we anxiously asked Mox if he had heard them. *"Wa utlwa de tau bosigo ya maabane?"*

"*Nnya*" was always his answer.

But one morning, after sleeping out with the plane on Passarge Valley, we taxied into camp and found Mox standing at the fire, his face beaming. He pointed to lion tracks imprinted everywhere on the ground, then led us through camp on a pantomime broken with bits of English and Setswana. He stalked to the bath and kitchen bomas, then pawed at the gap between two wooden posts where a line full of biltong had been drying. He pinched his ear, then pointed to the blue in my shirt and pulled at his chin with his fingertips, meaning it had been the lions with the blue ear tags and a couple of young males with scraggly manes. In his final act, he drew a J in the dust with his finger and patted his backside; one of the males had a J-shaped scar on his hip. It was the same two males who had serenaded Delia, Roy, and me from the airstrip some weeks before.

The three of us piled into the truck and drove the 400 yards to Bush Island, where Mox had last seen the pride. We drove slowly, giving the lions ample opportunity to see us and the Land Cruiser in advance. They sat up as we approached, and we watched their expressions and postures for signs of fear or aggression.

We need not have worried. As always, Sassy and Blue came straight for the truck, chewing its tires and peering at us over the half door, their whiskered muzzles and resin-colored eyes just an arm's length away. I was tempted to reach out and pick off a tick above Sassy's eye, but then thought better of it. The two scruffy young males, whom we named Muffin and Moffet, lay a few yards away from the lionesses. Despite their youth—they were only about four years old—they had apparently laid claim to the Blue Pride and its territory. Only time would tell if they could hold it against older and larger challengers.

We sat with the pride while they lay in the shade of the truck. It was just like old times. Except that Sassy, Gypsy, Liesa, Spooky, and Spicy were now full-grown adults. Together with Blue and old Chary, they made quite a pile of lions.

After we darted the Blue Pride, more than sixteen individuals, from five different prides holding territories along the Deception, Passarge, and Hidden Valley fossil rivers, were wearing radio transmitters that we could home in on from the plane or truck. Through the association of collared lions with their pride-mates, many of whom we had already ear-tagged, we had direct contact with more than thirty-six individuals. We also put transmitters on six brown hyenas, members of the Deception Pan clan, and another clan near Cheetah Pan.

Now that all the collars were in place, all we had to do was keep track of the lions daily with the airplane during the remainder of the rainy season, and then document their migration. Throughout the dry season, the brown hyenas would remain close to the valley, making it easy to find them from the air. We began to feel the tensions of the past few weeks drain away. We had done it! The stage was set for our aerial telemetry studies of lions and brown hyenas.

On the morning that we had finished collaring the last hyena, we proclaimed the rest of the day a holiday and headed for camp. When we parked between our two tents, we were met with a rush and flurry of wings as Chief, Ugly, Big Red, and forty other hornbills settled on the guy ropes, clucking for their daily ration of mealie-meal. "Horn billy-billy," Delia sang out to them as she started down the path into the shade of our tree-island home. Ugly settled on her shoulder, pulling at her earring with his curved yellow beak, and Chief struggled to hold a perch on her head. The whole flock followed her toward the kitchen, where Marique, the Marico flycatcher, swooped to the ground in front of her, shaking his wings and vibrating all over, begging for his share of the handout. I had to wait my turn after a hundred or so camp birds, William the shrew, and Laramie the lizard. Then I, too, was remembered and fed.

Late that afternoon we sat on the riverbed near camp, watching the orange sun turn silvery grass-heads into a sea of fire before it slipped below West Dune. Soon after, the valley echoed with the mournful cries of Captain, Sundance, Skinny Tail, Gimpy, and other jackals, their calls a lullaby to the lonely beauty of the Kalahari going quietly to sleep around us. The color drained from the sky, and the silhouette of West Dune quickly faded in the dusk. The click-click-click—like marbles striking together—of barking gekkos and the plaintive scoldings of plovers announced the coming of night. Finally, as the rush of cool air drained off the dunes, we headed back to camp.

Mox had built a fire and laid out antelope steaks for us before going to his camp. "*Go siami, Ra*," he called softly, meaning that he was finished for the day and was wishing us goodnight. The soft scuffle of his boots on the clay path to his camp sounded friendly, comfortable, at home. I was glad he was with us.

We weren't ready to eat, and for a long while just sat silently staring into the leaping fire. When the flames had died down a bit we could see beyond, and lying on the chips next to the woodpile a few feet away, were Muffin and Moffet. Sometime earlier they had joined us, and now they watched and listened as we quietly talked. We had to remind ourselves that they were wild lions. What we felt at such times could not be expressed with any one of the usual emotional terms. It was an amalgam, really, of several emotions: excitement, gratitude, warmth, companionship.

Later they stood up and stretched, and then walked to one of the same trees that Bones had so often scent-marked. No more than ten feet from us, they turned, raised their tails, and jetted scent into its branches. Carrying flashlights, we followed them as they ambled into the kitchen. They seemed as big as horses, standing in the three-sided reed boma. Muff cocked his head and put his muzzle on the table, and I could have put my hand on his head as his fleshy tongue lapped up the meat Mox had put out for supper.

Meanwhile, Moff was smelling the shelves. When he reached the twenty-five-pound bag of flour, hanging high on a post, he clamped his jaws on it and pulled. The sack ripped open and white flour showered his muzzle and mane. He stepped back, sneezing and shaking and flinging the flour all over the kitchen. Then he grabbed the bag and strutted from camp, leaving a long white trail behind him. Muffin followed him, and after they had pulled the sack to pieces, they lay quietly next to the kitchen, like big mounds of sand in the moonlight. Miming their soft coos, we walked quietly to within six feet of them and sat there, listening to the squeaks and rumbles of their stomachs. Half an hour later they stood up, roared, and then walked north up the valley.

* * *

Each morning at sunrise we lifted off into the still, cool air to locate our collared lions and hyenas. I had turned Delia's seat around so that she sat facing the tail and could use the plane's food box as a work table. She would tune to the frequency of a lion or hyena, and by listening to its signal in her earphones and switching it back and forth between the two antennas, she would direct me toward the animal. When the signal peaked, we were directly over it. By taking compass bearings on two or three geographical features, we could plot our position on aerial photographs of the Deception research area and have a record of the subject's exact location for that day.

With position coordinates established, we would drop to just above the ground. Diving and turning steeply, heavy g forces pressing us into our seats, we tried to spot the lions. Delia took notes on habitat type, the number of lions in the group, what, if anything, they had killed, and the area's prey concentrations, all while facing backward toward the plane's rollercoaster tail. I don't know how she did it; I would have lost my breakfast in five minutes. Yet she continued to fly with me every day for more than two and a half months.

When I had gained a bit more experience and could safely fly at low levels while tape-recording my observations and operating the radio, I began making the flights alone. While I was in the air, Delia visited the hyenas or worked on data in camp. A couple of years later, after we had bought a base station radio for the plane, we often stayed in touch with each other between one lion position and the next, so that if I'd had to make a forced landing, she would have known where to look for me.

One of the most exciting pictures that began to emerge from the radio-tracking was the relationship between the Blue Pride and the Deception Pan clan of brown hyenas. No matter where the lions were in their wet-season territory, the hyenas found them. The Blue Pride rarely made a kill that Star, Patches, or one of their clan-mates did not find. It became obvious that the brown hyenas depended heavily on the lions for food and that the clan's territory almost completely overlapped the Blue Pride's wet-season territory; even their scent trails often coincided. From the air we could see the valley and riverbed as a big gameboard, with the hyenas uncannily monitoring the predatory movements of the lions so that they could get at a carcass as soon as the predators had moved off. They were all players in a contest of survival.

At the outset we had been concerned that the plane would frighten the lions, making close aerial observations of them impossible. We needn't have worried. Very soon we could fly at grass-top level twenty-five or thirty yards away, without disturbing them. At this range, if we were quick, we could easily see a lion's radio collar and often the color of its ear tag. The lions' reactions to the plane varied. Muffin often made funny faces, rolling his eyes up without lifting his head as we glided over. Satan would crouch and sometimes playfully chase the plane a little way. Or if we sailed over his head, he would rear on his hind legs, pawing the air. Occasionally, when they were resting on the riverbed, we would land and taxi over to them and then picnic in the shade of the wing while we watched them.

* * *

Though their manes were not yet fully developed, they each weighed more than 450 pounds, and Muffin and Moffet made it obvious that they intended to hang on to their claim to the Blue Pride territory in Deception Valley. They strutted up and down the riverbed every night and early in the morning, bellowing, scraping, and spraying their scent on trees, shrubs, and grass clumps along the way.

One morning, however, a rift developed in the male alliance when Blue came rambling into camp with the males in tow. She was in heat and doing her utmost to beguile her two brawny suitors. She slinked and swayed bewitchingly before them, dusting their noses with the tuft of her tail. When two male lions court a female, usually one gives way—or they share her favors. But it soon became evident that in this case the issue had not been settled.

After lying for several minutes near the plane, Blue began to move toward Mox's camp, and together Muff and Moff approached her hindquarters as if to mount her. Instead they bumped shoulders. With growls and snarls, the two males stood on their hind legs cuffing, biting, and clawing each other. Blue ran to the other side of the tree island and cowered behind a bush. Muffin reached her first and whirled to face Moffet. Again they fought, and this time Blue made for the thick bushes at the edge of the riverbed.

Muffin came away from the second round with his left eyebrow split and blood draining over his face. The two males snuffled through the grass, each trying to find the female first.

It might have ended at this point if Blue, the reward, had not chosen that moment to peer out from behind the bushes. Muffin saw her and began trotting toward her. But before he had gone halfway, Moffet charged in from the rear. They fought viciously, rolling over and over, uprooting grass and shrubs as they raked and battered each other with heavy forepaws.

When they broke up, Muffin took final claim to Blue—by now thoroughly intimidated by the fighting—and lay down facing her in the hot sun. Moffet had gone to a shade tree to rest. Blue grew more and more uncomfortable in the heat, and she began to look toward the place where Moff was resting. But when she rose to join the other male, Muff curled his lips, wrinkled his brows, and growled menacingly. She cowered and was held captive all morning, panting heavily in the sun. The situation was finally resolved when Moffet sought more luxurious shade farther away. After that Muff allowed his lioness to rise and they both moved to the spot Moffet had abandoned.

For several days, while Muffin courted Blue, and for another week after that, he and Moffet were separated, even though before this, it had been unusual for them to be apart at all. Ten days after their scrap, we were awakened early in the morning by Muffin's bellows as he approached camp. After spraying scent on the small acacia tree in the kitchen, he moved north along the riverbed. Another lion answered his calls from farther up the valley, and the two moved toward each other, bellowing continuously. When Moffet emerged from the bush near North Tree, the two males trotted toward each other. They rubbed their cheeks, bodies, and tails together again and again, as if trying to erase the conflict that had come between them. Then they lay down together in the morning sun, Muffin's paw over Moffet's shoulders. It would take more than a rift over a female to break the bond between them.

* * *

We had spent years crashing through the bush in our truck to gather single tidbits of information on lions and brown hyenas. Now that we were using the plane and radio-tracking equipment, a stream of data began flowing into our field books. We knew where Muffin, Moffet, Blue, and the rest of their pride were on any given day and how far they were from the Springbok Pan pride, as well as from four others. To learn whether or not one of the lions had made a large kill, we simply took to the air, tuned its frequency, and flew over its head. I could depend on finding each of our collared animals from the air virtually 100 percent of the time, and could usually tell who they were with, in what habitat, how far they had traveled in the night, and whether or not they had cubs. It took no more than an hour and a half to two hours to find all of our collared animals in the rainy season. It was a field researcher's dream.

17

Gypsy Cub

Delia

> . . . the things which will not awaken are giving life to those that do . . . and thereby shall live again this spring . . . and always . . .
>
> —*Gwen Frostic*

ALOFT IN EWG one morning, Mark circled the two male lions again, confirming what he saw below. Lying under the same tree, no more than three feet apart, were Muffin and Satan, rivals from the Blue and Springbok Pan prides. Each rested his chin on an outstretched paw, not moving a muscle, glaring intently at his opponent across the boundary of their adjoining territories. Moffet was nowhere around.

After Mark got back to camp, we drove over to the lions and found them still trying to stare each other down. It was now midday and the shade had moved, leaving them in the hot sun. Slowly Muffin's eyelids began to droop. His head nodded drowsily and then slipped to one side. Immediately a deep growl rose from Satan's chest and Muffin's head snapped up to meet the challenge.

The stare-down continued into the afternoon. Whenever one of them grew uncomfortable and had to change position, a low growl would grow in his throat. As it increased in volume he rearranged his hindquarters, barely moving his head, and never taking his eyes from the other.

Just after sunset both males slowly got to their feet, growls tearing from their throats, neither daring to look away. Step by deliberate step, they backed cautiously away from each other, finally turning and disappearing into their respective territories. Not a shot had been fired, but they had tested each other's strength just the same; it had been a draw.

Male lions who form an alliance with siblings or peers, as Muffin and Moffet had done, are more successful at gaining and maintaining possession of a pride and its territory than are single males.[1] The odds would be against Satan if he ever confronted Muffin and Moffet together.

* * *

The boundaries of adjoining pride territories were not entirely discrete, and there was some overlap: Members of the Springbok Pan Pride and the Blue Pride occasionally hunted on Cheetah Pan, at the border of the two territories, as long as the other group was not around. Yet the male lions, in particular, spent a great deal of time and energy during the rainy season defending their territories. They roared, raked, scraped, sprayed, and fought, if necessary, to maintain the claim to their areas and, ultimately, to the prey and reproductive females each encompassed. Muffin and Moffet spent hours roaring and scent-marking their boundaries, and they were especially vociferous in the period right after they assumed control of the Blue Pride territory.

Mark played a dirty trick on Muffin and Moffet one morning when they lay sunning themselves on South Pan. Earlier, we had tape-recorded Moffet's voice roaring an answer to Satan. Now Mark parked the truck about ten yards from where Muffin and Moffet rested peacefully, their heads on their paws, eyes closed, soaking up the sweet warmth of the new sun. He held the recorder to the open window and switched it on.

When he heard his own voice, Moffet leaped to his feet and whirled around to face the truck. Mark turned off the recorder instantly, but there was no switching off poor Moffet. Thoroughly agitated by this strange voice, and squeezing out thunderous roars from deep within his belly, he took several steps toward the truck, then stopped, head erect, ears perked, eyes searching. When he got no answer, he roared again, and looked back at Muffin, as if to say, "Come on! Get with it! Some fool's trying to take over our territory!" But Muffin, his head still resting on his paws, looked indifferent. After Moff had finished his fourth chorus of bellows, he walked to where Muff lay and roared again. As though he had no choice in the matter, Muffin stood up and, somewhat half-heartedly, added his bellow to the performance. After that, both of them roaring, and pausing only to scrape-mark, they set off at a fast walk, right past the truck, toward their phantom intruder.

A few nights later Muffin and Moffet were on their southern beat when Satan's roar came drifting over the dunes. They stopped abruptly, listening, and then roared in return, raking their hind feet through the sand. For three hours, while slowly moving closer together, the males called back and forth across Cheetah Pan.

Several hours before dawn, Satan stopped answering the challenge, and a silence settled over the valley. Muffin and Moffet each killed a hartebeest from a small herd on the territorial boundary between the Blue and Springbok Pan prides. They were feeding on their kills when Satan stepped into the clearing behind them. He stood watching from twenty yards away until Muffin and Moffet turned. Their eyes burned with aggression.

With tremendous roars and a shower of grit, they jumped over the carcasses and slammed into him. The charge drove Satan back several yards, his hind feet ploughing furrows in the loose sand. Claws extended, he lashed out with his heavy paws, snapping Moffet's head to the side. Then, rearing to full height on his hind legs, his wide-gaping mouth exposing long canines, Satan turned and took Muffin head on. Looking like massive prizefighters, they bit, pummeled, and slashed each other's shoulders, manes, and faces. Great cords of muscle stood out like steel cables across their backs.

By now Moffet had recovered from Satan's blow, and he attacked him from the rear, biting and clawing his back while Muffin hammered his head with both forepaws. With his enormous strength, Satan whirled and sent Moffet rolling into the thornbushes, but Moffet struggled to his feet, and he and Muffin charged Satan once again, driving him into the base of a tough desert bush. Heavy branches two inches thick splintered like matchsticks.

Muffin pressed his frontal attack, but Satan was punishing him severely, stabbing deep into his shoulders and chest with his long canines. Meanwhile, Moffet was again mauling Satan's back and flanks, crisscrossing them with open slashes. Though the bush partially protected Satan's rump from Moffet, it would not allow him to escape.

Muffin's face was gushing blood from a gash that ran from his right eye to the end of his nose. He was weakening under Satan's penetrating bites and thunderous blows, and his sides were heaving with exhaustion.

With Muffin weakening, Satan moved away from the bush. But as soon as he exposed his hindquarters, Moffet caught his left hind foot between his teeth and bit down with tremendous force. Satan roared with pain, but confronted as he was by Muffin, he could not divert his attack. Moffet held on, and this seemed to give Muffin new strength. He pressed in on Satan, biting and beating his head with a series of blows that sent tufts of black mane and broken branches flying into the air and blood splattering all over the ground. Satan's deep snarls and roars were gradually losing their power and changing in pitch to a near whine. Moffet now clamped his jaws around Satan's lower spine, and biting hard, he crushed the nerves and vertebrae with a dull grating sound. Satan slumped to the ground.

The brothers stood over the fallen lion for a minute. Then, panting heavily, Moffet turned back toward their hartebeest kills, with Muffin staggering after him.

For a long while Satan lay unmoving, his stertorous breath gurgling in his throat. Flesh and mane dangled from his torn neck, and blood oozed from his broken spine. Then, very slowly, he raised himself on his forelegs and began struggling away to the south, dragging his useless hindquarters. But he managed only fifteen yards before he collapsed again, urinating blood and gulping air. Again and again he half raised himself and crawled toward his territory. But each effort cost him more of his waning strength. Finally, with a great shudder, he collapsed and took a last deep breath.

When the new dawn arose Satan was dead.

* * *

Sitting backward in the cockpit, I tried to keep my attention on the telemetry instruments in front of me, but from the corner of my eye I could see the white tail of the plane dipping and swerving just above the treetops.

"Hang on. I'll make one more turn. Try to find them," Mark called over the intercom.

I clutched the seat, and the plane banked slowly over the crest of West Dune. The ugly warning horn squawked on and off as Mark held the plane on the edge of a stall. Fighting the urge to close my eyes, I scanned the ground under the acacias for a sign of Sassy and Gypsy, who for some time now had been separated from the other females of the Blue Pride.

"There they are—at the edge of that clearing!" I shouted.

"Okay—that's where they've been for the last few days. We'd better get the truck and have a closer look."

This style of flying, for hours every day, eventually began to unnerve me, but even later, when Mark began doing aerial locations alone, I didn't feel much better. This was high-risk flying, and with his attention divided between the telemetry work and the plane, there was a greater chance that he would have an accident. But he insisted that for both of us to be in the plane locating the lions was a waste of man-hours.

Now we flew back to camp, loaded the radio gear into the truck, and followed Sassy's signal up the face of West Dune. The long bodies of the lionesses were sprawled in a patch of drying grass on the crest of the dune. Except for the constant flicking of their tails to ward off the flies, they did not budge as we approached.

When we were six yards away, we stopped. A tiny head with woolly ears and dark eyes peered over Sassy's belly. Another pair of soft round ears and sleepy eyes appeared, and then another, until a line of five wee faces stared at us. Sassy and Gypsy, whom we had known since they were youngsters, now had infants of their own.

The cubs toddled around their mothers on stumpy, unsteady legs, stumbling into one another and falling backward onto their plump, fuzzy bottoms. Their straw-colored fur was peppered with freckly brown spots. When eventually they settled down again, three of them suckled Sassy and the other two went to Gypsy.

The mothers were about four years old, and as far as we knew, these were their first litters. They kept their cubs in the "nursery," a grass thicket with an unusually tall, spreading Terminalia tree at its center, near the top of the dune.

We were particularly excited to find the cubs because, in order to develop recommendations on how to conserve Kalahari lions, we had to know more about aspects of their reproductive biology: how often these lions bred, how many cubs they had, how the mothers fed their litters through the long dry season, and the number of cubs that usually survived from each litter.

Studies in the Serengeti of East Africa have shown that lionesses are notoriously poor mothers. Only after they have had enough to eat themselves do they allow their cubs to feed on a kill. They often abandon their young, sometimes for no apparent reason, other than that they seem to prefer to socialize with their pride-mates rather than face the responsibilities of motherhood.

Although prey is relatively abundant for most of the year on the Serengeti Plain and life is generally easier for predators than in a desert like the Kalahari, only twenty percent of infant lion cubs survive to adulthood.[2] Of those that do not survive, one-quarter die of starvation, often because their mothers simply fail to lead them to kills. Another quarter die from predation or accidents, and one-half die of undetermined causes. According to George Schaller, adult lions live many years, have a fairly low death rate, and do not rear very many young.

We thought things might be different in the Kalahari. If mortality among adult lions was higher, if their lifespan were shorter in the harsh desert environment, maybe they would take better care of their offspring. We stayed with Gypsy and Sassy as much as possible, hoping to gather this and other information.

Lionesses in a pride often come into estrus, breed, and give birth synchronously, in any season of the year. Then females with cubs will frequently separate from the pride to form a small group of their own until the young are old enough—at about four months—to keep up with the movements of the adults. At birth, lion cubs weigh only about three pounds and are almost totally helpless; their eyes usually do not open until between their third and fifteenth day of life. Gypsy's and Sassy's cubs were probably between two and three weeks old.

For the rest of that day the mothers lay with their infants in the shade of the nursery tree. Mostly they slept, a ball of cubs cuddled under Sassy's neck or next to Gypsy's forelegs. All five, snuggled together, were about the size of Sassy's head. Now and then a cub would waddle over to suckle one of the mothers, and the others would follow. Neither Gypsy nor Sassy ever appeared to notice which cub she was nursing. In the Serengeti, pride-mates communally suckle one another's young; now we knew the same was true in the Kalahari. They would suckle for five to eight minutes before wandering a few feet away or falling asleep at the mother's side.

At sunset, Sassy rolled onto her stomach and alertly scanned the three-mile strip of riverbed visible between the dunes. Gypsy, sensing the mood, lifted her chin and watched. Then abruptly they both stood up, rubbed their faces together, and stretched their long backs like bows, pushing their forepaws through the sand. Then, without looking back, they walked northward. Three of the infants followed their mothers through the grass for a short way, but Sassy and Gypsy quickly disappeared in the bush. The cubs all scrambled deep into their thicket beneath the nursery tree, where they would hide until their mothers returned. There was nothing to suggest to any predator that the lion family was there, except for the pugmarks left between the grass clumps on the face of the dune.

By exchanging roars with the other females, the two mothers joined the rest of the pride in the north end of the valley for a springbok hunt. When they had finished feeding, just after midnight, they returned to the nursery. Their soft coos brought the meowing infants tumbling from their hiding place. While the cubs wobbled about between their mother's legs, Gypsy and Sassy lapped their faces and backs, their rough, heavy tongues pushing them to the ground. Rolling each infant over, the mother licked the cub's underbelly and beneath its tail while tiny paws pushed at her muzzle. Then the two females began to nurse their youngsters.

Toward morning Muffin and Moffet came by the nursery and lay down next to Sassy. One of the cubs tottered up to Muffin and stuck its tiny face up to his giant whiskered muzzle. He ignored the pesky infant until it walked between his two front legs and turned to snuggle beneath the shag of his full mane. Mildly irritated, Muffin slowly raised the right side of his upper lip, wrinkling that side of his face and showing his long canine in a crooked, half-hearted snarl, as if this puny cub couldn't possibly be worthy of more threat. The tot turned its ears back, scampered to Sassy and pushed under her chin, looking back with round eyes at the crotchety old Muffin.

The males took no part in rearing the cubs, and perhaps only visited the nursery so that they could follow the females when they left to hunt.

Though both females nursed the five young cubs, it soon became apparent that Sassy was a much better mother. When the least bit of bickering arose from the tangle of tiny bodies at Gypsy's teats, she would often swing her head around and snarl and then roll onto her belly or walk away, leaving the infants crying for more milk. Soon all five cubs would be fighting over Sassy's four teats. Meowing loudly, the odd one out would go to Gypsy, and sometimes she would nurse it, sometimes not.

As the days passed, Gypsy stayed away from the cubs for longer and longer periods. Sated and apparently content, she would lie around all day with her other pride-mates. Meanwhile, Sassy was doing more than her share to raise both litters.

One day when the cubs were about eight weeks old, we found that Sassy and her three young were gone. Gypsy was lying on her back nursing her two cubs, but when they fought briefly, she bared her teeth, wrinkled her nose, and hissed wildly at them. Then she walked away and they were left gazing after her, their ribs showing through their scruffy coats.

Gypsy joined the pride on Leopard Trail and lay around with them for the rest of the day. The next morning, instead of returning to her cubs, she relaxed in the shade with her head snuggled along Liesa's back. Except for her swollen teats, she showed no sign that she had two hungry infants waiting for her.

Both of Gypsy's cubs were in poor condition, but one was especially scrawny and weak; it would not survive much longer without milk. Flying in Echo Whisky Golf the next morning, we found Sassy and her cubs with the old lioness Chary several miles from the nursery. By circling low in the plane we could see that Chary had four cubs of her own, several weeks older than Sassy's. The two females were lying together, peacefully nursing their young.

We switched channels on the radio and found Gypsy with Liesa, almost ten miles from her cubs. Later, when we drove to the thicket, we found that the weakest cub had died. Alone and emaciated, the other one was hunkered down between two forks of the tree, watching us with frightened eyes. If we did not feed it, the cub would probably be dead within twenty-four hours, but there was still a remote chance that Gypsy would come back for it. After much agonizing, we finally rationalized that, although it would be a lot of trouble to have a lion cub in camp, we would also learn a great deal. If Gypsy did not come back to her infant by the next day, we would adopt it.

The next morning the roving mother had moved even farther from her cub, and we knew it probably would not survive another day without milk. We took a cardboard box and an old blanket to the nursery to rescue the abandoned infant, but to our surprise, we found Muffin lying under the tree with it. The cub staggered on trembling legs to the big male, feebly pushing its tiny muzzle into his belly, groping for milk-filled teats that were not there. For several minutes it just stared up at Muff, dizzy with hunger, and then it stumbled back to the tree and with its head hanging down, it swayed forward and back, bumping, bumping, bumping its forehead into the trunk, over and over again. Its wasted body made its head and paws seem over-large. Finally, in the last stages of starvation, it just stood there leaning the top of its head against the bark.

We weren't sure how Muffin would react if we tried to take the cub, so we decided to come back that night when he had moved off to hunt. In the meantime it might starve to death, but at least no other predator would harm the infant so long as Muff was there.

It was an unusual day for late in the rainy season. Instead of moderate temperatures with a light breeze, it was muggy and still. The hornbills sat quietly in the trees, their bills open, wings cocked out from their bodies, trying to cool themselves. Nothing moved but the flies, which buzzed our faces or sat on our towels, rubbing their grimy feet in apparent glee.

Late that afternoon, a long black tunnel of low clouds rolled in from the southeast. Skimming rapidly over the dunes, it filled the valley and rushed toward camp. The sun dipped lower in the western sky, and the clouds turned brilliant shades of pink and mauve streaked with gold. But when they swirled overhead, the air became a frenzy of wind and sand.

We hurried to ready camp for the storm, zipping the tents, tying down the plane, and putting equipment boxes up on blocks—Mox was on leave in Maun, so there was no one to help us. Suddenly, the wind slapped the trees, thunder cracked, and tongues of lightning split the wounded sky.

Lashed by rain and hail, we finished tightening the guy ropes on the tents. Mark yelled over the roar of the wind, "Get in the truck—we've got to get out from under these trees!" We jumped into the Toyota and drove twenty yards from camp. The ziziphus and acacia trees reeled about madly above the tents, and sheets of rain scudded parallel to the ground. We could barely see the camp or the plane through the gale.

"There goes Echo Whisky Golf!" Like a wild horse, the plane reared up against its tie-down ropes, the starboard wing high in the air. The line holding the tail wheel snapped, and as the aircraft weathercocked into the wind, the port wing tore its stake out of the ground. The plane slewed around and slammed into a fuel drum and the fence.

Mark bounded over the fence and grabbed the starboard wing tip to keep the aircraft from flipping over while I staggered against the wind toward Echo Whisky Golf.

Mark shouted, "Grab the other wing and hang on or we'll lose the plane!" I stood on my toes to reach the wing. We clung to the plane in the blinding rain. The powerful wind caught under the broad airfoils and lifted our feet from the ground for seconds at a time. My arm and back muscles throbbed with pain, and I worried that I would lose my grip.

The lightning was a buzzing blue hue in the sky, and dangling from the metal wing, I felt like a lightning rod. The sleeping tent gave one last mighty heave against the wind, and collapsed in a tattered heap, draping itself like a wet spider web over the poles.

A few minutes later the wind slackened slightly, and we were able to tie drums of fuel to the wings to help stablilize the plane. We quickly inspected for damage and discovered that the port-side stabilizer had been crumpled by a drum.

Again the wind slammed into us, this time from the north, and once more we hung onto the wings, pounded by wind and hail. By now I was extremely weak. My arms felt as if they were being pulled from their sockets, and the cold sent sharp spasms through my back and shoulders. Just when I knew I could hold on no longer, the wind eased a bit. My fingers slipped from the wing and I sat down in the mud, utterly exhausted.

Mark came sloshing through the water and helped me into the truck. "Well done, Boo," he said, putting his arm around me. "We'd have lost her for sure if you hadn't hung on." He wrapped his shirt around me and hurried away to restake the plane. I felt a warm stickiness on my leg; when I reached down I discovered it was blood. I switched on the flashlight and saw a deep gash in my calf, probably made by the fence. I tried to stop the bleeding with tissue.

Mark jerked open the door of the truck. "I'm going to try to fix the tent. Come and help me if I whistle."

I sat shivering uncontrollably, hoping that he would not need my help. Although the wind had slackened, the rain was still pelting down, and the plane stood in a growing lake of muddy water. Moments later I heard the faint shrill of Mark's signal. I jumped from the truck, losing my sandals in deep ooze.

He heaved up the tent's center pole and we both struggled through the muck to retie the guy ropes. A few poles were broken, one side sagged, and the floor was covered with inches of muddy water, but at least it was a roof over our heads.

When Mark lit the lantern, he saw my bloody leg. I tried to tell him what had happened, but my teeth only chattered. He wrapped me in a dry blanket, and then bound my wound. When he started for the door I asked, "Aren't you going to dry off?"

"First, I'm going to get some hot food." And he ran out into the storm again.

Minutes later he was back, carrying a tray with mugs of steaming soup and tea. The dripping tent was beginning to warm from the lantern, and we sat on the tin trunks drinking our hot soup, feeling quite cozy.

Five hours after the storm had hit, it finally ended as suddenly as it had begun. All that remained was an occasional grumble of thunder and great drops of water that plopped from the trees onto the tent. We sat listening to the quiet and warming ourselves. A jackal called from North Bay Hill. Then from south along the valley, a lion roared—and we remembered the cub.

We grabbed the driest blanket, filled a canteen with hot water, and drove across the valley toward the dune. The thirsty earth had already soaked up a lot of the rain, though much of the riverbed was still under water. There were split and scattered trees everywhere in the fractured woodland. Using the spotlight, we finally found the nursery. Muffin was gone. Next to the tree the crumpled cub lay like a soggy rag doll, his eyes staring sightlessly into the night.

* * *

As far as we knew, Gypsy never went back to the nursery. She went on hunting and sleeping with the Blue Pride females until her udders lost their milk. From her behavior, it appeared that Kalahari female lions were no better mothers than those in the Serengeti, but it was too early to draw any firm conclusions. Gypsy, young and inexperienced, had been just one example of how not to rear lion cubs in the Kalahari. New mothers are often poor mothers and improve with experience.

The dry season was beginning, and we continued our study of maternal care of desert lions by watching Sassy and Chary and their seven cubs. Now that Sassy had joined Chary, an old and experienced mother, perhaps their litters would have a better chance of surviving.

Sassy's cubs were now about two months old, Chary's about three. They all played and fought as brothers and sisters, rolling over and over, mouthing and pawing at one another's faces and forequarters like kittens. They often attacked their mothers, and sometimes Sassy joined in the game. Chary, although patient with all the cubs, never joined in the tomfoolery.

In carnivores, as in all animals, play is not just for fun. The types of behavior important for hunting—stalking, chasing, jumping on a moving object—require coordination and practice, and they are the very ones exhibited in play. Lion cubs do not have to learn all the motions for hunting; they are born with most of this information in their genes. But by play-fighting and play-hunting, the cubs polish the skills needed for bringing down a moving prey.

One afternoon as a cub rested next to Sassy, a fly lit on the tuft of her tail. Lying with his chin on his paws and his eyes crossed, the cub watched the fly roam around the tassel. Sassy flicked her tail and the youngster pounced on it, rolling over in a somersault. Another cub joined in, batting and pawing at the tail snaking around on the ground.

Sassy jumped to her feet, whirled around, and pawed playfully at her cubs' heads. They reared up and swatted at her, and she took off through the grass. Instantly, all the other cubs joined in pursuit.

Eventually old Chary fell into the long line of lions racing after Sassy. In and out of the thorn shrubs they twisted and turned, swatting at whomever they encountered. Sassy, stopping abruptly, took a long, thin stick in her jaws and pranced through the tumbling cubs, her head and tail held high. The youngsters pulled at the baton, rolling over and over in the sand, trying to yank it from her teeth. None of them stood a chance of out-tugging the adult. But then Chary, her sagging back swaying, grabbed the other end. The lionesses romped and chased each other, pulling and tearing at the skinny stick as they swung about. Eventually the cubs all lay down in a row, and watched their mothers rolling and fighting over the twisted twig. When only a plug of shredded wood was left, Chary and Sassy gave up the contest and, panting, sauntered to their shade tree. When she passed the truck, Chary turned her ears and avoided looking at us. I could have sworn that she was embarrassed by her brief loss of control.

Later on, Chary and Sassy killed a young hartebeest in the woodlands of West Dune. They had fed for twenty minutes when Muffin and Moffet trotted up, chasing the females from the carcass. The lionesses returned to the cubs' hiding place, but instead of nursing them, they started walking slowly in the direction they had just come from, and cooing softly, encouraging their young to follow them to the kill. Muffin and Moffet completely ignored the youngsters and made no protest when they fed with them, but Chary and Sassy never got another bite.

Now that the cubs were old enough to eat meat, the pattern of their daily lives changed. The females would leave their litters hidden in the grass to hunt and to feed themselves. They would then return and lead their young to the kill—sometimes several miles away. Whenever Muffin and Moffet found the females on a carcass, they chased them off, but they always shared the meat with the cubs. Chary and Sassy also continued to nurse their young, but less frequently and for shorter periods.

The mothers seemed to be making every effort to insure that their offspring were well cared for. But with the skies clearing, the grass dying, and the antelope dispersing as the dry season began, their kills were becoming fewer and smaller. And the cubs were getting larger and hungrier.

18

Lions with No Pride

Delia

and my tribe is scattered . . .
—Stanley Kunitz

OFTEN, in those wild open spaces of the Kalahari, even a tent seemed too confining. So some nights we pulled our canvas cots onto the ancient riverbed to sleep under the stars. The fresh smell of drying grasses and the soft, cool air were more effective than a sedative. By this time we knew almost every species of bird or insect that squawked or clicked around us, and these familiar sounds, along with the cry of a jackal, would send us off to sleep. Periodically during the night, I would check on the position of the Southern Cross, following its gentle sweep across the lower sky, before going back to sleep again.

Once, about four o'clock in the morning, a loud rustling in the bushes suddenly opened my eyes wide. The massive form of a lion loomed in the starlight not five yards away, and he was walking directly toward us.

"Mark! The lions are here!" I whispered urgently, feeling around on the dark ground for the flashlight.

Buried deep in his sleeping bag, his voice thick with sleep, Mark mumbled, "Don't worry, if they get too close we'll move inside the tent." At that moment the lion was actually standing at the foot of Mark's cot, looking down at us.

"Mark," I said, trying not to move my lips, "they're right *here*. Get up!" I found the flashlight, slowly raised it, and switched it on. Moffet's amber eyes blinked in the light. Now Muffin walked in from the shadows of camp and stood two or three yards behind him. We were lying at the base of one of their favorite marking bushes.

Mark poked his head from his sleeping bag and peered at the lions over his toes. Moffet squatted over his hindquarters and began scraping back and forth with his hind paws while dribbling urine loudly onto the ground between his legs. He was marking his territory.

Even if it was Muffin and Moffet, I didn't like the idea of being between them and their tree. I struggled out of my sleeping bag and, without taking my eyes from the lions, began moving toward our tent, sixty yards away at the other end of the tree island.

As I passed the head of Mark's cot, he was feeling around on the ground for his clothes. "I can't decide what to put on," he said, standing there nude and half asleep.

"What difference does it make, for heaven's sake!?" I hissed between my teeth. The two lions watched Mark stumbling around, gathering up his clothes and his sleeping bag. Finally, I grabbed Mark's arm and pulled him toward the tent. At the edge of the trees we looked back at Muffin and Moffet, rubbing their heads together, paying no attention whatsoever to our bungling getaway. I wondered, myself, what all the fuss had been about.

* * *

The rains of 1978 had been generous, but they ended prematurely. The blustery dry-season winds had begun much earlier than usual, and the grasses had turned to straw much sooner. The skies were dull grey from wind-blown dust and sand, and the savanna looked as dry in June as it had in August of previous years.

As always, the short grasses on the shallow, heavy soils of the ancient riverbed dried faster than the vegetation on the dunes. The plains antelope moved from the river channel to the bush and tree zones on the duneslopes, where the leaves stay green longer. Slowly the herds broke up, and the smaller groups dispersed into thousands of square miles of rolling bush savanna.

Each dawn we hurried to Echo Whisky Golf to look for the lions from the air. We were afraid that if we missed a single day's radio-location, they might travel to some distant part of the Kalahari where we could never find them again. But weeks passed and the prides still had not migrated. True, they had abandoned the dry river channel, now that the antelope had gone. Muffin and Moffet no longer marched up and down Mid Pan marking their scent trees, and Blue and the other females stopped visiting camp. Yet the Blue Pride lions were not very far from their wet-season territory. With most of the large antelope gone and no water to drink, how were the lions surviving? By following them with the truck and radio gear at night, we began to get some answers.

* * *

Moffet had been separated from Muffin and the females for several days and had not eaten. Moving through the thornbush east of the valley, he quickly broke into a trot, his head low as he zigzagged after a chicken-sized korhaan scurrying through the grass ahead. When he was ten feet from the bird, it took flight, but Moffet lunged forward and, standing on his hind legs, swatted it down with a wide forepaw. Lifting his lip, he chewed into the feathery breast of the bird, sneezing and shaking his head to clear the down from his nose. Minutes later, feathers still clinging lightly to his mane, he began hunting again.

At first we did not take Moffet's new sport of bird hunting seriously, for surely a 450-pound male lion did not intend to feed himself on such morsels. Later that same evening, however, he killed a four-pound springhare and chased a mongoose to its burrow. The diet of the lions was changing drastically.

The Blue Pride still preyed on the occasional giraffe, kudu, or gemsbok in the dune woodlands, but because these large ungulates were scarce and widely scattered over the savanna, the lions hunted smaller animals more often. Instead of killing 500-pound gemsbok, as they had done during the rains, now they fed on fifteen- to twenty-pound porcupines, steenbok, honey badgers, bat-eared foxes, or kori bustards. But these prey are hardly enough to make a meal for one or two lions, and they certainly wouldn't feed an entire pride. The seven females of the Blue Pride who lay around together in the wet season, always touching and reassuring each other, were forced to break up into smaller groups, so that when a kill was made there would be enough meat to go around.

From the air we found that Chary and Sassy and their cubs had again separated from the main pride and were roaming near Crocodile Pan, about five to six miles east of Deception Valley. Instead of hunting on the borders of fossil riverbeds, they prowled the bush savannas and woodlands, where a few bands of gemsbok and giraffe, and more small prey, were available. The lionesses had to travel from five to ten miles almost every night to find food.

Gypsy and Liesa hunted near Paradise Pan; the rest of the pride roamed interdunal valleys two to three miles west of Deception. The Blue Pride had splintered into small groups of females, with Muffin and Moffet trekking from one group to the other. Because of the time needed to locate the different fragments of their pride, the males had to spend more time apart from their females and do much more of their own hunting.

The pride's home range had more than doubled in area, to about 600 square miles. Still, the lions had not really migrated in the true sense of the word, but had simply expanded their range greatly to the east and west. We drew a map with colored dots showing their daily locations and their patterns of distribution over the range. It looked as if it had been sprayed with BB shot.

The other prides had responded to the dry season in the same way, by breaking up and traveling greater distances away from the valley in search of prey and by hunting smaller animals. The drier it became during the winter months, the more the diet, range movements, habitat utilization, and social system of the lions differed from the wet season. We began to fly on moonlit nights to better document these changes.

* * *

Midnight takeoff: Cast in soft moonlight, the pewter desert fell away below us. Except for our gas lantern, set out on the airstrip to guide us home, not another light on earth could be seen as we sailed over the quiet, forgotten world of the Kalahari. Our faces glowing eerie red from the cockpit instrument lights, we followed the night movements of the lions and hyenas below.

Straining to recognize the subtle landmarks beneath us, we found Happy of the Springbok Pan Pride one night, on the boundary of the Blue Pride's territory. Within two weeks after Muffin and Moffet had killed Satan, another male, Diablo, had taken over the Springbok Pan Pride. The females had adjusted to their new male, and in recent weeks we had even seen Happy and some of the others mating with him. But now, as we circled overhead in the moonlight, we could see that Happy was within a few yards of Muffin and Moffet, who were patrolling the border of their territory. We were curious to know whether the two males would chase this foreign female back into her own territory or mate with her—if she was in estrus. In the Serengeti, male lions will court females from other prides, but we had never had the opportunity to observe this in the Kalahari. We flew back to camp, and then drove south to look for the lions.

When we found Muffin and Moffet, they were walking fast through brambles near Cheetah Pan, their noses to the ground. They stopped abruptly and looked up; Happy's eyes met theirs at less than thirty yards. The two lions stared intently at her for a few seconds, their tails twitching. Happy stood above the males on a low, scrub-covered sand ridge.

The lioness walked slowly forward, her head tall above the grass, her ears perked. Chests rumbling and tails lashing, Muffin and Moffet sprang to their feet and chased her for over 100 yards. But Happy was too fast for them, and when they broke off the charge she stopped just out of reach. They stared aggressively at her, raking their hind paws through the grass and roaring.

Again Happy walked cautiously toward them, and again they chased her, roaring and swatting the air just behind the tuft of her long tail. After each chase she ventured closer to them, but they seemed less and less inclined to pursue her. When she managed to get within twenty yards of them, Muffin and Moffet lay down side by side and watched what amounted to a feline burlesque.

Her hindquarters swaying sinuously, eyes half closed and jaws parted, Happy slunk toward the mesmerized males. Muffin quickly stood and strutted toward her, but she galloped away. When he stopped, she turned and wound her way toward them again, this time passing within a few yards of their noses. Muffin stood as tall as he could and, with all the savoir-faire he could muster, swaggered toward Happy. She lowered her hindquarters suggestively, inviting him to mount her. But when he stepped to her rear she suddenly spat and cuffed him hard across the nose. Muff roared and drew back, his ears flat and his long canines exposed, as Happy minced away, her tail flicking flirtatiously. After a few more attempts by both males to gain her favor, Muffin and Moffet seemed to tire of the game, and they walked back north into their own territory. Happy followed about thirty yards behind, apparently unconcerned that she was on foreign soil.

We knew that Liesa, Gypsy, Spicy, and Spooky of the Blue Pride were finishing a warthog kill on the crest of West Dune. Muffin and Moffet, with Happy trailing by fifteen yards, were moving directly toward them.

Since it was not unusual for male lions in the Serengeti to associate occasionally with females of another pride, it had not been totally surprising to see Muffin and Moffet interact with Happy. However, we knew that Serengeti pride females form closed social groups that do not accept new female members or tolerate foreign females in their territory.[1] There the pride is sacrosanct: a stable social unit of closely related lionesses and their young, who associate with the male or males who help defend the territory. A lioness may be kicked out and become nomadic, but these nomads do not join other prides. In the Serengeti, a single pride lasts for generations, with the same kin line, and at any one time, it has in its membership great-grandmothers, grandmothers, mothers, daughters, aunts, and female cousins.

Now Muffin, Moffet, and Happy padded steadily toward the crest of West Dune. We followed in the truck, preparing our flashes, cameras, and the tape recorder for the coming fight between Happy and the Blue Pride females.

By the time we could see the four Blue Pride females in the spotlight ahead, they had finished the warthog and were casually licking one another's faces. The two males greeted the lionesses, smelled the skeleton, and then lay down a few yards away. Happy sauntered past Spicy and Spooky and lay down next to Muffin and Moffet. Incredibly, there was not the slightest sign of aggression on the part of any of the lionesses. We switched off the tape recorder and pulled the cameras back inside the truck. It was astonishing: A foreign female had ambled into the heart of the Blue Pride camp, and its members had hardly noticed!

For the next four days, Happy was courted, first by Muffin and then by Moffet, just as though she were a Blue Pride female. During the heat of the day Muffin lay as near to her as he could, watching her every move. If she sought out better shade, he strutted so close beside her that their bodies rubbed together. Sometimes he would initiate copulation by standing at her rear. More often, however, she would walk back and forth in front of him, her tail flicking and hindquarters swaying, or she would brush her body along his before crouching in front of him. When he stood over her to copulate, he nibbled at her neck and she growled and flattened her ears. As soon as Muffin had finished, he would step back quickly to avoid getting clouted by Happy's paw, for invariably she would whirl around, snarling fiercely, and swat at him. Then, lying on her back, her legs extended, she would roll over and over in the grass, her eyes closed in apparent ecstasy.

They mated in this stereotypic fashion every twenty to thirty minutes for part of two days and all of two nights. Small wonder that Muffin did not object when Moffet took over the courtship at sunset on the third day.

During the day Happy rested—Muffin or Moffet always at her side—under the same bush as Spicy, looking very much as if she belonged. Then, on the fifth night, she walked south alone and returned to Diablo, Dixie, and the others of the Springbok Pan Pride.

This mixing of females between prides had never been reported in lions. Was this wandering lioness an aberration, a passing "stranger in the night"? Was her behavior unique? We could hardly think so. Since Happy had been so readily accepted by the Blue Pride females, it appeared that such exchanges of lionesses between prides might occur quite regularly.

* * *

The desert winter ended overnight—there was no spring. In late August there was a gradual warming of the days, but the nights remained bitterly cold. Then one silent morning in early September, the temperature suddenly shot upward.

When the hot-dry season had settled over the Kalahari, the thermometer often reached one hundred and twenty in the shade during the day; at night it fell to as low as forty or fifty. Differences of more than sixty degrees, sometimes even seventy, were not uncommon in a twenty-four-hour period. The relative humidity was lower than five percent at midday, and the sun beat down unmercifully, burning the last traces of life from the vegetation. The blossoms of the acacia and catophractes bushes—the blanket of pink and white magic that usually spreads over the Kalahari in the driest time of the year, providing succulent food for the antelope—never appeared that year. Here and there a puny flower hung with its withered brown face to the ground, only to shrivel and fall to the sand. The wind blasted across the scorched valley and the dry, brittle grass disintegrated, leaving stubbles sticking up from the cracked earth like broken broom heads. We had survived four dry seasons, but this was the worst.

By October there were almost no large antelope left on the dunes and in the sandveld around Deception Valley. During the rainy season over fifty percent of these animals concentrated on the ancient riverbed; now less than one percent wandered across its barren surface.

Chary and Sassy were still nursing their five- and six-month-old cubs, yet they had not had a drink of water for five months. In order to get meat for their growing families they searched farther and farther east, toward the game reserve boundary, where pockets of antelopes browsed the woodlands. They often traveled more than fifteen miles a night for several nights before they managed to kill a lone gemsbok.

Then one morning Mark found the two mothers and their young, together with Muffin and Moffet, outside the game reserve. They had crossed over the boundary into cattle country, as Bones had done, and again it was hunting season. Old Chary, with her sagging back and somber ways, was wise. She had survived many dry seasons, and probably a drought or two, by hunting outside the game reserve; she seemed to know the dangers.

A cow must seem the ideal prey to a lion: fat, slow and clumsy. But even though Chary led Sassy and their cubs to within 300 yards of cattle posts, they never killed a single domestic animal, as far as we knew. Instead, they preyed on the antelope moving out of the reserve to find water. Of course, neither Chary nor the others would have been rewarded for their discretion, had they been seen by ranchers.

Muffin and Moffet did not always stay with the females, and they were neither as old nor as wise as Chary.

We were answering a lot of the questions about Kalahari lion conservation: They could survive at least eight months with no drinking water, and instead of migrating in a single direction, they dispersed into huge ranges to find enough dry-season prey. They left the protection of the reserve not to find water, as we once suspected, but to get enough to eat. In all, the nine females of the Blue Pride increased their range by 450 percent, from 270 square miles in the wet season to over 1500 square miles in the dry months; the Springbok Pan Pride increased their pride area by 650 percent. These tremendous increases in range inevitably took the prides into areas where they were in danger of being shot.

With this expansion of range, the territories that they had defended so vigorously—even to the death—only weeks before, appeared to break down. The overlap in pride areas, which had existed to a minor degree, increased tremendously, and now it was Diablo who padded down Leopard Trail through the Blue Pride's old territory. Meanwhile, Muffin and Moffet roamed far into the range of the East Side Pride, often more than twenty miles outside their wet-season territory on Deception Valley, for more than two months at a stretch. When they did come back near their wet-season home range, they only stayed for two or three days at most before heading off again.

A dry-season silence fell over Deception. The lion roars and jackal calls no longer drifted down the valley at dawn. It wasn't just that the lions were too far away to be heard; even when they were close to the valley they did not call. From our camp on the valley floor we neither saw nor heard any signs of the lions. No wonder that for years we had accepted the common belief that they migrated to some unknown place for the dry months. Without the airplane and radio-telemetry equipment, we would never have known that some of them still prowled within the reserve, at times less than a mile from camp.

In the hot-dry season, the prides broke up into even smaller groups than in the short winter of June, July, and August. Two lionesses, at most, shared the kills they were able to make together, and they were often on their own. Muffin and Moffet were with the females only twenty percent of the time, compared to fifty-seven percent in the wet season. By contrast, Serengeti pride males are with females seventy to ninety percent of the time throughout the year.[2] Muffin and Moffet were often as far as forty miles from their Blue Pride lionesses.

The social organization of Kalahari lions under these extreme environmental conditions was turning out to be very different from that of East African lions. The most significant difference was the behavior of the females. We soon learned that Kalahari lionesses switched prides and pride areas frequently during dry seasons, as Happy had done on a number of occasions.

As Chary, Sassy, and their cubs traveled in and out of the game reserve, they occasionally met and socialized with members of the East End Pride, the Blue Pride, and other prides, and with some females we did not recognize. It didn't seem to matter which pride the lions had belonged to before the drought, they appeared to develop these new social affinities easily. These associations between individuals of different prides were usually temporary, unless the local concentration of large antelope prey was dense enough to allow the group to stay together and still find enough for all to eat. This happened on occasions when antelope concentrated on a flush of new grass after a fire.

We could hardly wait for the results of each new day's aerial locations. Every observation was a new bit of insight into the flexible social behavior of the lions under the environmental pressures of the Kalahari dry season. The flow of social and asocial events—who associated with whom, how many were in the group, and the nature of these relationships—was very dynamic.

Some of the lionesses transferred between groups more often than others: Happy associated temporarily with lions of four different prides eighteen times in nineteen months, and she eventually ended up roaming with Spicy of the Blue Pride. We were even more amazed one morning when Kabe, an ear-tagged female from the Orange Pride, strolled out onto North Pan. We had not seen her for three years, and she was traveling with a young male and two young females from the Springbok Pan Pride. A few days later she abandoned her young companions and joined Dixie of the Springbok Pan Pride—but inside the Blue Pride's old wet-season territory. If all this seems somewhat confusing to read about, imagine how we felt observing it at first hand, after seeing these lions grow up, hunt, sleep, and play together in their own prides for years. The whole lion social system, which we had spent years figuring out, seemed to be coming apart at the seams.

Without exception, all the lionesses we monitored associated with members of different prides. The cohesion and pride structure that were so permanent and fundamental to the social organization of Serengeti lions had temporarily disintegrated in the Kalahari population. It was a startling example of how a species can adjust its social system to extreme environments.

We could no longer be certain that the females of a pride were related; it was impossible to know the family origins of the older ones, whom we had not observed from birth. We had always assumed that Chary, the oldest, had grown up in the Blue Pride, but she may have been born and raised in the East Side Pride. And we could not ascertain the paternity of cubs born under these conditions, for the females of the Blue Pride mated with males from four different prides.

Chary, Sassy, their cubs, Muffin, Moffet, and many of the other lions continued to prowl outside the game reserve boundary. Perhaps when the rains came again, some of them would return to their original pride areas. Perhaps—but for now there wasn't a cloud in the sky.

19

The Dust of My Friend

Delia

In a rising wind
the manic dust of my friends,
those who fell along the way,
bitterly stings my face.
—*Stanley Kunitz*

THE DRY SEASON of 1978, like all the others, had a few good points, in spite of the dust and flies: The grass had died down, so it was easier to follow research subjects; we didn't have to worry about preparing camp for rain; and the animals in our tree island, attracted to the water and mealie-meal, had become more numerous and tame.

One of the new arrivals in camp was a grey-backed bush warbler we called Pinkie, a tiny fellow who could fit in the palm of your hand. With pink legs like toothpicks, a plump posterior, and an up-turned tail, he looked homemade.

Nearly every day Pinkie hopped around inside our sleeping tent, pecking under the trunks and boxes and behind folds in the canvas, in search of insects. A clutter of books, journals, and papers stacked at the head of our bed was Pinkie's favorite hunting ground for flies and beetles.

One afternoon when we were resting, Pinkie hopped from a book onto Mark's bare shoulder, then skipped across his chest and down his belly to his navel. He stood on tiptoes for a moment, craning his head this way and that and peering inside. Mark's stomach began to shake with laughter, but staring benignly, Pinkie rode it out. Then suddenly he sent his sharp little beak down, true as an arrow, right into Mark's navel. I don't know what he was after, or if he was rewarded, but he seemed quite satisfied as he hopped across the floor and out the door of the tent.

By now, there were seven Marico flycatchers in camp, including Marique, and on cold nights they slept all in a row, snuggled together on an acacia branch. The ones in the middle stayed warm and cozy, but after a while, those on the end would get chilly. In what looked like a scene from Disney, the outsiders would jump up, their eyes still half closed, hop along the feathered backs of their buddies, and wiggle their way into the better-insulated center spot. Soon they would be fast asleep again. A little later, the birds at the end of the row would find themselves cold, and they would repeat the performance; and so this continued all night long.

By far the fastest-moving character in camp was William, the shrew. He had Mickey Mouse ears, frizzy whiskers, and a long, incredibly dexterous rubber-hose nose. William, never still, was always darting along his own private paths with quick, herky-jerky starts and stops, like someone driving with one foot on the accelerator, the other on the brake. His nose constantly twitching, he zoomed in and out of the bushes, competing with the hornbills and flycatchers for mealie-meal.

One of William's routes through camp took him under our chairs in the ziziphus tree "tearoom." Since shrews have a high metabolic rate, they have to eat a tremendous amount every day. For this reason William was always in a hurry; still, he paused now and then to tickle our toes with his elephantile nose as he passed by. He was one of camp's main attractions.

At times we had a number of mice in camp, but the population plummeted after Dr. Rolin Baker of Michigan State University requested that we make a collection of Kalahari rodents for the university's museum. We didn't have the time to spend on such a project, so we taught Mox how to live-trap mice, sacrifice them humanely, and make study mounts of them. We agreed to pay him for each specimen, plus an extra tip for every new species he collected.

Mox set about his new responsibility with a great deal of enthusiasm and pride; at last he was involved in the science of the project. He hid traps in the corners of the tent and behind the tea crate. Every morning, after he had finished his other duties, he took a pair of pliers from the toolbox in the truck, and stalked from one trap to the next, gathering his specimens. He would take all morning to stuff three or four mice, but when he had finished, they would be perfectly shaped and very natural in appearance.

At noon one day we were reading under the ziziphus tree, when I heard Mox clear his throat behind us. He was standing at attention, proudly displaying his latest collection of rats and mice. They were all precisely arranged along a board, their feet tucked under them, their tails hanging down. These were his best yet; except for their cotton-filled eyes, they might have been sleeping. I started to tell Mox what an excellent job he had done, when I noticed a nose jutting out from the row. In the middle, his long snout stretched across the board in front of him—forever for Michigan State—was William.

* * *

Since the Frankfurt Zoological Society had provided us with an airplane, we hoped they would continue to fund our project, but as 1978 drew to a close and the new year began, we were out of money once again. Richard Flattery, the Standard Bank manager, kindly arranged a temporary loan with no collateral; he knew full well we had nothing to offer and he never raised the issue. To save money, we grounded Echo Whisky Golf and waited until January to go to Maun, when surely there would be word of a grant waiting for us in our mail.

Long before we were packed, Mox stood waiting at the plane, ready for the flight to Maun. He was dressed in his best, which had improved considerably since he first came to work with us. A big black comb crowned the back of his head, and he wore dark sunglasses with wide blue-and-red rims. Mark's jeans, plastered with patches, covered his spindly legs, and he wore the tennis shoes that Mark had retired after the wild dog tried to bury them. He was going to the village for the first time in more than three months and he was as excited as that territorial springbok watching his females return after a long dry season alone.

After landing at the airstrip in Maun, we took Mox to the Standard Bank, where we paid him his usual wage, plus the money for his rodent collection. The total was something over 200 pula—about $250. This was more cash than he had ever seen before. Together with Richard Flattery, we did our best to encourage him to open a savings account, but he seemed to have an inherent distrust of banks. When we insisted that this was the safest place for his money, he turned and hurried outside into the yard, where some goats and donkeys were grazing.

We caught up with him. "Mox, what's wrong?" I asked him gently. He kept his eyes on the ground for some time. Then he slowly looked up at me.

"Cowboys."

"Cowboys?"

"Ee, *cowboys*." He held out his right hand, its index finger and thumb like a six-shooter, his face in a frown. In broken English he explained.

Some months before, he had apparently seen a cheap cowboy movie, shown at the village center by one of the Peace Corps volunteers. In the film, the bank had been robbed. And although Botswana had yet to have its first bank robbery, nothing we could say would change Mox's mind. He was convinced that at any moment, masked men could ride up to the Maun bank on thundering horses and, in a cloud of dust, make off with all the money inside. He was sure his savings would be safer hidden in his mother's *rondavel*.

We borrowed Richard's Land Rover and drove Mox to his clay-and-thatch home. All the young children rushed to greet him, admiring his sunglasses and dancing around him. He patted each on the head. We arranged to meet him at the same place in two days' time and drove away.

Anxious about news of a grant, we hurried to collect the mail from our box at Safari South. In a stack of two-month-old Christmas cards was a cable from Frankfurt Zoological Society. We walked to a quiet corner of the yard, where I tore open the envelope. The message had been badly scrambled by the wire operator at the post office, but the gist of it was that we had been saved again: The society intended to fund us fully for the next two years.

Mark swung me high above his head. "You know what?" he asked. "Get yourself all fixed up—I'm taking you out to dinner."

And so we celebrated Christmas (a month late), our sixth wedding anniversary, and our grant, by dining at Island Safari Lodge on the banks of the Thamalakane River. The innkeepers, Yoyi and Tony Graham, gave us a free bottle of champagne and a cottage for the night. It was hard to believe—a tablecloth, wine glasses, waiters, a real shower, a real bed. We were more in love with each other, and with our work, than we had been when we first stepped off of that train in Gaborone, so many years before.

After two days of letter writing and shopping, we stopped in front of Mox's mother's rondavel, ready to head for the airstrip and Deception Pan again. A young girl was stirring a pot of steaming mealiemeal next to a fire, while several other children played in the sand. They all stood quietly watching as we walked to the hut. No one spoke, and when we asked about Mox they looked at us blankly.

An older teen-age girl I recognized came out of the house. No, she knew no one named Mox, she told us flatly, as if bored with the question. Several neighbors gathered around our truck. They all shrugged their shoulders—no one had ever heard of Moxen Maraffe.

For two days we drove around looking for him. Twice more we stopped by his mother's hut, and although there was no sign of him, we had the feeling that he was hiding inside. Mox had simply decided to disappear, and his clan was helping him. We finally gave up and drove away for the last time.

At first we were hurt and angry. We could well understand if Mox wanted to quit his job. Living in the desert far from his family was not a lively life for a young bachelor. But he had meant a lot to us, and we had thought he felt the same way. At least he could have told us he was quitting, instead of just disappearing. One of the hunters in Maun, though, told us that the fact that he could not face us with bad news was, in a way, his parting sign of affection.

Mox had acquired considerable recognition among the villagers. Not only did he fly in an airplane, but he was the *kgosi*—the chief—who worked with the people who shot lions and then brought them to life again. He was no longer the village buffoon. Respect and a new identity—these were the most important things he had brought back from the Kalahari, but they were of no use to him as long as he remained isolated.

Although we always asked about him when we were in Maun, we never saw Mox again.

* * *

After receiving the grant from the Frankfurt Zoological Society, we flew to Johannesburg in January 1979 to buy new tents and supplies and to have the plane inspected. On our first night we decided to go to town, perhaps to see a show.

Lofty towers, spires, and slowly spinning restaurants soared high above the city's nightlife. There were so many glaring lights, the stars were lost. Horns, engines, shouts, and sirens. Fumes and crowds.

Mark took my arm and pulled me away from a dark alleyway. I stepped on the remains of a greasy bag of fish and chips. Until I had lived on the desert sands I had never noticed how filthy city sidewalks were.

We stayed close together, stopping, dodging, turning to avoid bumping into people on the sidewalk. Suddenly, as we neared the movie theater, we recognized a face. I grabbed Mark's arm and we ducked into a small bookstore and peered over a shelf; one of the few people we knew in Johannesburg passed by. Then we looked at each other.

"Why did we do that?" Mark asked.

"I don't know."

We kept much too much distance between us and the person ahead of us when we stood in line to buy our tickets. Once inside we found two seats alone in a corner of the theater. The space around soon filled up with talking, laughing moviegoers, and when the movie began, the laughing and talking didn't stop.

"Let's get out of here."

Back on the street, we found a small café with sidewalk tables nestled among potted trees—real trees. We ordered two glasses of white South African wine and sat in silence, watching the city's nightlife.

* * *

The next morning we went into a gift shop to buy some small presents for the people in Maun who had helped us so much over the years. Shelves sparkled with rows of fine china, lead crystal, and silver. An attractive green-eyed woman in her thirties offered to help us. We declined the various items she suggested as not appropriate for Maun or for our budget.

"Are you from Botswana?" she asked.

I explained that we had been living in the Kalahari for six years, studying lions and brown hyenas.

"Oh . . . my father once lived in the Kalahari," she replied.

"Really? What was his name?"

"You probably wouldn't have known him—he passed away some years ago. His name was Berghoffer—Bergie Berghoffer."

For a second Mark and I were unable to speak. "You—you're Bergie's daughter!" I stammered.

We had wanted to contact Bergie's family for more than five years, to show in some small way our love for him and our appreciation for all he had done to help us. But we hadn't known either of his daughters' married names.

She introduced herself as Heather Howard and called her husband, Mike, down from upstairs to hear the flood of stories we had to tell about Bergie. They remembered his talking about "crazy Yank friends who had pitched up in the Kalahari, with nothing but a Land Rover, to study the wildlife." They had always wondered what had become of us. Sadly, we had to decline their invitation to dinner that night; we were returning to Botswana that afternoon. We promised to call them on our next trip to the city.

But we didn't contact them on our next trip, or on the one after that. Whenever we had to go near their shop we worried that we might accidentally run into them and have to explain why we hadn't phoned. We couldn't understand our behavior. Though we longed to see people, we avoided doing so. Mark and I each felt the other was the only person on earth who understood this idiosyncratic social behavior, and our contentment with each other only exaggerated the problem of dealing with other people.

It was almost a year after we had first met Heather and Mike that we finally called on them again. On a sunny afternoon we drove through the rolling green fields of the South African highveld to their home, beyond the outskirts of the city. It was very good to see them again, and they never inquired about the long lapse between our visits. Perhaps they understood better than we; after all, Bergie had spent much of his life alone in the wild.

Heather was pleasant, but pensive. We chatted for a time, and then she explained that, in his will, her father had asked that he be cremated and his ashes scattered in some quiet, grassy glade someplace in the wilderness. In all those years since his death, she said, the family had never felt that the time was quite right. Now that we had met again, they believed that Bergie would be pleased if we would join them in granting his last wish.

We walked through the meadows to a creek that rushed and swirled over rocks. There was a gentle breeze and there were butterflies. As I tossed his ashes to the winds, I could see Bergie's face smiling at me; we were setting him free again.

Some of his ashes caught on a spider's web that stretched between tall, waving reeds. I turned and looked at the distant, smoky haze of the city sprawling beyond the hills of green. I doubted if Bergie—or any of us—would be in the wilderness for very long.

* * *

In February 1979 we flew back into the Kalahari, our plane loaded with equipment and supplies. After several days of unpacking, sawing, and hammering, we stood back and looked at our new camp, with its five tents. The little yellow mess tent, trimmed in brown, was nestled in the center of the tree island, near the ziziphus tree. Inside was a dining table complete with tablecloth and chairs, and on each side there were orange-crate buffets that held pottery dishes, baskets, and glasses. A path wound through the trees to the sleeping tent, which held a real bed that Mark had made from packing crates. The office/lab tent had a large working table, bookshelves, a typewriter, file cabinet, and another table, to serve as a desk. There was a storage tent with a gas freezer and refrigerator and a new three-walled reed kitchen boma.

If only Bergie could see us now.

20

A School for Scavengers

Delia

. . . in short, we see beautiful adaptations everywhere . . .
—Charles Darwin

WE HAD CONTINUED our brown hyena research along with the observations of lions all during the 1978 wet season and the winter months that followed. Star was more than eleven years old now, and her once thick coat of long, dark hair had thinned, exposing bare patches of coarse grey skin. Most of her blonde cape was gone, battle scars stood out on her leathery neck, and her teeth were worn to nubs from years of crushing bone. She seemed a little slower getting up—a little stiff, perhaps—and a little more apt to rest during a night's foraging.

From the air, Mark found her radio signal in the same spot on West Dune for four consecutive days. This was unusual for a brown hyena; a desert scavenger cannot afford the luxury of such roots. We could think of just two reasons why Star had not moved: She had slipped her collar or she was dead.

With the radio receiver in the truck, we homed on her transmitter on the duneslope west of camp. As we eased through the scratchy thornbush, the signal grew stronger; but there was no sign of Star. I steeled myself for the moment. Any second now, we would find her body, torn and broken on the sand, her bones picked clean by vultures.

Mark stopped the truck, switched off the ignition, and pointed ahead. About fifteen yards away, Star's weathered old face peered at us above a small scrub. Shaking chalky sand from her coat and flicking her tail, she walked to an opening in a small sandy mound, lowered her head to the hole, and made a low purring sound. Out wobbled three tiny cockleburs of charcoal fur—not only was Star alive and well, but she had cubs in a den only 300 yards from camp! Their dark eyes looked up at their mother, and she nuzzled them with her big muzzle as they stumbled around her feet.

At last we had another opportunity to observe a brown hyena mother caring for her young. We feared that Patches and Shadow had abandoned their cubs because we had tried to study them, but Star was so totally accustomed to us that we felt sure our presence would not disturb her. We named the female cub Pepper, and the two males Cocoa and Toffee.

Although by this time we knew a great deal about brown hyena feeding ecology, we still did not understand their social system. It was a mystery to us why they lived in a clan. Since they were scavengers and did not need each other for hunting large prey—as do other social carnivores—why did they associate in a group? Why did Patches, the dominant female, share food with Star and Shadow, when she could take it all for herself? Why would the clan share a common territory, if they did not need each other in some way?

Star had enlarged an existing springhare hole for her den. Three deep trenches in the sand led to separate tunnels underground, each concealed by a thicket of acacia bush. During the day she slept in the patchy shade about fifteen yards away, and every three to four hours she summoned the cubs by purring at the entrance. They toddled from the den and greeted her with wild enthusiasm, crawling around and around her, all the while squeaking hoarsely. They tottered about "grinning," their ears flattened and their tails curled over their backs, and Star licked and nibbled at each of them. Then she lay in one of the cool sandy runs and nursed them for twenty to twenty-five minutes.

When they were only three weeks old, the cubs began playing outside. At first this consisted mostly of stumbling into each other and falling down. But when they could keep their balance well enough, they practiced muzzle-wrestling and neck biting. Star seldom joined in the play, but lay there patiently while they tried with all their might to bite off her ears, nose, and tail or pounced on her round, dusty belly. Unlike lion and human mothers, Star never lost her patience. When it appeared that she could take no more of their mischief, she rolled them onto their backs, and while they squirmed to get away, she groomed them. As soon as they could escape, they would scamper away and begin chewing on one another again.

Just after dark, she led them into the safety of the den, and there they remained while she walked for miles in search of food. But since she had to return to nurse her young every four or five hours, she was unable to spend as much time foraging as the other hyenas, or to range very far from the den. This limited the amount of food she was able to find during the months that she was raising her litter.

One night when the cubs were six weeks old, Star gingerly clamped her powerful jaws over Pepper's back and carried her down the airstrip, across the valley floor, and into the bush on North Bay Hill, where she installed her in a new den. She then returned for Cocoa and Toffee. We did not know why Star moved her cubs, but it is common for some carnivores, such as jackals and wolves, to move their infants to two or three different lairs during their development.

Whatever the reason, it provided us with an excellent opportunity to investigate the interior of a brown hyena den. Armed with flashlights, notebooks, and measuring tapes, we walked to the abandoned site. When we reached the area, Mark squatted to examine the sandy spots around the entrance.

"What are you looking for?" I asked.

"Tracks. We'd better make sure that a leopard or warthog hasn't moved in here since Star left."

We searched through the hundreds of tiny brown hyena tracks for any sign of a new, larger predator.

When Mark was satisfied, he said, "Looks okay. You go into that entrance, I'll take this larger one."

I crawled head first into the open trench and then into a tunnel about two and a half feet high. By lowering my head and shoulders I could just squeeze inside. I pointed the flashlight into the pitch-dark. Ahead, the tunnel ran straight for about twelve feet and then made a turn to the left. I kept thinking that if a warthog or leopard had taken up residence in these dark corridors, it must be feeling very threatened, with us grunting, coughing, and crawling toward it from opposite directions. I could imagine angry eyes lurking around the corner ahead.

Flat on my belly, pulling with my hands and pushing with my toes, I inched forward. Now and then my head hit the roof and sand rained down on my neck and back. Still leaning on my elbows, I crawled down a gentle slope, shoving the flashlight ahead of me.

When I neared the end of the passageway, I stopped and listened. I could hear Mark's muffled bumps and scrapes drifting over from another run. Slowly, I shone the flashlight around the corner, half expecting the hiss-growl of a trapped leopard. I snatched it back. When nothing happened, I pulled myself forward and peered around the bend.

In front of me was a central chamber about five feet in diameter and three feet high, with hairy grey roots hanging down from the ceiling. This was apparently where the cubs had spent most of their time; there were little depressions in the sandy floor where they had slept. Three small tunnels and two larger ones led from the chamber.

I still could not see Mark, but sounding as if we were talking in a barrel, we called descriptions of the den back and forth to each other. We determined which tunnels were connected underground, and we measured their dimensions.

I was impressed by how clean the den was; Star was an excellent housekeeper. There was no dung or litter lying around, only a few bones, and there was no odor except for the dank, musty smell of earth. The skull of a young giraffe and a gemsbok scapula were the only furnishings.

"Hey! There's something biting me!" Mark yelled from the other tunnel. I didn't know whether he meant a mouse or a leopard, but then I began to feel fiery stings all over my body. I was so startled that it never occurred to me to turn around in the chamber and exit head first. Instead, I began belly-crawling backward, upslope, as fast as I could go. Frantically pushing with my hands, pulling with my toes, and constantly bumping my rear on the ceiling, I finally reached the entrance. Standing in the sunlight and fresh air, we found that we were covered with fleas.

We stripped off all our clothes, doused ourselves with water from the canteen, and skulked back to camp. For once, I was glad that Mox was not there to greet us.

There may be several good reasons why a female brown hyena moves her infants to a new den—perhaps to provide the growing cubs with a larger home or to protect them from predators who have discovered the first one—but I remain convinced that, at least in part, it is an attempt to avoid the flourishing flea population.

At two months of age, Pepper, Cocoa, and Toffee played for longer periods at sunset, scampering up to ten yards away from Star and their new den. However, at the slightest rustle in the grass—or even at the sight of a crow overhead—they always ran back to their mother's side or disappeared into the den.

When Star was ready to forage, she would stand up and shake

herself, and then walk away without a glance at the cubs. Now that they were slightly older, she made no special effort to tuck them away safely in the den. Pepper and Cocoa would gallop after her for about fifteen yards, then they would run back to the den; Toffee, always more cautious, watched from the safety of the entrance. All three would stand silently until they could no longer hear Star's footsteps in the dry vegetation, and then they played or explored around the den area for ten or fifteen minutes before going inside. At this age, the cubs were only slightly larger than house cats and good prey for lions, leopards, cheetahs, or jackals.

By the time Pepper, Cocoa, and Toffee were two and a half months old they had plump, round bellies. One night Star took Cocoa by the neck and walked west through the bush. Following close behind in the truck, we saw her move from North Bay Hill down onto the valley floor, and then northward, the cub dangling from her mouth like a limp rag.

Mark had found Moffet under the Topless Trio that morning, and now Star was headed along the dark riverbed directly toward the lion's position. Through binoculars we could just make out Moffet's large body lying perfectly still under the tree. Lions often stalk and kill brown hyenas, and unless Star changed course, she would walk directly into him. She might be able to escape, but she would probably drop Cocoa in the process.

I raised the glasses and watched anxiously as Star carried her cub closer and closer to the lion. Brown hyenas do not seem to have very keen eyesight, and unless Moffet moved, she probably wouldn't see him until it was too late. The night air was dead calm; his scent might not reach her until she was just a few yards away from him. Star continued on her way, oblivious to the danger ahead.

Moffet rolled over and gathered his feet under his heavy body, his big head raised and his eyes locked on Star, plodding toward him over the riverbed. From having observed lions stalk brown hyenas previously, we guessed he would wait until she and her cub were within twenty or thirty yards, then he would charge. By the time she could react he would be practically on top of her.

But when Star was only eighty yards away from him, she stopped and peered ahead. Then she turned abruptly and made a wide detour around the lion. Moffet dropped his muzzle onto his paws and apparently went back to sleep.

Star trekked north for over two miles, and during the whole time

Cocoa never stirred. The moon had not yet risen, but the calcrete shoal on the riverbed reflected the bright starlight, and we could easily see the hyena's dark form moving through the dry grass. Turning northeast onto the dune, she wound her way through thick thornscrub. She continued for another half mile, stopping now and then to look and listen. We could not understand why she was taking Cocoa so far.

We broke through the next stand of tall brush into a large clearing, and quickly switched off the engine. We stared ahead, dumbfounded. Before us lay an enormous den complex comprised of several great mounds of grey sand over fifteen yards long. Standing on each mound were young brown hyenas of different ages, and obviously belonging to different mothers. Here were the missing cubs, the ones we thought Shadow and Patches had abandoned. All the clan's young were at one communal den—the first such den ever seen by humans!

This, at last, was the answer to all the questions we had been asking for years about the raison d'être of brown hyena society. These scavengers associate in a clan, sharing food and territory, because they raise their young communally in a supreme cooperative effort to contend with the harsh and fickle Kalahari environment.

It happens too rarely in science that, after years of effort, a new discovery practically falls into the researcher's lap. We sat speechless. Star lay Cocoa softly on the sand and stood back. All the other cubs came forward and smelled their new denmate. Cocoa did not seem afraid or timid, he lifted his small black nose and sniffed the assortment of cubs that greeted him. While Star went to bring Pepper and Toffee to the nursery, Cocoa explored his new surroundings.

* * *

The Kalahari environment, with its sparse and unpredictable food supplies, makes it difficult for a female brown hyena to find enough to eat for herself and her growing cubs. We were to learn later that usually only one female in the clan gives birth to cubs each year, and thus there is a limit to the number of young at the communal den. With all of the cubs safely inside, each female is free to roam alone for several nights until she locates food that can be carried back to the cubs. Since each mother does not have to return to a private den several times each night, the clan's collective foraging time is increased, insuring a more regular supply of food to the young. Every adult female, whether or not she has ever bred, brings food to the cubs at the den.[1] And some of the males provision as well. Because they must forage alone, yet rear their young communally, brown hyenas are a curious blend of the social and the solitary, reflecting the capricious nature of the land over which they roam.

* * *

With the discovery of the communal den, our lives took on a different routine: In the early morning Mark flew around locating the lions and hyenas, and then later we would drive to some of the lions nearest camp. In the early evening, while he was transcribing his notes from the tape recorder, I drove to the hyena den and watched them for part or all of the night.

I took along notebooks, a flashlight, cameras, a tape recorder, a sleeping bag, fresh bread, and thermos bottles of soup and hot tea. In the back there were extra cans of food and a jerrican of water, in case I had to stay longer than planned. When I arrived at the den there were usually no hyenas in sight, and I would watch the sunset and listen to the Kalahari night fall: A jackal would call on North Dune, a korhaan would give a territorial squawk, and hundreds of barking geckos would begin their nightly serenade. After dark I could see the flicker of Mark's campfire three and a half miles away.

One sunset, before any of the hyena cubs appeared from the den, the truck suddenly shook. Startled, I looked around to see what it could be. Just when I was beginning to think I must have imagined it, the truck moved again. I opened the door to see if a grass owl had landed on the roof. Nothing there. Again the truck shuddered, and now I was really getting spooked. Then I looked through the back window, and there I saw Moffet's big furry head slowly appearing over the tailgate. He stuck his nose into the bed of the pickup, sniffing at the toolbox and spare tire. He lowered his head again, taking the trailer hitch in his jaws, he rattled the truck as if it were a toy.

"Hey, Moff, stop that!" I called out the window. He gave one last tug and then walked over to within two feet of the open window. Raising his head, he looked deep into my eyes. I said, very softly, "Look, I was just kidding. If you want to shake the truck, go right ahead."

Moffet yawned enormously, shook himself, and walked over to the hyena den, where he jetted scent onto a small tree. He disappeared into the brush, and the J-shaped scar on his flank was the last I saw of him.

Those nights alone on that duneslope, with the stars hanging close overhead, were some of the most special of my life. And slowly I began to know the hyena cubs. Pippin, the oldest, was over three years and really a young adult. He foraged on his own, but still visited the den to play with the younger cubs. Chip was the next oldest, and he, too, foraged away from the den area. Sooty and Dusty, a younger brother and sister, remained at the den site all the time, along with Puff, a very young female. Finally, there were Pepper, Cocoa, and Toffee, the newly arrived infants.

The night after we discovered the communal den, I saw Patches come along one of the paths worn through the grass, carrying a fresh springbok leg in her jaws. All the cubs jumped up at the sound of her approach, their hair standing on end. The younger ones dove into the den opening; for all they knew, the sound was that of a lion or some other predator. When Patches was close enough to be recognized, the older cubs bounded toward her and circled round her in greeting for several minutes. She laid the bone on the sand and sniffed each cub that paraded under her nose, licking their ears and backs. After Sooty had paid his respects to his elder, he grabbed the springbok leg and rushed into the den, and all the others followed. Patches slept on the mound while the cubs fed inside.

Later the same night, Shadow strolled out of the bush and the cubs circled around her, kicking up fine dust until a white cloud hung over the area. She flopped onto one of the mounds, and Puff began to suckle, her paws kneading the soft udders. I had just concluded that Shadow was Puff's mother, when Dusty also began suckling. Because of the differences in their ages, Puff and Dusty could not both be Shadow's cubs; she was nursing at least one that was not her own. Later we saw Patches and Star nurse each other's young. Communal suckling had only been seen in a few other wild carnivores, including lions and wild dogs; it had never been recorded in hyenas before. It was further proof of the cooperative social system of the browns.

Since the lactating females in the clan nursed all the cubs, and since all the females brought food to the den, at first it was not obvious who was the mother of whom. Fortunately, we had detailed records of the previous pregnancy and lactation periods of the females in the clan. By comparing this information with the ages of the cubs, and by sitting long hours at the den, we were able to confirm family relationships. We knew that Pippin was Star's cub from a previous litter, making him the half brother (Pippin's father had been displaced by another dominant male) of her present cubs, Pepper, Cocoa, and Toffee. Chip was Patches's cub, and Puff belonged to Shadow; we did not know who was Dusty and Sooty's mother.

With Star, Patches, and Shadow bringing food, and Pippin visiting the den to clear loose sand out of the tunnels and play with the cubs, one might expect the communal den to be crowded with hyenas, but this was never the case. Adult females did not visit every night and they rarely appeared at the same time. If they did happen to meet at the den, they barely acknowledged one another. We never saw the clan's immigrant adult male, the cubs' father, visit them or bring them any food.

Because they had to spend so many hours foraging, most of the time there were no adults at the communal den to protect the young. Clan members slept under bushes or trees widely scattered throughout the territory, some up to five miles from the den. An adult might occasionally sleep near it during the day, but never closer than 200 to 300 yards.

The infants were protected by the den itself and by the presence of older, larger cubs. Pepper, Cocoa, and Toffee would wander up to twenty-five yards away in the tall grass, but at the sight or sound of any approaching animal, whether it be a porcupine or a lion, they would dive into one of the runs and dash underground. Minutes later, their ears, then their eyes, and finally their noses, would slowly appear like periscopes over the rim of the hole to find out if the danger had passed. If they saw that the older cubs had not taken cover, Pepper, Cocoa, and Toffee would bound out of the den to resume play.

Late one afternoon, a pack of eight wild dogs loped toward the den. The smaller cubs disappeared, but Chip, Dusty, and Sooty, who were three-quarters adult size, stayed on the outside and faced the predators. Standing on the largest mound, with every hair bristling, they looked quite formidable. The dogs circled the den area three times, occasionally trotting closer for a better view, but eventually moved away. However, when Moffet came by the den one afternoon, all the cubs, including Chip, Dusty, and Sooty, disappeared inside and did not come out again for more than an hour after the lion had left.

The cubs occasionally wandered too far from the protection of the den. When Puff was about the size of a small, stocky bulldog, one night she strayed farther away from the den than usual. Loud screams and sounds of a struggle came from the tall grass. By the time we arrived, a leopard was dragging her torn body toward an acacia tree. Even after Puff's death, Shadow, her mother, continued to suckle and provision the other cubs.

Every day at sunset, after the heat had broken for the day, the cubs would peer out of the four den openings. When they were satisfied that there was no danger, they would plod out of the runs and collapse on the mounds of excavated sand. Later, when cool air began to flow down the duneslopes into the valley, the cubs began smelling grass-stalks, twigs, old bones, and anything else they could get their noses into. These are important lessons for hyenas, who spend much of their time foraging in tall grass, where they cannot see more than a few feet ahead, and who must locate widely scattered pieces of carrion. As adults, they would also depend heavily on their sense of smell to warn them of dangers from lions and to maintain contact with one another by scent-marking.

Pepper, Cocoa, and Toffee tried to scent-mark long before their anal glands began to produce the viscous paste excreted by adults. Over and over again they raised their small fuzzy tails, turned, and squatted over a stalk, trying to leave their olfactory calling cards and always sniffing to see whether they had succeeded.

At about four months of age, soon after they were moved to the communal den, they discovered that they were able to make their own paste. They looked very proud of themselves, strutting around the denning area, raising their tails, and daubing white, gooey drops on everything—even on the tail of an unsuspecting adult and the legs of our camera tripod.

Games in which one cub tested itself against another were an important part of their development. From the first day they emerged from the maternal den, the infant cubs exhibited the same behavioral patterns in play-fighting as those used by adults in combat: muzzle-wrestling, neck-biting, nipping the hind legs, and chasing. Play was important in developing social ties among the young, and it probably sharpened the fighting skills that would later be necessary in the battle for status in the clan's social hierarchy.

Whenever Pippin arrived at the den, the cubs greeted him with great excitement, springing forward to circle him, pulling at his tail, and jumping up to nip at his ears. In typical big brother fashion, he led them on a merry chase in and out of the bushes, but he always let them catch him, as he tossed his head from side to side to avoid their snapping jaws.

If young cubs were not reared in communal dens, they wouldn't benefit from the protection and play experience provided by older cubs, and they wouldn't be as likely to learn from, and form social bonds with, all of the adult members of their clan.

* * *

By February 1979 we had been searching the dull skies for months for any sign of rain. February is usually the height of the rainy season, but there was seldom a cloud in the sky, and midday temperatures were breaking 110 degrees in the shade. Occasionally the massive head of a cumulus formation peeked over the eastern horizon, only to sink from sight, spilling its life-giving moisture on other lands. By the beginning of April, the clouds were gone and we had lost all hope. The rains of 1979 had failed completely. Except for one brief shower, it had been twelve months since the animals and plants in Deception Valley had tasted moisture, and there was no chance of relief for ten months to come. The Kalahari was locked in drought.

When the lions—now spread over immense areas beyond the dry river system—occasionally visited the valley, their kills were so small that nothing but blood-stained feathers, quills, or a horn or hoof were left for the brown hyenas. The cheetahs and wild dogs had disappeared when the last of the springbok had left the valley. Now ants, termites, birds, rodents, and an occasional steenbok were the only prey available for leopards and jackals, and most of these small prey were completely consumed. Star, Patches, McDuff, and Pippin walked over the grey desert twenty miles or more every night in search of food. They, too, lapped up termites and chased mice, hedgehogs, porcupines, and springhare. The food supply could only get worse during the coming dry season, and since there had been no rain, there were no wild melons to be eaten for moisture.

At eighteen months of age, Dusty and Sooty had begun to forage on their own. As Pogo and Hawkins had done years earlier, they tagged behind Star, Patches, or Shadow when one of them left the den. Pepper, Cocoa, and Toffee were often the only cubs left in their earthen home, which had become a quiet and lonely place. Sometimes several nights would pass while they waited patiently for something to eat. Star was the only female still lactating, and at six and a half months, the three cubs were still heavily dependent on her milk for nourishment and moisture.

One windy night, Star walked north along Leopard Trail to Bergie

Pan, crossed the riverbed, and moved northeast to the slopes of East Dune. By midnight she had traveled more than twelve miles and had not found anything to eat, for herself or to take back to her young. She poked her nose into the entrances to several rat and springhare colonies, but no one was home. She was tired and lay down to rest near a grove of broad-leafed lonchocarpus trees about a mile from the riverbed.

Muffin and Moffet had spent days roaming the sandveld areas east of Deception Valley, crossing the game reserve boundary into cattle country several times. This night, they moved back west into their former wet-season territory and started trudging up the face of East Dune. Having seen only one hartebeest, which had cantered away from them, they were lean and hungry.

Lying flat on her side, her scarred head and neck on the cooling sand, Star occasionally pawed some of the fine grains onto her wrinkled belly. Sometime later she heard a faint sound from downwind. Perhaps the wind had covered the lions' approach, or maybe she had slept too soundly. But when she jumped up it was too late. Muffin and Moffet rushed in, mauling her, and in seconds Star was dead.

21

Pepper

Delia

A little more than kin and less than kind.
—*William Shakespeare*

PEPPER, COCOA, AND TOFFEE had no way of knowing that their mother was dead. Hour after hour, night after night, they lay on the den mounds, their chins on their paws, watching the path on which Star usually approached. As the time passed, their lethargy deepened; they did not play. Every few hours they plodded slowly around the area, smelling once more the few splinters of dessicated bones. They spent the long hot days in the den's cool interior, conserving the moisture in their withering bodies.

Their bony shoulders stuck out at sharp angles, and their hair began to fall out. The days were incredibly hot and dry, as though there had never been water on the earth, but the nights, at least, were mercifully cool.

On the fourth night after her death, Pepper, Cocoa, and Toffee did not come out of the den. For three nights we sat watching the bare mounds in the moonlight, hoping for some sign of life. We had to find out, so we crept to one of the main entrances, knelt, and listened. No sound from inside, and no small hyena tracks in the sand. The cubs must have starved to death or died of thirst.

But when we stood up and turned to go back to the truck, a thud and a squeak drifted out of the hole. At least one was still alive—but for how long?

Around midnight, a loud rustling came from the grass west of the den, and Pippin, the cubs' half brother, stepped into the clearing, a freshly killed springhare dangling from his jaws. He laid the four-pound mammal in the sand, walked to the entrance, and purred loudly. Immediately all three of the weak and hungry cubs scrambled out to greet him with eager squeals. They circled Pip again and again and then ran to the springhare and dragged it toward the den. On their way they stopped to rush around him one more time, raising great clouds of dust in their excitement. Then, tearing and pulling at the food, they disappeared inside.

Pippin stood on the mound alone, his legs long and lanky and his body thin. Without moving his head, he rolled his eyes and gave us a long look, just as his mother, Star, had so often done. Then he shook his long hair, flicked his tail, and walked away into the bush.

"Mark! Maybe he'll adopt them," I whispered. Not only did Star's cubs now have a chance to survive, but this was a high point in our brown hyena study. Adoption in nature is extremely rare; group members in most species usually abandon orphans and devote their efforts to rearing a litter of their own.

Early the next evening, Dusty came to the den carrying a large piece of giraffe skin, which had quite a bit of fresh meat attached to it. Following a few steps behind was Chip, the older male cub. Squealing and grinning, their tails raised in greeting, Pepper, Cocoa, and Toffee rushed forward and crawled around their old den mates. Cocoa grabbed the skin and they vanished inside. If we had observed this scene without knowing the identity of the individual hyenas, we could easily have thought that this was a mother and father feeding their young. In fact, they were all cousins.

Over the following days, certain clan members began to care for Pepper, Cocoa, and Toffee. We now realized why we had been unable to establish who was the mother of Dusty and Sooty: She had died, and, like Star's cubs, they had been adopted by the clan.

Now that they were being fed by Patches, Shadow, Dusty, and Pippin, the cubs grew stronger. Though brown hyena young often suckle until they are ten to twelve months old, these three had been abruptly weaned from their mother's milk at the age of seven months. Despite this radical change in their diets, they seemed to thrive on the meat, skin, and bones brought to them, and their chances for survival looked better and better.

* * *

We observed the communal den for more than three years and made several interesting discoveries. For one thing, adoption occurs often in brown hyenas. In the period during which we watched the den, seventy percent of the cubs that survived were adopted orphans.

Most brown hyena females stay in the clan to which they are born; thus they are all related. Because we had been observing the clan for so long, we knew many of the relationships. Patches and Shadow were Star's cousins, making them Pepper, Cocoa, and Toffee's first cousins once removed; Dusty was an older second cousin; and, Pippin, we knew, was their half brother. The cubs had been adopted by their relatives.

Thus hyenas, long considered vermin and listed in a thesaurus as synonymous with "cur" and "viper," help other hyenas by feeding and adopting their cubs; not only are they very social creatures, they seem to be very selfless, as well.

But how selfless are they, really? In the midst of a drought, why did Patches, Shadow, Dusty, and Pippin provide Star's cubs with food that they could have eaten themselves? Why would they aid another's young at a cost to themselves?

Part of the answer can probably be found in the sociobiological theory of kin selection.[1] "Fitness" in the term *survival of the fittest* does not refer to how physically strong an individual is but rather to its survival and the number of genes that individual passes to future generations. Any animal, including humans, can increase its genetic fitness in two ways: directly, by producing offspring who carry one half of its genes; and indirectly, by enhancing the survival of its more distant relatives—cousins, nephews, nieces—who carry a smaller proportion of its genes.[2]

Since Pepper, Cocoa, and Toffee were Shadow's first cousins once removed, each cub carried some of the same genes she had. By keeping the three of them alive, Shadow would increase her genetic fitness. Shadow's only cub, Puff, had been killed. If Pepper, Cocoa, and Toffee had also died, Shadow would have lost one of her few chances to pass her genes to future generations. This is especially important since a brown hyena female does not have many opportunities in her lifetime to raise litters. Each of the cubs also carried one-quarter of the same genes as Pippin, their half brother; thus feeding them benefited him genetically.

So, according to the theory of kin selection, the clan members who were feeding the cubs were not being altruistic. In fact, the food they brought to the den to keep their cousins or half siblings alive was merely an investment in perpetuating their own lineage. Of course, the brown hyenas themselves did not realize why they were feeding the orphans. During the evolution of their social behavior, those who possessed the "helping" genes and participated in provisioning must have kept more of their relatives alive, than did those hyenas without the genes who did not provision; so the behavior evolved as part of the natural life style of brown hyena sociality.

Chip and Sooty, the cubs' male cousins, did not help feed them. And though they came to the den to play with Pepper, Cocoa, and Toffee, we suspected they were really looking for morsels of food. In fact, on many occasions Chip and Sooty actually stole the carrion that had been brought to the den for the younger resident cubs.

But why did Dusty, their female cousin, feed the cubs when their male cousins did not? They were all related to the same degree. The answer is probably that most females remain in their natal clan for their lifetime and benefit from an increased clan size, whereas most males emigrate and do not. Because cousins share only about one-eighth of the same genes, this alone may not be enough genetic incentive to induce a male to feed his cousins. He may benefit more by eating the food himself than by investing it in the survival of the few of his genes that are carried by them. Since he will eventually leave to become a nomad or to join another clan, he would not benefit directly from increasing the number of members in his natal clan. On average, half siblings share twice as many genes as cousins do, so that even though a male half sibling may also eventually leave the clan, by provisioning cubs he would increase his genetic fitness more than cousins would.

On the other hand, it benefits any female in the clan, no matter how distantly related to the cubs, to feed them, because she is probably going to remain in the clan. If she helps raise cubs, there will be more individuals in the clan to defend the territory and its food resources. Perhaps most important of all, there will be more females around to eventually care for her cubs.

Thus, brown hyena cubs are raised by all the females in the clan and by the males most closely related to them.[3] That the behavior is not purely altruistic should not make it any less special—that a birdsong has a function does not make it less beautiful. By understanding the selective pressures behind the evolution of behavior that at first appears to be altruistic in animals—and also in ourselves—we learn that there is a natural and necessary element of self-interest in these kinds of behavior.

I thought about these things as I watched Dusty, who did not yet have cubs of her own, bringing food to her younger cousins. Is there any true selflessness in nature—in man? Why had we come to Africa, worked so hard, for so long, under such adverse conditions? Was it only for the animals? Or was it partially for ourselves?

* * *

The cubs were being fed again, though in modest quantities, and once more they began to play. Late one afternoon Pepper roused herself groggily from her sleep. Yawning, she shuffled around the den area a few times and then bit the neck of Cocoa, who was still trying to rest, and chomped at his ears and tail. When he stood up to retaliate, she ran away at full speed, crashing through the dry grass and bush nearby. A few minutes later she dashed back to the mound, jumped high into the air above the den, and dove into one of its openings, a cloud of dust rising from the hole. A few seconds later, her black ears, eyes, and nostrils ringed with white calc dust peeped over the rim of the hole, apparently to see if everyone was watching. Everyone was. She sprang out of the den, ran over Toffee, and disappeared into the scrub again.

It was usually Pepper who came up with new games. One afternoon she minced over to the truck, slowly extended her muzzle to smell the bumper, and then galloped back to the den, hair standing on end. When she reached the mound, she looked back at the Land Cruiser, her eyes rolling. After that, walking very cautiously, she led her brothers single file to the truck. Standing side by side, they all sniffed the Toyota and dashed away. Each time, they gained more confidence, until finally they walked underneath the truck; I could hear them lapping, snuffling, and chewing every part of the undercarriage.

One night, after several hours of den observation, I started down the dune face, only to discover that no matter how hard I pumped the brakes, the truck would not stop. Gripping the wheel and swerving to avoid termite mounds, holes, and scrub bushes, I bounced down the sandy slope and shot out onto the flat riverbed. The rest of the drive to camp was uneventful, until it came time to stop. I slowed down, but misjudged my speed. Stamping the brake pedal against the metal flooring, I coasted through our usual parking spot and sailed past the sleeping tent, finally coming to a stop just three feet from the office tent. Mark, who had finished transcribing his notes and gone to bed, was up on his elbow peering out of the tent window with a flashlight. I parted the flaps and said as sweetly as I could, "Don't be upset, but I think the cubs ate the brakes." Indeed, they had chewed right through the brake hoses and drained away all the hydraulic fluid.

Since our study of brown hyena helping behavior would be the subject of my Ph.D. thesis, I observed the den for over 1000 hours, and the cubs became completely accustomed to me. One afternoon, instead of staying in the truck, I sat in the long grass on the edge of the clearing. When Pepper and Cocoa looked out of the den, they ambled up to me, stuck their snouts into my hair, and began sniffing my ears, neck, and face. I remained perfectly still, trying not to laugh when their cold, wet noses blew puffs of air down my neck and spine. Eventually they turned their attention back to the bones that were scattered around the mound at the den.

Sitting among the cubs, I could observe more details of their behavior and get a fresh photographic perspective. Pepper would even let me take measurements around her skull and neck with a tape while she sniffed around me. But I had to be very careful with all my gear; one time she grabbed my notebook from my lap and ran into the den with it. Fortunately, she dropped it just inside the entrance, so I was able to retrieve it without too much difficulty.

At times, Pepper would rake her oversized paw down my arm, just as she did to initiate play with Cocoa. And once, at eight months of age, she latched onto my little finger with her incisors and stared into my eyes, as if issuing a challenge. She could easily have bitten off my finger, so I dropped my gaze and quickly pulled my hand from her grasp. It would have been fun to play with her, but this would have interfered with the objectivity of our research. Besides, her powerful jaws could have been quite dangerous. Since I did not respond to their attempts to incite play, the cubs ultimately treated me as little more than an object of curiosity. Pepper would always shuffle to the truck when it arrived and smell me as I stepped out, but then she would usually ignore me for the rest of the observation period. I was always careful to return to the truck before an adult approached, for they were less relaxed when I was sitting in the open only ten yards from their communal den.

That dry season of 1979 was the toughest we had known because there had been no rainy season at all preceding it. By late September, the temperatures again soared above 120 degrees in the shade, and the daily relative humidity was less than five percent. The adult animals needed more food for their own moisture requirements, and they visited the den less often. Sometimes nothing was brought to the cubs for two or three nights, and for the first time since we had started our study of brown hyenas, both the adults and the cubs looked worn and haggard. Once again, Pepper, Cocoa, and Toffee remained in the cool den most of the time and seldom played.

Late one afternoon Mark and I were busy in the kitchen when, to our amazement, we saw Pepper walking toward us on the track. She was not quite a year old. Cubs usually don't leave the den until they are almost eighteen months old, and then they follow adults closely for three or four months before foraging on their own. Yet here was little Pepper out all alone, three and a half miles from the den. It must have been a frightening adventure for her; every hair on her thin body stuck straight out, making her look like a bottle brush. That she had begun foraging on her own so early in life was another sign that the cubs were not getting enough to eat from the adults.

Pepper came into the kitchen without a moment's hesitation. She walked to where I was stirring stew over the fire, smelled the wooden spoon, grabbed it, and tried to pull it from my grasp. I held on and won the tug of war, though I would have liked more than anything to have given her the whole pot of stew. For me, one of the most difficult aspects of observing the brown hyenas and the lions during the long drought was resisting the urge to help them in some way. But we were there to learn how they survived and whether the game reserve offered enough resources for their conservation, not to offer them comfort. We burned our garbage and buried it in deep pits in the sandveld, away from the riverbed. We kept food out of reach and tried to remember to empty the water basins—I felt guilty every time—so there would be nothing in our tree island for animals to drink. We did everything possible to discourage the hyenas from keying on camp as an oasis in the desert. When they learned that they couldn't get to the sources of the scrumptious odors, they usually ignored them.

All except Pepper, that is. After she had smelled all the shelves and boxes in the kitchen boma, she walked down the path toward the dining tent. She stepped inside the door, and before we could stop her, she grabbed the tablecloth and pulled all the dishes onto the floor with a loud clatter. Then, for the next hour, she snooped around every corner of camp, smelling the water drums, poking her head inside the tent doors, and standing on her hind legs beneath the hanging shelf. It was dark when she finally left, and we followed her in the truck to see how well developed her foraging skills were.

Her hair again on end, she walked north, sniffing here and there on the dry ground and lapping up a few insects. As she rounded Acacia Point, she stopped and stared north along the valley. In the spotlight we could see the large eyes of another predator walking toward us from about 100 yards away. Obviously frightened, Pepper backed slowly toward the truck, ducked under it, and hid behind a front wheel, peering out with widened eyes. Through binoculars we could see Chip, her cousin, approaching; she apparently had not recognized him from a distance. After Chip circled us and moved on, she came out and continued north along the valley floor.

Nearing the dry water hole on Mid Pan, Pepper was intercepted by two jackals. She stared at them briefly and then scurried toward the den, which was still two miles away. Emboldened by her fear, the jackals closed in, their noses to her tail. She turned back her ears and walked even faster. Apparently realizing that she was a rookie, one darted forward and nipped her on the rump. Pepper tucked her tail between her legs and drew in her hindquarters, but both jackals continued to snipe at her legs as she struggled along, now almost sitting on her backside.

This continued for several hundred yards, until Pepper abruptly came to a halt. As if she had just realized that she was twice their size, she drew herself to her full height, her neck hackles bristling, and chased the jackals all the way to the edge of the riverbed. We followed her until she returned safely to the den; except for a few ants and termites, she had found no food.

Several weeks later Mark was in Maun for the night and I was in camp alone. After dark I heard a racket in the kitchen and cautiously crept down the path to see who was there. Pepper rounded the corner and walked straight up to me, smelling my toes and fingers. I followed her as she sniffed around camp, and after she walked out of the island and went to stand on the flat riverbed. I sat down five feet away from her. She turned to look at me and then settled on her haunches, her head up. The moon was only a quarter full in the western sky, but I could see for several miles over the Kalahari. The dark line of the dunes was silhouetted against the lighted sky; the night was quiet. We sat together, two small forms on the desert floor. I had never felt so close to the Kalahari, to the natural world. After about ten minutes, Pepper flicked her tail and walked away without looking back. I wondered where *I* would go if I had to walk into the desert to find my supper.

Cocoa and Toffee also explored away from the den, searching for morsels. One night, just after leaving the den, Toffee, who had always been the most cautious, was grabbed and killed by a leopard. We found his remains stashed high in an acacia tree only 150 yards from the den. Sooty disappeared from the area, probably having emigrated from the clan. We found Shadow's wizened remains on the parched desert floor. She, like Star, had been killed and eaten by lions. McDuff, the dominant male, was dead of unknown causes. Only Patches, Dusty, Pippin, Chip, Pepper, and Cocoa were left in the clan. The drought was taking its toll.

Pepper and Cocoa began foraging away from the den with an adult, whenever they could find one to accompany them. Patches, the only adult female; Pippin, their half brother; and Dusty, their cousin, always allowed the cubs to tag along and shared any food they had with them. The young hyenas were entering subadulthood, and they must have learned a great deal about the scavenger's way of life on these excursions: the clan's territorial boundaries, the network of pathways through the home range, and how to find and appropriate carrion from other predators.

If they could not find an adult, the cubs wandered off on their own, usually returning to the den by midnight, when it was most likely that a relative would bring them food. Even through the worst of the drought, Patches, Pippin, and Dusty continued to feed the orphans whenever they could.

Mark was in our reed bath boma one night, taking a spongebath in the dark. He was bending over the basin, his head covered with soapsuds and his bare feet perched on a narrow board to keep them out of the sand. All of a sudden a tongue slithered across his toes. He let out a loud whoop and jumped back. At the same time Pepper's head jerked upward, hitting the table and upsetting the water basin. She turned and shot for the entrance, but she missed and rammed the log frame of the door with her head. This frightened her even more. Like a ricocheting seventy-pound cannon ball, she charged around inside the small hut, with Mark tripping and shouting in confusion as he tried to figure out what was in there with him. Finally, Pepper blasted right through the wall of the hut, leaving a gaping hole in the splintered reeds.

When they had both recovered their composure, Pepper shook off the bits of reeds clinging to her long hair and walked calmly down the path to the kitchen. There she picked up the empty water kettle—its handle still bore her mother's tooth marks—and walked off into the night.

22

Muffin

Mark

> From his slim Palace in the Dust
> He relegates the Realm,
> More loyal for the exody
> That has befallen him.
> —*Emily Dickinson*

BRILLIANT SHAFTS of sunlight stabbed through the leafless trees in camp. The rays of white heat stalked us into every corner of our island. It seemed as if there were no longer any seasons—only heat. Each day was like the last, each week, each month the same. By September 1979, Deception Valley had received only four inches of rain in twenty months. The Kalahari was an expanse of grey earth stretching out to a grey sky, as if reaching for rain that would not come.

One of our thermometers, nailed to a tree in camp, rose past 122 degrees and stuck; surface temperatures on the open riverbed were near 150. Every day we poured small puddles of water onto our canvas cots and wallowed there, in a stupor, for hours. Or, like roaches seeking the cooler darkness, we pressed ourselves to the floor of the tent or sprawled on a corner of the ground sheet.

The heat clung to us like a leech, sucking away our strength. When we had to perform some task—anything—we dragged through it in slow motion, exhausted. Often, when we stood up from our cots, dark spots would spread behind our eyes; dizzy, we would lower our heads between our knees until the nausea passed. The hours of torpor scrambled our brains and confused us. Sometimes we had to stop and think, "Why are we still here, trying to survive the fifth—or is it the sixth?—dry season... the first—or second—year of drought?"

Because the relative humidity was so low and the evaporation so intense, we did not sweat; that is, the moisture from our bodies was vaporized before it could dampen our skin. We drank quarts of water, hot and smoky from being boiled on the fire, but it tasted good just the same. When the sun finally sagged behind West Dune, our skin felt chilled beneath a sticky film of dust mixed with dry perspiration salts. We could hardly wait to sponge-bathe. But when we stood naked and wet in the boma, with the wind rushing through the flimsy reed walls, we shivered—angry that we were always either too hot or too cold.

* * *

Often apart, sometimes together, Muffin and Moffet roamed for months over miles of wasted desert. At times they were as much as thirty or forty miles from any of their scattered lionesses, and we seldom found them with their females anymore. It was a time of social disintegration, of enforced isolation, for members of the Blue Pride. The most the lions could find to eat was a rat here, a springbok there, a porcupine or steenbok (if they were lucky), but never enough to allow them to stay together as a pride.

Like us, Muffin and Moffet spent the hot days in torpor, lying on bare sand and fire-blackened stubble beneath any sterile bush that offered a little shade. They constantly worked their mouths, pushing their tacky tongues out through dry lips, slowly rolling their vacant eyes toward us when we collected their scats for analysis. Their bellies were high and tight against their spines, their manes thinned, ragged, and lusterless, like the hair of bed-ridden invalids.

It had been more than a week since they had fed on anything substantial. With no large antelope left in their former Deception Valley territory, they had moved east, hunting every night through the open woodlands near the border of the game reserve. Now the two lions lay panting next to a bush, the only sign of life in sight.

When the heat subsided that evening they walked east to the boundary of the reserve and crawled through the wires of the fence. They could smell not only prey but also water. Ahead, cattle stirred uneasily inside a boma of felled thorn branches. The lions silently stalked forward.

Suddenly a white-hot pain shot through Muffin's leg. He roared and lunged against the trap, his foot twisting in its jaws. Biting at the steel, he rolled over and over, shredding the muscles of his leg as he pulled at the chain and the log to which he was bound. Moffet rushed to him and smelled the mangled foot and trap, but there was nothing he could do.

All night long Muffin fought to get away, panting and staggering as he hauled the heavy log in circles over the sand. Moffet watched nearby. In the morning, a native rancher on horseback rode up, lifted his rifle, and shot Muffin in the face and chest. Moffet turned and ran west toward the game reserve, the man and his pack of baying dogs tearing through the scrub after him. A rifle cracked repeatedly and bullets slapped into the sand around the fleeing lion.

Later that morning I flew over the spot where I had last found Muffin and Moffet, near the fence. They were no longer there and I could hear Muffin's signal coming from far away in the east. With a heavy feeling growing in my chest, I banked the plane and headed out of the game reserve toward his transmitter. I kept thinking that maybe he'd gone to the river for water or followed a herd of antelope, but I knew by the unusual clarity of the radio signal that he was no longer wearing his collar.

Sixty-five miles east, the signal peaked over the village of Mopipi near Lake Xau. By flying low, back and forth over the thatched roofs of the huts, I pinpointed the one with the collar and transmitter. When I looked down, the skin of a large male lion was pegged out in the sand near a low shed. People were scurrying through the village, all pointing up at the plane.

I landed in a clearing nearby and was surrounded by a throng of natives clapping their hands, waving, and laughing. Scowling and silent, hurting inside for yet another dead friend, I made my way through the crowd and into the village to the hut I had singled out from the air. A middle-aged black woman came warily to the door and peered around its edge at me. "Someone from this house has shot a lion," I said. "You must have the collar that was around its neck."

Unable to understand what had led me to her rondavel, for a moment the woman seemed confused and frightened. I managed a weak smile to reassure her. Then I saw Muffin's worn and blood-stained collar hanging behind her on a post, its transmitter still functioning. She gave it to me and I asked her how many lions had been shot. She said she didn't know, but that her husband had brought only one skin to the village from the ranch. I told her I would be back in a few days to get the details of Muffin's death from him.

Airborne again, I tuned in Moffet's frequency, but I could not hear his signal. It was not easy to tell Delia that Muffin was dead and that I could not find Moffet.

For weeks I continued to search for Moffet from the air, but never heard his signal. I figured he must have been wounded and had wandered off to die. One of the bullets had probably smashed his transmitter.

23

Uranium

Delia

> He rips earth open for her ancient veins
> Of molten splendor; toppling floods give room
> Faced by his dams; the lightning knows his chains . . .
> He loves his handicraft and . . . scorns what doom?
>
> —*Gene Derwood*

THE SMALL, ROUND water hole on Springbok Pan had been dry for months. Its cracked grey bottom was patterned with perfect footprints of those animals, large and small, who had come in search of water. There were old prints, made when the water was fresh: A brown hyena had knelt to drink, a lion had slid in the mud, a porcupine had swished its bristly tail. Then there were the deep spoor left by those who had plunged through the mud to the last stagnant puddles in the center and the desperate hoof marks of a gemsbok who had pawed deep into the sludge for the last few drops of seepage. Finally, there were the tracks of animals who had come, smelled around, and left, with only the memory of how it feels to drink.

The water hole was surrounded by large acacia bushes and small ziziphus trees, and kneeling beside it, we were well hidden. We had driven to Springbok Pan hoping to collect lion and brown hyena fecal samples. Analysis of the scats was important because it supplemented our direct observations of what the predators were eating during the drought.

Suddenly a loud whop, whop, whop drifted toward us. Startled, we looked up to see a helicopter circling the trees. We backed deeper into the bushes, hoping we wouldn't be seen. We were confused, threatened, curious, annoyed. What was a helicopter doing here?

The chopper blew up a storm of dust as it landed. The rotor wound down, and three young men dressed in baggy jeans stepped onto the riverbed. Blue plastic bags full of soil samples were tied to metal trays mounted on the skids of the aircraft. We introduced ourselves, and they explained that they were field geologists on contract with an international mining company.

"What are you prospecting for?" Mark asked.

The chief geologist answered, his nervous glance dropping to Mark's shoulder and then to the ground. "Uh—well, we're really not supposed to say—but, uh—diamonds," he stammered.

A heavy pressure filled my chest, and my palms began to sweat. The vision of a massive diamond mine, with its great open pit, mounds of tailings, conveyers, trucks, and shantytowns looming over the gutted ancient river valley, flashed into my head. Perhaps there would be a parking lot where the brown hyena den had once been.

"Do you have a permit to prospect here?" I asked.

The geologist answered too quickly, "We're not operating in Deception Valley; we use it only for navigation. We're prospecting in the southern part of the reserve."

After a few stilted comments on how beautiful they thought the Kalahari was, the men walked to their helicopter and took off. Afterward we found sample holes and blue plastic bags littered at intervals all along Deception Valley.

A few weeks later a red-and-white Beaver—a single-engine bush plane of a type used in Alaska for years—circled our airstrip several times and landed. As it taxied to camp, I could feel that same tight feeling in my chest.

The pilot and his navigator introduced themselves as Hal and Caroline, mineral surveyors from Union Carbide. Caroline had sandy hair, a broad smile, and freckles. Hal, who was from Michigan, was tall, dark, and exceptionally polite. He explained that they were using a magnetometer to search for uranium in the Kalahari. We asked them into camp for tea, to discuss their operation. No one had notified us that they were coming or told us what they would be doing in the reserve.

The hornbills, flycatchers, and tit-babblers gathered in the trees above our heads, raising their usual cheerful ruckus. Our visitors were amazed at how tame the birds were and told us with great excitement that they had seen a lion from the plane that morning. How wonderful it was, they said, to be in a real, pristine wilderness among such wildlife. Pouring the tea, I quashed the urge to glare at them. How long did they think the Kalahari wilderness would last if they discovered minerals in Deception Valley?

They proudly explained that for the next several weeks they and others would be flying along the pans and dry river channels in the game reserve. The ancient riverbeds looked particularly promising for uranium deposits. If it were found in significant quantities, a drilling team would follow, to investigate the possibility of establishing an open-pit mine in Deception Valley—perhaps right where we were sitting.

We were horrified. After nearly six years of living alone in the Kalahari, suddenly we were being inundated by people in aircraft, who sat drinking their tea and cheerfully telling us how they hoped to contribute to the destruction of all that we had worked to protect.

"That's quite an airstrip you've made for yourself," Hal remarked. "We were wondering if we could use your camp area as a fuel station—the choppers and planes could easily land here to refuel."

"No," I answered abruptly. "I'm sorry, but we're working with sensitive animals here. That would cause too much disturbance."

"Oh, I see. Well, that's too bad. It would have been a big help, but we understand your position."

I thought to myself, The last thing we want to do is *help* you strip-mine the Kalahari, you stupid SOB. Out loud, I asked, "Would you care for more tea?" and smiled far too sweetly.

After a few more minutes of small talk they said goodbye and took off again in their Beaver.

* * *

One of the most important considerations for the conservation of Kalahari wildlife was the critical need to preserve pans and ancient river channels like Deception Valley. During years of adequate rainfall, the old river bottoms were covered with nutritious grasses, primary food for plains antelope during calving. The woodlands surrounding the valleys were essential browse for giraffe, kudu, steenbok, and eland, and for grazing antelope, who must switch to browsing in dry season and drought. These ungulates attracted predators, most of whose ranges were centered along the dry river systems.

Fossil river channels meandering through the dunes represent only a tiny fraction of the entire range area, but they are one of the most crucial habitats in the desert. An open mine, with its associated development, in Deception Valley or any of the other fossil channels, would be a disaster for Kalahari wildlife.

And now, seemingly overnight, Deception Valley held great interest for the mining industry. Surface uranium deposits had been discovered in dry riverbeds in Australia; the same could be true of the Kalahari.

We could hear the planes and helicopters flying over the desert every day for several weeks. Our reports to the Botswana government, urgently requesting that the game reserve be spared mineral exploration, received no response. All we could do was wait. The skies finally quieted down, but we had no idea what the results of the mineral survey had been.

Then one morning a deep rumble sounded from beyond East Dune, and we saw a column of dust that stretched for miles above the savanna. Standing on the riverbed near camp, we watched a convoy of trucks, ten-ton trailers, and a twenty-five-ton drilling rig roll single file into the valley. Union Carbide had come to the Kalahari to drill test holes for uranium, to determine if a mine would be profitable. We met the convoy at Mid Pan and talked to the drillers about their plans.

Doug, the geologist in charge, a young man with a plump face and a hang-dog expression, scuffed at the ground with the toe of his boot as he spoke. He promised not to allow his truck drivers to speed along the riverbed, not to chase animals or to frighten any brown hyenas that came to their camps at night, and not to drive at night, when the lions and hyenas were on the move along the valley.

"I know how important your research is—the Wildlife Department has told me—and I'll try not to interfere with your work."

We were greatly relieved with his apparent concern and shook hands warmly before he climbed into his truck. But we soon learned that his offer to cooperate had only been an attempt to placate us.

For years we had tiptoed around the old river at five to ten miles per hour. Now, ignoring our pleas and protests, heavy vehicles roared up and down the valley at fifty miles per hour, day and night, along the same paths Pepper and Cocoa used. They chewed deep ruts in the fragile surface of the riverbeds, scars that will last at least 100 years. Over and over again we cajoled, begged, and finally threatened, until we were given assurances that the trucks would slow down and not drive at night. The promises were never kept. The few springbok and gemsbok that had come back to the valley to re-establish their territories galloped away from the riverbed.

Discarded drums, beer cans, and other litter were left at each campsite the drillers set up along the valley. Long strands of blue plastic ribbons marked sites worthy of further investigation at some later date. Fluttering from the limbs and branches of acacia trees, they were a driller's trademark, a laying of claim to the valley.

We drove to the rig every afternoon, wherever it was operating, and asked anxiously about the results. Drawing lines in the sand with his boots, Doug assured us that they had not found uranium in significant quantities. He would not show us the official graphs.

Eleven days after they had come into the valley, the long convoy of heavy trucks pulled up next to camp. They had completed their tests, and they told us that they had not found significant amounts of uranium. We watched them disappear over East Dune, on their way to another fossil river for more drilling. We wondered if we could believe them.

* * *

Our research was beginning to show what it would take to conserve the Kalahari. But were we too late? Would it all be lost to man's greed for more minerals and for cattle? We were a lobby of two against powerful forces of exploitation. We had learned a lot about this ecosystem, but that was not enough. Other people had to care. The Botswana government had to view the Kalahari as a precious natural heritage rather than just a tract of exploitable resources.

We would do whatever we could. For starters, we tore down as many of the blue plastic survey ribbons as we could find.

24

Blue

Delia

> Green fields are gone now, parched by the sun;
> Gone from the valleys where rivers used to run . . .
> —*Terry Gilkyson*

BLUE STOOD on North Dune, the wind blowing into her face. The once sleek and powerful lioness was very thin, her waist drawn in, wasplike. Her hair had fallen out in several spots along her back, leaving circular grey splotches, and her gums were pale.

She lifted her head and called with a soft "coo"—to the east, to the south, to the west, her ears perked to catch an answer. For most of her seven years of life Blue had slept, hunted, fed, and bred flank to flank and nose to nose with at least some of the Blue Pride females. In other years her pride-mates would have answered her coo and sauntered from the bush to rub heads in greeting. But for a year and a half, during the same time that we had observed the brown hyena cubs develop, the drought had driven them apart. We had not seen her with another lioness for months.

Blue could not know that Chary and Sassy were over fifty miles away. With their seven small cubs struggling behind them, the two lionesses wandered the bleak plains east of the reserve. They occasionally met with strangers, both females and males, who accepted the cubs as if they were their own; the males even sharing food with the cubs, as Muffin and Moffet had done. Except for their faded ear tags, there was no way to know that Chary and Sassy had once belonged to the Blue Pride.

Now that the drought was in its eighteenth month, the pride had disintegrated; Blue was the only lioness left in its original territory. The others ranged over a huge tract of mixed woodland, bush, and grass savanna more than 1500 square miles in area, eating anything they could catch.

After losing her cubs through neglect, Gypsy had joined Liesa to wander far to the southeast of Deception Valley, preying on duiker, kudu, porcupines, and the smaller rodents. Happy, of the Springbok Pan Pride, and Spicy from the Blue Pride transferred back and forth among various prides, then formed an alliance of their own. Prowling in open bush and grass savanna due south of the valley, they preyed on springhare, steenbok, and other smaller mammals. In May 1979, each had given birth to two cubs within a few days of each other, as pride-mates often do. We could not possibly know who the fathers were, since the females had mated with males from three different prides.

The first time we saw Happy and Spicy nursing each other's young, it was an exciting moment for us. Previously, communal suckling in lions had been seen only among closely related females of the same pride. Happy and Spicy could not be close relatives since they were from different prides. This and similar observations had important implications for the evolution and ecology of cooperative behavior among lions, which was the subject of Mark's Ph.D. thesis.

We had not seen Moffet again, although whenever Mark flew, he turned the radio receiver to the lion's frequency. Once in a while there was a faint beep mingled with the static, giving some hope that Moffet still roamed somewhere in the desert. Yet when Mark turned the plane toward these phantom signals, they always vanished.

* * *

When we sat with Blue on North Dune I had the feeling she was grateful for our company. She slept in the shade of the truck, and with its doors open for the breeze, I could have nudged her with my foot. The tires still held a fascination for her, and lying on her back, legs in the air, she rolled her head to one side and gnawed gently on the rubber.

Ordinarily she would not have stirred until after sunset. But she was very hungry, and at four o'clock she began foraging north toward the dune woodlands. From the duneslope, she could see more than a mile north and south along the valley; not one prey animal was in sight.

She zigzagged in and out of bushes for more than two hours—stopping, listening, watching—but found nothing to eat. Panting heavily, she lay down to rest for a time, then continued toward West Dune at nightfall. Near an open sandy area, she stopped in mid stride, lowered her body slowly until her shoulder blades jutted above her back, and stalked toward a springhare hopping near its burrow. When she was fifteen yards away, she sprang forward. But her prey saw her coming. With dazzling speed and a series of quick turns, its bushy tail flicking deceptively behind, it dashed toward its hole. Blue gave chase, the sand showering off her feet. Her nose was at its tail when it shot into the opening of its burrow, but it did not make a clean entry, and in the second that it paused, Blue pinned the still exposed hindquarters with her paw. She seized the springhare with her jaws, pulled it from its hole and chewed slowly, rhythmically, her eyes half closed, as though savoring every morsel of her four-pound prey. Within five minutes, all that was left were a few drops of blood and tufts of hair on the sand. It wasn't enough meat to sustain her for very long; she continued to hunt through the woodlands.

Blue found no more food that night, or the next, though she walked eighteen more miles. She lay down often to rest and to scratch her irritated skin. Every day the scabby bald spots spread over more of her body and we feared that she had sarcoptic mange, a debilitating skin disease caused by a microscopic mite. These parasites can be present in a healthy animal without causing harm, but can flare up to provoke hair loss when the animal loses condition, as from malnutrition.

Despite her poor diet and condition, Blue's slender stomach began to swell slightly and her nipples enlarged. We worried that it would be difficult for her to have young during the drought with no other pride-mates to cooperate in the hunting and with almost no large prey in the area. It was with a feeling of pity that we found her one morning, nursing two kitten-sized male cubs in a thicket of tall grass. At a time when she could barely manage to feed herself, and with no water for thousands of square miles, she could ill afford to lose the moisture and nutrients needed to nurse a demanding family.

We went to see Blue every day to learn how she was raising her young in the drought. One of the first things her cubs, Bimbo and Sandy, focused their eyes on was our battered Toyota. Often the mother and cubs would lie in the shade of the truck, and we would have to be careful not to run over a tail or a leg when we drove away.

In the evening Blue left Bimbo and Sandy alone, tucked away in a thicket of tall grass and bush while she walked for miles in search of food. She would return hours later and stand fifty or a hundred yards away, cooing softly. The grass would stir, and the cubs would scamper out, answering her with rasping, high-pitched meows. As Blue washed them with her rough, pink tongue, they squawled and squirmed. Bimbo managed to struggle to his feet and attempt a getaway, heading for his mother's teats while she was busy with Sandy. But her huge paw bowled him over, and he found himself wrapped in her great tongue again. When the licking and nibbling was over, they all settled beneath a tree where Blue nursed them.

Food was so scarce that sometimes Blue had to leave her cubs for twenty-four to thirty-six hours in order to find a meal. Both cubs were thin, but Sandy, the smaller one, began to show signs of weakness. More and more often he simply sat in the grass, his eyes listlessly watching his brother bounding through the bush or playing with sticks. Whenever Blue ended a nursing period, it was Sandy who cried loudly for more milk.

One night when the cubs were about two months old, Blue cooed softly to them and started walking away through the grass. Bimbo and Sandy scampered along behind as she walked west down the dune face. But by the time she had gone halfway across the riverbed, the cubs were falling far behind. Bimbo trailed by twenty yards, Sandy by thirty, both meowing loudly. Blue stopped and waited, cooing, but when they caught up with her, she continued west without giving them a chance to rest. She led them to the top of West Dune, a trip of nearly three miles, and there she left them in a patch of tall grass at the base of a tree. Then she walked away to hunt.

Blue's last drink of water had been during a brief shower ten months before; her diet of springhare, mice, honey badgers, and bat-eared foxes was her only source of moisture. She often had to walk at least ten miles at night to find food, and more and more frequently she encouraged Bimbo and Sandy to follow her for at least part of the way. It was increasingly difficult for Sandy to keep up. He was barely two-thirds the size of Bimbo, his fur was thin, the hard angles of his tiny bones showing through his skin.

One morning we found Blue and Bimbo alone. Sandy had been left behind, or perhaps he had been killed by a leopard, jackal, or hyena.

Mother and cub lay together beneath a thornbush. The hot wind swept small waves of sand, soot, and ash between the blackened bristles of grass clumps left from the dry season's fire. Blue's ribs and pelvis were outlined under her skin, her gums were white, and her hair had thinned all over her back and belly. She nuzzled Bimbo; he stood on his hind feet and put his padded forepaws on her face. With her broad tongue she turned him onto his back and, while he licked her forehead, she nibbled at his shrunken body. Though she could barely feed herself, Blue gave no indication that she intended to abandon her one remaining cub.

She had been wearing her radio collar for eighteen months; the edges were frayed and the antenna curled like a stretched bed spring. It was more and more difficult to hear her faint signal from the air and several times we had been unable to locate her from the truck. Although we did not want to dart her with Bimbo so near, her old transmitter would have to be replaced. And it would also be a good opportunity to examine her physical condition more closely.

We waited until dusk, when mother and cub had fallen asleep under a large acacia bush; then, with the velocity control knob on the darting rifle set at its minimum and the silencer in place, Mark darted Blue from ten yards away. The dart lobbed slowly, and quietly penetrated her flank. She jumped up, lifting her feet one at a time high in the air, looking around on the ground as if a snake had bitten her. Bimbo watched his mother curiously for a minute, also looking around in the grass, and then both of them went back to sleep.

Fifteen minutes later, Blue had apparently succumbed to the drug; she did not wake up when Mark shuffled his foot in the grass to test her. As we eased out of the truck, Bimbo's head shot up and he gazed at us with piercing eyes. He had seen us standing in full view many times, but never so close and never walking toward him. While we slowly moved to Blue, he looked back and forth from his mother to us, but she slept more deeply than ever. If we were acceptable to her, we were apparently okay with him; he put his chin down on his paws and, from ten feet away, watched us treat his mother for the next hour and a half.

When we rolled Blue over and examined her closely, we found her in even worse condition than we had expected. She had lost almost all of the hair from her underside, and large patches on her flank and neck were covered with heavy scabs. It was most certainly a case of sarcoptic mange.

Treatment for this disease in the wild is quite complicated, because the animal has to be immersed in a dip of chemical solution to kill the parasite. We had neither the equipment nor the essential drugs.

"I think I have an idea," Mark whispered. "We can drain some oil from the truck engine and smear it all over her. If we do it well enough, and she doesn't lick it off right away, there's a chance it will smother the mites."

It sounded crazy to me, but I couldn't think of anything better. Mark crawled under the truck and drained three quarts of black oil from the engine, leaving just enough to get us back to camp. We poured it all over Blue, rubbing it into every inch of her fur with our hands. Bimbo cocked his head to one side and then the other as we rolled his mother over and coated her chest. When we had finished, Blue was a mess. Sand, oil, and ash had caked to form a sludge that made her look like the victim of an oil spill.

We bolted a new radio collar around her neck, made notes about, and photographs of, her tooth wear, and gave her an injection of antibiotic. From ten feet away we could see no signs of the disease on Bimbo's skin, so we packed all the equipment and returned to the truck; Blue was just beginning to lift her head and look around.

In two days Blue had licked most of the sand and grit from her coat, but a layer of oil remained, and she didn't seem to have suffered any ill effects from the treatment. In fact, she began to scratch much less often, and within a week the edges of the large scabbed patches turned pink with healthy skin. Once her hair began to come back, the healing process was remarkable. Within three and a half weeks after her oil bath, her coat had almost completely recovered and all of the wounds had filled in with new hair.

At three months of age, Bimbo was still almost completely dependent on Blue's milk and had not filled out to the stocky shape normal for his age. When he was nearby, he showed an interest in the few kills his mother made, but he was rarely with her when she hunted. Since most of her prey were small, Blue usually consumed them completely while he was in hiding several miles away.

One night Blue killed a female honey badger and its cub, and after eating the adult, she carried the young badger back to Bimbo. When she laid it on the ground he seized the back of its neck in his jaws and strutted around, holding his head high. Then he lay down, his paws around its back, and quickly ate the three pounds of meat. Clearly the time had come: Blue had to find more meat for her cub.

The next night, after leaving Bimbo at the base of East Dune, she hunted through the dry scrub of the interdunal valley, and then up the dune face. As she neared the crest she saw something she had not seen for a long time. Lowering herself, she stalked forward. Along the dune top, silhouetted against the purple night sky, a bull wildebeest led a long line of black forms through the bush. Shrouded in a cloud of dust, blacker than the night, hundreds of antelope wound their way along the dune.

The tip of her tail twitching slowly, Blue flattened herself in front of the herd. As the third wildebeest passed, she sprang forward, leaped onto its back, and threw her paw over its shoulder, her claws hooking deeply into the tough skin. The antelope groaned and bolted, dragging her along the ground and through sharp thornbushes. But she held on and threw all of her weight under the wildebeest's neck. When her struggling prey hit the ground, Blue released her grip on its shoulder and grabbed its throat in her jaws, pinching off its windpipe. Lioness and antelope lay together, the wildebeest kicking out at first, trying desperately to breathe, then growing still. Panting heavily, Blue chewed into the flank, licking the blood and eating the tender viscera.

A few minutes later she walked the two miles back to where Bimbo was hidden. She cooed softly and he scampered out, and his nose near the tip of her tail, he followed her back to the kill. Two jackals had found the carcass and were tearing at the meat; Blue loped forward and scattered them. Bimbo joined her and they began feeding, not hurriedly, but with relish.

Eventually, Bimbo slumped down against his mother and slept. For the first time in his life his belly was round and full.

* * *

Late the next night Patches, the brown hyena, smelled the pungent odor from the torn belly of the wildebeest. By midnight Blue and Bimbo had finished all but the skin, bones, and attached meat. Patches circled cautiously around the area until she was satisfied that the lions had gone. With hackles bristling and tail raised, she scattered the jackals, already snipping morsels from the carcass, and she began feeding on the large bones, sinew, and skin left by the lions.

Pepper and Cocoa, who had been subsisting on old bones and the occasional springhare, were inside the den. Suddenly an entire wildebeest leg, covered with skin and bits of red meat, dropped through an entrance in a shower of dust. With thumps and squeals, the two cubs pulled the leg into the inner chamber. Patches lay down on one of the mounds and slept; she had carried the heavy leg for nearly three miles.

The following night when we drove to the den, Pepper was lying on her side atop one of the mounds. Usually she would get to her feet and plod to the truck to investigate its interesting odors. But not this night. She merely cocked open one eye, peered at us briefly, pawed some dust carelessly over her stomach, and dropped off to sleep again.

Blue's wildebeest kill had fed two lions and three hyenas. But it was only one wildebeest, and in this part of the Kalahari they were rare.

25

Black Pearls in the Desert

Mark

> An ecologist must either harden his shell and make believe that the consequences of science are none of his business, or he must be the doctor who sees the marks of death in a community that believes itself well and does not want to be told otherwise.
>
> —*Aldo Leopold*

THE MORNING after Blue had made her wildebeest kill, Echo Whisky Golf and I beat the sun into the sky, trying to find the lions and hyenas before the turbulent desert winds came to life. With Blue's signal sounding in my earphones, I dropped over the trees into a dune valley, where I was surprised to find her and Bimbo feeding on a wildebeest. Where had it come from and why was it in our area? In all the time we had lived in Deception, we had seldom seen wildebeest, and there had been almost none in the last three years. It must have been an errant old bull who had left his herds 100 miles or more to the south. But since wildebeest are quite gregarious, I couldn't understand why he would have come all the way to Deception on his own.

I tuned Moffet's frequency and climbed higher, listening closely to the crackle of static in my earphones. It was hopeless, and so I changed channels to look for Geronimo of the Ginger Pride.

When Deception Valley lay curling away to the south behind me, I noticed plumes of dust, or possibly smoke, rising all across the savanna ahead and below. I had never before seen anything quite like this from the air. Flying nearer, I could see hundreds, thousands of black dots moving along in single file through the bushveld. Stunned, I shouted over the radio to our base camp, "Wildebeest! Delia, I've found tens of thousands of wildebeest! They're moving north!"

I pulled back the throttle and began to descend. Below, the files of antelope were winding through the bush savanna, like long strings of black pearls against the tan monotony of the Kalahari in drought. Although we did not realize it at the time, we had just stumbled upon the second largest wildebeest migration on earth.

In Maun we had heard the hunters reminisce about times when they had waited for hours on the main road to Francistown while hundreds of thousands of wildebeest crossed. But no one knew where they had come from or where they were going. Many people just assumed that the populations exploded in the years of good rainfall, and then died off in years of drought. Only a few months before the present migration, a countrywide aerial survey conducted by a foreign consulting firm had counted 262,000 wildebeest in their southern Kalahari range, a population second only to the Serengeti herds. But the research team had concluded that in Botswana these antelope never migrate.

Delia and I took off at first light the morning after I had spotted the migration from the air. Banking and turning 100 feet above the savanna, we followed the wandering trails south, away from the herds and deeper into the Kalahari, making notes on where the migration had begun, what range conditions were like there, what routes the population was following, how fast it was moving, where it was headed, and other details that we would need to describe this event.

In the five previous years, the Kalahari rains had been generous. The wildebeest herds had led a vagabond's existence, chasing scattered rain clouds and patches of green grass deeper into the southern part of the desert, far from the only lakes and rivers, 300 miles to the north. Even though they had nothing to drink for several months each dry season, they found moisture as well as nutrients in the fodder they consumed. The grasses on and around the hundreds of calc pans never completely dried out from one rainy season to the next. Each rainy season the wildebeest population had swollen with the birth of many new calves, and these grew sturdy and strong from the protein and minerals in the pan vegetation.[1]

This year, 1979, when the rains had failed, the grasses had turned from green to tan, and now, in mid-May, they were little more than bleached straw, crisp and brittle under the sun.

* * *

The wildebeest stood on a low sand ridge, their manes and beards and stringy tails flowing in the dry wind. It may have been instinct, or a behavior passed down for generations, but something told them to trek northward, to the only place they could get water to survive the drought. Probably for centuries, Lake Xau and Lake Ngami, the Nghabe and Boteti rivers, and the southern fringes of the Okavango River delta had provided refuge for Kalahari antelope in times of drought. The dust blowing from their tracks, the bulls and cows and their calves lowered their heads and began plodding north.

This was unlike the Serengeti migration, where herds of wildebeest often mass together in great numbers. Because they live in a marginal, semidesert habitat, the Kalahari population is more mobile and less concentrated to begin with; now it was moving in herds of from 40 to 400 antelope, scattered along a vast front measuring more than 100 miles from east to west.

Not all the herds headed in the same direction. One portion, probably more than 90,000 strong, had taken the route to the north; tens of thousands of others began walking toward the Limpopo River 300 miles to the east. Whether migrating north or east, once under way they spent little time feeding, for without moisture they could not digest what they ate. Their aim was to get to water, and perhaps to better forage, as quickly as possible. Without water they would starve to death in a savanna filled with grasses. And even when there is an abundance of fodder, it may lack sufficient protein and essential nutrients that antelope need for survival in drought. Trekking in the early evening, at night, and in the early morning in order to avoid heat and dehydration, for days the great long lines of wildebeest plodded onward.

The herds covered about twenty-five or thirty miles each night. From the air the dusty migratory trails looked like gnarled fingers reaching for the lakes and rivers. Some of the wildebeest had already come more than 300 miles, from southern and southwestern Botswana—even from across the border with South Africa. The desert was taking its toll of the very young and the old; they were left behind for the scavengers. The physical condition of each animal was pitted against the great distances that had to be traveled, with little to eat and nothing to drink, but evolution had prepared them for the trek, and the strong should survive.

Suddenly, the wildebeest stopped short. Confronted by something many of them had never seen before, they bunched together and milled about nervously. Stretched across their path were strands of high-tensile steel wire—the Kuki foot-and-mouth-disease control fence, extending for more than 100 miles across the northern border of the Central Kalahari Reserve. At its east and west ends it joins other segments of fence that hem in the desert with more than 500 miles of wire.

The wildebeest were cut off from the emergency water and riverine habitat that for eons they had counted upon in times of drought. Nothing they had ever learned, none of their instincts could help them deal with this obstacle.

Frustrated in their urge to continue north, with the river little more than a day or two away, the herds turned east along the fence. There was nothing else to do. Having walked for days with little nourishment and no water, they were already weakened, and now the long fence beside them added more than 100 miles to their trek.

As they plodded along the fence, they encountered many other herds, part of the same migration headed for the lakeshores and riverbanks. Each day they were joined by giraffe, gemsbok, and hartebeest, all needing water but trapped by the wire and posts.

Thousands upon thousands of antelope that had been spread out over vast areas of the savanna were now forced by the fences to take the same migratory route toward water. The grasses of the fragile rangeland were soon stomped and broken, ground into dust by the hooves of the first herds to pass. For those that followed, there was nothing to eat. Animals began to drop from hunger, thirst, and fatigue. A giraffe who could easily have stepped over the wire became tangled in it. He struggled to get free, but the coils of high-tensile steel sliced deep into his flesh until he pitched forward, breaking his foreleg at the knee. His hind legs still ensnared, he pawed at the ground for days, building small mounds of sand around him as he tried to rise again. He never did.

Eventually they came to a north-south fence called the Makalama-bedi, which forms a corner with the east-west Kuki line before running south along a portion of the east boundary of the game reserve (see map I, opposite). Here there was chaos among the wildebeest. To follow this second fence they had to turn south, directly contrary to the direction they needed to go for water. They stood in confusion, their heads hanging, until many began to sway and stumble and finally collapse. But they were tenacious and the end did not come easily. In contrast to the victims of the swift tooth and claw of a predator, the animals who fell prey to the fence died more slowly. Even as they lay, still pawing the dust, their eyes were often plucked out by crows and vultures while other scavengers chewed off their ears, tails, or testicles. A few thousand died along the fences, but the carnage had just begun.

Finally the wildebeest herds struck off south along the five-foot wall of wire. A day later they came to the end—the fence just stopped in the middle of the savanna, as though someone had forgotten to finish it. The herds swung around it. Now there was the sweet, unmistakable smell of moisture on the prevailing easterly wind. They followed the promising odor. But as soon as they had moved around the end of the fence at the border of the game reserve, they entered a safari hunting area. To reach the water they would have to risk being shot.

Two more days of walking, and the wildebeest who had survived the trek, the fence, and the hunters, shuffled out of the woodlands and onto a great plain black with thousands more of their own kind. The smell of water was stronger; it was only twenty-five miles away. They hurried forward.

Resident cattle, tended by natives from scattered kraals along the lakeshore, had stripped the once beautiful lake plain of every edible leaf and blade of grass. Now its surface was like concrete covered with several inches of grey powder, and the choking dust rose from the hooves of the wildebeest in the still morning air. Here and there a spindly bush stood rooted in the wasteland.

Wizened carcasses littered the plain. Dying animals lay on their sides, their legs moving rythmically, as if, in their delirium, they were still moving toward the water. Prime wildebeest bulls and cows, the breeding stock of the population, began leaving the long lines filing toward Lake Xau. Unable to take another step, their knees buckled, and their muzzles sank lower and lower, until their nostrils blew small potholes in the dust.

At dawn of the second day after leaving the game reserve, the surviving wildebeest had nearly reached the lake. But water was not

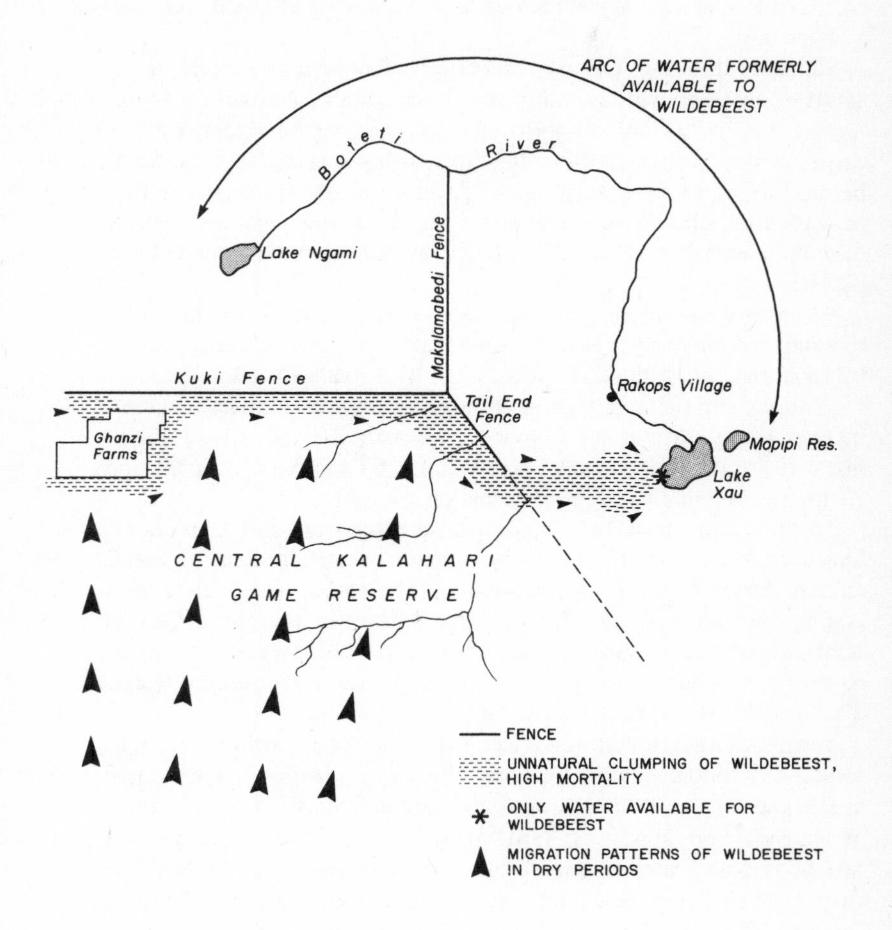
ARC OF WATER FORMERLY AVAILABLE TO WILDEBEEST
Boteti River
Lake Ngami
Makalamabedi Fence
Kuki Fence
Tail End Fence
Rakops Village
Mopipi Res.
Lake Xau
Ghanzi Farms
CENTRAL KALAHARI GAME RESERVE
FENCE
UNNATURAL CLUMPING OF WILDEBEEST, HIGH MORTALITY
ONLY WATER AVAILABLE FOR WILDEBEEST
MIGRATION PATTERNS OF WILDEBEEST IN DRY PERIODS

all they needed. There were no shade trees for miles, and there was nothing to eat. Time was short; they would have to drink and then get back to the shade and graze of the woodlands twenty-five miles behind them before the sun sapped them of their remaining strength (see map 2, opposite).

Suddenly the long, orderly lines began to splinter and circle; thousands of antelope were running from three trucks filled with waving, jeering men. Wheeling in tightening circles around the wildebeest, the driver of the five-ton Bedford bludgeoned his way through the herd, before turning to come back again. Several wildebeest hit on the first pass tried to hobble away. The driver turned sharply and, with clouds of dust boiling from the truck's wheels, he ran down the wounded one by one.

When they had struck down six wildebeest, the drivers slid the trucks to a stop and laughing tribesmen leaped out. Two men held each animal by its horns, and a third sawed through its throat with a knife.

With the sun rising higher and hotter, the survivors crossed a shimmering white salt pan and climbed a last barren ridge. Below them, not half a mile away, lay the blue waters of Lake Xau, pelicans and flamingos bobbing like flower petals on the surface.

To the north, more than 360 miles of river front and lake shores had once been available to the wildebeest during drought, as had a similar stretch of the Limpopo River, in the south. Now, fence lines and settlements had funneled a major portion of the entire Central Kalahari population into a tiny area, denying all but two or three miles of the riparian habitat to the 80,000 antelope who had come for water. The wildebeest had to drink here or die.

Sensing danger from the native huts on either side, the thirsty animals took a few tentative steps forward. The water was *there*. They could see it and smell it! They broke into a canter, heading for the lake. When they were about 200 yards away from it, bands of native men and boys with packs of dogs broke from cover near the kraals. The dogs were set upon the wildebeest and chased them in circles for long minutes. The dogs worked efficiently, holding exhausted animals by the hind legs, hamstringing and disemboweling them as they sank to the ground, the poachers rushing in with clubs and knives to finish them off.

Thousands of other wildebeest were prevented from going to the water by the disturbance. Some managed to reach the lake, where they

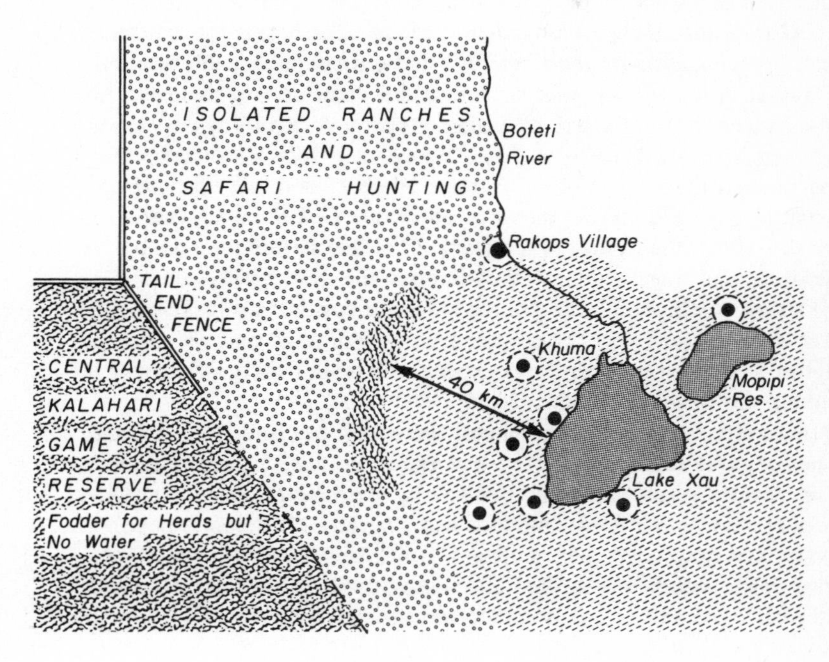

 SETTLEMENTS

 ONLY AREA WITH FODDER FOR WILDEBEEST

 AREA OF INTENSE POACHING AND OVER GRAZING BY CATTLE

 DAILY MOVEMENT OF WILDEBEEST FROM FODDER TO WATER

collapsed into its coolness. But many were too weak to rise or even to drink, and their muzzles sank slowly into the shallow water and the mud.

Above in EWG, we watched through binoculars as the slaughter continued along the shore. Trembling with rage, I pushed the control wheel forward and we plunged toward the lakeshore. The poachers were preoccupied with their butchery and did not see the aircraft until it was at ground level, roaring across the plain toward them at 160 miles an hour. We flashed by inches above a pack of dogs attacking a young male wildebeest; at the last second they let go of their prey and dodged away. The dogs scattered in confusion and the antelope began to run. We chased the dogs until they fled to cover. Three of the men threw their clubs at the plane an instant before they dove into the dust, scuttling on their bellies through the thornbushes.

During the migration, I continued to make periodic low-level flights over the huts and the herds in the early mornings and on moonlit nights. It seemed to deter the poachers, and from then on we saw less harassment of the herds.

Ironically, even if the wildebeest were able to drink, the lake was a nemesis for them. Once they had tasted its water, their migration was frozen in that one area. Because of the native settlements they would go no further north, and thus were barred from the river beyond. Every day they needed to get back from the lake to the shade and grass in the woodlands before the sun grew too hot, and then to recross the plains and salt pan at night. It was an incredible fifty-mile round trip.

Day by day this distance between water and food increased, as the masses of antelope denuded the rangeland of grass farther and farther from the lake. For a while the wildebeest survived like this, but inevitably the time came when all the water they could drink at the lake and all the graze they could get from the woodlands did not supply them with sufficient energy to make the long journey in between. At this point the antelope began the inexorable slide toward starvation and mass death.

September, and the start of the Kalahari *hot*-dry season, could not have come at a worse time for the antelope. Temperatures shot upward, and phalanxes of dust devils swirled across the parched plains. With the sun rising earlier and setting later, the wildebeest could not avoid making part of their trek in the heat of the day. It was the proverbial last straw. Mortality soared and carcasses littered the plains, salt pan, and lakeshore. Without rain to draw the suffering animals out of the Lake Xau trap and back into the Central Kalahari, most of them would die.

* * *

Extensive fencing began in Botswana in the fifties, when beef exports from cattle ranching became an important industry and the need arose to control periodic outbreaks of foot-and-mouth disease (FMD) among domestic stock. During such epidemics European (EEC) countries refused to accept meat products from Botswana for fear of contamination. It is understandable that Botswana had to take action to protect this lucrative industry, and the Department of Animal Health was charged with the task of devising ways to control the disease. To date, that department has erected more than 800 miles of cordon fences through the country's wilderness areas; and construction of another 700 miles is currently under way.

Because cape buffalo and some species of wild antelope can carry the FMD virus, their populations were suspected of being a reservoir of the infection that periodically contaminated domestic animals.[1] The fences were erected to segregate the country's stock population from wild herds, to separate infected cattle from others, and to divide the range into sectors that could be quickly sealed off during outbreaks. By preventing the movement of infected animals from one area to another, the fences would, in theory, make the disease easier to control. But foot-and-mouth disease continues to develop and spread across fence lines in Botswana.

The use of fencing to control FMD has become a very controversial issue, and research veterinarians disagree on the effectiveness of this means of disease control. In spite of extensive experiments it has never been demonstrated that wild animals transmit the FMD virus to domestic stock.[2] The epidemiology of the disease is poorly understood, and no one really knows how it is spread.

The fences had been devastating Botswana's wildlife long before our study was under way. In 1961, and again in 1964, as many as 80,000 wildebeest died in the area of the Kuki-Makalamabedi fence corner and between there and Lake Xau. George Silberbauer, government officer of the Ghanzi District in 1964, estimated that a tenth of the population in the Central Kalahari Reserve was dying every five days while trapped behind the Kuki fence during drought.[3] It is not known how many survived the 1964 mortality. Dr. Graham Child, an ecologist with the Botswana Department of Wildlife, wrote that the 1970 die-off was, "the severest mortality in living memory."[4]

Bergie Berghoffer had tried in vain to save thousands of dying wildebeest. For weeks he had hauled water from the Boteti River to troughs he had made from dozens of steel drums and placed near the fence corner. "It was a bloody disgrace," he said. "You could walk up to the poor blighters, put your hand on them, and they would just fall over."

Zebra, which once used Deception Valley as part of their wet season range,[5] have been eliminated altogether. We didn't see one in seven years. Great mixed herds of gemsbok, eland, and hartebeest, which George Silberbauer described as covering an area three by five miles near the Piper Pans, have been reduced to a small fraction of their former wet-season concentrations.

After the reduction of the Central Kalahari antelope by drought and disease control fences, the survivors have become even more important to the predator community. If the large antelope all die off, lions, leopards, cheetahs, wild dogs, and scavengers, like brown hyenas, will suffer a similar fate. Though we cannot know how many carnivores there were before the fences decimated their food supply, their numbers must have dwindled considerably.

Since the Botswana Department of Animal Health began fencing the Kalahari, the Kalahari Bushmen have found it increasingly difficult to hunt and kill antelope for meat, one of the few sources of protein for them and other rural native Africans. Coincidental with fencing for disease control, the amount of protein in their diet has fallen precipitously, according to Dr. Bob Hitchock, a former rural sociologist for the government.

The wildebeest crisis must now be considered in a broader context than simply antelope versus the fence. It is part of a larger picture, the competition between man and wildlife for such limited resources as grassland and water. Alternatives for controlling FMD, such as a sophisticated vaccination program, need to be considered more seriously. (For more details, see Appendix A.)

* * *

In many ways, Botswana has had a positive attitude toward wildlife; indeed, about one fifth of the country is either national park or game reserve. Government officials had always been courteous to us and had granted us permission to conduct research in the Central Kalahari Reserve. But we were continually frustrated in our attempts to stimulate interest and action from the government in order to help the wildebeest.

We wrote letters and reports to the Wildlife Department describing the migration and mortality. We made recommendations, including the establishment of a game scout camp at the Lake Xau area to control poaching and harassment of wildebeest, and the maintenance of a corridor from the reserve to the lake so that the antelope could drink. But there was little response to our requests.

The drought persisted into October, and the wildebeest were dying at an ever-increasing rate.[6] We felt frustrated and alone in our efforts to save them. In all our years in the Kalahari, we had never seen such suffering among animals, such degradation of habitat. It all seemed so pointless. Had the antelope been allowed to distribute themselves throughout the miles of riverine habitat, as they had done for thousands of years in times of drought, many fewer would have died.

Almost everyone we knew told us to forget it. "Cattle is too big an industry; you'll never get them to take down the fences." One or two friends warned us we might get expelled from the country for raising the issue. But Botswana is a democratic republic and we did not believe that the government would expel us on account of a wildlife issue. We felt compelled to do something before it was too late. We knew that the reports written by Dr. Silberbauer and Dr. Child describing previous die-offs had simply been filed away. We were determined to ensure that a solution be found before the next drought. Since no one within the country would listen to our recommendations, we decided to try to publicize the issue worldwide, to enlist the support of prominent people outside the country who perhaps could encourage the Botswana government to review the problem.

* * *

One day, over our radio, we received an invitation to give a slide presentation for Prince Bernhard of the Netherlands, who would soon be touring some of Botswana's wildlife areas. Shortly after that, Dr. Richard Faust of the Frankfurt Zoological Society and a group from The Friends of Animals—our major sponsors—were due to arrive in Maun. It was unbelievable luck. Two major figures in global conservation would be practically on our doorstep—at least within a couple of hundred miles of us—in a matter of weeks. We quickly wrote both Dr. Faust and Prince Bernhard, describing the wildebeest crisis and inviting them to camp, but we had almost no hope that the prince would accept our invitation to visit us in the desert.

Even so, we began to wonder how we would deal with it if he did accept. Where would he and his attendants sleep? We couldn't imagine his sharing our one sleeping tent, with its packing-crate bed and piece of foam rubber, with his staff. I also doubted that royalty would consent to fly in Echo Whisky Golf, and our airstrip was certainly too short for a much larger plane. What could we give him to eat and drink—biltong and hot, smoky water? We worried most about the toilet. The "thunderdrum," a bright red gasoline drum with a seat cut in the top, stood in the middle of the riverbed.

Given these uncertainties, we decided that we had better do whatever we could to prepare for the prince ahead of time, so that we would be ready if he decided to come back with us after our meeting at Khwaii. Delia washed the tent floors (sparing the spiders in their corners as always), emptied old birds' nests from some of the kitchen pots, screened the ants from the sugar bowl, and baked bread in the bucket oven. I waxed the plane, hung burlap on some tent poles around the thunder-drum, and buried a bottle of wine, saved for a special occasion, beneath the ziziphus tree.

On the day the prince was to arrive in Botswana, we flew to Khwaii River Lodge, a posh resort on the east edge of the Okavango River delta. We buzzed the lodge and landed on the long sod airstrip. A Land Rover met us and the driver chauffeured us to a group of white-washed rondavels set in a neatly manicured lawn. The dining house was of dark timbers; beyond it lay the Khwaii River flood plain, with scattered herds of lechwe antelope, and hippos lying like grey sub-marines in the blue waters.

When we arrived at the lodge, we were relieved to learn that the prince and his party were taking a game drive somewhere in the bush. We were somewhat uncertain about the proper way to greet him and hoped that we could find someone to ask. Should Delia curtsy, should I bow? Should we address him as Your Majesty or Your Highness? Odd considerations in the middle of the wilderness, but we didn't want to appear gauche.

That evening as we entered the thatched dining house and self-consciously made our way through the room full of people, we glanced from face to face, hoping to somehow spot the prince. We were passing the center table when a hand gripped my arm and a voice said, "My name is Bernhard—not Barnard, like the famous South African heart surgeon. You must be Mr. and Mrs. Owens." Suddenly we were facing the prince of the Netherlands, who had just let me know that I had misspelled his name in my letter about the wildebeest. A thin smile grew from the corners of his eyes and spread across his tanned and freckled face. His thinning hair was slicked straight back, and rather severe wire-rimmed spectacles were comfortable on his nose. I was reminded of a picture I had once seen of him as commander of the Dutch forces during the Nazi invasion.

"Anyway," he continued, "I'm glad to meet you. Please have your lovely wife sit here next to me."

During dinner he said casually, but with an unmistakable glimmer of anticipation, that he would be quite happy to fly to our camp in Echo Whisky Golf. Unfortunately, he would be able to stay only one day.

The next morning at six-thirty we met him and his secretary on the airstrip. At the dinner table the night before, the prince had given animated accounts of his old flying days: Gypsy Moths, short landing fields with hedges, and all. Now, as we took off, he looked at me and asked with a smile, "Do you mind?" I told him the heading for camp and gave him the controls. If he'd forgotten anything about flying he didn't show it, for he took us straight to camp.

After a quick cup of tea, we took to the air again and followed the route of the migration north to the Kuki fence. Dodging columns of vultures arriving for the day's feed on the carcasses, we followed the fence to its corner, and turned south. Miles away to the east, clouds of dust rose from the Lake Xau plains; thousands of wildebeest were returning to the trees after their long trek for water. The prince just shook his head, his jaw set grimly while we flew low over the black masses that speckled the plain as far as the eye could see. It was much hotter than it had been even ten days before, and the animals were dying at a much faster rate. We flew over a pall of destruction, death, and suffering. We hardly spoke on the way back to camp.

As we walked into camp after our depressing flight, Chief, one of our friendly hornbills, sailed from his perch and glided straight for a landing on the prince's pate. Over another cup of tea, Bernhard promised to help raise additional money for our research, and to inform the right people in Europe about the wildebeest crisis.

I dug the wine from beneath the ziziphus tree while Delia served up fresh bread from the bucket oven. Together with the hornbills, tit-babblers, and marico flycatchers, who hopped around the table, we had our lunch.

That afternoon Prince Bernhard met some of the lions, the brown hyena cubs, and the Pink Panther—who crawled into a hole and refused to come out. Just before dark, we touched down back at Khwaii Lodge. We gave our slide show that night, and went home the next morning to get ready to receive Dr. Faust.

Dr. Richard Faust is a man of phenomenal energy. He works all day seven days a week: from five to eight o'clock each morning as director of the Frankfurt Zoological Society; from eight to five directing the affairs of the Frankfurt Zoo; and from five to ten at night as director of the zoological society again. His trip to Africa was his first time off in seven years, and even then he was leading a party of the society's sponsors.

Now he stood on the truck's running board, his hair tossed by the wind, his face powdered with dust. We were driving from one wildebeest carcass to the next, counting, sexing, and determining the age of dead animals along the Lake Xau shoreline and salt pan. In the evening, we spread our bedrolls in the open just a few yards up from the water, and sat around our campfire. At sunset we had watched a young wildebeest standing in the dying heat waves on the bank above us, afraid to descend to the water to drink. Now the darkness was heavy with the stench of carcasses and the keening of night birds. No one spoke for a long time.

By ten-thirty our fire had burned down to embers. A subtle vibration began to fill the air. "Listen . . . do you hear something? There . . . like water rushing over rocks." The minutes passed and the sound became a rumble; a low moaning rose from the plains. "The wildebeest are coming!"

Black forms marched over the ridge above and a cloud of dust swept over us. I moved quietly to the truck and switched on the spotlight. A sea of antelope, their brilliant emerald eyes like spots of phosphor, was pouring over the bank, flowing around our campsite.

The legions passed us and entered the water, slurping and splashing as they drank. But each animal stayed in the lake for only two or three minutes. Then it was drawn into the black current of bodies eddying shoreward and then westward toward the plain. The return trek had begun almost immediately. All that way for a few gulps of water!

They had but a few hours to find shade before the sun began sapping the life from them again.

As I watched the antelope surge desperately into the lake and then out of it, I thought about the significance of the migration for the conservation of all wildlife in the Kalahari. The wildebeest, lions, and hyenas had taught us much: For all its great size, the Central Reserve does not provide adequate habitat for most of its highly mobile populations, both predator and prey. Without any permanent water holes in the reserve, and restricted by fences and human settlements from the country's only lakes and rivers, the antelope populations have almost no place to get water in severe drought. Though lions, leopards, brown hyenas, and other Kalahari predators can live indefinitely without drinking, they can do so only as long as there is prey available to provide them with enough food and moisture. We were convinced that if something wasn't done soon to allow these animals greater access to the Boteti River and Lake Xau, to stop the harassment by poachers, or to devise some other solution, much of the Kalahari's wildlife would disappear.

In the short term, the only hope for the antelope was rain—rain to grow green grass in the desert and to draw them away from Lake Xau. The only long-term solution was to designate the area between the reserve and Lake Xau as part of an even larger game reserve or, at least, as a protected corridor of access to the lake for the herds. The catch, of course, was that this would mean freezing the development of settlements and ranching in that area.

We were convinced that if tourism and other wildlife industries could be developed as a substitute for raising cattle, the overall living standard of local tribal people would be raised. At the same time a great natural resource would be conserved. But even while we were suggesting this to government departments in Gaborone, we knew there was little chance that they would accept the idea—too many important people have cattle interests in the Lake Xau area.

Dr. Faust was greatly moved by the wildebeest situation and pledged his continued support of our research. In the months following his and Prince Bernhard's visits, we spent many hours hammering away at the typewriter in our tent or working under the ziziphus tree, with the hornbills pecking our pencils. We drafted articles for magazines all over the world. We sent reports and circulars to other influential people, hoping that someone could convince Botswana to do something for the conservation of the wildebeest; or to convince the EEC, who insist upon the fences, to review their impact on wildlife.

We hardly dared hope that any of this would help change the attitudes of import-export businessmen or government officials. But we had done our best. Meanwhile we watched the bleak and smoky skies for clouds. There were none.

26

Kalahari High

Mark

> You could feel the rain
> before it came,
> the signals were that good.
> —*Rod McKuen*

ONE AFTERNOON in mid-October 1980, over two and a half years after the drought had begun, there was a cloud. After months and months of searing desert sky, a single pillow of water vapor stood alone above the Kalahari, teasing us. Several hours later, others appeared. They were scattered, but each grew darker and heavier in the sky to the east, between the valley and Lake Xau.

When rain began streaking the sky beneath one of the clouds, Delia and I ran to the plane. At 1500 feet, we flew beneath the soft, grey belly of vapor, the rain splattering against the windshield and streaming along the skin of the plane. We opened the windows and let our arms trail outside. The cool wetness coursed down and off our fingertips and the fresh smell rushed into the cabin. It was a Kalahari high.

We flew toward Lake Xau as other storm cells feathered the sky with moisture. Over the lake plain there were no clouds, but below, the black masses of wildebeest were bunching, looking west toward the desert sky. Then the whole surface of the plain seemed to move, as thousands upon thousands of antelope began galloping westward. Some natural sense of order prevailed, and they began forming several lines, some more than a mile long, each headed straight for a cloud and its veil of rain.

It must have been the mist and spray around the airplane, or our excitement, that kept us from noticing at first, but, with a pang of despair, I realized that the ground was still grey with drought. We had been flying in "virga"—rain that evaporates in the hot desert air before it reaches the earth. Some of the wildebeest nearest the clouds, where the rain should have been, had slowed to a plodding walk with their heads lowered. Others had come to a standstill. Could a wildebeest feel utter dejection?

I throttled back, put down some flap, and for half an hour we dawdled from one cloud to another, watching the herds below. Finally, with the falling temperature in late afternoon, dense white columns of water began to reach the ground. Circles of savanna turned dark and wet. Puddles formed. The wildebeest gathered to drink and to eat what soppy grasses they could find.

Three days later it rained again, then again a week after that. Green grass shot up everywhere; the wildebeest quickly began eating their way back into the Kalahari and the game reserve. They were, of course, only the survivors of a much larger number that had migrated, but at least the rain bought us time—another year to convince Botswana's government and the rest of the world that Kalahari antelope are worth saving.

The sky was still stacked with cumulonimbus the morning after the first rain, and we took off in the plane to find the lions. Just as Sassy's signal sounded loud in our headphones, big drops began spiking against the fuselage. We passed the signal's peak, our foreheads pressed against the side windows, squinting through the mist at the trees flashing underneath. I banked steeply and came around again. When I saw Sassy she was standing near a big acacia with Chary and all seven of their adolescent offspring. Preying on wildebeest far outside the game reserve, often within a few hundred yards of cattleposts, the two females had brought all of their young through the drought. By any standard they had been good mothers. Now they all stood near Hartebeest Pan, licking the water from one another's backs and faces under the pelting rain. When we banked away the youngsters were stalking and chasing one another, and we could see their paw prints in the wet sand.

Blue and Bimbo were drinking at a water hole west of Crocodile Pan when we found them. We made notes on their position. I had just turned to fly back to camp when I spotted a large male lion resting near Blue and Bimbo at the edge of a grove of acacia bushes. He was nearly under the plane and just a blur, so I hauled EWG around for another look. But the aircraft was drifting heavily in the wind and there were dozens of thickets. We could not find him again.

It was just after sunset when the rains finally arrived in Deception Valley. Pepper was smelling a scent mark near the communal den while Cocoa rested under a bush nearby. The two brown hyena cubs stood, their ears perked, as the first rain they had ever seen began kicking up puffs of dust on the mound all around them. They began licking moisture from twigs, old bones, and the ends of their noses, and finally, lapping it from puddles on the ground. At two years of age, at last they had their first drink of water.

The next morning Blue and Bimbo were near Dog's Leg, in the upper end of Deception Valley. As I flew past I could see them lying with a big blond male, probably the same lion we had seen them with the day before. I was glad to see that, after almost two years on their own, they had found another companion. Perhaps when the rains were well under way and the antelope came back to the valley, the lions would walk the riverbed again. The nights and early mornings seemed empty without their roars rolling from dune to dune. I flew to camp and plotted their position on our aerial photographs. Then we set out in the truck to have a better look at the three of them.

We found them in an opening between two dense thorn thickets. The male was lying on his side and didn't even turn as I stopped the truck.

"I can't believe how relaxed he seems," Delia remarked. But then he swung his head around.

Delia raised the binoculars to her eyes. I heard her catch her breath.

"Mark! It's Moffet! He's alive! I can see the mark on his hip!" Though his collar and transmitter were gone, in his right ear were the remains of a red tag. He had seen Muffin trapped and shot and had himself been chased by a man on horseback with a pack of dogs; he may even have been wounded. But he had survived all that, and the drought, too.

After a time, Delia and I eased out of the truck. Cooing softly, mimicking the social call we had used for so long to reassure lions, we crept forward. Lying apart from Bimbo and Blue, Moffet was feeding on a porcupine clamped between his broad forepaws. He watched us intently, and then sighed and continued feeding. We settled beneath a bush about five yards away. It was like old times with him again.

Bimbo, now nearly two years old, still had a youngster's curiosity, even though he was a 200-pound subadult with the ragged beginnings of a mane. He slowly stood up and walked toward us. When he was five feet from us, he stopped and looked away. He licked his forepaw and smelled the ground and then took another tentative step forward, placing his paw carefully on the ground as if he were walking on eggshells. More than anything I wanted him to accept us totally, to show that his curiosity outweighed his uncertainty. If he touched us it would be a sign.

Another step. He leaned toward me, his nose and whiskers only three feet away from my face. He came still nearer, and I could see the reflection of the desert in his eyes, the flecks of golden brown in his irises as they adjusted to the changing light. Again and again, he pushed his muzzle forward, and then stood back, turning his ears slightly. After a last, clumsy attempt, he hastily put his nose into some leafy branches near my head and sniffed loudly, as if that had been his intention all along. Then he walked away. He had almost touched me, but something held us apart. The last barrier still remained.

We sat for a long time and watched Moffet slowly finish his meal. Then he rubbed the quills from his face and shoulders and licked his paws. When he had finished cleaning himself, he got to his feet and walked toward us, his mane swinging, his pink tongue sliding along his muzzle. He stopped near our feet, his soft eyes on us, then walked on to lie down with Blue beneath their shade tree.

In the midst of thousands of square miles of wilderness Moffet, Blue, and Bimbo were at least somewhat buffered from man's careless exploitation of the wilderness. Perhaps they, Pepper, Cocoa, and the others would be allowed to retain a part of the earth, to survive and endure.

But then my attention was drawn to something in a nearby tree that neither of us had noticed before. Tied in the branches were blue plastic survey ribbons, fluttering in the breeze.

Epilogue

Delia and Mark

> The ecologist cannot remain a voice crying in the wilderness—
> if he is to be heard and understood.
>
> —*M. W. Holdgate*

BLUE, BIMBO, AND MOFFET are all that is left of the Blue Pride dynasty that once ruled a long stretch of Deception Valley. When we last saw him, Bimbo was a hefty young male with a scruffy new mane and a wanderlust. He would soon become a nomad, roaming far from Deception Valley in search of a territory and a pride of his own. In the meantime, he and his mother stay together in the pride's old home range, stalking through bushveld and woodlands to the east of the valley near Crocodile Pan. Now and then they meet Moffet, and the three of them hunt or rest together under a shade tree.

Moffet usually stays alone, preying on small animals and birds. He rarely roars, for he has no territory, but now and then he coos softly into the wind—perhaps listening for an answer from his old friend Muffin.

At the end of 1980 old Chary gave birth to three more young, probably sired by a male of the East Side Pride near the game reserve boundary. She and Sassy and their cubs range from twenty to fifty miles east of Deception, near Hartebeest Pans and beyond. In this picturesque area, where dense terminalia and combretum woodlands open out to parkland and rolling grass savanna, the lionesses prey on occasional kudu, duiker, hartebeest, and migrating wildebeest. Now that they have formed new associations with other males and females in these areas, they will probably never return to their old Blue Pride territory near Deception Camp.

Liesa and Gypsy are together near Paradise Pan, where, in 1980 Gypsy gave birth to three cubs. She was a much better mother the second time around, and by the time we left the Kalahari, her new cubs were healthy and growing quickly.

Spicy and Spooky, of the original Blue Pride, joined the Springbok Pan Pride, where Spicy reared her cubs with Happy's family.

Both Rascal and Hombre, who were young male cubs with the Blue Pride when we first met them, were later shot by ranchers near cattle posts just outside the reserve boundary. More than a third of all the lions we tagged or collared were shot by professional hunters, poachers, or ranchers before we left. We believe this mortality, directed mostly at males, is detrimental to the long-term welfare of the population. (See Appendix B for our recommendations concerning the conservation of Kalahari lions.)

Diablo, the dominant male of the Springbok Pan Pride, was ousted by three prime males that we called the All-Stars. He moved about twenty miles west of Deception Valley, where he associates with two young females. Happy, Dixie, Sunny, Muzzy, and Taco, the females of the pride, together with Spicy, Spooky, and two lionesses from other prides, briefly came back to their old stomping grounds during the short rains. However, they are now once again scattered over more than 1200 square miles of sandveld north and south of Deception Valley.

The entire Tau Pride, which had frightened Delia while she was checking for holes on the crude airstrip in Hidden Valley, were shot by ranchers when they left the reserve in the dry season.

* * *

Pepper has grown into a young adult brown hyena who still visits camp to steal the water kettle, just like her mother, Star.

Patches gave birth to four cubs late in 1980 and moved them into the clan's communal den, where Dusty and Pepper helped feed them. Dusty lost a litter of her own and began nursing Patches' cubs soon after they were brought to the communal den. Chip, the cubs' half brother, assists in rearing them by provisioning and playing with them, but Pippin, their more distantly related male cousin, does not.

Recommendations for the conservation of brown hyenas in the Central Kalahari are in Appendix C.

* * *

The rains that fell on Lake Xau in late 1980 temporarily drew the wildebeest back into the reserve after thousands more had perished. But the respite was brief. Apart from a few scattered showers, the drought continued through 1984. The herds still migrate to Lake Xau, which is now completely dry.

The boundaries of the Central Kalahari Game Reserve were drawn at a time when nothing was known about the shifting antelope populations. To conserve these animals, even in their present diminished numbers, a solution must be found for the migrating species.

We wanted the research on the wildebeest to continue, so we requested funds for the Deception camp to operate as a small research station. The Frankfurt Zoological Society agreed to finance the facility and a team of researchers to further investigate the wildebeest problem. Doug and Jane Williamson are following up on our preliminary research on the antelope with a more detailed study of their range ecology. They report that, in 1983 alone, more than 60,000 wildebeest died, just in the area around Lake Xau.

Publicity of the wildebeest issue has stirred considerable interest, and the Botswana government has received communications from all over the world expressing concern for the antelope. We have been told by an official in the Wildlife Department that the Botswana Ministry of Agriculture has agreed to allocate over one million pula to the Department of Wildlife and National Parks for research into the development of alternate water supplies for Kalahari antelope. The government has temporarily accepted the recommendation to freeze the development of settlements on the west shore of Lake Xau, thereby maintaining this migratory corridor for the wildebeest. The Kalahari Conservation Society has been founded in Gaborone, and discussions are continuing on the feasibility of developing water holes for wildlife inside the Central Kalahari Game Reserve.

Unfortunately, a game scout camp has yet to be established at Lake Xau, and poaching and harassment of the migrating antelope continues to be severe, the local people chasing the wildebeest with vehicles, setting dogs on them, and shooting, spearing, and clubbing them to death.

Recommended solutions to the wildebeest problem are described in Appendix A.

* * *

Although we never saw Mox again, we eventually learned that he was working on an ostrich farm at Motopi, a village thirty miles east of Maun on the Boteti River. According to the farmer, Mox often sits around the evening campfire telling stories about Bones, about being treed by the Blue Pride, and about our bungled attempts at radio-tracking Star for the first time. He still drinks beer and occasionally terrorizes the native women of Motopi; he also enjoys the well-earned title, *Ra de Tau*, man of the lions.

We are presently writing and publishing our research results and completing our Ph.D. degree studies at the University of California, Davis. Soon we will return to the Kalahari to continue our studies of Pepper, Dusty, Blue, Sassy, Moffet, and the other animals we knew for seven years.

* * *

We could have stayed in Deception Valley for the rest of our lives, filling up one field journal after another; its mysteries are for us an endless fascination. But such an indulgence would have accomplished little for the Kalahari. We had to process seven years of data, write, and publish our results for science and conservation. Just as important, we had to make the people of Botswana and the rest of the world aware of the wilderness treasures that lie in the Kalahari. None of this could be done from our tent camp.

We had lived through some difficult times in the desert, but the most difficult task of all was leaving Deception Valley.

Early one morning in December 1980, we bounced down the airstrip in Echo Whisky Golf and lifted into the desert sky. Boeing the springbok trotted out of the way and the hornbills in camp flitted about the trees. Neither of us could speak as Mark turned the plane north for a short run over the valley. We flew low over the trees where we had done surgery on Bones's broken leg, and over the hyena den, where we could see Pepper, resting beneath an acacia bush. We lingered over the shoulder of East Dune, where Muffin and Moffet had killed Star, and over the small clearing on Cheetah Hill, where Captain and Mate had raised Hansel and Gretel. Then we turned south onto a heading of 163 degrees and flew away from Deception toward another world.

APPENDIX A

Conservation of Migratory Kalahari Ungulates

IN DROUGHT, Kalahari ungulates, including wildebeest and hartebeest, migrate across the Central Kalahari Reserve and beyond its protection. The herds move toward the waters of Lake Ngami, the Okavango River delta, Lake Xau, and the rivers that connect these natural reservoirs. Besides water to drink, the antelope may also need more nutritious forage than can be found in the reserve during these dry times. Their migrations take them into areas where human settlement has increased over the last twenty years, and now there is direct competition between man and wildlife for such limited resources as water and grassland. In addition, fences erected to control foot-and-mouth disease (FMD) block the migrations and channel antelope populations into only a very small portion of previously available riverine habitat (see maps on pages 297 and 299).

Finding a solution to the conflict between people and the migrating desert antelope is not going to be easy. However, without immediate action, these ungulate populations may not survive the Kalahari's periodic droughts. The following recommendations deserve consideration:

1. Detailed research must be undertaken to qualify and quantify the role of cordon fences in the control of FMD. Little is known about how the disease pathogen is transmitted from animal to animal and, despite extensive experimentation, it has never been conclusively proven that wild ungulates can transmit FMD to healthy domestic stock.[1] Thus, no one can be certain that wild ungulates are a reservoir of infection that is held in check by fences.

Since the erection of the fences in the early 1950s, Botswana has experienced more than nine major outbreaks of FMD, which have spread over large sections of the country irrespective of the disease-control fences. In part, this has been due to the fact that FMD is caused by three different strains of virus, each of which may cause an outbreak in a different area almost simultaneously when environmental conditions are conducive. There is also good evidence that the virus may be spread through the air over considerable distances[2] or in damp soil clinging to vehicles,[3] which cannot easily be constrained by fences. So, there appears to be as much circumstantial evidence to suggest that the fences do not help control the development and spread of the disease as there is evidence to suggest that they do. What we do know, is that they have devastated migrating antelope populations all over Botswana.

However, taking down fences may not be a viable long-term solution to the wildebeest problem. There is great pressure for human settlement along the shores of Botswana's few rivers and lakes, so that even if the fences were removed, Kalahari antelope would probably be blocked from water in the near future. The government has never seriously considered proposals to develop tourism and other wildlife-based industries in these areas, which would probably raise the living standards of local people and at the same time preserve a great natural heritage. To prevent yet another wildlife disaster, research is needed that would determine how new fences that are being planned will affect wildlife.

2. Botswana should consider alternatives to fencing for disease control, the most obvious being a modern and efficient vaccination program. In the past, often fewer than fifty percent of all cattle in infected areas have been vaccinated during an outbreak. And, at least on one occasion, outdated vaccine was used. A new vaccine is currently under development in the United States that will provide cattle a lifelong immunity to foot-and-mouth disease.[4]

There are other alternatives that would reduce the need for fencing and make the beef-export industry less subject to the vagaries of FMD: the development of more meat-canning plants in areas where FMD is endemic; stricter penalties, such as confiscation of cattle, for movement of domestic stock from one area to another during FMD outbreaks; and patrols using light aircraft instead of fencing along borders of quarantined areas.

3. One partial solution to the wildebeest problem would be to extend a portion of the eastern boundary of the Central Kalahari Game Reserve to include the area around Lake Xau. If the government will not consider this, the area between the lake and the western shore of the reserve at least should be set aside as a permanent corridor for migrations, and further development of villages and ranches in this area should be frozen. The corridor would have to be maintained free from settlement even in years when migrations did not occur, but it could be used to support tourism, safari hunting, or other wildlife industry.

4. A permanent game scout camp should be established in the Lake Xau area to prevent the poaching of migratory antelope.

5. We do not highly recommend the use of boreholes in the reserve as a means of providing water for the ungulates. However, if such action is taken certain considerations should be made.

a. The abundance of a grass species gives no assurance of its quality as a forage for antelope. Research is needed to determine if graze and browse plant species in the Central Kalahari Reserve contain enough protein and mineral nutrients to sustain antelope during drought. If they do not, merely providing migratory antelope with water will not ensure their survival.

b. Artificial water supplies will tend to focus mobile antelope populations and, unless they are carefully managed, will result in regional overgrazing and desertification.

c. Artificial water supplies will also attract people, who will settle nearby with livestock and crops. This would prevent access for wildebeest and aggravate the already sensitive problem of what to do about such growing settlements as Xade, which has developed around a borehole inside the game reserve.

6. Pan and fossil riverbeds constitute only about eleven percent of the Central Kalahari Game Reserve, but their soils contain essential minerals and the grasses have a more favorable protein/fiber ratio than do sandveld grasses. Even though these habitats make up a small portion of the total range, fifty-seven percent of all ungulates counted inhabited them during the wet season in years when rainfall was ten inches or more. Our results show that these fossil riverbeds are important habitat for wildlife and should be protected.

7. The European Economic Community, and in particular Britain, which imports most of Botswana's beef, heavily subsidizes Botswana's cattle industry. EEC officials in Brussels rigidly insist on the veterinary cordon fences, despite the fact that no research has ever been done to demonstrate their efficacy in controlling foot-and-mouth disease; and regardless of the fact that in the thirty-odd years since the fencing program was begun, it has been directly responsible for the deaths of at least a quarter of a million wildebeest and untold thousands of other antelope. "Easy" money from these subsidies encourages overstocking that leads to overgrazing and desertification—and to further displacement of wild antelope populations. Many native people are becoming less able to meet their own needs for food and clothing, traditionally obtained from the products of wild animals, and they are growing very dependent on foreign-aid programs for subsistence. Meanwhile, the few wealthy cattle owners, those who own most of the country's domestic stock, are growing richer.

The European Parliament should revise this policy immediately. Foreign subsidies should encourage Botswana to develop wildlife industries, such as tourism, photographic and hunting safaris, game ranching, and others. The necessary funds could come from the annual beef "rebate" to Botswana, currently running at more than 14,500,000 British pounds. Wildlife industries are more sustainable over the long term because they are less likely to contribute to desertification, less expensive to maintain, and more likely to raise the standard of living of the general populace.

APPENDIX B

Conservation of Kalahari Lions

1. The Predator Control Act should be amended to require that before ranchers destroy predators, they must provide proof that the predators have actually killed their stock. An immediate investigation should be made by the appropriate authority, and if sufficient proof of damage exists, the destruction of the predator concerned should be the responsibility of the government authority and not the rancher. The official should confiscate the remains of the predator, the sale of which should be used to maintain a fund for the remuneration of ranchers for damage to stock by predators. Skulls of all predators should be aged by the Department of Wildlife for much-needed data on population structure and dynamics.

2. Based on our density figures, we recommend that Kalahari lion-hunting quotas be reduced by one-half and the price of a lion-hunting license for safari hunters be doubled. The skulls of all lions taken by safari hunters should be aged by trained personnel of the Department of Wildlife. (We remind the reader that this book is not a scientific treatment of our results. Complete and detailed accounts of density figures, range sizes, and habitat utilization will be published in appropriate journals.)

3. Safari hunters should be required to buy a lion-hunting license only if they have already shot a lion. Many hunters are shooting very young lions simply because they have been required to purchase a license in advance and cannot find older males. Because of this, hunting pressure on male lions does not diminish even when there are no older lions.

4. Laws against baiting and trapping of predators should be more strictly enforced. This practice results in the indiscriminate killing and maiming of animals that have not damaged domestic stock. Baiting is also an expedient method for drawing predators out of reserves and parks by poachers.

5. The Department of Wildlife should have two to three times more men in the field to improve enforcement of existing laws.

6. As discussed in detail in Appendix A, one of the most important measures for the conservation of lions and other wildlife in the Kalahari, is to readjust the

Central Kalahari Game Reserve boundaries to include at least the western shore of Lake Xau. Though, as we have seen, Kalahari lions can live for months without drinking water, many of them have to leave the protection of the game reserve to locate adequate prey during prolonged dry seasons and drought.

7. Until the above measures are taken, permission to shoot lions outside game reserves should be suspended in times of drought, when many of them must leave the protection of the reserve in order to survive.

8. A tourist facility should be developed at the southern tip of Lake Xau. Such a facility could include accommodation at a lodge overlooking the lake, canoe trips through the papyrus to bird blinds on the lake, trips by canoe up the river for fishing and game viewing, photographic safaris into the Makgadikgadi Pans Game Reserve and the fossil rivers of the proposed Central Kalahari National Park, and game-viewing flights from a local airstrip. The Lake Xau facility could be utilized by tour operators as part of a packaged deal for tourists to visit the Kalahari, the Makgadikgadi, and the Okavango. It would greatly stimulate the local and regional economy, while at the same time conserving and advertising a unique part of Botswana that is still relatively unknown.

APPENDIX C

Conservation of Brown Hyenas

1. Because they are scavengers in a semiarid ecosystem where carrion is often limited, brown hyenas naturally occur in small numbers. The species is seriously threatened by decreasing habitat, as more and more Kalahari wilderness is used for grazing cattle. The hyenas are commonly shot and trapped in Ghanzi, Tuli, and Nojani, and in most ranching areas. However, the threat they pose to domestic stock is probably exaggerated. With one or two exceptions, the few times we observed them hunting in Deception Valley, they never pursued anything larger than a rabbit. Even at the beginning of the rainy seasons, when springbok dams synchronously birthed their lambs, we never saw a brown hyena kill a springbok fawn. When one is found feeding on the remains of a domestic animal, it cannot be assumed that it is responsible for the kill. In many cases—perhaps in most—a brown hyena discovers or appropriates a carcass after a prey has been killed by other predators. Some ranchers in South Africa have begun to allow brown hyenas on their rangeland; the public must be educated to the fact that this species of hyena is predominantly a scavenger and does not usually endanger domestic herds.

2. Predators on which brown hyenas depend heavily for food, especially lions and leopards, are being shot at increasing rates by ranchers, poachers, and hunters. Conservation of major predator communities is essential in maintaining the present brown hyena population density in the Central Kalahari.

3. Veterinary cordon fences are killing off thousands of antelope that otherwise would represent a lasting food resource for brown hyenas and other Kalahari predators. Addressing this problem is critical to the conservation of the brown hyena.

4. Since the brown hyena is of little real threat to livestock, and since it is an endangered species, it should not be included in Botswana's Predator Control Act. Proof of damage to livestock should be required of ranchers before they are issued special depredation permits to kill brown hyenas.

APPENDIX D

Latin Names of the Mammals, Birds, and Snakes Mentioned in the Text

MAMMALS

aardvark	*Orycteropus afer*
aardwolf	*Proteles cristatus*
cape fox	*Vulpes chama*
caracal	*Felis caracal*
cheetah	*Acinonyx jubatus*
bat-eared fox	*Otocyon megalotis*
brown hyena	*Hyaena brunnea*
duiker, Grimm's	*Sylvicapra grimmia*
eland, cape	*Taurotragus oryx*
gemsbok	*Oryx gazella*
hartebeest, red	*Alcelaphus busalephus*
honey badger (ratel)	*Mellivora capensis*
jackal, black-backed	*Canis mesomelas*
kudu, greater	*Tragelaphus strepsiceros*
leopard	*Panthera pardus*
lion	*Panthera leo*
meerkat	*Suricata suricatta*
mongoose, slender	*Herpestes sanguineus*
porcupine	*Hystrix sp.*
rabbit, Crawshay's	*Lepus crawshayi*
serval cat	*Felis serval*
springbok	*Antidorcas marsupialis*
spring hare	*Pedetes capensis*
spotted hyena	*Crocuta crocuta*
squirrel, striped ground	*Xerus erythropus*
steenbok	*Raphicerus campestris*

warthog	*Phacochoerus aethiopicus*
wild cat	*Felis libyca*
wild dog	*Lycaon pictus*
wildebeest	*Connochaetes taurinus*

Birds

bulbul, red-eyed	*Pycnonotus nigricans*
bustard, kori	*Otis kori kori*
cormorant, reed	*Phalacrocorax africanus*
eagle, tawny	*Aquila rapax*
finch, scaly feathered	*Sporopipes squamifrons*
fish eagle	*Haliaeetus vocifer*
flycatcher, Marico	*Bradornis mariquensis*
goose, spur-winged	*Plectropterus gambensis*
hoopoe, scimitar-billed	*Rhinopomastus cyanomelas*
hornbill, grey (in Maun)	*Tockus nasutus epirhinus*
hornbill, yellow-billed (in camp)	*Tockus flavirostris leucomelas*
kestrel, rock	*Falco tinnunculus*
kite, black-shouldered	*Elanus caeruleus*
kite, yellow-billed	*Milvus aegyptius*
korhaan, black	*Eupodotis afra*
lily-trotter (African jacana)	*Actophilornis africanus*
night jar	*Caprimulgus rufigena*
ostrich	*Struthio camelus*
owl, pearl-spotted	*Glaucidium perlatum*
plover, crowned	*Stephanibyx coronatus*
shrike, crimson-breasted	*Laniarius atro-coccineus*
stork, white	*Ciconia ciconia*
stork, white-bellied	*Ciconia abdimii*
teal, hottentot	*Anas hottentota*
tit-babbler	*Parisoma subcaeruleum*
vulture, lappet-faced	*Torgos tracheliotus*
waxbill, violet-eared	*Granatina granatina*
weaver, masked	*Ploceus velatus*

Snakes

boomslang	*Dispholidus typus*
cobra, Anchieta's	*Naja haje anchieta*
mamba, black	*Dendroaspis polylepis polylepis*
puff adder	*Bitis arietans*
spitting cobra (Black-necked)	*Naja mossambica*

Notes

4 Cry of the Kalahari
  1. Moehlman, pp. 382–83.
  2. Trivers, pp. 249–64.

5 Star
  1. Kruuk, p. 126.
  2. Owens and Owens, 1979a, pp. 405–8.

10 Lions in the Rain
  1. Schaller, p. 33.

12 Return to Deception
  1. Mills, 1978, pp. 113–41.
  2. Skinner, 1976, pp. 262–69; Mills, 1976, pp. 36–42.
  3. Macdonald, pp. 69–71.

14 The Trophy Shed
  1. Bertram, p. 59.

17 Gypsy Cub
  1. Bygott, Bertram, and Hanby, pp. 839–41.
  2. Bertram, p. 59.

18 Lions with No Pride
  1. Schaller, pp. 34–42.
  2. Schaller, p. 38.

20 A School for Scavengers
  1. Owens and Owens, 1979b, pp. 35–44.

21 Pepper
  1. Hamilton, pp. 1–52.
  2. Dawkins, pp. 95–131.
  3. Owens and Owens, 1984, pp. 843–45.

25 Black Pearls in the Desert
  1. Young, Hedger, and Powell, pp. 181–84.
  2. Hedger, p. 91.
  3. Silberbauer, pp. 20–21.
  4. Child, pp. 1–13.
  5. Silberbauer, p. 22.

6. Owens and Owens, 1980, pp. 25–27.

EPILOGUE

1. Williamson, in press.

APPENDIX A Conservation of Migratory Kalahari Ungulates

1. Condy and Hedger, pp. 181–84.
2. Hedger, p. 91.
3. Siegmund, p. 255.
4. Abelson, p. 1181.

References

Abelson, P. H. 1982. Foot-and-mouth vaccines. *Science* 218: 1181.

Bertram, B. C. R. 1975. The social system of lions. *Scientific American* 232: 54–65.

Bygott, J. D., B. C. R. Bertram, and J. P. Hanby. 1979. Male lions in large coalitions gain reproductive advantages. *Nature* 282: 839–41.

Child, G. 1972. Observations on a wildebeest die-off in Botswana. *Arnoldia* (Rhodesia) 5: 1–13.

Condy, J. B., and R. S. Hedger. 1974. The survival of foot and mouth disease virus in African buffalo with nontransference of infection to domestic cattle. *Res. Vet. Sci.* 39(3): 181–84.

Dawkins, R. 1976. *The Selfish Gene*. New York: Oxford University Press.

Hamilton, W. D. 1964. The genetic evolution of social behavior, I, II. *J. Theor. Biol.* 7: 1–52.

Hedger, R. S. 1981. Foot-and-Mouth Disease. In *Infectious Diseases of Wild Mammals*, ed. John Davis et al. Ames: Iowa State University Press.

Kruuk, H. 1972. *The Spotted Hyena*. Chicago: University of Chicago Press.

Macdonald, D. W. 1979. Helpers in fox society. *Nature* 282: 69–71.

Mills, M. G. L. 1976. Ecology and behaviour of the brown hyena in the Kalahari with some suggestions for management. *Proc. Symp. Endangered Wildl. Trust* (Pretoria) pp. 36–42.

Mills, M. G. L. 1978. Foraging behavior of the brown hyena (*Hyaena brunnea* Thunberg, 1820) in the southern Kalahari. *A. Tierpschol* 48: 113–41.

Moehlman, P. 1979. Jackal helpers and pup survival. *Nature* 277: 382–83.

Owens, D., and M. Owens. 1979a. Notes on social organization and behavior in brown hyenas (*Hyaena brunnea*). *J. of Mammalogy* 60: 405–08

Owens, D., and M. Owens. 1979b. Communal denning and clan associations in brown hyenas of the Central Kalahari Desert. *Afr. J. of Ecol.* 17: 35–44.

Owens, D., and M. Owens. 1984. Helping behaviour in brown hyenas. *Nature* 308: 843–45.

Owens, M., and D. Owens. 1980. The fences of death. *African Wildlife* 34: 25–27.

Schaller, G. B. 1972. *The Serengeti Lion*. Chicago: University of Chicago Press.

Siegmund, O. H., ed. 1979. *The Merck Veterinary Manual*. Rahway, N.J.: Merck & Co.

Silberbauer, G. 1965. *Bushmen survey report*. Gaborone: Botswana Government Printers.

Skinner, J. 1976. Ecology of the brown hyena in the Transvaal with a distribution map for southern Africa. *S. Afr. J. of Sci.* 72: 262–69.

Trivers, R. L. 1974. Parent-offspring conflict. *Am. Nat.* 14: 249–64.

Williamson, D. T. 1984. More about the fences. *Botswana Notes and Records*. In press.

Young, E., R. S. Hedger, and P. G. Howell. 1972. Clinical foot and mouth disease in the African buffalo (*Syncerus caffer*). *Ondersterpoort J. vet res.* 39(3): 181–84.

Acknowledgments

Without the assistance of many people, our research and the writing of this book would not have been possible. We have not been able to mention in the text all of those who believed in us and helped us throughout the years. We deeply regret this and wish them to know that we will always remember their contributions.

Our very special thanks to the Friends of the Animals and the Frankfurt Zoological Society, under the direction of Dr. Richard Faust, who gave us an airplane and other sophisticated equipment essential for working in such a remote area. The society financed the project from 1977 to 1983 and is continuing its generous support. The personal interest and encouragement of Dr. Faust and Ingrid Koberstein, his assistant, kept us going when times were tough.

We are also deeply grateful to the National Geographic Society for our first grant, and to the Netherlands branch of the World Wildlife Fund and the International Union for the Conservation of Nature for their generous financial assistance. H.R.H. Prince Bernhard of the Netherlands helped us secure funding and was influential in our efforts to publicize the Kalahari antelope issue.

Our sincere appreciation also to the Okavango Wildlife Society for a grant that allowed us to purchase our first radio telemetry equipment and to continue our research at a critical time. We are especially grateful to Chairman Hans Veit, and to Kevin Gill, Barbara Jeppe, and Heinz and Danny Guissman for their support.

We owe much to Al and Marjo Price and their family, who, through the California Academy of Science, contributed generously toward the operation of our project's airplane.

The late Dr. Beatrice Flad, a warm and sensitive person who was at the same time tenacious in her defense of wildlife, gave her life for conservation. We appreciate her financial support during the writing of our results.

Thanks also to Dr. and Mrs. Max Dinkelspiel for their personal contribution toward a trip home when we badly needed to see our families.

We are very grateful to the office of the president of Botswana and to the Department of Wildlife and Tourism for permission to conduct our research in the Central Kalahari Game Reserve, for accepting our criticisms, and for considering our recommendations on the conservation of the Kalahari. We realize that it is not always easy to resolve the competition between man and wildlife, and we thank those officials who are sincerely attempting to do this for the betterment of all.

Besides our sponsors, there are people who contributed greatly to the running of the project in crucial ways: our lasting appreciation and warm thanks to Kevin Gill who graciously gave us the full use of his home whenever we were in Johannesburg and for treating us to mellow evenings filled with good wines, fine music, and stimulating conversation. Our thanks to Captain Roy Liebenberg for teaching Mark to fly, and for his assistance with radio equipment; to Roy, his wife, Marianne, and their children, and to Bruno and Joy Bruno for allowing us to be a part of their families on many occasions. Dave Erskine and Rolf Olschewski hauled thousands of gallons of aviation fuel through the desert to our camp. Dave also made windsocks for the airstrip, helped us with photography, made logistical arrangements with mine personnel, and made critical observations on the brown hyenas on occasions when we had to be away. Bobby and Mary Dykes (Delia's twin brother and his wife) gave us unending support in printing, sorting, and cataloguing our photographs, in shipping spare parts for our airplane from the United States, and in helping with project correspondence. They even brought our lion and brown hyena radio collars to Africa in their suitcase.

There are still many frontiers in southern Africa where people must depend on one another—sometimes even for survival. In Bulawayo, Zimbabwe, the Archers—Geoffry, Ruth, Margaret, and Jean—kindly gave us the use of their home, wonderful meals, and innumerable cups of tea, and a "bush shower" that helped equip us for life in the *bundu*. We thank the Tom Lukes and Graham Clarks, also of Bulawayo, for their warm friendship; Mr. and Mrs. White of Salsbury (Harare) for their hospitality; Ted Matchel and Ian Salt of the Zimbabwean Department of Wildlife and National Parks for advice on prospective study areas.

In Gaborone, Tom Butynski and Carol Fisher Wong put us up for several weeks while we were outfitting for our reconnaissance through Botswana. And over the years, whenever we arrived from the bush, Pietman and Marlene Henning of Gaborone always took us in, fed us, and gave us rest and friendship.

For seven years, whenever we came into the village of Maun for supplies, our friends provided us with everything from truck spares to parties and advice. We will never be able to thank them enough, for theirs was the truest expression of the pioneer spirit that still lives in small villages on the edge of the bushveld. Our thanks to Richard and Nellie Flattery, Pete Smith, Eustice and Daisy Wright, Mark Muller, Dave Sandenberg, Hazel Wilmot, Toni and Yoyi Graham, Diane Wright, Dolene Paul, Dad Riggs, Cecil and Dawn Riggs, John and Caroline Kendrick, Larry and Jenny Patterson, P. J. and Joyce Bestelink and Kate and Norbert Drager. Special thanks to Phyllis Palmer and Daphne Truthe for kindly reading messages and telegrams to us on shortwave radio.

There is a group of people in Maun who deserve special recognition: the professional hunters, especially of Safari South. When we first arrived with our back packs and dilapidated old Land Rover to study wildlife, the hunters managed to conceal the doubts they surely had about us and from the very beginning made us feel welcome. It would have been very difficult for us to begin our project without their advice and never-ending support. They gave us our only radio and talked to us often during the hunting season—our only communication with the outside world; they towed our truck when it broke down near the village; they loaned us the use of their airplane for game censusing; they gave us tents, chairs, tables; they flew Delia into Maun when she was very sick with malaria and did hundreds of other favors. Our sincere thanks to Lionel Palmer, Dougie Wright, Willie Engelbrecht, Bert Miln, John Kingsley Heath, Simon Paul, Wally Johnson, Junior and Senior; Tommy Friedkin, owner of Safari South; manager Charles Williams, and David Sandenberg. Though we did not condone all of their hunting practices, most of the hunters remained our friends.

We had many illuminating discussions with Steve Smith, Curt Busse, and Carol and Derrick Melton, who gave us a standing invitation to visit their baboon research camp in the Okavango delta. The evenings with the baboons scampering around us, the Christmas turkey that was cooked in a washbasin, and our swims in the hippo lagoon will never be forgotten.

We thank Dr. W. J. Hamilton III for accepting us as graduate students, for his support and encouragement while we were in the field, for his great patience with us as we write up our results, and for all the laughs both he and Marion, his wife, have given us when we needed them.

De Beers Consolidated Botswana allowed us to purchase aviation fuel from their stocks and to buy supplies at the mine store.

We would like to thank Lake Price and Warren Powell, who assisted us in the field for three months in 1979. They never complained about the long hours over the plotting board, the lack of water, or the rats and snakes in their shredded tent; or about the "turd patrol" (collecting, crushing, and sifting lion and hyena scats). Their contributions and companionship were invaluable.

We are grateful to Gordon Bennett for the generous use of his airplane and company facilities on several occasions; to Cliff and Eva Thompson, Hans Pearson, and Phil Parkin for donations of equipment. For their gracious hospitality in South Africa, we also thank Frank Bashall, Schalk Theron, Allistar and Maureen Stewart, Willy and Linda Vandeverre, and Liz and Jane Cuthbert.

To our families we owe special appreciation for their encouragement through the years. Delia's mother and late father sent endless "care" packages. Mark's father and Delia's mother brought much needed cheer to camp on their visits. Again, we are sorry that the many interesting details of their visits could not be included in the book.

Our good friends Bob Ivey and Jill Bowman have been involved with our project from the very beginning. Their encouragement and enthusiasm greatly inspired us, and they read and commented on the entire manuscript. We owe them much more than they will ever realize.

We are also grateful to Dr. Joel Berger, Carol Cunningham, Dr. W. J. Hamilton III, Dr. Murray Fowler (Chapter 25), Helen Cooper, and Dr. Bob Hitchcock for their constructive comments on the manuscript. Helen Cooper (Delia's sister) also helped with the epigraphs. We appreciate the encouragement, assistance, and lasting patience of our editors Harry Foster (Houghton Mifflin) and Adrian House (Collins) and the support and encouragement of Peter Matson and Michael Sissons, our agents.

Doug and Jane Williamson took over the wildebeest research and the operation of the camp during a four-year drought. In our absence they have made lasting contributions to science and the conservation of Kalahari wildlife under extremely difficult conditions.

We owe special thanks to Mox Moraffe, who assisted us for three and a half years in the desert. In his own quiet and humorous way, he gave us support and knowledge.

Mr. and Mrs. Langdon Flowers of Thomasville, Georgia, kindly invited us to stay in "Breezinook," their log-and-stone house on Greybeard Trail in Montreat, North Carolina, while we wrote much of this book. We are so very grateful for the peace and inspiration we found in this retreat and for the opportunity to get to know them better.

And last, we would like to thank Dr. Joel Berger and Carol Cunningham for teaching us what true friendship can be again, after seven years alone.

The Eye of the ELEPHANT

An Epic Adventure in the African Wilderness

DELIA AND MARK OWENS

To Helen and Fred,
Bobby and Mary,
and Mama—for doing so much.

And to Lee and Glenda, who keep us all smiling.

OOO

Library of Congress Cataloging-in-Publication Data
Owens, Delia.
The eye of the elephant: an epic adventure in the African wilderness / Delia and Mark Owens.
p. cm.
Includes bibliographical references
ISBN-13: 978--0-395-42381-3 ISBN-13: 978--0-395-68090--2 (pbk.)
ISBN-IO: 0--395-42381-3 ISBN-IO: 0--395-68090--5 (pbk.)
1. Wildlife conservation-Luangwa River Valley (Zambia and Mozambique) 2. Elephants-Luangwa River Valley (Zambia and Mozambique) 3. Owens, Delia. 4. Owens, Mark.
5. Wildlife conservationists- United States-Biography.
I. Owens, Mark. II. Title QL84.6.233084 1992
639.9'7961-dc20 92-17691 CIP

Printed in the United States of America
Maps by George Ward

Design by Melodie Wertelet
QUM 15 14 13 12 11 10 9 8
Permissions for quotations that appear in this book are listed on page 678.

CONTENTS

Authors' Note

This story is not meant to judge Zambia's past conservation practices so much as to project hope for the future. The events described in this book occurred under the previous one-party Marxist government in Zambia. In 1991 the Zambian people elected a truly democratic government, which has taken positive steps to address the conservation problems of the country. It is only because of this change in government that we have the freedom to tell our story. Scientists and conservationists have the responsibility and the right to report their findings. By telling the truth, no matter how controversial, they incur a measure of personal and professional risk; by not telling it, we *all* risk much, much more.

The names of the innocent in this book have been changed to protect them from the guilty; the names of the guilty have been changed to protect us. The rest of this story is true.

Principal Characters

Island Zulu	the "Camp-in-Charge" at Mano Camp
Patrick Mubuka	the "Camp-in-Charge" at Nsansamina Camp
Nelson Mumba Gaston Phiri Tapa	the game scouts at Mano Camp
Chomba Simbeye Chanda Mwamba Mutale Kasokola	the first Bemba tribesmen to work for us
Mosi Salama Bornface Mulenga	game wardens at Mpika
Sunday Justice Mumanga Kasokola	our cooks
Jealous Mvula Bwalya Muchisa Musakanya Mumba	our earliest informants
Chanda Seven Bernard Mutondo Mpundu Katongo Chikilinti Simu Chimba	the most notorious poachers of North Luangwa National Park
John Musangu Kotela Mukendwa	unit leaders at Mano Camp
Banda Chungwe	the senior ranger at Mpika
Evans Mukuka	our first educational officer
Marie and Harvey Hill	friends in Mpika
Chief Mukungule	chief of the area west of the park
Chief Nabwalya	chief of the area between North and South Luangwa parks

Chief Chikwanda	chief of the area near Mpika
Max Saili	our community service officer
Tom and Wanda Canon	volunteers from Texas
Ian Spincer Edward North	assistants from the University of Reading
The Lions	
Happy Sunrise Sage Stormy Saucy	the new members of the Blue Pride in the Kalahari
Serendipity Kora	lions of the Serendipity Pride along the Mwaleshi River
Bouncer	the male we radio collar on the plains
The Elephants	
Survivor	the male elephant who comes into our camp
Cheers	the male elephant who sometimes accompanies Survivor
Camp Group	the group of male elephants that forages near our camp
One Tusk Misty Mandy Marula	a family unit of female elephants
Long Ear and her daughters	another family unit of female elephants

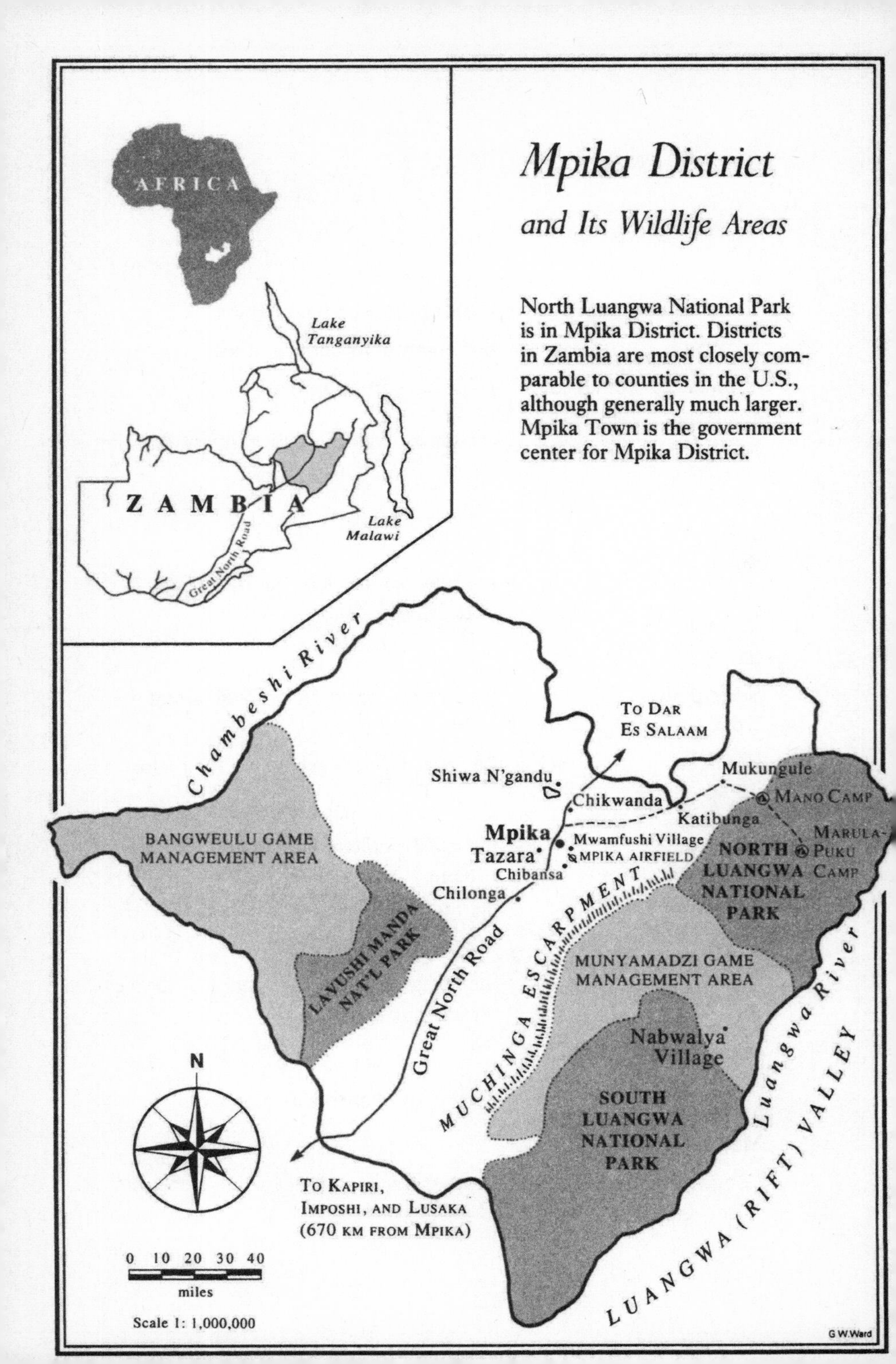

Mpika District
and Its Wildlife Areas
North Luangwa National Park is in Mpika District. Districts in Zambia are most closely comparable to counties in the U.S., although generally much larger. Mpika Town is the government center for Mpika District.
AFRICA
Lake Tanganyika
ZAMBIA
Great North Road
Lake Malawi
Chambeshi River
To Dar Es Salaam
Shiwa N'gandu
Chikwanda
Mukungule
Mano Camp
Katibunga
Mpika
Tazara
Mwamfushi Village
Mpika Airfield
Chibansa
Chilonga
Marula-Puku Camp
North Luangwa National Park
Bangweulu Game Management Area
Lavushi Manda Nat'l Park
Great North Road
Muchinga Escarpment
Munyamadzi Game Management Area
Nabwalya Village
South Luangwa National Park
Luangwa River
Luangwa (Rift) Valley
N
To Kapiri, Imposhi, and Lusaka (670 km from Mpika)
0 10 20 30 40
miles
Scale 1: 1,000,000
G.W.Ward

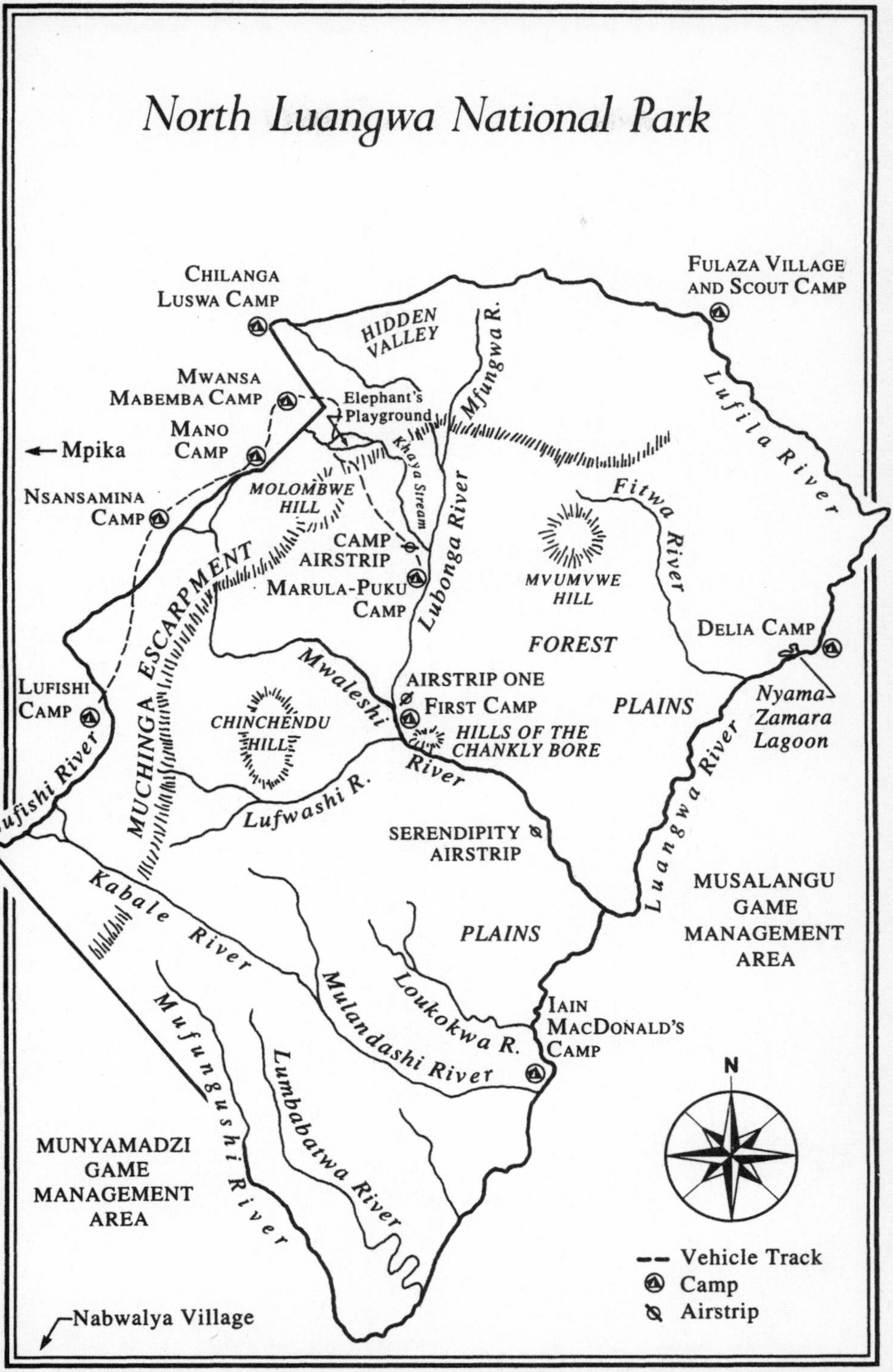

North Luangwa National Park

CHILANGA LUSWA CAMP
HIDDEN VALLEY
Mfungwa R.
FULAZA VILLAGE AND SCOUT CAMP
MWANSA MABEMBA CAMP
Elephant's Playground
MANO CAMP
← Mpika
Khaya Stream
Lufila River
NSANSAMINA CAMP
MOLOMBWE HILL
Fitwa River
CAMP AIRSTRIP
MARULA-PUKU CAMP
Lubonga River
MVUMVWE HILL
MUCHINGA ESCARPMENT
DELIA CAMP
FOREST
Mwaleshi River
AIRSTRIP ONE
FIRST CAMP
PLAINS
Nyama-Zamara Lagoon
LUFISHI CAMP
CHINCHENDU HILL
HILLS OF THE CHANKLY BORE
Lufishi River
Luangwa River
Lufwashi R.
SERENDIPITY AIRSTRIP
MUSALANGU GAME MANAGEMENT AREA
Kabale River
PLAINS
Mulandashi River
Loukokwa R.
IAIN MACDONALD'S CAMP
Mufungushi River
Lumbabatwa River
N
MUNYAMADZI GAME MANAGEMENT AREA
Vehicle Track
Camp
Airstrip
Nabwalya Village

PART ONE ○○○

The Dry Season

Prologue

DELIA

DAWN IN LUANGWA. I hear the elephant feeding on marula fruits just outside the cottage. Quietly pushing aside the mosquito net, I rise from the bed and tiptoe through the dark to the washroom, which has a tiny window high under the thatched roof. All I can see in the window is a large eye, like that of a whale, blinking at me through the pale morning light.

One step at a time, I ease closer to the window until I am just below it. Then, standing on an old tea-crate cupboard, I pull myself up to the sill and see Survivor's eye only a foot away. Long, straight lashes partially cover his pupil as he looks toward the ground searching for a fruit. Then, as he picks one up with his trunk and puts it into his mouth, he lifts his lashes and looks directly at me. He shows neither surprise nor concern, and I stare into the gray forever of an elephant's eye.

Such an incident may take place in other areas of Africa, but not in the northern Luangwa Valley of Zambia. In the last fifteen years, one hundred thousand elephants have been slaughtered by poachers in this valley. Here elephants usually run at the first sight or scent of man. I want to remember always the deep furrows of folded skin above Survivor's lashes, his moist and glistening eye, which now reflects the sunrise. Surely this will never happen to me again; the memory must last a lifetime. And I must never forget the way I feel, for at this moment I can see everything so clearly.

○ ○ ○

We first came to Africa in 1974 and settled in Deception Valley, a dry, fossilized river in the Kalahari Desert of Botswana. For seven years we lived in tents among the bush-covered dunes, the only people other than a few scattered bands of Bushmen in a wilderness the size of Ireland. The lions and brown hyenas there apparently had never seen humans before. They accepted us into their prides and clans, revealing previously unknown details of their natural history. Our tree-island camp was in the center of the Blue Pride's territory. These lions — Blue, Sassy, Happy, Bones, and later Muffin and Moffet — often sat beyond our campfire or raided our pantry. Once, when sleeping on the open savanna, we awoke to find ourselves surrounded by lions an arm's length away.

We left Deception at the end of 1980 to complete our graduate work and returned in 1985, when this story begins. Our greatest hope was to find whichever Blue Pride lions might still be alive, and to continue the research for another five years. We would search every dune slope, dried water hole, and acacia grove until we found them.

But we had another objective, too. The Central Kalahari Game Reserve — long forgotten and ignored by the outside world — was now the center of controversy. Powerful cattlemen and politicians wanted to dissolve the reserve and divide it into large private ranches, even though the sandy desert savannas could not sustain cattle for long. We had a quite different recommendation: that the area be conserved for the benefit of the local people through wildlife tourism.

Despite the pressures on the Kalahari, surely few places on earth had changed so little during the four years we were away. There was still no development of any kind in the reserve. At our camp we would still have to haul water in drums for fifty miles, live in the same faded tents, drive on the one bush track we had made years before. Once again our only visitors would be lions, brown hyenas, jackals, springbok, giraffes, hornbills, and lizards.

Lost again among those dunes, we failed to realize that even though the Kalahari had remained much the same, the rest of Africa had changed. We had survived drought and sandstorms. Now we would be caught in another kind of storm — one that would uproot us and blow us like tumbleweeds across the continent in search of another wilderness. And there the storm would continue.

○ ○ ○

Survivor lowers his lashes again as he feels around for another fruit, finds one, and raises it to his mouth, smacking loudly as he chews. He looks back at me again. I can see not only into his eye, but through it. Beyond are thousands of elephants in massive herds wending their way along mountain trails and down into the valley, there to stroll slowly across stilled savannas surrounded by thick, luxuriant forests. Giant, gentle mothers and playful youngsters romp and bathe in wide, sweeping rivers, unafraid. Powerful males push and shove for courtship rights, then stand back from each other, shaking their heads, their ears flapping in a cloud of dust. Through Survivor's eye I can see the wilderness as it once was. The storm continues, but a ray of hope shines through. Because of it, some of wild Africa may be saved.

Slowly Survivor curls his trunk to the windowsill and takes in my scent as he looks directly at me again. I wiggle my fingers forward until they are pressed against the flyscreen, only inches from his trunk. I want to whisper something, but what could I say?

The eye of the elephant is the eye of the storm.

1
Flight to Deception

MARK

> Every time that I have gone up in an aeroplane and looking down have realized that I was free of the ground, I have had the consciousness of a great new discovery. "I see," I have thought. "This was the idea. And now I understand everything."
>
> — ISAK DINESEN

○ ○ ○

AIRBORNE OVER THE KALAHARI for the first time in years, I felt as though I was meeting an old friend again in some secret corner of the earth known only to the two of us. During our seven years in this vast wilderness, I had got Kalahari sand in my shoes, and civilization with its fine hotels, its restaurants, its hot baths and other conveniences, had not been able to shake it out. The farther north I flew, the farther into the desert. Seeing the familiar pans, the fossil river valleys, the vast, undulating bush savannas with giraffes browsing flat-topped *Acacia tortillas* trees, I knew I was going back where I belonged. It was early April 1985.

While planning the flight to Botswana, I had been anxious that the six-year drought might have so changed the Kalahari's features that I would be unable to find our old camp. I was supposed to have met Delia there two days ago, but last-minute problems with the plane in Johannesburg had delayed me. During her long drive into the Kalahari by truck, and even after she reached camp, there was no way to alert her. If I didn't show up soon, she would think I had been forced down somewhere.

Scanning the plane's instruments, my eyes locked onto the gauge for my right tank. Halfway to Deception, its needle was already nudging the red. I was losing fuel — fast. I straightened up in my seat, looked along each wing for any sign of a leak, then checked my carburetor mixture again. Nothing wrong there. Wiping my forearm across my eyes, I tried to stay calm.

My right tank was virtually dry while the left one read completely full, but I had set the fuel selector to draw equally from both. The line from the left tank to the engine must be blocked. If so, I would run out of gas within the next few minutes. I had to land immediately.

I looked out of the window and down 4500 feet. Six years of drought had flayed the Kalahari, the dry, hot winds searing all signs of life until the terrain looked like ground zero at the Nevada nuclear test flats: sterile, forbidding, unfamiliar. I swallowed hard, leaned forward in my seat, and began urgently looking for a place to make a precautionary landing. If I flew on, the engine might quit over bush savanna or woodlands, where a forced landing would end in an outright crash. No one would ever find me.

A perfectly round, brilliantly white salt pan appeared off to the left about fifteen miles away. I banked left and headed straight for it, pulling back the throttle to conserve avgas (aviation gasoline). The gauge for the right tank was now rock solid red, and several times the engine seemed to miss strokes. When the pan was finally below me, I took a breath and began setting up the plane for a landing.

But at 500 feet above the ground I noticed deep animal tracks in the surface. If I put the plane down here, its wheels would sink into the salt and powder. Even if I could find and fix the fuel problem, I would never get airborne again.

It occurred to me that I couldn't be positive that the left tank was blocked until the right one was dry. I would switch to the right tank and deliberately run it out of fuel while circling over the pan. If the engine quit I could land there safely, even if I was not able to take off again.

I circled overhead, waiting for the engine to die. It never did. The left tank began feeding fuel, its gauge slowly drawing down. Later I would learn that the plane's mechanics had cross-connected the lines from the fuel tanks to the fuel selector console. "Right" drew from the left tank; "Left" was drawing from the right. Worse, higher air pressure from a bad vent in the right tank was forcing its avgas into the left tank, bloating it. The excess was being pumped out through a leaky fuel cap on top of the left wing, where I couldn't see it. It took forty precious minutes of flying — and fuel — to figure all this out. Now even if I made a beeline for camp, I might not make it.

And my problems were just beginning. Within five minutes of leaving the pan, I realized I was lost. Nothing below me looked even vaguely familiar. Surely the drought could not have wiped out all my old landmarks. Where were the Khutse Pans, the "mitochondria" pans, the squiggles of fossil river that used to tell me my position in the desert? They were subtle, but four years ago I had known the Kalahari so well from the air that they were like road signs to me. Even though haze had cut my visibility to about two miles, it seemed impossible that I had flown past each of these features without seeing any of them. I tightened my grip on the controls and held my compass heading. Something familiar had to come along.

Forty-five minutes after leaving the pan, I was totally disoriented; and a stiff head wind had reduced my ground speed from 150 mph to 120. It would take even more fuel to get to camp. Desperate to see something — anything — recognizable, I spent precious avgas climbing to 9500 feet, where I hoped I could see farther over the desert. The result was the same. All below me was a whiteout of haze. I had to be miles off course, but which way I couldn't tell. The same mechanics who crossed the fuel lines had put a steel — rather than a nonmagnetic brass — screw in the compass housing. It was off by thirty degrees. But of course I didn't know it at the time.

I fought off the urge to leave my flight path to chase after smudges in the bleak landscape, hoping to find something familiar. I couldn't afford to gamble away the avgas. So I flew on, not daring to look at the gauges anymore.

An hour later I still had no idea where I was — and I knew for certain that I would run out of fuel before reaching camp. I could only hope that I would be near a Bushman village where I could get water, or at least some wild melons, to keep me alive. But I had seen none of the settlements that I knew from years ago. I must be many miles off course.

I switched the radio to 125.5, Botswana's civil air traffic frequency, and picked up the microphone. "Any aircraft listening on this frequency, this is Foxtrot Zulu Sierra. Do you read me?" There was no response. I repeated my sign several times, but the only answer was the hiss of static in my earphones.

I changed to 121.5, the emergency frequency, and called again: "Any aircraft, this is Foxtrot Zulu Sierra. I am lost over the Kalahari somewhere between Gaborone and the northern sector of the Central Reserve. My fuel is critical . . . Repeat, fuel critical. Forced landing imminent. Does anyone read me?" No one answered. I suddenly felt as though I were the last survivor of some apocalypse on earth, calling into outer space with a one-in-a-billion chance of being heard and rescued by some intelligence.

My ETA for Deception Valley had come and gone. Still there was only an anonymous void below me. The left fuel gauge was faltering in the red; the right one was completely empty. I flew on, scanning ahead for a place where I could crash land with the least amount of damage to the plane and to myself.

I spotted a hint of white off to the right of my track about thirty degrees. Lake Xau! But as I flew closer, the depression taking shape in the windshield became too round, too white, to be the Lake Xau I remembered. Sure, Xau had been dry for a couple of years, but this looked too small, too much like a permanent salt pan. I couldn't see the lake bed or the Botetile River that flows into it.

If it wasn't Lake Xau, it could be Quelea Pan — in which case I was fifty miles off course to the west, deeper into the desert. It had to be one or the other. If it was Xau, I needed to turn west and fly sixty miles to get to Deception Valley; if it was Quelea, I should head east for fifty-five.

I glanced at my fuel gauges. Now both were dead red. I rolled my wings up and down and the left needle wiggled, but only slightly. There was barely enough avgas in the tank to slop around. I had to find camp or a suitable place to land immediately. I couldn't afford to waste my fuel flying closer to the pan to identify it. If I couldn't make it to camp, I wanted to get as close as possible.

If I turned west and it wasn't Xau, I would fly away from camp into a more remote part of the desert, where my chances of ever being found were nil.

There was no time left for agonizing. I turned the plane.

2

Home to the Dunes

DELIA

What aimless dreaming! The drone of the plane, the steady sun, the long horizon, had all combined to make me forget for a while that time moved swifter than I.

— BERYL MARKHAM

o o o

SCANNING THE HORIZON, I wondered again why Mark hadn't flown out to look for me. I was two days late; if he'd made it safely to camp, he would have buzzed me by now. I searched once more for the white plane moving against the blue; but the Kalahari Desert sky, the largest sky on earth, was empty.

Endless, barren plains — the wasted remains of Lake Xau on the edge of the Kalahari — surrounded me. For six days I had been driving the old Toyota Land Cruiser, burdened with supplies, from Johannesburg, across the Kalahari toward our old camp in Deception Valley.

Mark and I had arranged to meet at camp on April 4, my birthday. If he wasn't there when I arrived, I was to radio to the village of Maun for an aerial search. On the other hand, if I wasn't in camp, he was to fly along the track looking for me. My trip across the tired scrubland had taken much longer than expected. That Mark had not flown to look for me meant only one thing: he had not made it to camp.

The track I was following twisted and turned across the southern tip of the dry lake bed. Driving back and forth, leaning over the steering wheel, I looked for signs of the old track that had for many years led us into the reserve. The plains looked so different now after years of drought; faint tracks wandered off in odd directions and then faded altogether in the dust and drifting sand.

I climbed to the roof of the truck for a better view, squinting against the glare. A hot wind blew steadily across the wasteland. Dust devils skipped and swirled. I couldn't find a trace of the old track; either it had faded from disuse or I was lost.

There was another way into the reserve: I could drive to the top of Kedia Hill and head due west along an old cutline. It was a longer but more certain route. I turned onto the track to the hill and pressed down hard on the accelerator.

As I reached the edge of the plains, I looked back. This was where, only four years ago, a quarter of a million wildebeests had trekked for water — and died. In one day we had counted fifteen thousand dead and watched hundreds of others dying. They had migrated for several hundred miles only to find that their way to water was blocked by a great fence. For days they had plodded along the barrier until they had come to the lake plain, already overgrazed by too many starving cattle. Now it lay naked, empty, and abused. Not one wildebeest, not one cow, was in sight.

The conflict between domestic stock and wild animals had not been resolved, but we had submitted some ideas to the government that we hoped would benefit both people and wildlife. I was reminded of how much work there was yet to do to conserve the Central Kalahari. I left the plains and headed up Kedia Hill.

Ivory-colored sand, deeper than I had ever seen, was piled high along the track and in places had drifted across the path like powdered snow. The truck's canopy and heavy load of supplies made it top-heavy; it swayed along in the spoor, leaning drunkenly from side to side. I urged it up Kedia's rocky, forested slopes and easily found the old survey track. It had been made in the early '70s by our late friend Bergie Berghoffer, who had once saved us from the desert. I felt as though he was here now, showing me the way with his cutline, which pointed like an arrow straight into the Kalahari.

Several hours later I came to the sign we'd made from wildebeest horns to mark the boundary of the Central Kalahari Game Reserve. I stepped out of the truck for a moment to be closer to the fingers of the grass and the face of the wind. Other than the sign there was nothing but weeds and thornscrub, but we had darted the lioness Sassy just over there, under those bushes. As we put the radio collar around her neck, her three small cubs had watched from a few feet away, eyes wide with curiosity. We had known Sassy herself as a cub. If she had survived the drought, the hunters, the poachers, and the ranchers, she would be twelve now, old for a Kalahari lion. "Where are you, Sas?"

I expected Mark to zoom over the truck at any moment. He would drop down low and fly by, the belly of the airplane just above my head — one of his favorite tricks. But there was no sign of the plane.

I drove on, the truck's wheels churning steadily through the deep sand. I was glad to see that the survey ribbons left by the mining prospectors were no longer hanging in the tree. They had been shredded by the sun and blown away by the wind. The Kalahari had won that round.

Seeing fresh brown hyena tracks in the sand, I jumped out and bent down to look at them. They had been made last night by an adult moving east. I was torn between savoring every detail of my return to the Kalahari and rushing on to camp to see about Mark.

An hour later my heart began to race as I reached the crest of East Dune. I scrambled to the truck's roof and squinted under my hand, trying to see if the plane had landed at camp, nearly two miles away on the dry riverbed. The heat waves stretched and pulled the desert into distorted mirages, making it difficult to distinguish images. Even so, the broad white wings would have been visible against the sand — but the plane was not there.

Jumping to the ground, I flung open the door and drove furiously down the sand ridge. Oh God, what do I do? It had all sounded so easy to radio Maun if Mark was not here, but we had not radioed the village in four years. What if the radio didn't work? What if nobody answered?

The truck plowed on. The engine was overheating badly and complained with a deep rumbling noise — too much noise. If something was wrong with the truck, I was in bad trouble. The sound grew louder.

VAARRROOOOOM! A rush of air and thunder roared in from behind me and passed over my head. Instinctively I ducked, looking up. The belly of the plane filled the windshield as Mark skimmed ten feet above the truck. He zoomed down the dune slope and soared south toward camp. Stopping the truck, I leaned my head against the steering wheel with a rush of relief. Then I pounded it with my fists. "Damn! Where has he been? He always roars in at the last second." But I smiled. He was safe, and we were back in the Kalahari. Now I could enjoy my homecoming.

I climbed onto the roof again. I was standing in exactly the same spot from which we had first looked down on Deception Valley eleven years ago. At that time the ancient riverbed had been covered with thick, green grass and majestic herds of gemsbok and springbok. Now, stretching north and south between the dunes, the valley floor looked naked and gray, with only an occasional antelope standing in the heat. Then I noticed the faintest hint of green; only someone who had lived for years in the desert would call it green, but it was there. It had rained a few inches very recently, and the grass was struggling up through the sand. The Kalahari was neither dead nor tired, she was merely waiting for her moment to flower again.

Other people have neighborhoods that they come home to, streets with houses, familiar faces, jobs, and buildings. As I gazed down on Deception Valley, I saw my neighborhood, my home, my job, my identity, my purpose for living. Standing atop East Dune, I was looking down on my life.

Quickly I drove over the dune and across the riverbed. Mark had landed on our old strip and was rushing to greet me as I rounded Acacia Point several hundred yards from camp. I jumped out of the truck and hugged him.

"What happened? Why didn't you buzz me?" I asked.

"I almost didn't make it." Mark looked a little dazed as he recapped his flight. ". . . so I reached a point when I had to decide to go east or west. I turned west and after a few minutes recognized Hartebeest Pans. At least I knew where I was, but any second the engine was going to quit and it was still ten more minutes to the valley. When I finally landed at camp, I cut the engine and just rolled out of the cockpit onto the ground. It was a few minutes before I could even move." He had drained the tanks and measured the rest of the fuel; less than ten minutes of flying time had remained. I hugged him again and we turned toward the thorny thicket that had been our home. Camp — a lifetime in seven years. We walked back into it.

○ ○ ○

When we first decided to make this tree island our home, thousands of green branches had reached for the sky in a tangle of undergrowth. Now drought had gutted its luxuriant thicket, and its trees were gray and leafless. But here was the bush that the lions Muffin and Moffet always marked, and there was the old fireplace that had warmed our lives for more than two thousand nights. The lions of the Blue Pride had ransacked camp many times, pulling bags of flour, mealie-meal, and onions out of the trees around the kitchen boma — an open enclosure of grass and poles.

During our absence another couple had used the camp while studying desert antelope, but they had departed more than six months ago. The same faded tents lay draped across their poles, their flysheets ripped and tattered by cheeky desert storms. One side of the tent that held our lab and office had collapsed, and a small pool of rainwater from the recent shower lay bellied in its canvas. Mark planted the tent back on its poles, gingerly drew back the flaps, then with a stick chased a spitting cobra from inside. In the sleeping tent, the packing-crate bed sagged under the weight of a sodden mattress, and the tent floor was caked with mud.

The kitchen boma, with its thick, shaggy thatch roof, was still standing at the other end of camp. Inside were the cutting board Dolene had given us, the fire grate Bergie had made for us, and the blackened water kettle, scarred by the teeth of hyenas who had pirated it so often.

I looked around hopefully for the yellow-billed hornbills, those charismatic, comic birds with whom we had shared the island during every dry season. But I didn't see any. The recent light rain must have lured them back to the woodlands to mate, as it did every rainy season.

"Look who's here!" Mark exclaimed. I whirled around to see a Marico flycatcher fluttering to a branch ten inches from Mark's head. It immediately began shaking its wings, begging for something to eat. I slipped away to the cool-box in the truck and returned with a piece of cheese, one of the Marico's favorite snacks. I tossed a few bits to the ground at our feet. Without hesitation the bird swooped down, stuffed its beak with cheddar, and flew to the other side of camp.

Unloading boxes and trunks of supplies from the truck and the plane, we began the enormous job of cleaning and unpacking. Mark built a fire with some scraps from the woodpile, while I washed mud, spiderwebs, and a mouse's nest from the table in the kitchen boma. We made tea and laid out a lunch of bread, cheese, and jam on the table.

"We've got to start looking for lions right away," Mark began as soon as we sat down. April was supposed to be the end of the wet season, but according to the rain gauge only two inches of precipitation had fallen instead of the usual fourteen. Although this was enough to fill the water holes, it would evaporate in a few days. Soon the lions would be following the antelope away from the valley to their dry-season areas; we had to find and radio collar them before they left, so that we could monitor their movements with the radio receivers in the airplane and truck.

Even before our departure in 1980, the lions of the Blue Pride were already roaming over more than fifteen hundred square miles, and as much as sixty miles from their wet-season territory, in search of widely scattered prey. After four more years of drought, who could say where they were or whether they were still alive. They had led us to exciting new scientific discoveries: that they could survive indefinitely without water to drink — obtaining moisture from the fluids of their prey — and that their social behavior was different from that of other lions who lived in less harsh environments. We were anxious to continue our research for many years, and to determine how the die-off of tens of thousands of antelope had affected the lions. Their radio collars would have failed long ago; finding them would be a long shot. But if we could locate even a few, we could document not only their longevity and their ability to survive drought, but also their range sizes and the changes in pride composition during such periods.

Working feverishly that afternoon, we pulled everything out of the sleeping and office-lab tents and scrubbed the mud-caked floors. An elephant shrew with two babes clinging to her backside had to be gently evicted from her nest in the bottom drawer of the filing cabinet, and we found another snake behind the bookcase. While I continued with the cleanup, Mark prepared the darting rifle and radio collars for the lions.

Late in the afternoon, Mark carefully excavated our "wine cellar," a hole dug long ago under the thick, scraggly ziziphus trees. We had buried a few bottles in 1980, to drink on our return. The spade clanked against glass, and Mark pulled up a Nederburg Cabernet Sauvignon 1978. Sitting on the dry riverbed at the edge of camp, we watched the huge sun rest its chin on the dunes as we sipped red wine by the fire. Slowly Deception Valley faded away in the darkness.

ο ο ο

Awakened by the distant call of jackals, we had a quick breakfast around the fire. Then, pulling the old trailer, we drove to Mid Pan to collect water. We stopped at the edge of what amounted to an oversize mud puddle with antelope droppings and algae floating on the surface. We stood for a moment, silently staring at the sludge, and we seriously considered driving out of the reserve for water. But that would take too much time — lion time. As always before, we would boil the water twenty minutes before drinking it. Squatting on the slippery mud, we scooped our cooking pots full, avoiding the animal droppings as best we could, and poured it through funnels into jerry cans. A full can weighed roughly sixty pounds, and Mark lifted each onto the trailer and emptied it into one of the drums. By the time we had collected 440 gallons, our backs and legs ached.

That evening, our second in the valley, I cooked a supper of cornbread and canned chicken stew, which we ate by lantern and candlelight in the cozy thatched boma. Then, weary but warmly satisfied with the day's work, we slid into a deep sleep in our shipping-crate bed. Not many sounds would have awakened us that night; but just as a mother never sleeps through her baby's cries, the deep rolling roar that drifted over the dunes brought us both awake at the same instant.

"Lions!"

"To the south. Quick, get a bearing."

Lion roars can carry more than five miles in the desert; the fact that we could hear them didn't mean they were close. The best way to find the big cats would be from the air, so we took off at dawn. Swooping low over the treetops, we searched for them or for vultures that might lead us to their kill. Looking in all the favorite places of the Blue Pride, we saw small herds of springbok, gemsbok, hartebeest, and giraffes. But no lions.

The next morning we heard their bellows from the south again and Mark suggested, "Look, we've heard lions to the south two nights. Let's camp down there. We'll have a better chance of finding them."

There was no track in that direction, so I drove across the dunes, making a turn just before Cheetah Tree and keeping to the east of a low ridge of sand. I chose a campsite near a clay pan where Mark could land. Seconds later he appeared, seemingly from nowhere, flew by once to check for holes, then landed. We built a fire under a lone tree overlooking the gray depression; as we ate our stew, we felt as if we were camped on the edge of a moon crater. Knowing that the lions could wake us anytime during the night, we sacked out early on the ground next to our truck, the compass by our heads.

Lion roars. Three A.M. We bolted up in our bedrolls, and Mark took a bearing on the roars. Within minutes we were driving toward them. After we'd gone a mile through the bush, we stopped to listen again. Another bellow surged across the sands, breaking over us with the resonance of a wave thundering into a sea cave. We turned the truck toward the sound and drove about two hundred yards. Mark switched on the spotlight and a medium-size acacia bush jumped to life with the reflections of eleven pairs of eyes — an adult male, three adult females, and seven cubs. They were feeding on a fresh gemsbok kill.

Mark turned off the engine, lifted his binoculars, and searched the lions for ear tags or any familiar markings we knew. But we had never seen these individuals before.

Without a minute's hesitation, all seven cubs sauntered over to investigate our truck. Only three and a half to four months old, they almost certainly had never seen a vehicle before. They walked to Mark's door and peered at him, seven small faces in a row; they smelled the tires and bumpers and crawled under the truck. Their curiosity satisfied, they began tumbling and play-fighting in a small clearing nearby, their mothers watching with bland expressions.

We sat quite near — within thirty yards — habituating them to our presence so that we could dart them that evening. By the time the sun warmed the sand, they had settled into the shade of a large bush; soon all of them, including the cubs, were asleep.

Moving to a shady spot of our own, we had a lunch of peanuts and canned fruit, then checked all of the darting equipment again. Just before sunset we drove back to the lions and found the adults feeding, while the cubs climbed all over them. Perfect. Their attention would be on the carcass, not on us, and they would be unlikely to associate the pop of the gun or the sting of the dart with our presence.

We sat very still, not making a sound, waiting for one of the lionesses to stand so that we could dart her without risk of hitting a cub. The dose intended for a three-hundred-pound lion could kill a twenty-pound youngster.

Several minutes later, one of the largest females stood and turned full flank to us. Mark loaded the dart, took aim, and squeezed the trigger. Nothing happened.

"What the . . . !?" Mark pulled the gun back through the window and thumbed the safety "on." The gun fired and the dart flew out the window into the bushes. Mark cocked the unloaded gun and pulled the trigger; it didn't fire. When he clicked the safety on, it did. Whatever the problem was, we had no time to fix it. The more the lions gorged themselves, the more drug it would take to sedate them. Mark would use the safety to fire the rifle. He took aim again as one of the females stood up; but as he did, a cub crawled under her neck.

Mark waited a few seconds, his cheek against the gun stock, while the cub moved past the lioness. He thumbed the safety on and the gun fired with a muted pop. Just as the dart lobbed out of the barrel, another cub stepped from under the female's belly. We watched helplessly as the dart arched lower and lower, striking the cub in the flank. He squealed, spun around, and stumbled off into the thick bush.

"Good God!" I cried.

"Where did it come from? The cub I was watching moved off!"

We had darted lions and other carnivores more than a hundred times, and nothing like this had ever happened before.

"Should we go after it?" I asked.

"There's nothing we can do. That cub doesn't have a chance. Let's concentrate on getting collars on the adults," Mark said. "First, we have to see about this damned gun." As saddened as we were about the cub, I knew Mark was right. We drove off about four hundred yards and while I held the flashlight, Mark repaired the gun on the hood of the truck.

After driving back to the lions, Mark darted the female that he'd missed, then the male, whose golden mane tinged with black was one of the most beautiful we had ever seen. The two darted lions moved off into the bush where, seventeen minutes later, they slumped down under the influence of the drug.

I put salve in the male's eyes, while Mark injected him with antibiotic. We collared and measured both him and the female, keeping an eye out for the two undarted lionesses, who had disappeared into the bush.

After checking the breathing and pulse of the darted lions, we moved off a hundred yards and sat for an hour until they were yawning and stretching, fully recovered. Then as Mark began driving back to the plane, I saw a small lump that looked like a rag on the cold sand.

"Mark! It's the cub!" We jumped from the truck and walked to the infant.

I watched for the adults as Mark squatted beside the cub, slipping his fingers between its front leg and chest and feeling for a pulse. The cub's body was already cool. Several seconds went by, then Mark felt a little blurb of pressure beneath his fingertips. Pushing his fingers deeper into the fur, he detected a single subtle pulse.

While I rushed to the truck to get the drug boxes, Mark massaged the cub, trying to stimulate his heart. He gave the little lion an intravenous injection of Doprim, a respiratory stimulant, and a massive intramuscular injection of antibiotic. Within minutes the cub's pulse was stronger but he was still hypothermic. We gently laid a canvas tarp over him, covering everything but his face, and heaped a pyramid of sand over his body for extra insulation. I stroked his muzzle once more, then carried the drug boxes back to the Cruiser.

Mark was making a fifteen-second count of the cub's pulse when we heard a loud splintering crash and a growl. Mark whirled and saw a lioness crashing through an acacia bush forty yards away. As he sprinted for the truck, I grabbed the spotlight and flicked it on, trying to dazzle the lioness. But the light shone directly into Mark's eyes, blinding him instead. Holding his arm over his face, he staggered forward. I dipped the light so he could see. The lioness stopped at the cub, sniffing it briefly. Then she bounded over it and ran toward Mark, her big feet drumming on the sand.

With one hand I swept the darting equipment from the front seat onto the floor and slid into the driver's seat, ready to start the engine. Once more I held the light on the charging lioness.

Blinded again, Mark slammed into the side of the front fender of the truck and stumbled back. He reached up for a handhold, tried vaulting onto the Toyota's hood, but missed and fell to the ground.

Swinging the light back and forth over the lioness' eyes, I opened the door, screaming "Get in! Get in!" Jumping to his feet, Mark fumbled frantically for the door. Finally he found it and dived in, crawling over me to the other side of the front seat.

The lioness broke off her charge only eight yards away. Her tail flicking, she walked back to her cub, sniffed its head and the sand over its body, then strolled back to the gemsbok carcass. The other lions were feeding again and had ignored the commotion. Both of us slumped against the back of the seat and breathed deeply. We would name that lioness Stormy.

We drove the truck to a lonchicarpus tree several hundred yards from the newly collared lions. I dug out some baked beans and we ate them cold out of the can. It was after midnight; we had been working almost continuously for twenty-two hours. My eyes felt as though they had sand in them, and Mark's shins and knees throbbed from hitting the truck.

We reeked of lions, the way a cowboy smells of his horse — a dank, earthy, not altogether unpleasant odor. But because carnivores sometimes carry echinococci, parasites that can infect the human brain, we splashed some cold water and disinfectant into a basin and washed thoroughly. Too tired to drive to the plane, we laid our foam mats and sleeping bags in the back of the Land Cruiser and crawled inside. Toolboxes at our feet, jerry cans at our heads, and the back door standing ajar, we slept.

We opened our eyes to a crisp Kalahari dawn, sunlight streaming over the dunes. After a quick breakfast we drove back to the dune crest to check on the lions. As soon as Mark switched off the truck, the collared female yawned deeply and began licking her front paw. We named her Sage and the male Sunrise. Stormy watched us carefully for a few minutes. Then even she began to nod and snooze in the morning sun, apparently at ease with us. Saucy, who along with Stormy had avoided being collared last night, slept with her head on Stormy's flank. Sitting among the heap of lions, we were pleased to have a new pride, though disappointed that we had not found the old one.

We drove to the spot where we had left the darted infant. The small pyramid of sand was flat; the cub and tarp were gone. I was hopeful that he had recovered, but Mark pointed out that he wouldn't have taken the tarp. "A hyena or a jackal may have got him," he said.

I drove Mark back to the plane and he took off from the clay depression, the plane bouncing over the rough ground. He flew over, checking the radio collars from the air, then headed on to camp.

Returning to the lions, I circled them in the truck, searching for the darted cub but finding no sign of him. I parked under a shade tree and began copying the notes I'd made the previous night. Dozing in the hot truck, I lifted my head from time to time to check on the lions. Now and then they shifted their position for better shade, and so did I.

Just before sunset one of the cubs bounded from the thicket, chased by another. Then three ran full speed across the clearing and behind a bush. Two dashed into the open, tearing and pulling on the dead gemsbok's tail. Were they the first pair, or two new cubs? Now four tumbled through the grass in a mock hunt, and one of them dashed out of view as two others pulled a piece of canvas. They were playing with the tarp! Two more cubs bounded into the scene. Seven! There were seven cubs! The one we darted was okay; in fact, I could see no difference between his behavior and that of the others. I counted again, just to be sure. Seven. I smiled.

The adults also moved into the clearing and lay in the last rays of sunshine, while the cubs attacked their ears, muzzles, and tails. As Stormy began walking south, Sage stood, stretched, and followed. The cubs trotted to catch up, and finally Saucy and Sunrise trundled after the others in a long, rambling line. As the sun set, I watched their golden bodies glide through the blond grass until they disappeared. Then I headed for camp to tell Mark the good news.

○ ○ ○

CRASH! A tin trunk full of canned food hit the ground in the kitchen boma. I looked at my watch; it was 5:30 A.M. We jumped from bed and pulled on our jeans. We had been in the Kalahari for almost six weeks and had darted eight lions in three prides. But still we had not found the Blue Pride.

Pushing back the flap of our tent, we peered out and saw the female lions romping around the campfire. Sage was dragging the ax handle in her mouth, while Stormy pawed at its head. Saucy was standing inside the grass boma, sniffing the pots on top of the table. We tiptoed down the path through camp to get a better look.

Two of the still unpacked boxes of food supplies lay on their sides with tins of oatmeal and powdered milk scattered around the campfire. Saucy chomped into a pot with her teeth and, holding it over her nose, pranced from the boma. The others chased her.

Their bellies were high and tight to their spines, a sign that they had not fed for several days. We had been following them for the previous five nights and they had not made a kill. Their cubs were nowhere to be seen. Seven cubs were too many for inexperienced mothers in these dry times; under such conditions the young are often abandoned.

Then my eyes met those of a fourth lioness, standing just beyond the trees of camp. We stared at each other for long seconds. She was old; her back sagged, and her belly hung low. For some reason she did not join in the play. Was she too old for it? Or had she played this game too many times before? We looked for ear tags or scars; there were none.

"Hey! Come on, that's enough," Mark called as Stormy stuck her head into the supply tent. He clapped his hands loudly and the lioness backed up, looked us over, then ambled back to the kitchen, where she grabbed a dish towel and ran out of camp. The other two followed and they chased one another around the plane. After a while the three young lionesses calmed down and, with the old one, walked north along the track. We grabbed some peanut butter and crackers for breakfast, got into the truck, and followed. They paused on the other side of Acacia Point, then broke into a trot to greet Sunrise, the newly collared male, who was swaggering from the bushes of East Dune onto the dry riverbed. After rubbing sinuously along his mane and body, the pride continued north toward the water hole on Mid Pan.

At the water's edge they lay flank to flank and drank for several minutes, their lapping tongues reflected in the water. Sunrise lifted his tail and scent-marked a thicket — the same thicket the Blue Pride lions had always sprayed when they passed the water hole. As the pride settled down under a shade tree at the base of East Dune, we returned to camp to prepare the darting equipment. Tonight we must collar Stormy, Saucy, and the old lioness.

When we returned in the late afternoon, Sunrise was feeding on a twenty-five-pound steenbok in the tall grass of East Dune. He had probably taken it from the lionesses moments earlier. Fifty yards away Saucy and the old lioness were feeding on a freshly killed gemsbok. But Stormy, Sage, and their cubs — the ones who most needed the meat — were nowhere in sight.

Mark darted Saucy and the old lioness with the sagging back, and they wandered away from the carcass into the bush, where we could treat them without disturbing Sunrise. Working quickly, we collared Saucy first. Then Mark nudged the old lioness gently with his foot to be sure she was properly sedated. Crouching beside her, he pushed back the hair on her left ear, uncovering a black plastic pin and a tiny piece of yellow plastic — the remains of an old ear tag.

I thumbed quickly through the identification cards of all the lions we had known. Blue — blue tag in right ear; Sassy — red tag in right ear; Happy — yellow tag in left ear . . .

"Mark, it's Happy!" We sat down next to the old lioness and stroked her. As a young female of the Springbok Pan Pride, she had invaded the Blue Pride's territory, won acceptance from its resident females, raided our camp with them, sat with us in the moonlight, slept near us, and — finally — had beguiled us, as she had the males Muffin and Moffet. We had spent hundreds of hours with her as we tried to understand the ways of desert lions. She had often swapped prides and males and had wandered away from Deception Valley many times, but she had always come back. Now she was a matron who had made it through one of the worst droughts the area had known.

We gave Happy a new yellow tag and radio collar, measured her body, and took pictures of her worn teeth. During all of this we touched her more than was necessary. By the time we finished, I had memorized her face.

Happy lifted her head slightly and looked around. Reluctantly, we backed away to the safety of the truck to watch her recover. When we were satisfied that both darted lionesses were recovering well, we drove the truck around some bushes to the gemsbok carcass. Sunrise was sleeping a short distance away, his belly round and heavy with meat. Feeding on the carcass were Sage, Stormy, and the seven cubs.

The cubs were already very full, their small bellies bulging like melons. They pulled at the fresh meat for a few more minutes, and then three of them plopped down and fell asleep. The other four tumbled around the grassy clearing, spending most of their time bouncing on Sunrise's expansive stomach. We were almost too elated to leave, but the deep yawns of the lions were contagious. We headed toward camp.

The drying grasses of the dunes glowed in the light of the full moon, which was so bright in the cloudless sky that we drove without headlights across the valley floor. But as we stepped from the truck at camp, the light began to dim, giving the desert a shimmering blue-gray cast. We looked up to see that the earth's shadow was stalking the moon; a full lunar eclipse was under way.

Pulling the foam mattress and sleeping bags out of our tent, we laid them on the ancient riverbed, next to several *Acacia tortillas* trees at the edge of camp. Their twisted, thorny branches had somehow spited the drought by producing flowers, then corkscrew pods full of seeds. From our spot we could see five miles along the valley and watch this secret desert drama before drifting off to sleep. Slowly the earth drew its shadow across the face of the moon, and the Kalahari grew dark and silent.

Moments later the stillness was broken by the clopping of heavy hooves. Three stately giraffes glided into view above us, silhouettes against the darkening sky. Apparently they had not noticed the two lumps on the ground, and it was too late for us to move without frightening them. We lay still, swaddled in our sleeping bags, literally at their feet. They spread out a few yards away, browsing the pods from the acacias. Lying almost under the giraffes' bellies, in this silky light we felt as if we were being absorbed into the desert.

The next morning, May 13, the entire eastern horizon was lined with patchwork clouds, blushing deep pink at first, then transforming into a quilt of gold when the sun found the dunes east of Deception Valley. As we ate pancakes around the campfire, I looked out over the valley; all seemed well with the Kalahari. We had heard reports — perhaps only rumors — that the government was planning to turn the lower two-thirds of the reserve into cattle ranches. Even though thousands of wildebeest had already died along the fences, there might still be time to resolve the conflict between cattle and wild animals. Knowing that Happy had lived through the drought gave us renewed hope that the reserve itself would survive.

Mark walked to the office tent for the radio schedule with Sue Carver, our contact in Maun, more than a hundred miles to the north. Meanwhile, I cleared away our dishes and fed the Marico flycatchers.

"Hello, Mark. I have an important message for you," I heard Sue say, her voice crackling.

"Hi, Sue. I'm ready to copy. Go ahead."

"It's from the Immigration Department. They say that your research permit has been denied and that you are to report to the Immigration Department in Gaborone immediately. Repeat, you must report to the Immigration Department immediately."

3
Against the Wind

MARK

Some things just
don't go on. some circles
come undone. some sparrows

fall. sometimes sorrow,
in spite of resolution,

enters in.

— PAULA GUNN ALLEN

○ ○ ○

"ARE WE BEING JAILED?" I asked. His face set in stone, the immigration officer said nothing and continued rolling my fingers over an ink pad, then pressing them on white cards, one each for the military, police, and immigration authorities. The day before, we had flown to Gaborone, the capital of Botswana, and this morning had been detained at immigration headquarters.

"Please, I would like to telephone the U.S. embassy," I said.

"No."

He finished taking my fingerprints, and I watched as he began with Delia. Another man took my elbow firmly and started to lead me away.

"Wait, please, don't separate us . . . ," Delia pleaded in a small voice. Pulling my arm free, I walked back to her side and said to the second man, "Just wait till he's through, okay?" He released my arm. When they had finished taking Delia's prints, another officer pushed two forms across the desk toward us. "You must sign these."

"*Declaration of Status as Prohibited Immigrants (PI)*" leaped off the page. They were throwing us out of the country! Before I could read any further, he snatched the forms away.

I swallowed hard and asked politely, "What does it mean if we sign these forms? I would like to see an attorney first."

The officer stood up abruptly and strode across the room. When he returned, he was followed by a giant of a man six and a half feet tall, weighing about two hundred fifty pounds. The big man glared down at me. "What is your problem?" he rumbled. "Sign, and then you can go about your business."

"I'm sorry, but we can't sign this without reading it first." I tried to explain. "When we were intercepted and brought here, we were on our way to the permanent secretary to the president with this letter appealing the denial of our research permits." I held up the envelope.

"After you sign, you can go to the president's office or wherever you want. And you can appeal the PI ruling. But you must sign these forms now!" He slapped the sheets onto the desk in front of us. I started to protest again, but he leaned over until his face was inches from mine.

"Sign, or the law will take its course. Do you understand what that means?"

I looked at Delia and put my signature on the PI notice. She did the same. The instant I lifted my pen from the form, he jabbed his finger at a paragraph near the end of the page.

"You will note in this subsection," he said, "that when the declaration is by presidential decree, as in this case, there is no right of appeal."

"But you just told us . . ."

"If you read the form, you will see that what I say is true and that I have no choice in the matter," he cut me off.

For the first time we were allowed to read the document we had signed. It stated that the president himself had ordered our deportation, that we could not appeal his decision, and that no reason need be given for it.

The big man led us to a small room where he stood facing us, his back to the wall, arms folded across his barrel chest. A uniformed policeman was seated behind a desk.

"As of this moment you are in Botswana illegally," the policeman said.

"But why?" Delia spoke up. "We've done nothing wrong. What are we charged with?"

"I'm just a cog in the machine. And even if I knew, I couldn't tell you. You must be out of the country by five o'clock. Do you know what the law expects of you now?"

It was already two-thirty. They were giving us only two and a half hours to get to the hotel, pack, go to the airport, plan our flight, check through customs and immigration, preflight the airplane, and take off.

"Look, please, we have thousands of dollars worth of equipment at our camp," I pointed out. "We need time to go back there and dispose of it. And what about the weather? We're in a small plane. Clouds are building up. It may not be safe for us to take off."

He leaned toward us, scowling. "I say again, if you are not out of this country by 5:00 P.M. the law will take its course! Do you understand?"

We rushed back to the hotel, threw our clothes into our suitcase, and stopped briefly at the American embassy to report what had happened. At four-thirty-five we hailed a cab to the airport. Fifteen minutes after takeoff, the Limpopo River slipped by below us. On May 15, 1985, as we left Botswana's airspace, we passed from wild, innocent Africa with its sweeping savannas of plains game and wide rivers of sand into a new era of confusion, turbulence, uncertainty, and danger. At the Limpopo we flew into a strong head wind.

4
Beyond Deception

DELIA

> The woods where the weird shadows slant,
> The stillness, the moonlight, the mystery,
> I've bade 'em good-by — but I can't.
> . . . . .
> There are valleys unpeopled and still;
> There's a land — oh, it beckons and beckons,
> And I want to go back — and I will.
>
> — ROBERT SERVICE

○ ○ ○

STANDING IN THE MIDDLE of a field, five hundred miles south of Deception Valley, I looked up at the moon. At this moment the same full moon was hanging over the desert, and I wished that I could somehow see the reflection of the dunes and the old riverbed in its face. Was Happy still with Stormy and Sunrise? How were Saucy's cubs, and Sage's? Like the wildebeest, we could no longer move freely into the desert; we were another casualty of the fences.

Botswana gave no official reason for expelling us. Informally, the ambassador to Washington told us that his president, Quett Masire, had been angered by our reports on the fences that blocked Kalahari migrations and resulted in the deaths of hundreds of thousands of desert antelope. But our accounts were accurate, and we believed it our responsibility to report the disastrous effects of these fences on wildlife (see Appendix A). Later another Botswana official confided that we were really deported because powerful ranchers-cum-politicians had wanted to establish their private cattle ranches in the Central Kalahari Game Reserve, and they knew we would speak out against their scheme. One of the longest-running scientific studies of lions and other carnivores in the wild and one of the largest wildlife protectorates in the world were both being tossed aside for the financial benefit of a few people.

Writing appeals, reports, letters, we tried frantically to get back to the desert. Many people, including U.S. congressmen from both parties, Atlanta's Mayor Andrew Young, and then Vice President George Bush, requested that Botswana's officials allow us to return. But they refused to discuss the issue — even to respond to the vice president of the United States. Months passed.

Time was being wasted; lion time, hyena time, conservation time, a lifetime, it seemed. We wrote more letters, made more phone calls. But there was no answer from Botswana.

After eight months Mark accepted the fact that we were banished from the Kalahari and wisely decided that we should search for a new wilderness to study. But hope still stalked me. Even after all this time, I believed a letter would arrive or a telephone would ring with the message that we had been misunderstood, that Botswana had relented and would allow us to go back to Deception Valley.

I gazed at the farm cottage where we were staying, outside Johannesburg. All but smothered in flowering vines, it was another home that had opened its arms to us, another wonderful family, another friendly dog. We had been living out of suitcases for months, always in someone else's back room or guest cottage — from California to Johannesburg — and had had so many different addresses that our mail rarely caught up with us. A trail of unanswered letters and spoiled dogs lay behind us.

One day I noticed a tab of paper pinned on a friend's bulletin board. Amid Gary Larson cartoons and holiday photos was a quote by Alexander Graham Bell, "Sometimes we stare so long at the door that has been closed to us, we do not see the many doors that are open." I read it twice, a third time, then walked to where Mark was writing and said, "It's time to find another Deception Valley." We would go in search of a new wilderness, and with a new idea.

For years we had believed that, at least in some places, wildlife can be more beneficial to a country and its people than exotic agricultural schemes. Too often aid and development agencies sweep aside the valuable natural resources in an area so they can get on with "real" development. They chop down lush forests and kill off wildlife, only to plant crops that deplete the soil of nutrients and yield poorly; they irrigate arid lands until they are sterilized by mineral salts; they overgraze grasslands, turning them to deserts.

This is what had gone wrong in Botswana. The Kalahari was teeming with wildlife whose migrations had adapted them to long droughts and sparse grasslands. These animals could be used for tourism, game ranching, safari hunting, and other schemes that would bring revenue to a large number of local residents, including Bushmen. Instead, the World Bank, the European common market countries, and the Botswana Development Corporation wanted to replace wildlife with cattle. Large-scale commercial ranchers in the Kalahari had already killed off hundreds of thousands of wild animals, overgrazed the desert, and depleted the water from fossilized aquifers. They had left a wasteland that was good for neither wild nor domestic stock.

In most places on earth, Nature long ago figured out what works best, and where. Often the best improvement humans can make is to leave everything alone. Nowhere is this more true than in marginal lands. The least we can do — before we chop down trees or build long fences — is watch for a while, to see if we can make the natural resources work for us in a sustainable way. Perhaps if local people who live near national parks could benefit directly from them, for example through tourism, they would recognize the economic value of wild animals and work to conserve them.

It was an idea worth exploring. But first we had to find a place.

○ ○ ○

Standing over a map of Africa, we eliminated one country after another. The continent seemed to come apart in pieces: Angola and Mozambique were torn with civil wars; Namibia was under attack from SWAPO (the South West Africa People's Organization), and human overpopulation had just about finished off the wildlife in western Africa. Sudan was out: the Frankfurt Zoological Society, our sponsors, had recently lost a camp to the Sudanese Liberation Army, which had kidnapped the staff members and held them for ransom. As Mark's hand swept across the map, wild Africa seemed to shrink before our eyes.

The region most likely to have large wilderness areas was tucked under the shoulder of the continent in Zimbabwe, Zambia, Zaire, and Tanzania. We began to outline the hundreds of details for a three-thousand-mile expedition north from South Africa through these countries. Mark would fly the Frankfurt Zoological Society airplane and I would drive the truck with its trailer; we would meet along the way at potential sites. We contacted the American embassies to find out where we could get aviation and diesel fuel, and where it would be safe to land without fear of partisans or bandits. We bought, labeled, and packed camping gear, foodstuffs, and scores of spare airplane and truck parts that would not be available on our route.

Finally, a year after being expelled from Botswana, we were almost ready to depart. Several travelers had recently been murdered along the main roads through Zimbabwe and Zambia, however, and the American embassies in those countries had issued travel warnings to U.S. citizens. So that I would not have to drive alone, Mark prepared to fly our plane to Lusaka, Zambia. He would leave it at the airport, then return to Johannesburg on a commercial flight so that we could ride together to Zambia.

On the morning of May 19, 1986, Mark drove to Lanseria Airport just north of Johannesburg, where our Cessna was hangared, to make his flight to Lusaka. Standing in the open door of the plane, he was loading his duffel bag and flight case when a man rushed up behind him and panted, "Excuse me, I believe you're flying to Lusaka?"

"That's right," Mark answered.

"Any chance of a lift?" the man asked hopefully.

"No problem," Mark assured him. "What's the hurry?"

"Haven't you heard? The South Africans bombed Lusaka this morning. And they hit ANC [African National Congress] hideouts in Botswana and Zimbabwe!"

"Lusaka! Are you sure?"

"Yeah. I'm a UPI reporter; I've got to get there quick." Mark stared at him for a moment, then said, "I don't know about you, pal, but I'm not flying to Lusaka today."

Our Cessna 180K was the same model that South African defense forces used for reconnaissance flights, and it still bore its South African registry. After canceling his flight, Mark returned to the cottage where we were staying. We sat at the table reading the latest news releases: "South African Defense Force hits three capitals in the biggest operation so far launched against ANC targets."

Our plan not only called for Mark to fly into Lusaka, which had just been bombed, but to fly the length of Zimbabwe, which had also been attacked and was known to have antiaircraft guns and surface-to-air (SAM) missiles. It would be foolhardy to fly over these territories with a South African–registered plane. But since we had purchased the plane in South Africa, by international law it had to retain that registry until we officially imported it into another nation and reregistered it. And that we could not do until we had settled in a new country.

"I'll give it a week; maybe things will cool down," Mark said, looking over his paper at me.

"Why not fly over Botswana instead of Zimbabwe? There are fewer antiaircraft batteries and missile installations in Botswana," I suggested.

"Much longer flight, and I might not have enough fuel. Don't worry, Roy told me how to avoid missiles."

Roy Liebenberg, a former military pilot, had taught Mark how to fly. They still kept in touch. His most recent bit of advice: "Stay real low so they can't get a lock on you. If you see a launch, climb straight for the sun until the missile is right behind you. Then chop the power, break hard right or left, and dive for the ground." Roy had also warned Mark about flying into Lusaka International Airport. Understandably, the Zambians were somewhat trigger-happy since the South African raid, and apparently they had accidently shot down two of their own military planes.

"I can't believe we're having this conversation," I said. Mark shook his paper and went back to his reading.

After several days, news of the attacks died away, and it became apparent that South African forces had made surgical strikes against ANC headquarters rather than more general attacks against the Botswana, Zimbabwe, and Zambian governments. Mark phoned the American embassy in Lusaka, and although the official with whom he spoke understandably did not want to give any guarantees, he said that life in Lusaka was going on "pretty much as normal and a flight should be fine."

On May 26, a week after the raids, Mark filed an official flight plan informing the Lusaka control tower that he would arrive at their field that evening. The plan went through by telex and no specific instructions or warnings were issued, so Mark took off. He flew checkpoint to checkpoint over Botswana and Zimbabwe for five hours. Darkness had rolled in beneath him by the time he was over the eastern end of Lake Kariba, the outline of its shore only faintly evident from the cooking fires of remote villages. Lusaka was still fifty minutes away.

When he approached Lusaka airspace, the controller did not answer his radio calls. Mark tried again and again. No response. He could not know it, but soldiers were manning antiaircraft guns at the end of the runway. The tower controller had alerted them to the approach of an unauthorized South African–registered plane. Cranking the guns around, they fixed their sights on the Cessna.

Even though Mark had not heard from the controller, he had no choice but to land; his fuel was almost gone. Approaching from the east, he lined up on the main runway and flew directly toward the antiaircraft battery.

When the plane was off the end of the runway, the gunners began to finger their triggers. Suddenly a Land Rover roared to a stop, and a colonel in the Zambian air force jumped out, yelling and waving his arms as he ran toward the gun battery. Seconds later Mark glided over the end of the runway and touched down.

Standing about a hundred fifty yards away in its own pool of harsh light, the terminal building looked deserted. Mark climbed out, stretched, unloaded his luggage, and began tying down the plane for the night. All at once, six soldiers stormed toward him from the building, their Kalashnikov (AK-47) rifles leveled at his stomach. "Halt! Do not move!"

Two of the soldiers grabbed Mark by the arms and steered him into the building and to a room with a faded blue "Police" sign over the door. The others followed with their AKs still leveled at the prisoner. They sat Mark on the bench and stood back, waiting.

Soon the colonel strode into the room, pulled a chair in front of Mark, and sat down facing him. For seven hours he grilled Mark on who he was and what he was doing in Lusaka. Fortunately, Mark had a briefcase full of introductory letters from the U.S. embassy, research permits, customs clearances, and a copy of his official flight plan. Finally, at 3:30 A.M. the colonel shook his index finger in Mark's face. "I was called to the antiaircraft battery as you were approaching the field. My men wanted to open fire and shoot you down. If I hadn't been there, you would be dead right now."

The next day Mark returned to Johannesburg on a commercial flight, wondering where a biologist fits on this tormented continent.

○ ○ ○

Our trunks were packed, and preparations for the journey north were complete. We were having supper in the A-frame cottage in Johannesburg, on our last night before departure, when the phone rang. Kevin Gill, our longtime friend, confidant, and legal counsel, was on the line. Some of our mail was still being delivered to his home, where we often stayed, and he told me that we had received an official letter from the government of Botswana. This was their first communication since they had deported us a year ago.

"Would you like me to read it to you, Delia?"

"I guess so, Kevin," I said.

There was a brief silence and the sound of shuffling papers. "Yes, it's what I thought." The letter from Mr. Festes Mochae, personal secretary to the president, was short and to the point: "The president has carefully considered all these appeals and has decided to lift your status as Prohibited Immigrants."

I muttered a word of thanks to Kevin, hung up, and ran to Mark. For months we had tried to get a reversal of the deportation. We had finally given up and set our sights on a new goal. And now we could go back to the Kalahari. We stared at each other in a confusion of emotions.

We had been cleared of any wrongdoing, but a lot of international pressure — from the United States and Europe — had been brought to bear on Botswana for deporting us simply because we reported an environmental problem. Other scientists had visited the desert and confirmed that our reports of the dying wildebeest were accurate. People were outraged about the fences; we were no longer the issue. Still, because of all the controversy we knew that we would not be welcome in Botswana at this time. We had no choice but to carry on with our plan to search for a new location. One day we would go back to Deception Valley to look again for a lioness named Happy. But that would be much later.

○ ○ ○

"Toyota Spares." "Airplane Spares." "Everyday Tools." "Everyday Food." "Food Stores." "Cooking Kit." "Bedding and Mosquito Nets." "Lanterns and Accessories." "Reference Books and Maps." "Cameras." "First Aid." "Mark's Clothes." "Delia's Clothes." Carefully labeled heavy trunks filled the truck, along with a mattress, folding chairs and tables, a chuck box, and two jerry cans of water. In the trailer were five drums of aviation gas, a drum of diesel fuel, three spare tires, a pump, a tent, shovels, axes, two high-lift jacks, ropes, and tarps. Driving our tired old Land Cruiser and worn-out trailer, their homemade bodies patched and repatched with scrap steel, we inched our way up Africa. None of the rusty blue trunks of supplies gave a clue to the dreams and the hopes that were packed inside.

During one portion of our journey through Zimbabwe, we were a hundred miles directly east of the Kalahari. Low, dark clouds stretched endlessly across the sky to the west, and we thought that perhaps rain was falling on the desert. Maybe the long drought had ended; maybe Happy, Sage, and Stormy would at last get a taste of water. On June 2, 1986, we crossed the Zambezi River, and headed north toward another season.

○ ○ ○

"We thought we would try Liuwa Plain National Park next," Mark said to Gilson Kaweche, chief research officer for Zambia's national parks. We had just spent five weeks exploring Kafue National Park in east central Zambia, often camping in places that had not seen a human in more than twenty years. Kafue was big and beautiful — the size of Wales — but hordes of commercial poachers were exterminating all the wildlife there. The park and its problems were too big for our resources.

Kaweche shifted uneasily in his chair at our mention of Liuwa Plain. "Ah, well, I'm sorry to say that security is a problem there, because of the UNITA [National Union for the Total Independence of Angola] rebels. Anyway, most of the animals in that park were shot long ago."

"I guess in that case we could try West Lungu Park first."

Kaweche's brow wrinkled as he concentrated on the doodle he was drawing. "Yes, but unfortunately in Lungu you will have a similar problem with security: some Zairian smugglers have been laying landmines along the roads. It would be highly risky for you to go there. I doubt my government would permit it."

"And Sioma Park, down in the southwest? What is the situation there?" I asked.

"Well, again it's the security problem. Sioma is right on the Caprivi Strip, which is South African territory. Freedom fighters from Angola cross the strip into Botswana on their way to South Africa. The South African army is trying to stop them. It would be unsafe for you to work there."

"How about Blue Lagoon, on the Kafue River . . . ?"

"I'm afraid the army has taken over that national park."

"How can the army take over a national park?"

"The military can do anything it wants." He chuckled.

One by one, we asked about the nineteen national parks shown on the maps of Zambia. Most were parks on paper only.

"We'll have to try Tanzania," Mark said to me. Our permits to look for a research site there had not yet been approved, so we would have to enter the country as tourists. If we found a suitable place for our research, we would request permission to stay.

I glanced up again at the map on the wall, my eyes traveling along the route that would take us through Zambia to Tanzania. More than four hundred miles up the road from Lusaka was another national park. "What about North Luangwa?" I asked.

"I'm sad to say that we have about written off the North Park," he replied. "It is just too remote and inaccessible to protect. No one goes to North Luangwa, so we have no idea what's happening there. I've never seen it myself, but I've heard it is a beautiful place."

"Anything wrong with our stopping there to take a look, on our way to Tanzania?"

"No," he said, "just give us a report on what you find." Gilson went on to warn us that this was not a "national park" in the American sense. There were no tourist facilities, no roads, and no one living in the park — not even game scouts. It was a 2400-square-mile tract of raw wilderness. Seasonal flooding of its many rivers made it impassible in the rainy season. The sectional map that Gilson spread over his desk gave no hint of even a track leading into the valley. Remote, rugged, and inaccessible — North Luangwa sounded like our kind of place.

After thanking Gilson, we visited Norman Carr, an old poacher-cum-game-ranger-cum-tour-operator, who in his eighty-odd years has come to know the valley better than any other African. Carr leads walking safaris in South Luangwa National Park, and his tough hide and infinite knowledge of trees, birds, and mammals are testimony to his expertise.

"Forget it. North Luangwa is impossible. You'll have a bloody time getting around in the dry season because of all the deep ravines and sand," he said. "And you can't drive around in the wet season because of all the mud. Those flash floods — they'll wash your truck away, even your camp."

Maybe. But we were determined to see for ourselves. Besides, if North Luangwa was not the wilderness we longed for, where else could we go?

PART TWO ○○○

A Season for Change

Prologue

MARK

THE SUN SINKS SLOWLY behind the mountains of the scarp as One Tusk, the elephant matriarch, steps cautiously from the forest along the Mwaleshi River in Zambia. Holding her trunk aloft, she searches the wind for danger. She is thirsty, as are the four young females in her family, one with an infant that gently presses his head into his mother's flank. Weeks earlier the rains tapered off, and by now most of the water holes away from the rivers are liquid mud. The elephants have come a long way since yesterday without drinking. They hurry forward, eager to cool themselves in the river after the heat of the day. But the matriarch holds them back, perhaps remembering an earlier time when poachers had chosen such a place for their ambush. She waits, her mouth dry with fear and drought, as the little calf nuzzles her mother's withered breast.

At that same moment, in Mwamfushi Village, far upstream of the elephants, another mother holds a crying infant to her flaccid breast. The stingy rains have turned the millet and maize to yellow, shriveled weeds. There will be starvation in the village this year unless the men go hunting in the park — unless Musakanya, her young husband, goes poaching.

For the past two weeks the family has lived on little more than *n'shima,* a paste of boiled maize meal dipped in a gravy made with beans. They crave meat, and Musakanya knows where to get it. He shoulders his rifle and walks down a dusty footpath that sixty miles later will end in the North Luangwa National Park. At the edge of his village, under the tree where they always meet on these expeditions, he joins Bwalya Muchisa and Chanda Seven, two friends who will poach for more than meat; they are going for ivory.

5
Into the Rift

MARK

Wilderness is not dependent upon a vast, unsettled tract of land. Rather, it is a quality of awareness, an openness to the light, to the seasons, and to nature's perpetual renewal.

— JOHN ELDER

○ ○ ○

SEVERAL DAYS AFTER our meeting with Gilson Kaweche at the National Parks headquarters, Delia drives and I fly the four hundred miles from Lusaka to Mpika. We sleep a cold, windy July night on the airstrip. At sunrise the next morning we take off down the runway into a strong wind. Zulu Sierra rises like a kite over a forested hill and within five minutes the last thatched hut has slipped from view below us. Soon after, the forest floor begins to show its first ripples and rills — the effects of titanic stresses along the Rift Valley. Two massive tectonic plates, one on each side of this gigantic trench, are drifting apart, tearing Africa in two. Taller mountains loom ahead, like sentinels guarding the valley. We climb over them, and fly along great ridges of rock, then over deep canyons, partly hidden by tropical trees and luxuriant sprays of bamboo, that seem to plunge away to the very center of the earth. Rushing rivers and waterfalls cascade over walls of sheer granite.

Suddenly a huge jawbone of rock runs northeast-southwest across our track as far as we can see — the Muchinga Escarpment, the western wall of the great Rift. Massive blunted mountains are rooted in this jaw like mammoth crooked molars, and whitewater streams burst between them, coursing untamed down the apron of the scarp and into the valley. According to our charts, these rivers — the Lufishi, Mwaleshi, Lufwashi, Mulandashi, and Munyamadzi — stream off the scarp to join the larger, wilder Luangwa

River. Flowing along the eastern border of the park, the Luangwa wanders to and fro over the valley floor, spreading the rich alluvium its tributaries have eroded from the plateau to the west beyond the Muchinga. It flows from Tanzania into Zambia, on to the Zambezi, and thence to the Indian Ocean between Mozambique and Malawi.

As we fly between two rounded cusps of the escarpment, the earth below us disappears, just drops away, leaving nothing but white haze under the plane. I pull back the throttle and we descend more than three thousand feet through the murk to the valley floor. Leaning forward, I watch for any peaks that might reach up to gut the belly of our plane, while Delia tries to spot a topographical feature that will tell us where we are.

Minutes later, the serpentine shape of a sandy river gradually emerges from the haze, as though we are regaining consciousness. Flying low, we follow the Lufwashi's tortuous route as it cuts its way out of the mountains along a ridge peppered with herds of sable antelope; then past saber-horned roan antelope and zebras cantering over the rocky, rolling foothills of the scarp's apron; and on around an enormous monolith above which hawks and eagles soar. From there the Lufwashi remembers its way along more gentle slopes to its confluence with the Mwaleshi River.

Families of elephants standing in gallery forests lift their trunks, sniffing the air as we pass overhead; and thousands of buffalo pour from the woodlands into the shallow river to cool themselves and to drink. Rust-colored puku antelope, the size of white-tailed deer, are sprinkled across every sandbar, along with impalas, eland, hartebeests, warthogs, and every bird known to Africa, it seems.

When we reach the broad Luangwa, we see herds of hippos crowded bank to bank, blowing plumes of spray, their jaws agape at the airplane. Fat crocodiles, wider than a kitchen table, slither off the sandbars into the water. And not a sign of human beings.

Along the Mwaleshi again we find the poachers' track and follow its scribblings across the scarp's apron into the foothills and mountains. Delia notes the times, compass bearings, and topographical features that we will use to navigate back into the valley on the ground.

After we land back at the Mpika airstrip, Delia grins at me and holds up both thumbs. Never before have we seen so much wildlife in one place. Now we have to find out if it will be possible to live and work in this remote, rugged wilderness. We taxi to the side of the airstrip and tie down Foxtrot Zulu Sierra. For a few Zambian kwachas Arius, a toothless old tribesman and the government's keeper of the airfield, agrees to keep watch over our plane while we drive into the valley.

Following Delia's notes, we drive up the Great North Road until we find the rutted clay track that we hope will lead us into the park. It follows the northern base of the Kalenga Mashitu, a twenty-mile ridge of rock, through a cool, deep forest of spreading *Brachystegia* and *Julbernardia* trees. With their splayed limbs and luxuriant crowns, these trees dominate the classic miombo woodland found at higher elevations throughout central Africa. Occasionally we see neat thatched huts nestled in the hills below Mashitu's rocky spine. Bending over each hut is an enormous green and yellow banana palm, providing shade, shelter from the torrential seasonal rains, and fruit for the family below it. From a settlement of about a dozen round huts, a gnarled old woman hobbles to the track holding up a bunch of bananas. As I am paying her for them, about thirty women and children gather behind her and begin to sing, their voices like wind chimes on the cool, moist air. After listening to three or four songs, we applaud the choir and drive on — while they are applauding us.

Soon after, the track forks and we stop to study Delia's notes. As we stand outside the truck, a small band of men approaches, the narrow blades of their hand axes hooked over their shoulders. The men curtsy with their hands clasped, eyes downcast in the traditional sign of respect, as we ask which track to take to Mukungule Village. Before answering, the spokesman grows an inch or two, then declares: "This track, she is good!" He hurries over to pat the ground of the left fork with both hands. "If you take it, you shall touch Mukungule." He smiles hugely, exposing his brown and broken teeth. Still hunched over, he rushes to stand on the other fork. "Aaahh, but this one, she has expired." His expression falls as he stomps on the expired track, as if to be sure "she" is dead.

"Natotela sana — thank you very much." We offer the only Bemba words we have learned, then drive away, leaving the men clapping and curtsying in farewell.

We take the living track and, four hours after leaving Mpika, it begins to wind through fields of maize and millet. We creep across a bridge of limbs and branches that snap, crack, and groan under the two-ton Cruiser, which sways drunkenly and threatens to break through to the water below.

Minutes later we "touch" Mukungule, its huts of ragged thatch and mud-wattled walls standing among maize patches overgrown with tall weeds and grass. The track leads us right past the fire circle of a family's boma, and even though we leave tire tracks through their "living room," they step back, laughing, waving, and cheering. "Mapalanye! Mapalanye!" The hellos of the women and the children's squeals of laughter mingle with the flutter and squawks of retreating chickens to create a raucous, but somehow musical, welcome. Several women, wrapped in brightly colored chitengis, pause from "stamping their mealies," their long poles poised above the hollow tree stumps they use as stamping blocks, or mortars, for crushing the maize kernels. An older woman sits on a stump in front of her hut, her foot working the treadle of an old Singer sewing machine as she stitches a brightly patterned cloth.

A throng of young people crowd around our truck as we stop. One lad softly and shyly strums his guitar, homemade from a gallon oil can, with a rough-hewn wooden neck and crude wooden tuning pegs. Nails driven into the neck and bent over under the wire strings form the frets. With a little encouragement from us and his friends, he begins a twangy tune. We listen intently for a while until it begins to seem that this song has no end; we slip away.

As we pass Munkungule's last hut, the grass in the track is suddenly taller than the truck. I stop, and Delia climbs up to ride on top so that she can guide me. An hour and a half later, but little more than six miles farther, the track forks again. Ahead of us on the left the four mud-wattle and thatch houses of the Mano Game Guard Camp pop up like mushrooms growing out of the tall grass and maize patches.

Set on a barren acre above the Mwaleshi River, this camp is home to four game scouts and their families. Four hundred yards from the main camp, at the base of a small kopje, are two other houses and a storeroom for the "Camp-in-Charge," his deputy, and their families. In Zambia game guards, or scouts, are civil servants who are given military-style training in firearm tactics, wildlife law, and a smattering of ecology, then charged with patrolling the country's national parks and other wildlife management areas to guard against poachers. Gilson Kaweche had told us that there are four other scout camps, spaced about twelve miles apart along the western boundary of the park; but together they have only seven scouts. Mano, with its six scouts at the center of the chain of camps, is the only one with enough men even to mount patrols. In fact, the Lufishi camp has been closed down, its single scout suspended for collaborating with commercial poachers. In all, thirteen scouts are charged with protecting the North Park — an area larger than Delaware.

We take the left fork and I stop the truck near a circle of twelve to fifteen men sitting on the bare red earth of the main camp. They look up at us with somber faces, their eyes red and watery. In their midst a large clay pot is brimming over with the frothy local beer; several reed straws stand in the mash. One of the men is wearing a pair of green uniform trousers, suggesting that he is a game guard; the others are dressed in tattered shirts and pants, probably obtained from local missionaries. After greeting them I ask for the Camp-in-Charge, and a stocky Zambian with prominent ears and black hair graying at his temples slowly stands up and walks unsteadily toward us.

"I am Island Zulu, Camp-in-Charge," he announces grandly, his head cocked to one side, as I hand him our letter of introduction from the director of National Parks. A man with a red bandana wrapped around his head saunters up.

"I am Nelson Mumba, Camp-in-Charge at Mwansa Mabemba," he says through a crooked smile, one front tooth missing. "We have no food or ammunition for patrolling, and no transport. We are supposed to be given mealie-meal every month, but it never comes," he complains. "Our families are hungry. Even now our wives are working in the fields so that we can eat." With his bandana, he looks like a pirate as he points to a group of women hoeing in a nearby maize patch.

"That's terrible!" Delia commiserates. "Have you told the warden?"

"Ha! The warden," Zulu shoots back. "He cares nothing about us. He has not been here in more than two years."

At this point I'm not sure what the scouts expect us to do about their problems. I explain that we are looking for a site for a major project, and if North Luangwa turns out to be the right place, we will help them all we can. Mumba mutters something, spits into the dust, and they all walk back to their beer circle. As we pull away in our truck, they are sitting down at the beer pot, reaching for the straws.

After fording the clear, rushing waters of the Mwaleshi River, we camp near a small waterfall hidden in the deep miombo woodlands. From here the Mwaleshi tumbles over the three-thousand-foot scarp mountains, and we will have to do the same. The thick forests prohibit us from following the river, so we will have to find it again when we reach the valley floor.

To test whether or not we can work in North Luangwa, we will try to drive down the scarp, then along the Mwaleshi to the Luangwa River and back. From our reconnaissance flight, the floodplains along these two rivers appear to be among the most important habitats in the park. If we cannot get to them, there is probably little reason to settle in North Luangwa. This trek will not be easy, for most of the way there is no track.

No one who cares about us knows where we are going, or for how long. Our Land Cruiser is nearly worn-out; we don't have a radio, a firearm, or fresh antivenom — none of which are available in Zambia even if we could afford them. In an emergency, it will be a minimum twenty-hour drive to the nearest hospital in Lusaka

— which is often critically short of everything, including AIDS-free blood. Despite all of this, we decide that having come this far we may as well go ahead.

Early the next morning we snatch our mosquito net from the tree limb above our bed on top of the truck, stuff down some raw oatmeal, and start driving. The trail is gentle at first, wending its way through the lush miombo (*Brachystegia*) forest with tropical birds flitting overhead.

But as we round a rocky outcropping, the track abruptly disappears; we will have to drive over the side of the mountain without one. A steep slope, studded with jagged rocks and deep ruts, drops off through the woodlands in front of us. Immediately the truck charges forward, going too fast. I slap it into low gear, but the heavy trailer lurches forward, ramming the Land Cruiser in the rear. Its back wheels heave off the ground, sliding sideways into a jackknife. The drums filled with aviation fuel slide forward, slamming against the trailer's front gate. Spinning the steering wheel, I gun the engine to keep the truck ahead of the trailer. The Toyota sways heavily, rumbling faster and faster over the boulders as I pump the brakes on and off. Still wet from the river crossing, they are not slowing us.

"Get ready to jump!" I shout to Delia. She grabs for her door handle as we rattle and bounce down the steep grade.

I stand hard on the pedal until the brakes begin to hold. Fighting for grip, the tires clutch at the sharp rocks embedded in the slope. Thumb-sized chunks of tread tear loose with a popping sound.

We bottom out of the quarter-mile grade bouncing and barely under control. We are going much too fast. But every time I jab at the brake pedal, the rig tries to jackknife. Finally, as I desperately feed in just enough brake to slow us down, but not too quickly, the truck's rear wheels settle back onto the slope and stay there. Shaking her head, Delia relaxes her grip on the dash and I release my choke hold on the steering wheel. The Luangwa has taught me my first lesson: get into low and go slow-slow when descending the Muchinga Escarpment.

Over the next hour and a half we descend three more steep

pitches and many smaller ones, until it feels as though the truck is standing on its nose. Finally we drive out of the shadows of the miombo woodlands onto a rocky ridge with a panoramic view of the valley: miles of golden grassland cover the rolling knolls of the scarp's apron and the valley floor in front of us; the mountains of the Muchinga Escarpment curve away to our right, disappearing in the distance. Chinchendu Hill, a giant two-by-four-mile monolith eight hundred feet high, juts from the valley floor about five miles away. In the language of the Bisa tribe, "Chinchendu" refers to a big man who stands firm, broad, and tall. To our left, about six miles away, a conical hill resembling a rhinoceros horn is shrouded in blue haze from the heat and smoke of wildfires sweeping the valley. Locally known as Mvumvwe Hill, it and Chinchendu will be our two main landmarks as we explore this part of the valley.

Not many tsetse flies bothered us on our drive down the scarp. But by now we have dropped nearly two thousand feet, and the temperature has risen at least ten degrees to about 87°F. Tsetses swarm inside the Cruiser, biting every exposed patch of skin, even through our shirts, shorts, and socks. Delia soon counts twenty-one bites on her legs. Too hot to roll up the windows, we beat at the flies with our hats, crush them against the windshield, and finally light cigarettes Delia brought for bartering with soldiers at roadblocks along the main road from Lusaka. We puff like fiends until the blue nicotine smog forces the flies to retreat.

The truck and trailer jolting and clattering, we drive on toward the confluence of the Mwaleshi River and the Lubonga, its smaller tributary. Two hours after leaving the scarp, we stop to study Delia's notes again, but cannot determine which way to go.

Walls of *Combretum obovatum,* a thorny scrub that stands twelve feet high, stretch across our path. Twisting and turning along the dusty valley floor, we try to navigate through the maze of thick brambles. Time and time again we fight our way through a brier patch only to find a deep, ragged stream cut blocking our way. Standing on the steep banks, looking down at the uprooted trees lying in these dry washes, I remember the flash-flood warnings Norman Carr gave us in Lusaka: "Don't get caught in the valley after the rains come in November. If you do, you might not get out — until it dries up in May or June."

Large and small hoof prints cover the ground, but we see few animals. All the vegetation except the crowns of the trees is parched dun-brown by the sun and heat. Leave it to us to discover another desert!

Nearly three hours after leaving the scarp, the soothing blues and greens of two rivers, one on either side of us, wink enticingly through the tangle of dry scrub. A bit later we push through a stand of tall grass and on our right is the Mwaleshi, its white, sandy bottom showing through sparkling water; on our left is the Lubonga, its tributary, little more than a dry-season trickle. We have arrived at the precise confluence of the two rivers.

A small herd of puku — freckles of red and brown in the brilliant green grasses — stand on the riverbank forty yards downstream; and fish eagles sit high in the treetops along the wide, shallow river. After the desolation of the obovatum scrubland, we drink in this scene, as we will the water; and the squints and frowns we wore from the glare only moments before dissolve from our faces. We run to the Mwaleshi, scoop it up in our hands, and douse our faces and necks. But it is not enough. Leaving the heat behind, we jump off the bank, fully clothed, into the water. Crocs be damned.

The sun is setting by the time we cross the river. High on a bank above the confluence, we unroll our mattress on the top of the truck, set out our table and two chairs, and light a campfire. It has been rough going, but we've made it halfway to our objective: the Luangwa River. To celebrate I splash some "pirate" rum, made in Zambia, into the orange squash in our plastic mugs, and we toast our first night in the valley. Below us herds of puku and zebras drink from the river, its water the color of molten steel in the glow after sunset. A neighborly kingfisher hovers at eye level, then tucks its wings and arrows into the pool at our feet. Later, after a dinner of canned chicken stew and a bottle of Drankenstein wine, we climb into our sleeping bags on top of the Cruiser.

Each night for weeks Delia and I have been playing a game, and tonight is no different. Burrowing down in my bag, I sigh, "Boo, tonight I'm going to show you a shooting star, or at least a satellite. This is it — get ready — I know we're going to see at least one." We gaze up at the heavens, looking for a sudden streak of blue or a faint yellow spot of light moving faster than the more distant stars. Within a few minutes we are asleep, somehow saddened that we have seen neither. In the Kalahari, where the arid skies are much clearer, it would have been different.

During the next two days we search up and down the Mwaleshi for a temporary campsite and landing strip. We find only one place where the loops in the river course are far enough apart to allow room for takeoffs — especially those lengthened by the heat and the resistance of rough ground and grass. The place we choose would make Cessna's insurance company shudder. It is a comparatively level surface, but cut short by the river at one end and a tree-covered hill at the other. Worse yet, a big sausage tree, thirty feet high, stands in front of the hill near the end of the strip.

I pace the runway several times, but cannot stretch it to more than 338 yards. According to the pilot's operating handbook for the Cessna 180K, a takeoff on a grassy surface in this temperature should require 330 yards; then add another 215 yards before the plane can clear a 50-foot obstacle — a tree, for instance. If we're hot and heavy, we may have to fly around that tree after takeoff. If not, well, we've got 8 yards of runway to play with and another 200 or so to clear the tree.

Using axes, shovels, and picks, we spend a blistering hot afternoon chopping out tough, spindly shrubs and leveling off termite hummocks to make our airstrip. To finish it, we mark both ends of Airstrip One with piles of buffalo dung. Before dawn the next morning we unhitch the trailer, stash it in tall grass near the airstrip, and head for Mpika to get our plane. Without the trailer to get us stuck in every sandy crossing, the drive back up the scarp to the village takes only eight hours. Just thirty minutes after takeoff I land on our new runway. Because the drive back will take Delia much longer than my flight, she will have to camp along the track and meet me here tomorrow.

I drag some thornbushes close around Zulu Sierra's belly, then spread my bedroll on the ground under the plane. A few years ago

Norman Carr's best friend was pulled out of his tent and eaten by a hungry lioness in the Luangwa Valley. So I am a little wary of sleeping in the open. In the Kalahari we often slept not only on the open savanna, but *with* lions. In this unfamiliar habitat, however, my primate ancestors, speaking to me down long lines of evolution, are warning me to be careful.

In the late afternoon I sit on the riverbank, watching a pied kingfisher dive for dinner. Deception Valley seems of another world, another time. It hurts to remember how much we left behind there, in the Kalahari: Sunrise, Happy, Stormy, Sage, and the other lions; and Dusty, Pepper, Patches, and Pippin, our brown hyenas. What can ever replace them, or fill the need they have created in us?

Night shadows begin stalking the riverbanks. A Goliath heron drifts by, its wings whispering in the still dark air. Through the quiet current a large V-shaped ripple cruises slowly upstream toward me. I retreat to my plane — my tin of technology — and sit by my campfire, out from its wing. A lion calls from upriver, another answers from down. Then it seems too quiet, so I lie under the plane, my three-foot-high thornbush boma pulled around like a comforter. Soon I am asleep. And I dream of another land, with larger lions, with deeper roars; of standing with my arm across the shoulder of a big male named Muffin. Together with Delia I look to the distant horizon, far across the dunes.

○ ○ ○

"Munch — munch — munch." Roused from sleep, I slowly raise my head and look out from under the plane. Four hundred fifty buffalo are mowing and fertilizing the gravel bar along the Mwaleshi River where I landed last evening. They are headed straight for me, some of them only fifty yards away. I crawl forward and stand up, leaning back against the propeller and peering over my thornbush boma. None of the buffs notice me. Their broad muzzles pressed to the ground, tails flicking while ox peckers flit about their backs, the mean machines mow on. Now and then one snorts or grunts loudly, shaking its bulldozer boss and wide-sweeping horns to shoo the flies, slinging saliva onto the grass.

The airplane means nothing to these buffalo since they have never seen one before, and because I am frozen against the propeller they haven't yet distinguished my human form. Buffalo have a hard time seeing anything that isn't moving, even at close range, and I am downwind from them so they haven't smelled me.

Grumbling and mooing, they continue to graze toward me. By now the closest cows are only twenty yards away, and I can smell their dank, musky scent. People who surprise buffalo at close range may get gored, stomped, tossed, and even chewed. Last year two game scouts from Mano were killed by them. At ten yards the nearest buffalo are too close, but they still haven't noticed me — and they are still coming. The only thing to do is to stay still and hope they move on.

But tsetse and dung flies are crawling over my face, and the urge to brush them away is unbearable. Cautiously I begin raising my right hand toward my chin. The lead cow, not more than eight yards away, lifts her head, stops chewing, and looks directly at me, a large sward of grass jutting from the corner of her mouth. The wrinkles over her eyes deepen, her muscles stiffen, and air explodes from her black nostrils. Some large bulls at the edges of the herd immediately lift their heads and key on her. I stop my hand midway up my chest.

Fifty buffalo are now staring at me. Dung flies are crawling over my cheeks and forehead, sucking moisture from my nostrils and the corners of my eyes and mouth. Tsetse flies are biting my neck and arms. I don't move.

The cow in front of me relaxes and lowers her head to the grass, but the older, more experienced bulls behind her stalk forward, sighting down their black cannon-sized muzzles at me. Close to the cow they stop, still glaring at me. My hand crawls to my chin, covers my nose and mouth, and freezes there. The bulls snort loudly, shaking their heads and stamping their feet.

I allow my fingers to wander over my nose and cheek, chasing away the maddening flies. The bulls snort and stomp again. The cow raises her head. She shakes her horns and my stomach tightens.

Then she spins away and clomps off, stopping fifty feet away to look back at me. But the bulls still move toward me, snorting and stamping the ground with their heavy hooves. I wipe my face with my hand and then twiddle my fingers at them. They stop again, raise their heads, then lower them, never taking their eyes off me. The cow begins to graze. Two of the males swing their heads to look at her, then they also graze.

I too relax. Moving slowly, I poke up the fire and minutes later pour a pan of boiling water over some coffee grounds. Then I sit down under the nose of the airplane, savoring my hot, thick "camp coffee" as I watch the herd graze past me. Some are so close I swear I can see the plane's reflection in their eyes, see puffs of dust around their nostrils, hear the coarse grass tearing as their teeth crop it off.

The sun rises slowly behind the herd, cradled between the banks of the river, setting fire to the fringe of hair around their ears and the whiskers on their muzzles. My coffee tastes especially good this morning, in North Luangwa.

Late afternoon. I am still wound up from the morning's encounter. Delia arrives from Mpika in a cloud of dust, and as I tell her about my communion with the buffs, she rolls her eyes and sticks her tongue in her cheek. Fortunately there is plenty of "B.S." to prove my story.

Up at the first hint of dawn, we load the trailer with the gear we won't need on our reconnaissance to the Luangwa, and stash it in an obovatum thicket. We enclose the plane in a thornbrush boma again — to keep hyenas and lions from chewing its tires and tail — and by seven o'clock we are on our way southeast along the river. We have traveled less than a mile when a mean range of scrambled hills blocks our way. They are covered with brambles and chopped up by dry stream channels; there is no way around them. The Mwaleshi is too wide and full of quicksand for us to ford it. We will have to drive over these "Hills of the Chankly Bore," as we call them.

Near the river a narrow gully leads up a steep slope and through the leading edge of the hills. Here we ax down hummocks and chop out briers. But when I try to climb the grade with our rig, I lose traction halfway up. So I back down and try again — and again. Finally, we winch up the truck first, then turn it around to winch up the trailer.

Only minutes after we've descended the Hills of the Chankly Bore, a wide, sandy river lies across our path. No matter which way we turn, a gauntlet of steep slopes and stream and river cuts blocks our way. By placing short planks in front of the wheels to keep them from sinking, we finally make it across. Fifteen minutes later we are down to our axles in mud on the edge of a lagoon. Almost as soon as we have winched out, we drive a brittle mopane stump through one of the Cruiser's tires while trying to push through a solid wall of obovatum briers. We change the tire and hack our way through the thicket with machetes, but then the truck's right front wheel falls into a deep hole hidden in tall grass. At one point it takes four hours to go a thousand yards through a woodland of dead snags.

Through all of this the Mwaleshi flows serenely by our side, twinkling in the sunlight. It is as though the river is teasing us during our ordeal. We see an occasional puku or waterbuck, but where are the mighty herds of buffalo, like the one that surrounded the plane, and the zebras, eland, and impalas we saw from the air? Eventually ten eland trot by, watching us as if they were spectators at a one-truck demolition derby. But their magnificence is lost on us: we are down to our axles in sand again, and shoveling furiously in the 110°F heat. Each obstacle we cross we will have to recross on the way back. There will be no quick way out.

Every evening we park our truck under a tree with a limb at the right height for our mosquito net, climb to the Cruiser's rooftop carrier, take down our chairs and folding table, stand the high-lift jack and spare tire out of the way, and lay our sleeping bags on mats on top of the truck. I have already lost a pair of boots to hyenas, so we keep most of our gear inside the truck or on top of it while we sleep — surrounded by our boots, extra clothes, toothbrush kits, towels, jacks, and spades. Stacked on the front seat are binoculars, books, and camera gear to keep them from getting soaked by the dew. Each morning everything has to be put away before we can move on. We have been living like gypsies for four months, exploring wildlife areas in Zimbabwe and Zambia, and we are anxious to settle somewhere.

On the fourth morning we drive through a dense woodland. As we emerge on the far side, a forest of stark, dead mopane trees and utterly bare ground stretches before us. In this "Torrible Zone," as Delia calls it, the trunks and branches of these skeletons — peeling, split, and rotting — all seem to have been killed at the same time, frozen in the act of life by some cataclysm. The gnarled roots clutch at soil baked by the sun to a dusty pancake. As far as we can see, not a single blade or leaf of green promises life.

"Mark, look over there!" I stop the truck and we walk to a thin grove of trees near the edge of the dead woodland. Five elephant skulls, bone white and half the size of bathtubs, are scattered about the area with pelvises, leg bones, ribs, shoulder blades, and other remains. Horrified, we notice skeletons lying everywhere: one here, five over there, six there.

"The bastards!" I kick the dust.

Hurrying from one skull to the next, we examine each one. All have small holes, where small holes should not be in elephant skulls. All have had their faces chopped off, their tusks hacked away.

Now we understand why we have not seen a single living elephant, or a sign of one, in the eight days since we entered the park. We are standing in the midst of a killing field, where gangs of poachers have slaughtered every great gray beast they saw. It is an elephant's Auschwitz. Looking around at the carnage, I can't help but wonder if the death of these elephants might somehow be related to death of the forest. The magnitude of the poaching problem in North Luangwa hits us like a fist in the stomach. Although we have not yet run into poachers, it must be only a matter of time until we do. There will be no ignoring them, running from them, pretending they do not exist. If we stay here to work, we will have to do something about them.

Sobered, we continue to follow the Mwaleshi River toward its confluence with the Luangwa. For hours the bush is so thick we cannot see the river, and we stay on course only by using a compass. We are driving through tall grass and obovatum thickets when suddenly the front of the truck falls out from under us with a crack. The Cruiser jams to a stop like a shying horse and pitches us against the windshield. We rebound into our seats and rub our heads, coughing in the haze of dust rising from the truck's floor.

After checking to see that Delia is not seriously hurt, I open my door, which is now at ground level, and get out to check the damage. The right front end is sitting bumper deep in a washout that was hidden in the grass. The spring has broken, letting the chassis down on the axle. If the axle had snapped, we would be stranded. We don't have enough spare blades to fix the spring properly; I'll have to jerry-rig something.

With the high-lift jack we raise the truck and block it up on pieces of dead wood. Using a small battery-powered drill, I make center-bolt holes in three tire levers, then wire them in place where the broken spring blades were.

Two hours later, the truck is ready to roll again. "I can't believe we still haven't reached the Luangwa," Delia sighs, slumping down in the grass, her arms covered with the claw marks of the obovatum, matted hair hanging low over her forehead. "Let's discuss this a bit. It's taken us four days so far. We have no radio, nobody knows where we are, we don't know where we are. If the truck breaks down and you can't fix it, it's going to be a long walk back to Mpika. We're digging ourselves in deeper and deeper."

I sit down beside her, pull a grass stem, and begin chewing on it. At last I say, "That's what we've been doing for years."

"Right; fine. I just thought we ought to stop and consider for a minute." A silent minute later — "Let's go," she says.

After another hour we finally break through a hedge of obovatum scrub into an avenue of trees growing on a high bank above the sandy Mwaleshi. Standing on the top of the bank, we are greeted by a sweeping view of the river valley. The sun is setting over the escarpment, its rays in a fiery dance, skipping over ripples and sandbars in the water. The floodplains near and far are spotted with wild animals: six hundred buffalo grazing across a grassy plain; fifty zebras ambling toward the river to drink; a herd of waterbuck lying on a sandbar downstream; impalas browsing at the edge of the mopane woodland. Nearby a herd of Cookson's wildebeest — found only in Luangwa — gallop about in a sun dance. "WHOOOO — HUH — HUH — HUH! MPOOOSH!" The sound, like a humpback whale playing a bassoon, echoes from our left. "Hippos!" I grab Delia's hand and we run downriver toward the calls. Not more than a hundred yards away, we round a last bunker of bushes and there is the Luangwa, with the Mwaleshi flowing into it. Where the two rivers join is a large pool crowded with a hundred hippos, their piggy eyes on us, their nostrils blowing plumes of water in the setting sun as they twiddle their ears.

After our tangle with the bramble and the broken woodland, Africa has won us back.

We sleep with the hippos that night, their grunts, sighs, hoots, and bellows the refrain of a strange orchestra in the river below. And in the forest near our bed, a leopard's hoarse cough sets off shrieks, screams, and chattering from a troop of baboons. Later, just after I have gone back to sleep, the cool air draining downriver from the mountains of the escarpment carries with it the trumpet of an elephant, and finally the heavy, insistent roar of a lion.

Born in Tanzania, the Luangwa sweeps between fifteen-foot banks and past broad sandbars for 460 miles southwest through Zambia. Like a snake, the river writhes, twists, and even coils back on itself in sharp hairpin turns, its water occasionally breaking through the land neck of a turn, or silting across the mouth of a sharp bend to pinch off an oxbow lagoon. A few tracks, but no major roads intrude on this stretch. It is one of the wildest rivers left in Africa.

During the next three days we make our second airstrip, Serendipity Strip, on a long floodplain near the Mwaleshi-Luangwa confluence. When it is finished, I fly the plane down from Airstrip One, build another bush boma around it, and then by truck and plane, Delia and I begin exploring north along the high banks of the Luangwa.

Every day we are more and more convinced that we want to live and work in North Luangwa. No one has ever done research on animal behavior or conservation here, and it seems a good place to test the concept that if the villagers nearest the park receive direct benefits from its wildlife, they will want to help conserve it. The people of the Bisa and Bemba tribes should be no exception. But every time I contemplate hauling tons of avgas and other supplies over the scarp, especially during the rains, trying to track research subjects through a maze of stream cuts, or persuading a dozen underequipped game guards to protect such a huge area from well-armed commercial poachers, I just shake my head. True, we have made it to the Luangwa; but we are not yet convinced that we can operate here.

We have carried so many spare parts, tools, and extra jerry cans of fuel with us that there was too little space left for food. Our supplies are already low, and we face a major trek back to Mpika for more. Three days after setting off north along the Luangwa, we chart a course back to Serendipity Strip. Two days later, in the late afternoon, we are lying in the hot, shallow water of the Mwaleshi at our first base camp, our toes and noses sticking above the water.

○ ○ ○

The sun is high and hot by early afternoon when we say our goodbyes on the riverbank. I check my watch as Delia begins driving to Airstrip One. She will go halfway this afternoon, then camp for the night and meet me there when I land tomorrow. Sleeping again under the belly of the plane, I am both comforted and aroused by Africa's symphony of the night.

My only visitor is a honey badger, who snuffles around my feet as I sit on the plane's main wheel having my cup of early-morning coffee. In the afternoon I fly northwest along the Mwaleshi and spot our truck crawling along below, approaching the Hills of the Chankly Bore. Our timing has been almost perfect; Delia will arrive at Airstrip One only minutes after I land.

But she does not. Standing under the wing, shading my eyes against the late-afternoon sun, I can see our truck and trailer three-quarters of a mile away, entering the steep cut through the last hill before the airstrip. Then it disappears. Half an hour later Delia still has not arrived. Something is wrong.

I walk and then run toward the hills, dodging bushes and stumbling through the chest-high grass. Once Delia started down the cut, she could not have stopped the heavy rig on the slope's loose gravel; one way or another she must have made it to the bottom. But I cannot see the truck or trailer through the undergrowth — until I round the last thicket. The Cruiser is on its side, jammed between the high, narrow sides of the ravine, its roof downslope. Behind it the heavy trailer has jackknifed into the bank. Delia is nowhere to be seen.

"Delia! Are you all right?" I yell as I sprint toward the truck. The only sound is the hiss of battery acid spilling onto the hot engine. "Delia . . ." A stirring comes from inside the Cruiser.

"Oh no, Mark! Look what I've done! I just couldn't stop it," she moans, stepping out through the driver's window.

"Don't worry about the truck." I smile. "It's easier to service on its side." She forces a weak grin as I hug her.

She tells me that she stopped at the top of the steep ravine, shifted to first gear, and eased the Cruiser forward. But I had forgotten to warn her that I had unlocked the trailer's brake, to make it easier to maneuver in reverse; and as she hauled the heavy rig over the lip of the slope, it leaped forward, compressing its hitch and slamming into the rear of the truck. Jammed back in her seat by the impact, she pumped the brake and fought the steering wheel as the Toyota rolled ever faster into the divide. The walls of the cut were so close to the truck that she could not jump out without being crushed. Trapped inside, she tried to ride it out.

Halfway through the chute and still gaining speed, the truck's right front wheel struck a rock embedded in the wall of the ravine. The steering wheel tore itself from Delia's hands and spun sharply to the right. Immediately the truck turned and began to climb the steep canyon wall. At the same time the top-heavy Toyota rolled dangerously to its left. Delia grabbed the wheel and clung to it, trying to straighten the truck, but was not strong enough.

The trailer forced the truck farther up the wall, Delia still pulling frantically on the steering wheel. The Cruiser rolled onto its left side. Shoved by the trailer filled with avgas, it continued down the slope, its roof leading the way. Inside, Delia was thrown out of her seat, slammed against the roof, and battered by an avalanche of toolboxes, food crates, and camping gear. After the rig slid to a stop, she clawed her way out of the rubble. She was dazed, but fortunately not seriously hurt.

○ ○ ○

Using the little daylight left, we organize the jacks and winches that will set the truck back on its wheels, then sleep on the riverbank near the overturned vehicle. Before sunrise the next morning we rig the high-lift jack under the rooftop carrier. I run the truck's winch cable through a pulley that I've secured around a tree at the top of the hill. With poles cut from nearby trees, we fashion a sling for the Toyota's canopy and attach to it a yoke of chains. Then we hook the cable to the yoke.

Before trying to lift the truck, we tie the trailer to another tree upslope from the rig, so that when the Cruiser finds its wheels it won't run away again. Alternately jacking and taking up on the winch, we slowly lift it. About noon it staggers back upright. We fill its battery with water from the river, add some oil to the transmission, and crank it up. Aside from minor damage to the left front fender and the canopy, it is fine. Delia comes out even better, with only a few bruises and scrapes on her left arm and leg.

Nevertheless, turning over the truck seems to solidify all the doubts about working in North Luangwa that have been simmering in our heads for days. Granted, the park is beautiful and it has an incredible variety of wildlife. But we can no longer shake off the thought that, true to its reputation, North Luangwa is too rugged, too remote, too inaccessible. That we are tired and really need to find a place, and that there are few comparable wildernesses left in Africa, does not make the rivers easier to cross or the slopes easier to climb. To drive even a short distance we have to make war on the landscape, mount a major expedition. And this is the dry season. Everyone has told us that when the rains come, we will be flooded out. It is a hard day's trip to Mpika for basic supplies, and aviation fuel will have to be brought from Lusaka, sixteen hours away. The poachers shooting elephants in the park may not take kindly to our plans, and because our licenses have not been approved, we have no firearms. On our limited budget, the nightmare logistics seem almost insurmountable.

The bruised truck standing to one side, we share a can of beans for lunch while sitting in the warm water of the Mwaleshi. Our conversation keeps turning to the hope that our permits for Tanzania will have arrived in Mpika. "If not, I think we should just get our things, pull out, and head for Tanzania as tourists," Delia echoes my thoughts.

After repacking the truck, we camp at the base of the Hills of the Chankly Bore. The next morning I awaken to the sound of splashing in the river. Lifting myself on one elbow, I see two big-maned lions thirty yards away, romping across the Mwaleshi, kicking up spray as they whirl and slap at each other. Their powerful bodies reflect the new light of the morning sun and at least for the moment make us forget the rigors of the previous weeks.

Not more than an hour later, on our way to Airstrip One along one of the Mwaleshi's floodplains, Delia puts her hand on my arm and points to a forked tree leaning out from a steep gravel bank. Four lion cubs are tumbling in play around the base of the large *Trichelia emetica* tree. As our truck creeps closer, they climb a short way up the two trunks of the tree and peer curiously at us with bright, round eyes. Below, the ears and eyes of three lionesses slowly rise above the tall grasses.

When we drive closer, the cubs climb down from their perches. One of the females lowers her ears, turns, and disappears; another lays her ears back slightly and looks away, as if mildly annoyed and determined to ignore us. The ears of the third stay fully erect, and she raises her head a bit higher. Twenty yards from the tree I switch off the truck and we sit quietly, letting the lions get used to us.

All at once the cubs come to the edge of the grassy patch and peer at our truck. First one, then the others, come slowly toward us on stumpy legs, their eyes amber-colored pools. When the first cub is ten feet away, he stops and stares through my window, raising and lowering his head as though trying to get a better look at me. Each cub smells the right front tire and circles the Cruiser, eyeing it up and down. Then they waddle back to sit between the forelegs of the lionesses in the grass.

A little later one of the lionesses leaves the others, climbs a low termite mound, and sits watching for prey. We drive over and park just twelve yards from her. We name her Serendipity. It has been fourteen months since we were last close to lions, and it is as though some drought has broken.

I look at Delia and smile. "How many places are left in Africa where we can wake up with four hundred buffalo around our bed, golden lions romping through the river near our camp, and a lioness sitting beside our truck?"

Although we are down to our last tin of beans and have barely enough diesel to get us up the scarp, we decide to stay one more night in North Luangwa before going on to Mpika. Perhaps we will see Serendipity's pride hunt later this afternoon. We set up camp on the banks overlooking the confluence of the Lubonga and Mwaleshi rivers, in the same spot where we slept on our first night in North Luangwa.

When the heat finally breaks late in the afternoon, we climb into the Cruiser to search for the lions. "Elephants!" Delia points to where the river curves eastward. A small family of six elephants is walking out of the forest, heading for the river five hundred yards downstream from us. The largest female has only one tusk. They stop, lift their trunks to test the air for danger, then take several more steps before stopping again, one foot raised, their trunks swiveling like periscopes. They are nearing the water's edge when suddenly One Tusk whirls in our direction. Flapping her ears wildly and swinging her huge bulk around, she runs back into the woodland. The others follow and within seconds they have disappeared.

The river must have carried our scent to them. We are barely larger than dots on their horizon, yet they vanished as soon as they sensed us. Constantly harassed by poachers, they are so frightened by humans that they will not drink even at such a distance.

At this moment, in August 1986, we pledge to each other: no matter what it takes, or how long, we will stay in North Luangwa until the elephants come to drink at the river in peace.

But to stay we must find a way to survive the floods.

6
Floods

DELIA

Except by the measure of wildness we shall never really know the nature of a place.

— PAUL GRUCHOW

○ ○ ○

SPEARS OF SUNLIGHT stab through the forests of the Muchinga Escarpment as I steer the old Cruiser carefully down the rutted track into the Luangwa Valley. Riding with me is Chomba Simbeye, a wiry, twenty-one-year-old Bemba tribesman who knows this part of the valley well. Mark will fly to meet us in three days, assuming Simbeye and I can clear Airstrip One for a safe landing.

Instead of being gone for three or four weeks as Mark and I had imagined, it has taken us more than a year to obtain all the permits to operate in North Luangwa. Now it is late October 1987, leaving us only a month to build an all-weather airstrip and base camp before the rains and floods come. Unless we finish the strip by then, we could be stranded for months.

We have been told that the poachers operate on foot and are especially active during the rains. That's another reason why we are determined to get settled in the park before then. We're not sure how we'll stop the poaching, but we've got to find a way.

At the Mano Game Guard Post a few scouts laze about, while their wives suckle infants, wash clothes in brightly painted basins, or pound maize for the evening meal. With a slab of whittled wood, one of the women stirs her simmering stew in a battered tin pot, occasionally flavoring it with a sprinkle of blossoms from a large straw basket.

Because I am unarmed, Mark has insisted that I take a game guard with me into the park. Tapa, a tall, slender man with shy, round eyes, volunteers to come. While he prepares his *katundu,* or belongings, the other scouts complain to me that they are still not getting ammunition or food from their command headquarters in Mpika. Just hours earlier the warden, Mosi Salama, told me that Mano had been given its monthly rations. I don't mention that we've heard from an honorary ranger that scouts often sell their government-issued food and ammo, or use the weapons to poach. If we are going to stop the poaching in the park, we will have to win the scouts' cooperation. Like anyone else, they need encouragement, equipment, and identity before they will do their jobs. If the government can't afford to give them food, medicine, and decent housing, we will raise the money somehow. Then they will no longer need to poach and will begin patrolling. My daydreams ease me down the rugged scarp.

After three hours of driving the familiar steep, rocky grades the three of us reach the confluence of the Mwaleshi and the Lubonga, that enchanted place where Mark and I vowed to stay in North Luangwa. A herd of puku lie on the sandy beach and a few waterbuck stand ankle deep in the slow-moving current. I would love to linger a while, but we are still two miles from Airstrip One and I want to get there by sunset. The dry season has reduced the Lubonga to a trickle of clear water flowing over ripples of loose sand. The old truck bores through, but the trailer bogs down in the wet sand midstream. We unhitch, and abandon it until later.

Just as the sun melts into the purple mountain peaks, we round a small stand of forest. The wide, shallow waters of the Mwaleshi sweep past tall banks on the far side, and the floodplain on our side opens into a sheltered grassland, tucked between high buffs. Several piles of bleached bones lie half buried in the tall grass — all that is left of Airstrip One.

There isn't enough time before dark to set up a proper camp; we'll just prepare for the night. Tapa and Simbeye gather wood, build the fire under a large fig tree, and set up the chairs and tables. I unpack my bedroll, put water on to boil, then walk the fifty paces to the river to bathe. There is a steep bank between camp and the river, so I have my privacy. I undress, check carefully for crocodiles, and plunge into the clear, shallow water. As I roll along the sandy bottom, the heat of the day and the frustrations of the previous months float away, drifting down the Mwaleshi to the Luangwa, into the Zambezi, and on to the Indian Ocean. I feel free, alone, strong, and happy. I laugh out loud as I splash.

Dusk is deeply upon us when I climb back up the bank, and Simbeye warns me that it is very dangerous to stay in the river so late. I thank him for his concern and lie that I will be more careful in the future. He and Tapa have built such an enormous fire — to frighten away lions, they explain — that it lights up the entire canopy of the fig tree and makes the already warm camp unbearably hot. The heat drives us to the edge of camp — much closer to the lions, if any are about — where they teach me words in their language until dark.

Simbeye, a cheerful, self-confident young man, is from the village of Shiwa N'gandu, which means Lake of the Royal Crocodiles. In the past the chiefs of the Bemba met at the lake each year for a ritual croc hunt. Simbeye squats by our fire, boiling mealiemeal in a crusted, sooty pot to make n'shima, the staple food of his people. We eat with our fingers, dipping thick pasty balls of n'shima into a relish of beans and onions. Simbeye, speaking in a low, raspy voice, tells me tales of Bemba folklore.

Sometime long ago, he says, there was a mighty tribe of warriors in the land that is now Zaire. One day a strange woman, who had ears almost as large as an elephant, wandered into the village of the chief, Chiti-Mukulu. Most thought she was ugly, but knowing that she would make a good wife, Chiti-Mukulu married her. She bore him three sons, who indeed were very strong but were always getting into mischief and causing much trouble to the chieftain. When they became young men, Chiti-Mukulu banished them from his lands and they were forced to travel far away to the south. Some of the other warriors joined them and they started a new tribe, calling themselves the Bemba. After many months of plundering the villages of other tribes, they came upon a beautiful valley bordered by mountains, where wild animals thrived in thick forests. They chased out the local residents and formed Bembaland, which is now Zambia's Northern Province.

To this day the "paramount," or highest, chief of the Bemba

bears the name Chiti-Mukulu. It is never the son of the chief who inherits the throne, but his nephew. When I ask why, Simbeye explains to me that a man can never, never be certain that the son of his wife is his own child. But he *can* be sure that his sister's son is his true blood relative. It is one of the clearest cases of kin selection — passing one's genes to the next generation through kin other than offspring — I have ever heard.

Soon after we eat, I drive the truck some distance from the tree; I'm not going to miss the night sky because of the bonfire. Instead of making my bed on top of the Cruiser, I lay my safari mattress and sleeping bag on the grass. Tonight I want to sleep on the ground, between the earth and the moon. The truck will be close enough for a retreat if lions come.

As I lie next to the earth, the moon covers me with its platinum blanket, not bringing warmth like the sun, but a caress of hope. The silky light transforms every leaf and blade of grass on the plain to shimmering silver. Puku and impalas standing next to the river fade into subtle impressions against the pale sky. I smile before I sleep. I too am in my place, for I am a moon person.

Awake at 5:25 A.M., I watch first the hills and then the river awaken from darkness, stretching out in the orange-pink dawn. Just after six, Simbeye whispers, "Madam, wild dogs — at the river." I look downstream to see three wild dogs, their bold black, white, and brown coats standing out vividly in the sunrise. They gallop through the shallow river, splashing a spray of water against the sun.

By six-thirty we have packed our beds, eaten breakfast, and walked to the airstrip, a mere hundred yards away. We slash grass, fill in holes, level ant mounds, chop down small bushes, and clear away logs and stones. By eight o'clock the heat is unbearable. Every fifteen minutes I walk to the river, and wet my shirt and hat to keep cool. I have never liked Airstrip One; it is only half the length required by regulations. But I can't bear to cut down the enormous sausage tree at the southern end; Mark will have to avoid it, as he did last year.

At noon we break for lunch. In the midday heat waves, the far riverbanks wiggle and dance. While Tapa and Simbeye rest and eat in camp under the fig tree, I take a can of fruit cocktail, some sweaty cheese, the binoculars, and a book to the river. The shallow water is hot, but as soon as I am wet the breeze brings goose bumps to my bare skin. As I sit in the river reading my book and eating lunch, a pair of Egyptian geese land nearby and paddle around next to a sandbar.

More work through the afternoon: we clear the strip, mark the ends with new piles of bleached bones and buffalo dung, and cut thorn branches to make a hyena-proof boma for the plane. At dusk Simbeye and Tapa build another big fire, but again I camp far away, closer to the moon and the stars.

In the morning we complete the thorn boma, rescue the trailer from the sand, pitch the tent, and fill it with our tin supply trunks. Mark and I will have to continue sleeping on the truck or ground, since we don't have another tent. Using branches from a fallen tree, we construct little tables for the pots and pans, and bury the film cooler.

The same pair of geese keep me company at lunch — a good thing, because the heat makes my book boring. The work is finished, more or less. If it wasn't so hot I might do more. Instead I read until four o'clock, then explore the river to the south on foot. Simbeye and Tapa insist on escorting me, so we set off across the plain together. I stop abruptly.

"Listen. Moneni ndeke!" I shout. They echo me, "Moneni ndeke. The plane is coming."

We run all the way back to camp and I grab a roll of toilet paper to use as a wind sock. Mark circles overhead, waggling his wings in salute as I stand on top of the Cruiser, letting tissue play out into the slight breeze. Mark buzzes the strip once to check our work, then glides in for a perfect landing.

Simbeye, Tapa, and I show Mark around the little camp with more enthusiasm than it deserves. While the Bembas go to collect more firewood, Mark and I walk to the river to bathe. Together we frolic in the water, laughing and talking endlessly about our separate trips into the valley — one by air, one by road. Tomorrow we will search for a permanent campsite; we are not sure we could drive to this one during the rains. The pair of geese forage about in their spot by the sandbar, and I imagine that they are pleased that I too have a mate.

○ ○ ○

Wiping sweat from our brows, we stand on a high bank of the Lubonga, studying an old floodplain that runs for a thousand yards along the river. Fifteen huge marula and sausage trees shade the sandy ground. A dry oxbow, where the river once ran, surrounds the plain on three sides, and on the east bank the Lubonga trickles gently over the sand. But this is the dry season. If the oxbow and river flood when the rains come, the plain will become an island and could easily be cut off. Our twenty-year-old map definitely shows this stretch of plain as an island, with water on all sides.

For ten days we have searched from the air and hiked through the heat to locate a suitable base camp. The site must be accessible year round and have drinking water, shade, and a nearby site for an all-weather airstrip. This floodplain has water and shade, but the only possible airstrip is three miles away. And the question is whether or not it will flood during the rainy season.

"We're looking for a camp in a valley, which is at the bottom of one of the biggest valleys on earth," Mark points out, chewing on a grass stem. "It's a sump within a sump; when it rains, we're going to get wet. But we haven't found a better place. I'm willing to gamble; what about you?"

A massive line of cumulus clouds poised along the eastern scarp reminds us that we are in a race with the weather.

"We don't have much choice. What shall we name it?"

The marula trees wave their massive limbs in the gentle breeze as if inviting us to shelter here. Nearby a herd of puku is grazing along the Lubonga.

"How about Marula-Puku?"

○ ○ ○

The days of celebrated sunrises, river lunches, and goose watching are over. Each day more and more squadrons of clouds assemble to the west and north, massing like a mighty army over the scarp mountains. We must build a primitive structure at Marula-Puku and complete the all-weather airstrip on the rocky ridge upstream. The Land Cruiser will never pull through the infamous Luangwa mud, so the Frankfurt Zoological Society has sent us a new Unimog — a nine-foot-tall, six-ton, all-terrain vehicle that is a cross between a tractor and a truck. With sixteen forward and reverse gears and a low center of gravity, it can climb steep slopes without turning over. We have to collect the "Mog" from Durban, South Africa, and drive it fifteen hundred miles back to camp. All this before the rains.

Simbeye and I leave at dawn the next morning for the long trip up the scarp to Shiwa N'gandu to hire a work crew and to Mpika to buy supplies. At Mano the game guards beg me to transport their corn into Shiwa for grinding, to take one of the wives to the hospital, and to carry four scouts to Mpika to collect their pay. In the village of Mukungule one of the headmen needs a lift to Chinsali to attend a funeral. The chief's wife has to transport her bean crop to market — some say she is smuggling it to Zaire for a better price. The school headmaster needs paraffin for his stove.

By the time we leave Mukungule the old truck has eleven people on board — I'm not sure how many children — and heaves under the weight of corn, beans, two live chickens, and everyone's katundu. My daypack has only a few crackers and sardines for my lunch, not enough to share with my passengers. Not wanting to eat in front of them, I stay hungry.

At four-thirty we reach the Great North Road and stop at the few grass huts of the village of Kalalantekwe for the night. I promise to collect those going to Mpika, including the sick woman, the next day. Simbeye and I drive past the blue waters of Shiwa N'gandu Lake along a dirt track, lined with huge trees, searching for a place to camp. I ask Simbeye if he can hire five men from nearby villages to work for us, and arrange for some women and children to cut thatching grass for us to haul into the valley.

Simbeye assures me he will do this and that one of the men he will hire is an excellent cook. I have not considered hiring a cook at this stage. With so much work to do and so little food to eat, it seems rather extravagant, but I ask the name of the cook.

"His name, Madam, is Sunday Justice."

"Sunday Justice!"

"Yes, Madam."

"Well, bring him for sure, and four others."

After several miles Simbeye shows me a place to camp near a rushing stream sheltered by massive palms. I drive him to his father's boma a mile away, where he will spend the night. The next morning at five-thirty sharp he returns, and as we drive back toward the main road he tells me that he has hired five men, who will be ready by noon, and that his sisters are cutting the thatching grass for us. Our first stop is to deliver the scouts' corn to the local miller, who lives down a crooked, sandy road. After much negotiating over prices, Simbeye and I unload the fifty-pound bags on the doorstep of the tiny, one-room mill house. We stop on the Great North Road to collect our passengers, then drive the forty miles to Mpika, where we leave everyone at their desired destinations, and still make it to the open-air market by eight o'clock.

Women and girls, clad in multicolored chitenges (strips of cloth wrapped around the waist to make a skirt), squat behind small piles of onions, cabbages, tomatoes, rice, and dried fish spread on the ground in the center of the Mpika market. They are surrounded by cement-block stalls that offer bath soap, matches, washing powder, and a meager selection of canned foods, including the ever-present corned beef and baked beans. Spry young men — coiled to run from authorities at a shout — call out prices for black-market goods such as sugar, flour, and cooking oil. The market sways to the beat of the gumba music blaring from a small stall. It looks rather quaint and picturesque, as most third-world open-air markets do; but in this part of Africa, one man's postcard is often another man's misery. A toothless old woman tries to sell two onions, another a handful of potatoes and some dried caterpillars.

We go separate ways to buy bags of cabbages, onions, beans, ground nuts, rice, and salt. Carrying a large bucket, I approach a young man selling sugar at one kwacha a cup. Several other women, holding various containers — the lid from an aerosol can, a roll of newspaper, a plastic cup — queue up behind me. As they look from my large bucket to the shrinking pile of sugar, concern grows on their faces. I step back to let them buy first, and they bow and clap their hands in the Bemba fashion of greeting and gratitude.

At Mpika Suppliers, a general store lined with shelves of colorful cloth, basic hardware, and foodstuffs, we buy cement, whitewash, nails, and mealie-meal. There is no flour or bread at the bakery stand, and we can't find milk, honey, jam, meat, eggs, cheese, or chickens for sale anywhere in the village.

I make a courtesy call on the district governor, Mr. Siangina, at his hilltop office overlooking Mpika Village. Charming and very enthusiastic about our project, he says he welcomes any program that will stimulate the economy and discourage poaching.

Next I visit the game warden, Mosi Salama, with whom we have met on several occasions. He is built like a bowling pin with a cheshire cat smile and eyelashes as long as a moth's antennae. Mosi greets me on the veranda of the lime-green concrete-block building that is the Mpika headquarters for the National Parks and Wildlife Services. He assures me again, smiling broadly all along, that he did issue the ammunition and food to the Mano scouts. When I inquire further, he gives me the surprising news that an officer from the Division of Civil Aviation, Mr. Banda, and the National Parks pilot, Captain Sabi, have driven all the way from Lusaka and are sitting in his office waiting to see me. As soon as I enter, without shaking my hand Mr. Banda says, "I'm afraid there is a very big problem with your program. You have been landing your airplane in North Luangwa National Park without permission from our department."

Immediately I relax. "Oh, it's okay. See, I have the papers right here." I dig in my briefcase, pull out a thick file of permits, and shuffle through them. "Here is the permit from the Zambian Air Force giving us permission to operate our plane in North Luangwa. And this is the permit from the minister of tourism granting us permission for our project, which as you can see in this paragraph, explains that we will be flying an aircraft in the park. This is a photocopy of Mark's Zambian license and a three-month blanket clearance for operating in this area from your own department."

Captain Sabi and Mr. Banda lean their heads together to read the documents. After a moment Mr. Banda shakes his head. "There is no permission here to land your airplane in North Luangwa National Park."

"Operating surely includes taking off and landing." I smile and try to make a joke. "Did they think we were going to fly forever and not land?"

"You cannot land an airplane in Zambia on an unregistered airstrip. You will have to operate from Mpika," Captain Sabi informs me.

"Mpika airstrip is fifty miles from our study area. How can we operate from there? We plan to build a proper airstrip. In the meantime, as we informed the ministry, we have cleared some temporary strips." I try to make another joke. "Mark's been a bush pilot for years; I'm not sure he could land on a real strip." No one smiles.

"You cannot land your plane anymore until you have constructed an airstrip that the DCA approves," Mr. Banda insists. "It must have concrete markers, a wind sock, all the requirements."

I slump in my seat. We have spent more than a year obtaining permits. This new requirement will set us back months, for we will be unable to conduct aerial surveys or antipoaching patrols until we have completed the strip. I look at Mosi to appeal for help. He appears thoroughly disgusted, but whether at me or at these men I can't be sure. He gives me no support whatsoever.

"All right. Thank you." I stand and walk out of the room, managing a slight smile when I imagine what Captain Sabi and Mr. Banda would think of Airstrip One, with its short runway and looming sausage tree.

○ ○ ○

There is nothing quite like the sensation of returning to a bush camp. I don't know whether it is more exciting to be the one waiting in camp, listening for the distant drone of the engine, or to be the one coming home. In the silence of the wilderness, the one in camp can hear the truck approaching from so far away that there is a sort of meeting of the hearts before the other arrives. As I pass the mopane tree, the one with the marabou stork's nest, I know that Mark can hear the truck, and he knows that I know. The rest of the journey is like an extended hug, so by the time I roll into camp, we are both warm and smiling.

Around the campfire we talk about my trip, until I cannot avoid the bad news any longer. When Mark hears that we cannot operate the plane in the park until we have a proper strip, he is upset; but we vow to work even harder to get the strip completed before the rains. Meanwhile, we just won't fly.

The next morning Mark drives the Cruiser and trailer, loaded with building materials, from our little camp to the Marula-Puku site. He, Simbeye, and the other men begin building the mud-wattle hut that will be our shelter in the rains. Our new workers are young tribesmen in their early twenties, dressed in ragged Western clothes but without shoes. They have never held a job except for helping their fathers tend the tiny maize and groundnut patches on their subsistence farms. The only tools they know how to use are axes, hoes, and shovels. But while they have had no more than five years of schooling, they are eager to learn. Of the five new men Sunday Justice, Chanda Mwamba, and Mutale Kasokola in particular radiate good humor and an uncommon willingness to work hard, as does Simbeye. Today I had said, "Good morning, guys," and they had laughingly repeated the word "guys" over and over. The name stuck and they call each other "guys" to this day.

Sunday Justice, bright-eyed, short, and chubby, stays with me to unpack the supplies. We store beans in a large can, tissue and soap in a large blue trunk, and sort through the other groceries. As we work, I explain to him that we hope to save the park by making it benefit the local people; we may even hire some of the poachers to work with us.

"That is a very good idea, Madam. You should go to Mwamfushi Village, where there are many poachers."

"Tell me, Sunday, can we fly to that village?"

"Oh no, Madam, that village is very much on the ground." I smile behind his back for a long moment.

All morning I have noticed Sunday stealing glances at the plane, parked in its thorn boma.

"You like the airplane, don't you, Sunday?"

"Yes, Madam. I myself always wanted to talk to someone who has flown up in the sky with a plane."

"Well, you can talk to me," I say, as I pour salt into a jar.

"I myself always wanted to know, Madam, if you fly at night, do you go close to the stars?"

I explain that on earth we are so far from the stars that being up a few thousand feet does not make any difference in how close they look. But I don't know if he understands, so I end by saying, "When you fly at night, you *feel* closer to the stars."

When we have finished unpacking and organizing camp, I show him our few kitchen utensils and try to discover how much he actually knows about cooking. He can bake bread, but only in an oven, he tells me. It seems that I will have to teach this African how to cook in a traditional black pot. In our wooden bowl I mix the ingredients for cornbread — omitting eggs and butter, of course, because there aren't any — and show him how I bake it in the pot, putting hot coals on top and underneath.

"Now this is something you have to be very careful with," I say as I hold up a frying pan with a nonstick coating. "See, it is not an ordinary pan. Food won't stick to the bottom. It's like magic."

"Oh, a Teflon pan," he nods. I stare at him. How often do you find a man who knows about Teflon, but wonders if you can fly to the stars? More often than you would imagine, I decide.

All morning the sun shoulders us with heavy heat, but to the west a blanket of dark clouds is draped across the mountains of the scarp. Our temporary base camp is on the other side of the river from Marula-Puku, about fifty minutes downstream. If it rains in the mountains, the river could flood, making it impossible to cross until the dry season. After giving Sunday a few more chores to do, I wander down to the riverbank to see if the water has risen in the last few days. It is hard to tell, so I kneel down in the sand and lay a line of small stones at water level. Each day I will check the stones to see if the water is rising. We cannot yet camp at Marula-Puku; we must stay near the plane to guard it against hyenas and poachers.

"What are you doing, Madam?" Sunday has come up quietly behind me.

"Well, Sunday, I need to know if the river is rising, because we will have to leave this camp and move to the other side before it gets too high. I can measure the water level by these stones."

"It won't be like that, Madam."

I stand up and look at Sunday. "What do you mean?"

"Today this river will be here." Sunday points to the water lapping against the sand by our feet. "And tomorrow when the rains come, this river will be there." He points a hundred yards across the floodplain to a spot far beyond the camp and airplane. I look back and forth from the river to the plain. If the river rises that high, the Cessna will float away like a raft.

"Sunday, you mean the water will come up that far in one day?"

"Maybe one hour. If these rains come to these mountains, the water, she comes down all together." As if on cue, the clouds to the west release a slow, distinct thunder, which rolls heavily over the hills.

"Sunday, come with me." Back in camp, I begin flinging boxes open and sorting through gear. "Take everything I give you and put it in a pile under the tree." I separate daily essentials — food, clothing, cooking gear — from valuables — camera equipment, film, tools, spares. Pointing to the latter, I say, "We'll have to carry this stuff to Marula-Puku."

At daybreak the next morning, Mark and I transport all of the valuables to Marula-Puku camp, which is on higher ground. Leaving the other men at work on the Bemba house, we head down the Mwaleshi to collect the cache we hid last year. I dig out our handmade map that shows how to find it: "Drive 15.6 miles along the north bank of the river to our Palm Island campsite; go 1.3 miles north through the trees, past two large termite mounds; cache is hidden under *Combretum obovatum* bush."

In spite of the dense October heat and our race with the rains, the journey along the Mwaleshi is as wondrous as ever. There is still no track, but we know the route now and avoid the worst sand rivers, the deepest gullies, the muddiest lagoons. Puku, waterbuck, zebras, and impalas graze on the broad plains as we drive along. A herd of more than a thousand buffalo shake the earth as they canter across the grassland. White egrets, stirred by the stampede, soar like angels against the black beasts. Small bushbuck peer at us from the undergrowth with Bambi eyes.

After only thirty minutes of slogging across dry riverbeds and small savannas, we approach a very familiar plain. We turn inland toward a stand of *Trichilia emetica* trees hanging over a bank. I touch Mark's arm and he stops the truck. Up ahead, under the same trees where the cubs played last year, lies the Serendipity Pride. Two adult males with flowing manes, three adult females, and four stroppy yearlings stare at us from the grass. The young female, the one we called Serendipity, stands and walks directly toward us, her eyes not leaving us for an instant. The males, apparently still shy, slink away in the tall grass. The four cubs trot behind Serendipity toward the Cruiser, and once again in this old truck we find ourselves surrounded by lions.

Serendipity stares at Mark from two feet away, then smells the front wheel for a long moment as the Blue Pride lions had done so many times. The four cubs — all legs and tails — soon tire of this odd beast with its strange odors of oil and fuel, and bound away in a game of chase.

We long for the day when our camp will be finished, so that we can spend more time with the lions. It will be fascinating to compare the social behavior of these lions with those we know in the desert. Forget the cache. Flash floods or not, tonight we stay here to watch the lions.

In the late afternoon they rouse themselves, stretch, and stroll toward the river. Serendipity leaves the others and walks across a small plain to a ten-foot termite mound that towers above the grass. With one graceful leap she springs to the top of the mound and balances on all fours. Her tawny coat blends with the gray clay, as she searches through the grass for any signs of supper.

After only a few moments she slithers down the mound in one silent motion and stalks through the grass toward the riverbank. The other lionesses raise their heads to full height, watching Serendipity's every move. The cubs stop their play and look at the females. The bank drops down about eight feet and Serendipity jumps out of sight onto the sandy beach. At that moment a male puku emerges from the grass, his black eyes searching the beach. Serendipity vaults over the bank to within five feet of him. In one motion she springs forward, reaching out a powerful paw and tripping her prey. At the same instant the other two lionesses dash from their positions just in time to pounce upon the struggling ungulate.

In seconds the three adults and four youngsters have their muzzles into the open flesh. The lionesses feed for only a minute, then walk away licking one another's faces. A hundred-forty-pound puku doesn't go very far among seven lions, and they leave the rest for the cubs.

Serendipity and the two other lionesses walk across the white beach and lie next to the water's edge. On the far bank a small herd of buffalo hold their muzzles high, snort, then disappear into the golden grass of sunset. Beyond them a herd of zebra grazes unaware. The lions will have to hunt again tonight, but prey is plentiful and water laps at their toes. We can't help thinking of the desert lions, who lived for two years eating prey as small as rabbits and had no water at all to drink. What would happen if the Kalahari and Luangwa lions traded places? Could these lions survive in the endless dry dunes of the desert?

After dark all seven lions cross the river in a long line, and we camp near their *Trichilia* tree. In the morning, when there is no sign of the pride, we continue our trip down the Mwaleshi to recover our cache.

Tall grass has grown up along the base of the bush, so the cache is even better hidden than when we left it. We cut the thorn branches free and pull out drums of diesel, jars of honey, jam, and peanut butter, even canned margarine from Zimbabwe. We sling the winch cable over a tree limb and load the drums into the trailer. After a not-so-refreshing swim in the hot river, we begin the long haul back to Marula-Puku.

○ ○ ○

Making endless trips up and down the jagged scarp — to collect poles for the hut, to haul more thatching grass, to meet Mark after he flies the plane to Mpika — we race to finish Marula-Puku camp. The heat and flies must be feeding on each other; both have become fat and unbearable. When the hut's mud walls reach eye level, it becomes obvious that, although their spirits and intentions could not be better, the Bembas are not the builders they claim to be. One corner of the hut crumbles before it has dried and we are doubtful the house will withstand the rains. But it is too late to start over, so we smear the cracks and holes with gooey mud and tie bundles of grass to the roof.

Afraid to stay in our little camp on the far side of the river any longer, we move to Marula-Puku one morning in early November. I am greatly relieved to have all of the gear at one campsite. While Mark joins the hut-building crew, Sunday and I set up our new temporary camp nearby. Sick of making camps, I hope this will be the last one for a while. Once more Sunday and I store the blue trunks in the tent, hang the cornmeal in the tree, put up the tables and chairs. As we work, white-browed sparrow weavers — the same species that shared our Kalahari camp for seven years — serenade us from a wispy winter-thorn tree (*Acacia albeda*). In the lower branches of the acacia they too are busy building their nests, but unlike other species of weavers, these seem unconcerned with neatness. They twist grass stems of various sizes and shapes into a messy bundle that looks like something that might be cleaned out of a drain. But their familiar song and perky chirps lighten my heart. If they can sing while they build, then so can I.

By midafternoon we have all the gear set up at Marula-Puku and I walk to the other side of the island to help the men with the hut. As I kneel in the sand, spreading mud with my fingers, I feel the wind pick up and stir the muggy air around us. A cloud mass looms to the northwest, but such formations have been marching harmlessly overhead for days. Suddenly a hot wind rushes into the valley, ahead of a low, swirling wall of black-gray clouds. Jumping to our feet, we grab gear and supplies and throw them into the unfinished hut. Mark and I run toward the tent, but lose sight of it in the dust and sand. Finally, we stumble over it lying on the ground. Pots and pans, books, chairs, plates, cups, and clothes are scattered for yards around. The sand stings our faces and eyes as we stagger through the storm, chasing bits and pieces of camp and throwing them into the truck.

The sandstorm lasts for thirty-five minutes and then retreats as quickly as it came. Not one drop of rain has fallen, and the valley is left standing in a still, dry heat. Silently we wander through the remains of our camp, standing up a table here and a chair there. The sparrow weavers are chirping furiously — their nests have been blown to the ground — but the next morning when we rise, they are rebuilding with crazed enthusiasm. I watch them briefly and do the same.

The ominous date of November 14 — when according to British meteorologists the rains begin — is less than two weeks away, when Mark and I drive to the top of a wooded hill to lay out the airstrip. We have chosen this site because it will drain during the rains, making it usable all year. This will be an easy job, I think, but the woods are so thick that it is impossible to see ahead far enough to lay out a straight line for the runway. After pacing off fifty yards, we run into a huge termite mound, so we try another heading and run into a deep gully. Deciding we must do a proper survey, we get the compass and hammer a row of three stakes into the ground every fifty yards, one in the middle of the strip and one on each side.

About this time a greater honey guide, a small gray bird with a black throat, notices us and gives his distinctive "chitik-chitik-chitik" call, inviting us to follow him to honey. Honey guides lead humans to bees' nests, and when the hive is opened for honey, the birds eat the bees, the larvae, and the beeswax. It is not at all difficult to follow a honey guide. He gets your attention by flitting about in a tree near you, making his raucous call. As soon as you approach, he flies off in the direction of the bees' nest. And just to make sure that you are still there, he stops often in trees along the way, calling over and over.

The honey guide at the airstrip sees us walking directly toward him and flies about in excited, exaggerated twirls. In this unpopulated area, he can't very often have a chance to lead people to honey, and he is more than ready. Just as he is about to fly to the next tree, we hold up our compass, turn a sharp ninety degrees, and march off in another direction. He is silent for a moment, then flies to a tree in our path and calls even more vigorously than before. Again we are nearly under his perch when we swing ninety degrees and pace off fifty yards in another direction. The airstrip is to be more than a thousand yards long, so forty times we stalk across the woods in one direction, only to change course and prance off in another. The poor honey guide has obviously never seen such stupid people. He takes to flying right over our heads, flapping his wings wildly. Now and then he lands on a limb nearby and glares down at us with beady eyes.

Sweat mats our clothes and grass blades sting our legs as we trundle along through the trees. Thinking it was going to be an easy job, we did not bring enough drinking water and our throats are burning. Finally, we hammer the last stake into the ground and climb into the truck. As we drive away, the honey guide is still perched on a branch, giving an occasional "chitik-chitik" with what seems a hoarse and raspy voice.

○ ○ ○

The Bemba hut, with its scraggly grass roof and big windows framed with palm stems, looks more like a lopsided face with a crooked straw hat than a house. But because we must, we declare it finished. At five-thirty the next morning we are all at the airstrip site, armed with six axes, six hoes, three shovels, and the truck and chains. We have about three thousand small trees to cut down, and three thousand stumps to dig up. The ground will have to be leveled and graded by hand. It is impossible to know where to begin, so we just start slashing, chopping, digging, and shoveling. Two hours later, the temperature is already above 90°F. Mark and I wet our clothes from the jerry can with river water that smells strongly of fish and buffalo dung. The Bembas, born of this heat, smile at this. They are not yet hot. "Wait until noon," they laugh.

After a while a routine emerges. Mwamba, Kasokola, Sunday, and I cut down the small trees and pull them to the side; Mark and Simbeye follow and yank out the stumps with the chain and truck. The others chop out stumps too large for the truck and fill in holes. In the midday sun the seventy-five-pound chain is so hot I cannot hold it, but all day long Simbeye runs barefooted from one stump to the next, carrying the burning links across his bare shoulders, refusing to let anyone relieve him or even to rest. As we work, the guys sing softly in a language I do not understand, but with a spirit I certainly appreciate.

To the south we see a flat-topped mushroom cloud rising from the parched earth — the poachers are setting wildfires that burn unchecked across the park. No doubt they are also shooting elephants for ivory and buffalo for meat, yet the game guards have not mounted a single patrol. Without roads or our plane there is nothing we can do to stop the killing and burning. I hack with rage at a small bush; we *must* finish this airstrip.

Where is the rain? For days we have worried that it will come; now we worry that it won't. Stranded or not, flooded or not, anything is better than this heat.

Each day we work from 5:00 to 11:00 A.M. and from 2:30 to 6:00 P.M. Some afternoons I stay in camp by myself, hauling water from the river in buckets, boiling drinking water, baking bread, collecting firewood, and washing clothes. All that is left of the Lubonga River is a few stagnant, smelly pools that we gladly share with the buffalo, puku, and zebras. They come late every afternoon to drink, and frequently I collect water with buffalo standing nearby. They seem to have lost their inhibitions — and so have I, for they used to be the one animal that really frightened me. Shrinking resources make either fierce enemies or strange friends.

At night Mark and I sleep on top of the truck, where it is cooler than inside the hut. Still, the temperature is often more than 100° at midnight, so we lie under wet towels trying to stay cool. We awake just before dawn to watch the stars retreat into the brilliant colors of sunrise and to see the water birds — saddle-billed storks, yellow-billed egrets, Goliath herons — soar along the river on their way to work. Commuters, we call them. They do not take shortcuts across the bends in the river, but follow its winding course, maybe for the same reason that we would — to get a better view.

One morning, while hacking at a small tree on the western end of the airstrip, I am surprised to see a straggling line of game guards walking toward us, some in tattered uniforms, others in civilian clothes. Nelson Mumba still has a red bandana around his head, Island Zulu carries the bent frame of a cot, Gaston Phiri totes a live chicken under his arm. Mark and I greet them and explain that we are building an airstrip.

"We'll use the plane to spot poachers and to count animals from the air," Mark says.

They nod and he continues. "In fact, we were thinking, if you would help us build an airstrip near your camp, we could use the airplane to take you on patrols in the park."

"Ah, but we cannot build an airstrip," answers Mumba.

"Why not?" I ask. "We'll lend you some tools." I hold up my ax.

"We are officers; we do not do manual labor," Mumba says, looking to the others, who nod in agreement.

"Not even if it makes your lives easier?"

"We do not do manual labor," he repeats. Mark, sensing my rising anger, changes the subject. The new subject is not much better.

"Are you going on patrol?" he asks.

Two of the scouts answer "yes," three say "no."

"Are you going to shoot for meat?" I ask.

"We have the right, if we want to," Mumba answers in a surly voice.

Mark explains to them, although we are sure they already know, that according to government regulations no one, including game guards, can shoot animals inside the park.

They talk to one another in Chibemba, their eyes darting back and forth at us. Mark adds that if they hunt in the park, we will be forced to report them to the warden. This is not the way I want this conversation to go; we want to work with the guards, to encourage them. I try to think of some way to salvage the situation.

"Look," I say, "we know it's rough living in your remote camp. When we get our project going, we want to work with you, help you. We'll buy you new uniforms, camping equipment, things like that. But in return you must do your jobs. You're hired by the government to protect these animals, not kill them!"

They talk some more in Chibemba and then announce that they must be going. We shout friendly farewells — "Good luck on your patrol" — but these words bring no response and wither in the heat.

Mark and I stand, watching the scouts hike over the hill. We disagree about how to fight poaching. He believes that we should get personally involved — flying patrols, airlifting scouts, going on antipoaching foot patrols with the guards. I argue that we should supply them with good equipment and encouragement, but we should not personally go after the poachers, for then they will come after us. Unarmed, we make an easy target. We have discussed these points over and over, but have not come to an agreement.

"Better get back to our manual labor," Mark jokes.

"Sorry, I'm an officer," I say as we both begin shoveling again. We've been working on the strip for over a week, and while half of it is clear of small trees, it still looks more like a spot where elephants have romped in the woods than an airstrip.

Two flat tires on the Cruiser force us to return to camp early in the afternoon. When we arrive, Tapa, the game guard enlisted to protect our camp, is nowhere to be found. Mark and I find him hidden in the tall grass, drying meat on a rack. Every day, while we have been clearing the airstrip, Tapa has been fishing, trapping, and drying meat. Stunned, we ask what he is doing, and he replies calmly that he is going to sell the meat in the village. "That is against the law, you know," I say. He shrugs his shoulders and continues to poke at the charred body of an otter, sizzling over the glowing coals. Although we do not report Tapa, we send him back to his camp without the food, and never again do we employ a game scout to watch our camp. It is beginning to seem that instead of the guards protecting the park, we need to protect the park from the guards.

While the men are busy mending the tires, I haul water and bake bread. Several times during the last few days it has rained high in the scarp mountains, and our little river is flowing gently with a few inches of water. We do not know when the real floods will come, so I have been pestering Mark for days to move our valuables again — this time to the airstrip, which is on still higher ground. Most of our gear is stored in the hut, but I'm worried that with the first rain it will be reduced to the mud from whence it came.

Bending over a basin washing clothes, I hear a distant roar and stand up to listen.

Simbeye and Mwamba shout, "The river, watch the river. It comes!"

Instead of running away from the riverbank, which would seem the sensible thing to do, we all run toward it and look upstream. A wall of water, three or four feet high, rounds the bend to the north. It rushes toward us, mad and muddy, looking like one river flowing on top of another. We watch in disbelief as the Lubonga, which was only five yards across, widens to more than a hundred yards, spreading over the rock bar on the opposite side.

Our bank had been a good twelve feet above the river; now the rushing water is only four feet below us, and rising. Huge trees and branches bob in the waves.

I scream over the roar, "Mark, it's going to come over the bank! We've got to move everything!"

"Let's wait and see," he shouts back. I wonder if we will stand here until our feet are wet before we do something.

"Here comes another river," Simbeye calls, pointing behind us, and we run to the northwest corner of the island. Savage brown water pours from what had been a dry gorge. It fills the oxbow to the north of camp with an instant roaring river thirty yards wide. Swollen rapids, topped with foam and debris, cover our track. We are cut off, stranded on the island. There is no longer any chance of moving to the strip. We run back to the main river, which has already risen another foot. Why haven't we listened to all the warnings about floods?

"Shouldn't we at least put everything on top of the truck?" I plead with Mark.

"I don't think it's going to come any higher."

"How on earth do you know?"

"Don't worry. It's going to be okay."

The seven of us stand on the riverbank, heads down, watching the unleashed fury of our little river. A large chunk of the bank falls into the hungry current. Mark motions for us to move back from the edge. The water is two feet below the top of the bank, but its rise seems to have slowed. Ten minutes later it is unchanged.

"See, it's going to be okay," Mark says.

"Right, fine, we're not going to be washed downstream," I agree. "But now we're stuck here; we won't be able to drive out for weeks."

"Oh no, Madam, it won't be like that," Sunday smiles. "This water, she will be gone tomorrow."

"The flood will only last one day?"

"This water," he explains, "she is coming from the mountains to the Luangwa River. When she is there, she will not come back. More water will come on a day from here, but this water, she will be gone tomorrow."

"See," Mark smiles, "no problem. This water, she will be gone tomorrow."

○ ○ ○

The flood begins to recede after a few hours, but it is only the first of many floods to come. With each rain, whether here or in the mountains, the rivers will become higher, the ground soggier, the track more slippery. The old Land Cruiser will no longer be able to drive us out of the valley. We must finish the airstrip and collect the Unimog truck, or we will not be able to operate in North Luangwa this season.

For now we are stuck in camp; we can't even drive to the airstrip until the flood recedes farther. Mark and I pull our folding safari chairs close to the riverbank and watch the Lubonga with new respect. She is still raging, and now that we know her moods, we will never take her for granted.

At sunset a small group of puku females gather on the opposite bank and stare at the river; one of their favorite sleeping spots is three feet underwater. After a while they settle down in a tight knot in the grass.

Darkness brings dazzling stars and the first lightning bug of the season. In a few days thousands of fireflies will sprinkle the night with their phosphorescence, like sequins fluttering and floating through the balmy air. But tonight this one is all alone, and seems lost and lonely as he flashes unanswered valentines above the grass. Usually lightning bugs fly no higher than the treetops. But this one soars higher and higher toward the starry sky as if, for lack of a mate, he has fallen in love with a star.

○ ○ ○

In a final dash to finish the runway before the rainy season, we start working on it at four-thirty every morning. As with most of our races with the African elements, we are losing. Nearly all the small trees have been cleared from the airstrip, but hundreds of stumps remain to be pulled, and three termite mounds as hard as concrete and as large as the truck must be leveled.

Now that much of the undergrowth has been removed, some of the animals can't resist the lush green herbs and grass that have been exposed. A male puku with one horn has already claimed part of the airstrip as his territory, and has become so habituated to our presence that he grazes nearby as we hack and chop. A family of warthogs and a small herd of zebras often forage at the opposite end of the strip.

One hot afternoon, as we are lost in a haze of heat and work, Simbeye calls softly, "Nsofu, there." Far on the other side of Khaya Stream, in a little valley, we see ten elephants moving through the tall grass. They are the first living ones we have seen since our return to North Luangwa. We watch them in awe and whisper softly when we speak, even though they could not possibly hear us at this distance. Adult males, three of them without tusks, feed on the prickly branches of the winter-thorn trees. Reaching with his trunk, one of them pulls down a branch of a fifteen-foot acacia. He strips the bark — twigs, thorns, leaves, and all — and stuffs it into his mouth.

We see these elephants on several more occasions, always in the distance, and although it seems a bit of an exaggeration, we start calling them the Camp Group.

November 14 arrives, ripe with legendary promises, but still there is no rain. Sunday was right, the river has become a gentle stream again, and only the driftwood high on its banks tells of the flood. But every afternoon giant cloud formations rumble across the sky. Simbeye keeps telling us that we must go now, that once the rains come we will not be able to drive up the slippery mountain track in the old Cruiser. "Only one more day," Mark keeps saying, as we pull more stumps and fill more holes.

Finally, the airstrip resembles a runway, although it is certainly not yet ready for approval by the Division of Civil Aviation. There are still several large hummocks, where termite mounds used to be, and scores of stump holes. But it is close enough to being finished that we can complete the job quickly in the Unimog when we return from Durban.

With no idea how long we will be away, we pack up all the gear and hide another cache of leftover fuel and avgas near the airstrip. With all the Bembas bouncing in the trailer, we drive up the scarp. We leave them at Shiwa N'gandu, with the promise that we will hire them again as soon as we return — in a few weeks, we hope.

We are near Mpika when fat raindrops pound the top of the truck, and curtains of white rain drift through the air. We look back. The valley, filled with cumulonimbus clouds, looks like an enormous bowl of popcorn. We have made it out just in time.

7
A Valley of Life

DELIA

> The most present of all the watchers where we camped
> were the animals that stood beyond the firelight,
> being dark, but there, and making no sound.
> They were the most remembered eyes that night.
>
> — WILLIAM STAFFORD, "When We Looked Back"

ooo

CARRYING THE HOT-WATER KETTLE, a towel, and a flashlight, Mark follows the footpath through the dark camp toward the bath boma. Surrounded by tall grass, the boma is a three-sided structure of sticks and reeds standing at the edge of Marula-Puku camp. Inside is a wash table also made of sticks, a jerry can of cold water, and a basin in which we mix hot and cold water for our baths every evening.

A rustling noise sounds from the grass. Mark pauses briefly, but walks on. Earlier a male waterbuck had been grazing near the sausage tree just beyond the boma; he is probably still in the tall grass. Mark mixes his bathwater, then switches off the flashlight to save the batteries. Standing naked under the bright stars, he begins to wash his hair, closing his eyes against the soapsuds. He freezes as he hears the rustling again from six feet behind him, just outside the boma. He quickly splashes water onto his face to rinse away the soap, then switches on his flashlight, hoping to get a closer look at the waterbuck. A wall of tall grass is all that he sees, but he can still hear the swishing sounds. He steps to the grass, parts it, and shines the light into the thick cover at his feet.

A lioness, crouched flat against the ground, glares back at him, her tail lashing. She is only four feet away, looking straight into his eyes.

"Aaarrgghh!" Involuntarily, Mark utters a primal growl and

jumps back. At the same instant the lioness springs to her feet, hissing and spitting at him, her canines gleaming white in the light. Mark leaps into the boma. The lioness whirls around and charges away through the grass to join five other lions ten yards behind her. Together the pride trots to the firebreak a little farther on, where they all sit on their haunches, staring at Mark. Suds dripping down his neck, Mark stares back, wondering if they will become frequent visitors to our camp like the lions we knew in the Kalahari.

○ ○ ○

It is early February 1988, much later than we'd planned, before we return to Luangwa — Mark in the new Unimog hauling a thirteen-ton shipping container, I driving the old Cruiser. The rains have transformed the Northern Province into a lush tangle of weeds, grass, and shrubs. The little villages are smothered in vines, dripping with today's rain and yesterday's moist blossoms. To stay dry the women have to cook inside their grass huts, the smoke smoldering through the thatched roofs. When we reach the village of Shiwa N'gandu, Simbeye, Kasokola, and Mwamba rush out of their mud and thatch huts to greet us. All smiles as usual, they are ready to return to Marulu-Puku. When I ask about Sunday Justice, they explain that he has gone to Lusaka to look for work. The thought of this gentle, soft-spoken, imaginative fellow walking the tough streets of Lusaka saddens me. But, happy to have the other men with us, we start once again down the scarp.

Island Zulu, Gaston Phiri, Tapa, and the other game guards leave their beer circle and shake our hands warmly in welcome. The children surround us calling "smi-lee, smi-lee," which at first I mistake as some form of Bemba greeting. Then I realize that I have always asked them to smile for the camera, so they think that "smile" means "hello." When I greet them in Chibemba, they collapse in giggles and run into their huts.

The Mwaleshi, now in full flood, does not give us such a warm welcome. The swollen river tears through the forest, splashing spray and whitecaps against boulders and logs. If we cannot get across the river, our hopes of working in North Luangwa during the rains will stop right here.

Using the bucket loader on the Mog, for three days we quarry stones from a rocky outcropping and dump them into the river to make a ford. On the morning of the fourth day Mark ties a rope around his waist and swims across, pulling the end of the winch cable with him. Once on the other side, he hooks the cable around the base of a large tree and recrosses the river. As he slowly eases the nine-foot-tall Mog into the river, its hood disappears under the roiling current. The cab rocks wildly as the truck climbs over the boulders on the river bottom. Water seeps in around Mark's feet, but the truck churns through the current and pulls itself up the muddy bank on the east side of the Mwaleshi.

After several more trips to ferry the rest of the gear across, we fill the back of the Cruiser with large stones for ballast and winch it over. Water pours out of every door and crack of the old machine, which must long for desert days gone by. The current would sweep away the shipping container, so we leave it in Mano.

On our way down the scarp the trucks get stuck so often in the greasy mud that we don't make it to Marula-Puku tonight, as we had hoped. We camp near "Elephant's Playground," a swale of long grass where we have often seen elephant tracks, dung, and broken trees, but never the elephants themselves. The next morning the grass is so tall — ten feet in places — that it is difficult to follow the track. Simbeye, Mwamba, and Kasokola climb into the Mog's bucket, and Mark raises them high over the truck so they can guide us.

The runway we had worked so hard to clear is covered by grass eight feet tall and hundreds of small mopane shrubs. "It's not as bad as it looks," Mark tries to cheer me. As we continue down the track, I dread what we will find at camp. From the tall north bank, all that can be seen of the Bemba hut is the soggy, lopsided thatch roof that appears to be floating on top of a grass lake. The oxbow around the island is a swamp with tall reeds bobbing in knee-deep water. But the main river, the Lubonga, is well within its banks, and only a shallow stream separates us from camp.

The adobe walls are cracked and crumbling, the roof windblown and certainly not waterproof, but the hut is still standing. As I walk silently inside, Simbeye says, "This is not a very fine house, Madam, but we will make it strong for you." I smile gratefully at him and look around. One big truck, one small truck, and five muddy people — a motley crew for the size of the project we have in mind. I look up at Mark. "Well, we'd better get started."

There is plenty of willing mud to repair the walls and plenty of ready grass to mend the roof. Within two days we have a primitive camp and a week later the grass has been cleared from the airstrip. The runway still has to be leveled, which will take another three months of backbreaking work, but after that we can fly the airplane to the valley.

Around the campfire each night, Mark and I talk endlessly about how North Luangwa can be saved from poachers. We will have to start by working with the game guards to enforce the laws against poaching, but that will be only the first step. The people who live around the park must be convinced that wildlife is more valuable to them alive than dead. Eventually, we hope that conservation-minded tour operators will run quality, old-fashioned walking safaris that will put money in the pockets of the local people. The government has agreed that 50 percent of the revenue from tourism in North Luangwa — once it starts — can be returned to the villagers.

Of course, we would rather North Luangwa be free and wild, but that is no longer a choice. It lost its freedom when the poachers fired the first shot. The challenge is to save it without breaking it of its wildness.

It will be some time before revenue from tourism will begin to flow to the villages near the park. In the meantime, we can help the people find other ways of making a living so they can give up poaching. We think of cottage industries, such as carpentry shops, beekeeping, maize mills, and sunflower presses. We can help them grow more of their own food, especially sources of protein such as poultry, fish, beans, and peanuts. Hungry people do not make good conservationists.

Most important, perhaps, we will start teaching the young

people that wildlife is the most valuable resource in their district. Most of the children have never seen live elephants, much less thought of them as anything other than a source of meat or ivory. Neither has the rest of the world. This is as good a place as any to start.

Then, of course, we have to learn more about North Luangwa, especially its wildlife and ecology. We will fly regular aerial surveys, taking a census of each wildlife species and noting its distribution in order to determine whether the population is stable or declining. We will also explore the park from the ground, but that will be difficult at the height of the rainy season. Even the Mog bogs down in mud between camp and the airstrip.

So, hiking in misty mountains and across soggy savannas, and wafting in the plane over the backs of buffalo, elephants, zebras, and wildebeest, we begin discovering this land of rivers and this valley of life.

○ ○ ○

"We're not going to make it tonight. Let's camp here." Standing in the drizzle, Mark, Kasokola, Mwamba, and I look up at the sheer forested cliff towering between us and our destination. Days before in the airplane, we had followed the Lubonga River from its source on the plateau above the Muchinga Escarpment. Beginning as a narrow trickle, it wound its way through the lush vegetation and rounded peaks of the tumbledown mountains. Now and then it cascaded over boulders, creating waterfalls hidden beneath tropical trees, ferns, and vines. At one spot, near the base of the mountains, the river surged through a small, pasture-like floodplain, the shape of a teardrop, tucked away in the folds of the steep-sided hills. We called it Hidden Valley. At this point along the river's course, a single mountain ridge blocked it from the plains beyond. But decades before, the Lubonga had found a weakness in the strata of the ridge and had crashed through, creating a narrow chasm, covered in ferns, vines, and sprays of bamboo.

Determined to reach this vale, we have hiked from camp along the Lubonga for two days through mist and torrential downpours.

By keeping records of the species of wildlife and plants we encounter in each habitat, we begin to understand the flux and flow among the plant and animal communities in the valley. Thinking that we would easily make it today, we have walked until late afternoon along the Lubonga. But from the base of the last rock outcropping between us and Hidden Valley, we can see that the route is more formidable than we thought from the air. Night will fall before we reach our destination.

"Okay, this is a great spot to camp," I agree, looking around at the lush plain that stretches to the small mountain. The Lubonga, in full flood, rushes through the narrow canyon and then meanders across the soggy bottomland. I lift the heavy backpack from my shoulders and ease it to the ground.

"Look — buffalo?" Kasokola points northwest toward a low stand of *Combretum* trees. Stooping over, Mark and I look under the scattered trees to see three hundred buffalo milling about in the mist, not a hundred yards from us. Some are bedding down in the soft grass for the night; others continue to graze toward us. Apparently they have not seen or smelled us, and as we set up our little fly-camp, some of the herd wander still closer, grunting and mooing until at last they lie down, very near our camp.

As Mark pulls the tent's guy rope, he looks over his shoulder, then points to the buffalo. We all stop in our tracks. A few large females have stood up and are blowing their alarm call as they stare at us. Suddenly the entire herd are on their feet. Blocked by the ridge, the river, and the steep canyon walls, they have nowhere to go except in our direction. Their feet sloshing in the soggy ground, they stampede past our campsite, then disappear in the gray swirling mist.

Up before the sun, we break camp and walk to the gorge. Our plan is to follow the river through the canyon to Hidden Valley on the other side of the four-hundred-foot ridge. But the river is so high that it crashes against the steep walls, leaving no space for hiking. We will have to climb over the ridge.

Following an elephant trail up the hillside, we pause here and there to clip samples from towering trees and tropical undergrowth for our plant presses. Water from the leaves drips down my neck, and my last pair of dry socks is soaked. When we reach the top, Hidden Valley, nestled in its own secret hills, lies quietly below us. Shrouded in a veil of mist, giant trees and bamboo line the tiny, grassy valley — only a few hundred yards wide. The Lubonga snakes gently through the marshy bottomland, and small herds of puku, buffalo, and waterbuck graze the lush, green foliage on the banks.

For the next two days we trek through the lofty forests and across the small dambos — sunken, grassy glades — recording animal and plant life. We see tracks of the rare sable antelope and come upon a family of wild pigs digging for roots. Elephant paths worn inches deep in the hard gravel of the ridges suggest that they have been traveled for centuries by generations of pachyderms winding around the hillsides.

One afternoon, leaving the Bembas in our little fly-camp, Mark and I follow the meandering Lubonga through Hidden Valley. We cross the meadow and follow the river up to where it springs from the hills. Here the heads of the tall elephant grass rustle as we pass, and in the distance the scarp mountains brood. We step into a small, marshy clearing and pause to watch two male puku sparring across the river.

Suddenly the long grass between us and the river moves and warns us of something big, bold, and bulky.

"Buffalo!" Mark whispers, pulling me behind him and raising his rifle. A huge bull staggers out of a reed-filled dambo only fifteen yards ahead, his hooves sucking loudly in the mud. He pauses, lifts his head, and stares in our direction, nostrils flaring, a bunch of grass sticking out of his mouth.

"Freeze," Mark whispers to me, thumbing the .375 rifle's safety off. The bull lowers his head and starts toward us like a Mack truck, his horns swinging from side to side. He is looking directly at us, but — incredibly — does not seem to see or smell us. At only ten yards away, he stops again and raises his massive head to scrutinize us, blowing puffs of air as he tries to take our scent. Lone bulls can be extremely aggressive and often attack with no apparent provocation. Turning my head carefully, I see a tall winter-thorn acacia tree forty yards behind me.

"Mark," I whisper between clenched teeth. "I'm going to run to that tree."

"No! Don't move!"

The buffalo raises and lowers his head, as if straining to make out the two forms standing in front of him. It is said that buffalo cannot see very well, but he can't possibly miss us at this distance. Holding his head at full height, the buffalo starts toward us again. This close, he is going to be very unhappy when he discovers us. I take a tiny step backward.

"FREEZE!" Mark hisses. The bull stops, shaking his head.

"I AM RUNNING TO THAT TREE!" I hiss back.

Without moving his lips, Mark vows, "If you move, I'm going to shoot you in the back!" I pause, considering my options.

Eight yards away the bull is raising and lowering his heavy black boss, and again blowing air through his wide nostrils. It's too late to run. I couldn't make it to the tree anyway, with my knees shaking like this. Slinging saliva and grass stems, the buffalo shakes his head and grunts. He stomps and rakes his right hoof. A dank, musky odor lies heavy on the air. Lowering his nose to the grass, he smells along the ground and begins walking again in our direction. After a few more steps he looks directly at me, drool falling from his mouth. Once again he tosses his head.

He turns slightly, then step by step walks right past us until he enters the tall reeds on the other side of the clearing.

When he is out of sight, Mark turns to me and grins. "See, it's okay."

Sitting down heavily on a log, I ask, "Would you really have shot me in the back?"

Mark smiles and sits next to me. "You'll never know."

○ ○ ○

On our last day in Hidden Valley, we hike with Kasokola, Mwamba, and Simbeye up into the mountains. Believing that we are the first people to explore this little corner of earth keeps us cheery and warm in spite of the constant drizzle.

But then we come upon a well-used footpath leading down from the scarp mountains to the valley. "Poachers," Mwamba says. Walking silently, we follow its switchbacks across the hills. Periodically there are clearings and old campfires, and occasionally large meat racks and piles of discarded bones. The path has been used regularly for years by large bands of commercial poachers.

We tell ourselves not to be discouraged; after all, we know that poachers hunt in North Luangwa. Even so, our hike to Hidden Valley has taught us that this is a very special place, and even more worth saving than we had believed before.

○ ○ ○

The stall warning blares constantly as the plane shudders and shakes, trying to maintain altitude. We are flying our first wildlife census of North Luangwa, which requires that we hold an airspeed of eighty knots at two hundred feet above the ground, along transect lines running approximately east and west across the park. Because of crosswinds and thermal air currents, it isn't easy to hold a precise heading, airspeed, and height above the ground, even over the relatively flat floor of the river valley. We have divided the park into sixty-five grids, and as we fly along we use tape recorders and a stopwatch to record the species of wildlife, the habitat type, and the exact time, which will later be computed against our airspeed to give us a rough grid position for the animals sighted. From these data we will calculate the distribution and density of the animal populations.

But the mountains of the Muchinga Escarpment cut a jagged line across the park, jutting more than three thousand feet from the valley floor in a series of ever steeper hills, deeper gorges, and higher cliffs. No matter how rugged the terrain, for purposes of the survey we must maintain a constant height above the ground. When we reach the first foothills, Mark pulls up the plane's nose and pushes in the throttle to climb over the first range of hills. But as soon as we have crested them, he hauls back on the throttle, drops flaps, and we sink into the next narrow valley. We level off, and before our stomachs can come down, a rocky precipice stares us in the face and we are climbing again. At the top of the next ridge, the earth plunges away to a seemingly bottomless ravine, then soars again to new heights. Mark pushes the stick forward and the plane dives through the gorge toward what looks like the center of the earth.

Under these conditions we cannot possibly maintain two hundred feet, and at times the wings slice within feet of massive trees and boulders. I try to concentrate: "5 buffalo, 10:25, brachystegia woodland; 3 wild pigs, 10:44, upland mopane." But more than once I close my eyes as the plane tries to scale a rocky cliff. The mountains stretch for more than thirty miles across the park and we must fly across them thirty-two times. The stall warning sounds continuously and the plane barely maintains altitude. I glance at Mark. Beads of sweat glisten on his forehead, and his hands strangle the stick as he fights the downdrafts and swirling air currents. I think we must have reached the top; but as I dare to look up, the tallest peak yet fills the plane's windshield.

Mark stomps left rudder and turns the plane away from the mountain. Gliding at a safe height above the ridges he flies us back to camp and lands on the airstrip. I step out on wobbly knees and control an urge to kiss the ground.

"Okay, that's just not safe," Mark says. In all our years together, I have never heard him say these words. I lean against the fuselage while he spreads the maps across the plane's tail. "This is what we'll do," he says. "Instead of flying east and west across the scarp, we'll fly northeast and southwest along it, and sample it independently of the valley floor. The peaks and valleys won't be as severe that way. As long as we design the transect lines correctly, we'll cover the same ground and not distort the data."

After redrawing the lines and calculating the new headings, we take off again. True, the ups and downs above the jagged earth are not as severe flying along the scarp, but the plane still struggles to fly and I still struggle to keep my eyes open. But "scarping," as we have come to call it, is worth it. The soaring forested peaks surround not only fall-away canyons but soft grassy glades and mountain streams. We see a herd of sable galloping through a meadow and a family of elephants walking on an ancient path through the hills. A leopard balances on top of a termite mound as he watches us pass. With each transect line, each hilltop and dale, we learn more about Luangwa.

○ ○ ○

In late February there is an unusual break in the rains. The ground dries up a bit, and we are determined to cut a track across the park to the plains that parallel the Luangwa for miles. From the air we have seen more wildlife on these seemingly endless savannas during the rainy season than anywhere else in Africa.

We fly from camp on the Lubonga River, past Mvumvwe Hill and all the way to the Luangwa, searching for the route with the easiest stream crossings and the lowest hills. Once we have decided on a general route, Kasokola, Mwamba, Simbeye, and I drive out and cut our way across the bush the best we can. Periodically Mark flies overhead and gives us detailed instructions by radio.

"Delia, you're heading too far north, you're going to run into a gully. Pull back to the last streambed, then head zero five five degrees for about four and a half miles till you get to a rocky cliff. I'll tell you where to go from there."

"Okay, Roger. I copy that." And on it goes for two weeks, until the guys and I finally reach the Fitwa River. It is too deep for the Cruiser to cross, so we turn back for camp to collect Mark and the Mog. We pack the truck with darting gear, camping gear, plant presses, and food in preparation for a long expedition to the plains to dart lions, take wildlife censuses, and sample the vegetation.

"Mark, do you really think the Mog can make it through this?" I stare at the angry Fitwa, raging between mud-slick banks that are fifteen feet high. We will have to ease the Mog down a fifty-degree slope of mud, ford the shoulder-deep current, then climb the opposite bank.

"No problem. Hold on, guys," Mark calls to Simbeye, Kasokola, and Mwamba, who are perched on top of the gear in the back. Mark shifts to the third of the truck's sixteen gears and eases forward over the edge. At first the Mog's four-foot-tall mud tires hold on the greasy slope, their ribbed tractor lugs biting deep. Then, as the entire weight of the truck heads downhill, the treads break loose and we begin a sickening slide toward the river. I grab for the handles in the cab and hold on. The truck hits the river, submerging its front end completely under water, spray, and mud. Mark rams the truck into a higher gear. It churns through the river, water boiling through its chassis, around its sides, and into the cab around our feet. Near the opposite bank he guns the turbo-diesel and the Mog claws its way up the slope — so steep that we are almost lying on our backs in our seats. The big tires spin, slide, and sling mud through the window into my lap.

"Hey! Hey!" Shouts come from somewhere behind us. Turning, I see our three helpers tumble off the back of the truck and into the river, followed by our mattresses, tents, and bedrolls. Splashing about in confusion, they grab overhanging branches and hang on against the swift current. With a free hand or foot they snare bits and pieces of our gear as they float by. I jump from the cab and slide through the mud to help them, as Mark maneuvers the truck to the top of the bank. Pulling Mwamba from the current I say, "Thank goodness you guys can swim!"

"I can't," he says with his ever-present smile. "But it would be a good thing to know how to swim when crossing a river with this boss."

Unbelievably, nothing is lost. We repack the soggy gear and carry on. Two days later we reach the plains.

As we emerge from the woodlands, the savannas stretch for miles in every imaginable shade of green. Dozens of different kinds of grasses wave with iridescent reds, greens, and yellows. Like a huge abstract watercolor, they boast an array of spiraling blossoms and sprays of soft seeds. Choreographed by the breeze, they bow, swirl, and pirouette. Wind and grass make perfect dance partners.

And it is here where most of the wildlife of Luangwa spend the rainy season. Large herds of zebras, wildebeests, eland, impalas, and puku graze the succulent wild rice (*Echinocloa*) and other grasses (*Erograstis, Spirobolis*) and attract lions, leopards, spotted hyenas, and wild dogs. In the late afternoon they pause to drink at hundreds of small water holes filled with knob-billed ducks, blacksmith plovers, jicanas, sperwing and Egyptian geese, and Goliath herons. Majestic crowned cranes strut nearby. Some of the smaller water holes are more mud than water, and in each a battle-scarred old bull buffalo wallows, caked in gray sludge, oxpeckers sitting on his broad back. Herds of more than a thousand younger bulls, cows, and calves mow the grass all around. Warthogs kneel to root up bulbs and subterranean delicacies. Greater kudu stand silently in the shadows of *Croton* and *Combretum* trees, and families of elephants pull up bunches of the tender grasses.

Amazingly, some of these "plains" are the same devastated and degraded woodlands we saw in the dry season. Then they looked like a portrait of ecological disaster — the soil a gray, dry powder without a single living plant to its credit, the mopane trees limbless and dead, the bushes leafless. We worried that this ruined habitat could never recover, but the rains have transformed it into a lush grassland that, in this season, is the most heavily utilized habitat in the park.

Most of this area was once healthy mopane woodland. But about fifteen years ago, when commercial poachers invaded the area and began killing unprecedented numbers of elephants, the harried survivors sought sanctuary deep in the heart of the park. Squeezed into these woodlands in unusually high numbers, the animals stripped the trees of their bark, leaving them vulnerable to diseases such as heart rot, and to the wildfires set by the poachers each dry season. This combination of pressures from elephants, disease, and fire has killed off hundreds of square miles of mopane forests, opening the way for the establishment of annual grasslands that appear only during the rains. The poachers have devastated the woodlands, just as they are devastating the elephants.

Now that the grasses have supplanted the dying woodland, there might seem to be no problem. But while grasslands favor buffalo and other grazers, forests are important to elephants, kudu, and other browsers. So poachers are reconfiguring the floral and faunal communities of the park. Who knows what changes in species composition or loss will occur if more woodlands are damaged by the bushfires that now sweep over 80 percent of the park every year.

○ ○ ○

Our radio tracking of lions in the Kalahari taught us not only about their natural history but about the habits of other carnivores, and the distribution and habits of their prey. We are anxious to put transmitters on the Luangwa lions so that we can learn more about their competitors and prey, and so that we can compare them with the Kalahari lions.

On the edge of one of the plains is a grove of large *Combretum obovatum* bushes that stand fifteen to twenty feet tall. The thorny branches of each bush hang down in a dense tumble, creating a spacious cavern within — a perfect place to hide. We put our pup-tent inside one of the combretums, and the guys erect theirs in another. In a clearing surrounded by a dense thicket, we build a campfire and set up the small table and chairs. With the Mog hidden in the bushes behind the camp, we are totally concealed from the wildlife on the plains.

We have always darted carnivores from a truck, but since the Mog is so huge, Mark worries that lions will not come within range of the dart gun. Instead, we will make a blind and operate from it. We hang a large piece of awning cloth between two combretum bushes not far from our little camp and hide our chairs, tables, and darting gear behind it. It is dusk by the time we finish, so we retire for the night in our tucked-away campsite.

At dawn we quietly cook a breakfast of oatmeal and fried toast over the campfire. Our plan is to set up a huge stereo speaker at each side of the nearby blind and play recordings of lions feeding, mating, and roaring their territorial challenge, in the hope that these sounds will attract a resident lion for darting. While I am making coffee, Mark plays the roars in the middle of our camp's little kitchen.

"It'll take a while for the lions to come," he says. "So we'll just finish our coffee, go to the blind, and play more roars there."

Meanwhile the speakers blare their great roars across the plains.

Quickly finishing their breakfast, Kasokola, Mwamba, and Simbeye take refuge in the Mog, where they wait for us to call them. Mark and I stand together, sipping our steaming camp coffee as we watch the herds of zebra and wildebeests on the plain.

"Hey! There's a lion!" Mark exclaims, pointing straight ahead. A large male with a full mane stands less than sixty yards away, his chin raised, moving his head side to side, apparently searching for the intruder who is bellowing in his territory.

"Hurry, let's get to the blind," Mark says, as he picks up a speaker and sneaks through the grass toward the blind. I lift the other speaker and follow. Without the taped roars to home on, the lion heads off in the wrong direction and disappears from sight.

In the blind we quickly hook up the stereo system and start playing the roars, taking cover behind the cloth. Almost immediately the lion reappears, trotting straight for us. Careful to stay below the level of the awning cloth, Mark loads the darting rifle with a drug-filled syringe. At fifty yards the lion slows to a saunter, his eyes wide, tail flicking. It only now occurs to me that nothing but a piece of cloth stands between us and him. The tape player continues to challenge the male, who hunches his shoulders as he stalks toward us, stiff-legged. He breaks into a trot again, his mane swinging loosely.

Mark turns off the speakers and takes aim with the darting rifle. Since the lion is coming straight for us, the only possible target is his forehead. Mark holds his fire. At forty yards the lion veers left and circles the blind, just out of range, then disappears behind our thicket. The brush behind us is so thick we cannot see him. Mark plays the roars again. We stand in the silence, watching and listening.

"He's right here," Mark whispers.

"Where?"

"Right *here!*" Moving very slowly Mark points to the end of the blind where it is tied to the bush. The lion's muzzle is almost touching the cloth as he peers into the depths of the thicket — and our blind. He is at most a yard from my right leg; too close to dart.

He looks up and down the strange material, sniffing loudly at its unfamiliar odors.

Apparently satisfied that no other male lions are hiding in the bushes, he turns and walks toward the plain. Slowly Mark lifts the rifle above the blind and darts him in the flank. The lion whirls around and stares at us. We freeze again. This is the most dangerous moment: if he associates us with the sting in his rump, he may charge. He spit-growls once, but turns and trots away. Five minutes later he sits on his haunches, relaxing as the tranquilizer takes effect. After another five minutes he slumps to the ground, immobile. With the guys' help, we collar, weigh, measure, and ear tag the lion.

For the next three days we set up the speakers at different spots on the plain, and try to call in other lions. But wherever we go, it is this same male who appears, still trying to chase imaginary intruders from his area. We name him Bouncer.

○ ○ ○

We have just returned to Marula-Puku from an expedition late one afternoon, and the men are mending a flat tire on the Mog. We have long ago given them the hut to live in; Mark and I sleep in a puptent near a small supply tent at the other end of the island. Our kitchen is merely a clearing under the marula trees, with crates and tin boxes arranged in a square. I am mixing cornbread batter and preparing to bake it in the black pot by the fire.

"KA-POW! KA-POW!" Gunshots from across the river.

"Poachers!" Simbeye shouts, pointing south.

More shots. Three, four, five, six, seven. I feel their concussion in my chest. Eight. Nine.

"Sons of bitches! AK-47s!" Mark swears. "Not more than a half-mile from here. They're probably shooting elephants."

All my doubts about our fighting the poachers dissolve in an instant. "We've got to do something!"

But with only one gun and no authority to go after poachers on our own, all we can do is drive to Mano to get the scouts. Their camp is eighteen miles northwest of Marula-Puku. Within minutes of the last shot Mark and I are in the Mog, clawing our way up the scarp. When we arrive, Mano camp is quiet and still, although scattered cooking fires glow here and there in front of each hut. Mark jumps down and quickly tells Island Zulu about the gunshots. A few scouts stand around, leaning against the truck. Tapa, who had dried fish and meat in our camp, yawns. Nelson Mumba, still wearing his red bandana, walks away. As honorary game rangers and directors of our project, Mark and I have the authority to order the scouts on patrol. But we do not want to command them; we want them to come on their own.

"We have no ammunition," Zulu tells us.

"What happened to it?" Mark asks. Mosi Salama, the warden in Mpika, swore to us that each man had been given his monthly allotment of five rounds. The scouts look at each other, speaking in Chibemba. As before, all agree that they have not received their allotment.

"I have one round," says Gaston Phiri, a lively, short man with the energy of a shrew. "But we have only four rifles, and one does not have a bolt."

Mark senses a faint willingness in Phiri. "Mr. Phiri, I will pay every man who comes with us two hundred kwachas for each poacher he catches."

"But we have no food for patrol," says Phiri.

"We will give you food," I interject.

Eventually six of them agree to come, but they will need two hours to get packed. We urge them to hurry, so that we can catch the poachers before daybreak, but Phiri tells us, "We cannot patrol at night. That is when the lions are hunting. Don't worry. The poachers will not move at night either."

It is midnight before we get back to Marula-Puku, and Mark and I are up again at four-thirty, getting a big fire going, making as much noise as possible to wake the slumbering scouts. They finally join us around the fire at five-fifteen. They unpack their worn knapsacks, which they have just packed, and Phiri puts a huge pan of water on the fire to boil their n'shima. The others lie around the fire smoking tobacco and chatting, waiting for the water to boil. I stoke the fire continuously, to make it hotter.

"Look, it's boiling," I say to Phiri.

"Yes, but it must boil for many minutes to get very hot."

I stare at him, wondering how I can explain that water cannot get hotter than it is at the boiling point. The poachers are probably breaking camp and moving on, and here we are waiting for water to perform a miracle. But I keep quiet, hoping that the poachers are also waiting for their water to exceed the boiling point.

Twenty minutes later the water is hot enough to satisfy the scouts. They toss in handfuls of mealie-meal, stirring vigorously, then eat the paste with the bully beef and tea we have provided. They breakfast in leisurely fashion, as is their custom; when they are finished, they wash their hands carefully in a basin of water. Then each man rolls a cigarette and smokes it down to his fingers. An hour and a half after rising, they are nearly ready to head out.

For patrol, we give them enough mealie-meal, salt, dried fish, beans, tea, and sugar to last a week. They repack their bags and at six forty-five announce they are ready. Mark steps forward to go with them, but Phiri holds up his hand.

"You can tell us, please, where you heard the gunshots. But you cannot escort us there. You are not a scout."

Mark is annoyed but accepts their position. He takes the compass and, pointing 170 degrees, shows them exactly where we heard the shots, and adds, "Don't forget. For every poacher you capture, you each get two hundred kwachas."

We wish them luck as they march out of camp in a ragged line. Four have uniforms, two do not. Their trousers are torn and patched. Four have boots, one wears a pair of rubber-tire sandals, and one is barefoot. Only two have proper rucksacks; another carries a plastic bag, and Phiri has an old gunnysack thrown over his shoulder. Island Zulu is still lugging his old cot frame and has three plastic mugs, red, yellow, and blue, tied to his pack. They have three rifles — one without a bolt, another without sights — and a shotgun that won't extract spent rounds. And they have only one round of ammunition. No wonder they are reluctant to go after poachers armed with AK-47s. Nevertheless, they are going. "Good luck," I say again softly.

Mark, Simbeye, and Mwamba go to the airstrip to grade it with the Mog's loader, while Kasokola and I remain in Marula-Puku.

Kasokola, the youngest of the Bembas, is shy and quiet, but smiles readily at the slightest prompting. He and I clear the grass where the office, bedroom, and kitchen huts will go, then drive sticks into the ground to mark the corners of each. After seeing what happens to a mud hut in the rains, we plan to build stone cottages with thatched roofs.

At eight-thirty I see the first vultures circling to the south, where the shots were fired. The carcasses are closer than we thought. The game guards should have found them easily by now and be on the trail of the poachers. I feel sickened that elephants were shot so close to camp, for if we can't protect the animals in areas right around us, what chance do we have to stop poaching in the rest of the park?

"They are coming, Madam," Kasokola says quietly.

I whirl around, "Who is coming?"

He points south. "The game guards."

The scouts are walking toward us, spread out in a line along the riverbank. It is eleven o'clock. Have they captured poachers already? I hurry toward them, as they emerge from the long grass. There are only six men; no poachers.

"Good morning, Madam," Gaston Phiri says loudly and cheerfully.

"Hello, Phiri," I answer quickly. "What is happening? Where are the poachers?"

Phiri raises himself to his greatest height, which is about the same as mine, and announces, "We have found two poached elephants! They are on the riverbank, only half a mile from here."

"Good," I say, "we sort of knew that." I point to the scores of vultures soaring less than a mile away. "But what about the poachers?"

Still holding himself erect, Phiri answers, "We thought you would want to take photographs of us with the dead elephants."

I stare at him in disbelief. "Phiri, we have plenty of photos of dead elephants. In fact, since we have been in this national park, we have only taken pictures of dead elephants! Since we have been in Zambia we have seen more dead elephants than living elephants. What I want is a picture of you with poachers. You are supposed to capture the poachers, not have a photo session with the dead elephants."

The scouts frown and look away, clearly disappointed that they are not going to be photographed.

"We have found the tracks of the poachers," Phiri continues. "We can chase them out of the park."

"Phiri, they will be miles from here by now. They probably left at sunup."

"We will go after them," he says, "but first we must have lunch. Can you give us some more canned meat?"

"We gave you a week's supply of food a few hours ago. We have only four tins left. Okay, here are two of them. But please try to capture those poachers!"

"Thank you very much! And anyway, we thought maybe you would like to take our photograph here before we go on patrol."

"Right. You're absolutely right. We should have done that this morning." I don't even bother to rush as I bring the camera from the tent. "Stand together over here."

They crowd together, holding up their rifles and making the most fearsome facial expressions and guttural growls. Too bad the poachers have not joined us for lunch — they might have had the fright of their lives. Little do the scouts realize it is a picture of despair.

The scouts do not come back to Marula-Puku. Later I ask Simbeye if he has heard anything, and he tells me that when the scouts left our camp they marched straight back to Mano to share the food with their families. Mark and I are disappointed, but realize we may be expecting too much of six men with one bullet and hungry families. We will have to equip them better, not only with rifles but also with tents and uniforms, and somehow ensure a more reliable supply of food at Mano. By candlelight we draw up a list of the scouts' most pressing needs and resolve to discuss it with the warden on our next trip to Mpika.

Two days later we see the elephants of Camp Group moving in the distance along Khya Stream. Now, instead of ten, there are only eight.

8
The Heart of the Village

DELIA

They learn in suffering what they teach in song.
— PERCY BYSSHE SHELLEY

○ ○ ○

THE SHARP EDGE of the hand-carved wooden stool cuts into my thigh, as I glance back and forth from Mark to the village headman, who is acting as our translator for Chief Mukungule. We are all sitting on various-sized stools in the thatched n'saka — except for the chief, who is enthroned on a seat taken from an old DC-10 aircraft. The chief's barefoot wife squats on the earthen floor near a clay pot of steaming sweet potatoes. Crowded nearby, their heads leaning toward us to catch the words of the translator, are twenty to thirty villagers of Mukungule.

"You see," Mark says, "if we can save the wild animals, the tourists will come from America to visit the park. They will bring money that will benefit your village. And if we can help bring back the animals around the park, your people can hunt them for meat — in a controlled way — so that there will always be some for food."

The headman stares at Mark for a long moment before turning to the chief and delivering his translation in Chibemba. Mukungule was born in 1910 and has been chief since 1928. He claims to have one hundred eighty grandchildren. His once-dark Bantu eyes have faded to a piercing ice-blue, but his personality is as warm and gentle as the African breeze. Most of his teeth are missing, no doubt the result of his insatiable appetite for sugar. He knows no English, but he smiles easily and communicates well with those ancient eyes, which have seen many things, including the coming and going of the British.

After an exchange in Chibemba, the headman turns to Mark, "We do not know this word 'tuureest.' "

I decide to give it a try. "Many people in the world like to travel, and they take money with them to pay for food and places to sleep. So the country they are visiting gains money. There are no elephants or Cape buffalo in America or Europe. The people who live there will come here to see these wild animals. They will pay a lot of dollars and pounds to see them. Your village could benefit from these visitors."

As the headman translates, the chief looks at us and nods his head slowly.

"But if the poachers keep shooting the elephants and buffalo, there won't be anything for the tourists to see. They won't come here. They won't bring their money."

I watch the villagers' faces; only the chief is nodding. Most of the people of Mukungule are of the Bisa tribe, which split from the Bemba tribe after the great exodus from Lubaland in Zaire in the nineteenth century. The older villagers, including the chief himself, remember well the days when they lived in the valley at the Lubonga-Mwaleshi confluence, the very spot inside the national park that we have come to love. The chief's ancestors, generations of chiefs, are buried under a tree only a few hills from our camp. Every October the headmen trek down the scarp to pay their respects to those spirits, by tying white swatches of cloth in the branches of the tree. It was their land, their home, their hunting ground, their burial place. As far as anyone knows, they were the first humans to live there — and until we came, the last. When the area was designated a game reserve by the British colonial government in the 1950s, the Bisas were asked to leave. Now we live near their ancestors and ask them to stop shooting the animals for meat and the elephants for ivory. We talk of "tuureests" coming from the moon with a kind of money they cannot imagine.

They left the valley willingly, the chief tells us, because the Mwaleshi hippos ate their crops and made farming impossible. In those days there was plenty of wildlife on the scarp, right here in Mukungule. As long as the Bisas hunted with bows and arrows, they could not kill too many animals and there were always enough to feed the tribe. Once guns were introduced, hunting was easier and no one controlled the numbers of animals shot. Soon all the animals west of the park were gone.

There is no butcher shop in this entire area, the chief continues, not even in Mpika. If a man in Mukungule wants to put meat on the table for his children, he must poach in North Luangwa National Park. I shift uneasily. Unfortunately there are so many people needing to feed their families, and so few animals left, that allowing people to kill "for the pot" would amount to a quick fix that would soon eliminate all wildlife in and around the park. For this reason, subsistence poaching — killing to put meat on the table — must be controlled as well as poaching for commercial gain. Both will lead to the near-term destruction of a valuable resource that can be used to raise the living standard of the people.

Talking a bit faster now, we explain that we understand their problems: there are no jobs in Mukungule, no meat, little protein. We want to assist them. If they will stop poaching, we will help them find other jobs and other sources of protein. Later, if tourists come to the park, there will be lots of work for the men; and the women can grow beans and groundnuts, raise chickens, build fish farms, and sell produce to the tour operators. While obtaining our permits to operate in the park, we persuaded the Zambian government to return 50 percent of its revenue from tourism to the local villages. But if the poaching continues, most of the animals in North Luangwa will be gone in five years. Then what will they do?

"You don't have to wait for the tourists to come," we tell them. "Anyone who will exchange poaching for a job can talk to us right now." We have raised funds for this purpose in the United States through our new foundation, the Owens Foundation for Wildlife Conservation.

As we rise to leave, bowing and clapping our respects to the chief in the Bisa and Bemba fashion, most of the villagers drift away, apparently uninterested in our offers. Only a small group of about ten women, standing to one side and not smiling, beckon to us. They are dressed in tattered Western-style blouses with faded chitenges wrapped around their waists. All are barefoot, although one is holding an old pair of high-heeled shoes, apparently to show that she does own some. With the help of the translator, and after much arguing on their part and confusion on ours, we agree to pay the women five kwachas for every bundle of thatching grass they cut and groom. We will need about two thousand bundles, which would bring them a total of ten thousand kwachas, probably more money than the entire village has ever seen. After making a circle of wire to show them the requisite size of the bundles, we arrange to return for the grass in seven days.

○ ○ ○

"KLOCK, KLOCK," the stones crack loudly against one another as we drop them onto the pile. One by one, we collect thousands of them — from the rock bars and the hillsides — to build our camp. For over a year we have lived in our small puptent, now tattered by the wind, and we long to unpack our trunks, put our books on a shelf, and not have to crawl out of bed every morning like caterpillars. We make bricks from sand and sun on the beach of our little river, and lay the foundations. Slowly, bit by bit, stone by stone, the cottages rise from the ground.

We level the last of the termite mounds from the airstrip and a charming representative of the Division of Civil Aviation, Arthur Makawa, travels from Lusaka to certify it. Once he has done this, he makes a mount for our wind sock and even helps collect stones for our camp. Finally the stone walls are complete, ready for the thatch roofs.

A week after our trip to Mukungule, Simbeye, Mark, and I drive back up the scarp, pulling the trailer to collect the thatching grass. Mukungule consists of widely scattered family bomas, surrounded by their fields. One cluster of mud huts is perched on a hilltop, another is nestled in a banana grove near the stream, and in the distance another is situated in a grassy field. In the center is a mud-brick, one-room courthouse and a three-room schoolhouse. We park next to a large family boma where five mud huts surround a cooking fire. Several small piles of grass bundles are stacked along the road. We call a greeting to two women, sitting at a fire, who wander over and speak to Simbeye in Chibemba.

"This is all they have collected," he tells us. "There were many problems. Some of the women snitched the cut grass from their neighbors and added it to their own piles. Then some villagers stole the grass for their own houses. The women became discouraged and quit working."

Even the bundles stacked by the road are less than half of the size agreed upon.

I look around. Villagers are standing by their huts and watching us. A few women have their heads together, giggling. What am I doing here, standing in this field of weeds talking about grass? I'm supposed to be studying lions, thinking about kin selection, calculating degrees of variance. How could I ever explain to our colleagues, who are waiting patiently for our scientific papers on brown hyena social behavior, that I am negotiating — unsuccessfully — the cutting of grass! I hug my arms to my chest and look to the sky.

"I miss Africa so much, and I am standing right in the middle of it."

"Let's get out of here," Mark says. "We'll try another village."

○ ○ ○

Tucked among the green folds of the escarpment hills, deep in the miombo woodlands, lies the small village of Chishala. It is closer to the national park boundary than any other village, and notorious for its poaching. We have been told that almost every adult male in the area has an illegal gun and hunts in North Luangwa. The pole bridge that once linked Chishala to the outside world was swept away by a nameless storm some years ago, so that now the road is only a footpath winding through the forest.

On a Tuesday morning we ease the Land Cruiser down the path, ford the river, and drive into the center of the village. In a shady spot near a crumbling mud hut, a couple of dozen men are sitting on the ground around a central pot frothing with homemade beer. Immediately, the men stop talking and stare at us. We have not been to this village before, but since there are no other white people in the area, they must know who we are. It is obvious from their cold glares and silence that we are not welcome.

I am tempted to turn around and leave, but Mark steps out of the truck, so I follow. Two of the men get up and walk quickly into the forest. The others continue to stare. One says something in Chibemba and they all laugh. When we are twenty yards from them, Mark calls a friendly greeting. No one responds. Suddenly an old woman rushes toward us, mumbling excitedly, and reaches out for Mark's arm. In the tense atmosphere her movement startles me, and I whirl around. She shrinks back, bowing and clapping in submission. Her sagging face, neck, and breasts are etched with a thousand fine wrinkles. Her deepset eyes are watery, and the hand that she still reaches out to us is knobbed and gnarled from the toil of primitive life. Pleading with us in Chibemba, she points to a cluster of banana trees where a young woman sits, holding a small, limp child.

Mark motions to me to get the first-aid box from the truck, then we both bow to the young woman and kneel beside her. The little girl in her arms appears to be two or three years old and is slumped against her mother's chest. Her thin arms and legs dangle from the soiled rags wrapped around her body. Her eyes are closed, but her tongue works constantly against her dry, cracked lips. When Mark carefully moves her head, it drops heavily to one side.

"Diarrhea?" he asks the mother. She nods and whispers in English, "Bad diarrhea, four days."

Mark asks the old woman to wash out an enamel cup, while I dash back to the truck to get clean drinking water. Mark stirs a rehydration mixture from a packet into the clean water and hands it to the mother. "She must drink this slowly." Holding the child's head up, the mother touches the cup to the girl's mouth and encourages her to sip the liquid. The tiny lips move and after a few swallows, large brown eyes open wide and stare into ours. Grasping the cup with both hands, the girl tries to drink faster, and Mark motions to the mother to go gently. I steal a glance at the beer circle. The men are watching us closely.

Rehydration, although not a cure for diarrhea, can produce a miraculous recovery from the symptoms. By the time she has drained the cup, the little girl is holding her head up and looking around at the strange white people and their big truck.

"Feeling better?" Mark asks. She buries her head in her mother's neck for a moment, then turns again to look at us. Her grandmother grins, claps, and bows to us, and the mother smiles shyly. The men in the beer circle are talking quietly to one another. One of them — the father — stands and walks over to the banana trees, squatting next to the mother and child.

Speaking in slow, short phrases, Mark explains to the parents that their daughter is still very sick and should be taken to the hospital. But the mother says she has no way of getting to the nearest clinic, which is in Mpika, sixty miles away. If we do not treat the girl ourselves, she could die in a few days. Mark takes some Bactrim from the first-aid box, cuts the tablets into quarters, and explains the dosage to the parents. We also give them more rehydration mixture. The mother bows her head and whispers, "Natotela — thank you." The father lowers his head and nods.

We gather our gear and walk boldly to the beer circle, greeting the men in Chibemba. Most of them smile and nod. Speaking through a translator, Mark and I tell them about our project and how we want to help them find other jobs so that they will not be dependent on poaching. The men laugh wildly at this. We tell them we have not come to arrest anyone. No matter how much poaching they have done in the past, it will be forgotten if they lay down their weapons and take up a new job.

"How soon?" one of them asks.

"Right now, if you want," Mark says.

Within thirty minutes, everything is arranged. The women will cut thatching grass and carry it on their heads to the grooming station. The young men and children will groom the grass on large combs, which they will build with lumber and nails that we will provide. Apparently the adult men will supervise. One old man, who calls himself Jealous Mvula, volunteers for the job of night watchman. We agree on a bundle size and a price, and when they calculate how much money they can make, a ripple of excitement passes around their faces. Telling them that we will be back in two weeks, we climb into the truck and drive away. I see the little girl, still in her mother's arms, waving good-bye to us.

Upon our return in two weeks we discover a veritable grass

factory. Swaying dramatically to balance the large bundles on their heads, women file through the fields toward the grooming station. Ten large combs have been constructed; young men and older children pull grass through the teeth to separate the leaves from the stems. Huge piles of grass, the size of haystacks, surround the decaying huts. Young men sing as they bundle the groomed thatch and throw it onto the heaps. The adult men are still sitting around the beer pot, but now and then they call orders to the others.

As we step out of the truck, the child we had treated runs up to us, smiling. Her mother, laboring under a large grass bundle, waves from a distance. Greeting everyone in Chibemba, we tell them how pleased we are with their work. Jealous has kept a detailed record of how many bundles each villager has collected or combed, and we calculate how much money we owe each of them. As we pass out the kwacha notes, people nod to us solemnly. Jealous tells us the village has made more money in two weeks than in two years of poaching.

While Mark and the men begin the scratchy, cumbersome task of tying hundreds of bundles onto the trailer, I sit on the bare earth in the shade of the banana trees and call to the children to gather around me. Holding up *International Wildlife* and *Ranger Rick* magazines, I begin to explain the pictures. But I do not realize that these children have never seen a color photograph. As I hold up a glossy centerfold showing an elephant family grazing on a savanna, the children "oooh" and "aaaah," clasping their small hands over their open mouths. Squeezed tightly together in a semicircle, they lean forward, taking in every detail of the photo. One young boy reaches out a finger to touch the shiny page, as though he expects the elephants to be there. I feel a tightness in my throat and a tear in my eye.

They do not seem to know that real elephants move silently through the forest just beyond the scarp mountains, and that their own fathers have slaughtered them for years. When I ask how many of them have seen an elephant, they all shake their heads. They are five miles from North Luangwa National Park and have never seen a live elephant!

Finally the truck and trailer are loaded with grass. The headlights look like eyes peering out from under a floppy straw hat. Brushing grass seeds and stems from his shirt, Mark joins me briefly, then we gently extricate ourselves from the circle of children, promising to return with more pictures. We have so few magazines that we will have to take them with us to the next village. One little girl helps me pick up the magazines from the ground, holding them with both hands as though they are the most precious things she has ever touched.

As we turn to go, the men in the beer circle call to Mark to join them; he walks to the edge of the gathering and greets them in Chibemba. Some are sitting on stools handmade from stumps, others sit cross-legged on the ground around the large clay pot full of home-brewed beer. A single drinking straw made from a reed stands up in the thick brew. The men take turns bending over the straw and drinking. With a sweep of his hands, one man invites Mark to share the drink. Diseases — dysentery, AIDS, cholera, tuberculosis — are common in these remote villages, as in most areas of Zambia. Yet Mark hesitates only briefly before bowing his thanks and kneeling beside the pot. Smiling at the men, he quickly pulls out the straw and turns it upside down. The men are silent for a moment, and I fear he has insulted them, but then they break into applause. Mark takes a long pull on the straw and exclaims, "Cawama sana — very good beer!" One of the older men walks to the pot and, with a great flourish, pulls the straw out, flips it over, and has his turn. The men rock back and forth, laughing.

As Mark thanks them and walks away, the men leave the beer circle and gather around us. Many are young — twenty-five to thirty-five years old — articulate, strong, and intelligent. For the first time, they admit openly that they are poachers but explain that they have no other jobs. "We want to conserve," says one man named Edmond Sichanga, who is dressed in clean, Western clothes, "but there is no job in conserving." I am surprised to hear him use the word "conserve," and even more surprised to hear him sum up in so few words one of the most critical environmental problems.

"That is often true in the short term," I say. "But in the long term, there will be more jobs if we can conserve North Luangwa."

"We can hire fifteen of you right now to work on the road between here and Mukungule," Mark tells them. "Then you will have jobs and a new road to your village. There will be more jobs later."

"That will be very good. Also we have another problem," Sichanga says, but now his eyes are twinkling with mischief.

"What is that?" Mark asks.

"We do not have a soccer ball. You can see over there, we have made a football field, but we have no ball."

"Okay," Mark says, "you stop poaching and we'll bring you a soccer ball. Is that a deal?"

The men raise their arms in salute. They shake our hands over and over in the Bemba fashion. Is it really going to be this easy to stop poaching in North Luangwa? We give out a few jobs and soccer balls and save the elephants?

The entire village stands along the road, waving and cheering as we drive away in our hay wagon. We creep along at a sluggish pace, and I lean backward out of the window to be sure the load isn't shifting too badly.

We have gone only a few miles when an African man dressed in a tattered coat steps in front of the truck and hails us. It is Jealous, the night watchman. On our first visit to Chishala Mark told him that we would pay for information about the poachers. He stops the truck. Jealous rushes toward us, his coat fluttering behind him, and hops onto the running board. Sticking his head through the window, he says: "These men of Chishala, they are not the big hunters. They kill a few elephants, but the men who kill many, the big poachers, they stay in Mwamfushi Village."

"How do you know this?" Mark asks.

"I have two wives. One lives in Chishala, the other in Mwamfushi."

"Who are the big poachers? Do you know their names?" We have heard of Mwamfushi Village; the game guards were chased away by men armed with semiautomatic weapons.

"The big hunters are Simu Chimba, Chanda Seven, Bernard Mutondo, and Mpundu Katongo. But Chikilinti is the worst — he is the godfather of them all." Jealous jumps from the running board and disappears into the forest. I quickly write down the names, underlining Chikilinti twice.

○ ○ ○

Fording transparent rushing rivers, building rickety pole bridges, clearing overgrown tracks, and slogging through the mud, we visit the remote villages along the western border of North Luangwa, each one more difficult to reach than the last. At every village we meet first with the headmen and elders, and talk to them about what jobs and food are available, what skills the villagers have, what materials they need to start small industries. We promise to help each village set up at least one cottage industry such as a carpentry shop, a sewing club, a fish farm. We talk with the headmaster of each school and organize a conservation program that includes a wildlife club for the children. Hauling around a generator to provide electricity, we set up our projector and show slides of wildlife to the children and adults. Each school has a counterpart in the United States, which will later send art supplies and letters to the Zambians. Smoke Rise Primary School in Atlanta, for example, is paired with the primary schools in Mpika and Nabwalya.

Not always welcome, we are sometimes warned and threatened. Over and over we hear that the worst village for poaching is Mwamfushi, and that it is not safe for us to go there. We keep visiting new villages and returning to old ones, slowly recognizing faces and making friends. Mr. Chisombe at Katibunga wants to build a fish farm. Syriah of Chibansa, only thirteen, wants to raise rabbits and ducks. The people of Fulaza, who for years have traded poached meat from North Luangwa for ground maize, need a grinding mill.

Determined not to make the mistake of creating welfare villages (as aid organizations unfortunately have done for years), we give nothing away. Anyone we agree to help must promise to stop poaching. And once their businesses are going, they must repay the original loans to our project. Before we hand out any money, they must contribute as much as they are able to their new enterprise. If they want a grinding mill, they must build the mill house with mud and grass before we will buy the mill. Then we know that they are committed to the enterprise.

Mukungule, where the women failed to cut the grass, is in the center of the region. During the months of 1988, as we go from one village to another, we often pass by the chief's n'saka with its airplane seat. The word has spread that Katibunga has a fish farm and that Chishala made fifteen thousand kwachas from cutting grass. One day I am driving alone from Katibunga while Mark is flying antipoaching patrols in the valley. Mrs. Yambala, a teacher in Mukungule, stands in the road and waves for me to stop. She invites me to sit under the trees with her and tells me that the women of Mukungule want to start a sewing club. They can sell ladies' blouses, baby clothes, and tablecloths to the wives of the game guards, who have cash, she says. I tell her that we will buy the materials and once they are able to sell their products, they can pay us back. Her husband, headmaster of the school, asks me to start a wildlife club for the children, as we have done elsewhere. I shake hands and tell them that we are happy to work at last with the people of Mukungule.

○ ○ ○

"Okay, everybody," I call out, standing near the banana trees of Chishala, where the villagers cut our grass. "Let's all go to the soccer field. We have a surprise for you." Jealous and the schoolteachers help me pass the message, sending runners to the distant fields and huts. I watch stooped and elderly villagers, vibrant young men, colorfully dressed mothers and children, move across the hills and through the meadow toward us. Soon an excited crowd has gathered at the field. I stand on the back of the truck, listening.

"Here he comes!" I shout. "See, the ndeke comes!" I point north to where our plane glides into view over the forested hills. The villagers wave and shout. Mark swoops in low, as though he is going to land on the field, and at the last second flings a soccer ball from the plane door. It falls among the young men and children, and a game begins on the spot. Everyone in the crowd, even an old man with a cane, takes a turn kicking the ball. After a while Sichanga, one of the men from the beer circle, picks it up, walks over, and thanks me. I can see that Mark has drawn an elephant on the ball and written, "Play Soccer, Don't Poach Elephants!" I point this out to Sichanga and his friends, who are now employed by our project to hand-grade the road from Chishala to Mukungule.

"Remember our deal," I say.

And they answer, smiling, that they remember.

○ ○ ○

The wide-open arms of the marula trees welcome us back to Marula-Puku after every village trip, when for days we have slept on the truck, eaten canned food, and bathed in cold streams. A roaring campfire, started by Simbeye, Mwamba, and Kasokola at the first sound of our truck, brightens the reed kitchen boma as we pull into camp. On the far side of the slow-moving Lubonga we can see puku and buffalo grazing. The guys greet us, no matter what time of day or night, and help unload the muddy truck.

The stone and thatch cottages, all but swallowed by the giant trees, are now complete. In a semicircle along the riverbank is an office cottage, a kitchen cottage, a bedroom cottage, and an open n'saka, the traditional Bemba meeting place. Solar panels power the few lights and two computers. At the back of camp is a workshop, stocked with tools and spare parts for the trucks. The camp is neat and efficient, yet its structures of local stone and grass blend into the riverbank so well that they are hardly noticeable from the far side.

One day as we pull into camp, Simbeye rushes up to us.

"Bosses, come, you must see," he shouts. As we climb down from the truck, he pulls on Mark's arm and leads us to the grassy area between the office and bedroom cottages.

"See, the tracks; he was right here." Simbeye points to the large footprints of an elephant only fifteen yards from our bedroom. "He has been coming here every night to eat the marula fruits. He is one of the Camp Group. There are eight, but only one comes here. The others feed on the hill."

"That's great, Simbeye! Did you actually see him? Isn't he afraid of you?" I ask.

"He comes only at night. He moves like a big shadow, so you cannot hear him. But I wait in the grass by my hut, and I see him come. He does not know I am there."

"Are you sure that it is the same elephant every night?" Mark asks.

"Yes, sir, I am sure. He is the one with tusks as long as your arm," Simbeye holds his hands about three feet apart, "and he has a small hole in his left ear."

After an early supper of cornbread and beans, Mark and I take up positions by the window in the bedroom cottage. Whispering in the darkness, we take turns peering into the night for large, moving shadows. But the elephant does not come. Finally, we fall asleep in our clothes on top of the bedcovers. In the morning there are no fresh tracks. The elephant must have known we were inside the cottage. After all, he is clever enough to have survived poachers' bullets for many years.

Early that morning, anxious to get back to the wildlife work, we drive to the airstrip to fly an antipoaching patrol. Suddenly Mark stops the truck. Eight bull elephants stand in a tight group only three hundred yards away, on the steep hillside overlooking the river. Wrapping their trunks around the bases of the tall grass, they pull up large clumps and munch on them. Not one looks in our direction. I hold my hands to my face, and Mark squeezes my shoulder. This may happen often in other parts of Africa — people watching a small group of elephants feeding — but never before have we been able to get so close. Instead of fleeing at the first sight of us, the elephants ignore us completely.

After that they show up regularly here and there. We see them from the plane near Hippo Pool, across the river feeding on marula fruits, late one afternoon in the valley beyond the airstrip. They keep their distance, but they do not run. Perhaps they have learned that they are safe near our camp.

The other elephants in the park are not so safe. Mark has been flying patrols daily, whenever he is not on a village trip with me. Every week he discovers four to six dead elephants. With each discovery we plead with the game guards to go on patrol, but there is always some reason why they cannot. They have not mounted a single patrol on their own since we arrived last year. The radios we ordered months before still have not been approved by the government. Every time we want to get a message to the game guards, we have to make the long drive up the scarp to Mano, or else Mark has to fly over their camp and drop a message in a milk tin.

A week after first seeing the elephants near camp, Mark takes off on a flight to drop a message to the game guards, asking them to patrol the hills around our camp to help protect the herd. No sooner is he airborne than he flies into a flock of vultures. Hitting one can be fatal, so Mark quickly banks the plane starboard to turn away from the birds. Looking down, he sees the mutilated carcasses of three male elephants, sprawled in pools of blood and splashed white with vulture dung. Swearing and flying dangerously close to the treetops, Mark circles the area looking for the poachers. Seeing no sign of them, he lands and drives madly up the scarp to collect the scouts. Four hours after spotting the elephants, we stand with the guards around the carcasses — huge, gray monuments to a dying continent.

"Bastards!" Mark paces around. "They're laughing at us. You know that, don't you?" Mark stares at Gaston Phiri. "They're laughing at you! They know that they can poach right here and get away with it."

"We know who shot these elephants," Phiri announces proudly. "We can tell by their boot tracks in the sand. It is Chikilinti, Chanda Seven, Mpundu Katongo, Bernard Mutondo, and Simu Chimba from Mwamfushi Village."

"Well, good," Mark says. "If we know exactly who the poachers are, we can go to the village and arrest them."

"Ah, but we cannot get these men," Phiri tells us. "They have juju."

"They have what?"

"These men are real men, but they have a magic from Zaire. They can make themselves invisible, so that we cannot see them. They can stand right here among us, but we will look through them. We ourselves can never capture them."

"Come on, Phiri! You don't believe that."

But Phiri insists, sounding hurt. "It is fact. It is like this: they stand under a tree, put on a special hat, pour magic potion over their heads, and turn in circles. Then they disappear."

"Phiri, don't you know it's impossible to be invisible?" Mark looks anxiously at the other scouts, hoping for support.

"Maybe for you, but not for these men. You may know what is written in your books. But these men, they know magic from Zaire!"

I drop my hands to my side and walk around in a small circle. Mark stands in silence, trying to control his anger, unsure of what to do.

"The men from Mwamfushi are the hunters," Phiri goes on, "but they use the men from Chishala as carriers."

"From Chishala!" I cry out. "Those men we gave jobs, and the soccer ball?"

Phiri just looks at me, and I get the message. How could we be so naive? Did we really believe we could win them over with a soccer ball and a few jobs?

"There is something else," Phiri says. "That man, the one who calls himself Jealous, the man who told you informations about the poachers. He was poisoned. His stomach is very sick, and his lips are burned very bad. He has been taken to the hospital in Mpika."

Mark lowers his head into his hands and stares at the ground. I walk away and look out over the golden, rocky hills. Something catches my eye. Five elephants — all that is left of Camp Group — move silently away through the trees. I make no sign that I have seen them, but I watch. As they reach the crest of the hill, I see the male with the small tusks — the one with the hole in his left ear. He has survived one more time. "Go well, Survivor," I whisper. "Go well."

9
Survivor's Seasons

DELIA

Here you must look
at each thing with the elephant eye:
greeting it now for the first time,
and bidding, forever, good-bye.

— ANNIE DILLARD

○ ○ ○

SURVIVOR, FOLLOWED by the four young bulls of his group, trundles slowly up the small, rocky hill. It is May and the elephants are on their way from the plains to the great scarp mountains. Even though it is a short migration of only fifteen to twenty miles, they take several months to pass through the belt of hills along the base of the escarpment. The tall, waving grasses and small trees and scrubs (*Terminalia, Colophospermum mopane, Combretum*) make good forage at the end of the rains, while the rushing rivers and hidden lagoons provide water. But one of the main attractions of the area is the large, spreading marula trees (*Sclerocarya caffra*) that drop their sweet fruits at this time of year.

The elephants know where the marulas are. Well-worn paths lead from one to the other, and under each the grass is matted down where the large beasts have fed for hours on the yellow fruits. They walk to one of the marula groves near Khya Stream. Swaying gently back and forth, they feel and sniff along the ground with their trunks, then pluck the fruits into their mouths with loud slurping noises.

The five animals are in their twenties and form a loose-knit group of independent males. Survivor was born into a "family unit" of closely related females, the oldest of whom was the matriarch. She was more than fifty years old and led the group to traditional feeding areas and watering points. A female calf born into a family unit will usually remain in it for the rest of her life unless the group becomes too large. Males, on the other hand, leave the group when they are ten to fifteen years old. Sometimes they wander on their own, sometimes they form groups with other young males.[1]

After eating all the fruits they can find in this grove, Survivor and his group move to a floodplain along the stream, where they feed on the tall elephant grass. Only their gray backs show above the grassy plumes as they pull up bunches of stems and eat the tender shoots. By late afternoon they become thirsty, but do not go to the river because the poachers know the elephants' watering spots and often ambush them when they come down to drink. Since the poachers do not shoot at night, the elephants wait until dark to quench their thirst.

Maybe Survivor can remember the days when his family unit went to the river every afternoon to drink and play. He and the other youngsters would frolic and splash in the water, while the adult females used their trunks to spray their broad backs. But it is no longer safe to linger there. After dark Survivor's group goes to the water's edge and drinks quickly, looking around frequently and listening. They move away immediately and return to the thick vegetation where they cannot be seen.

Day after day, the group feeds on the fruits, small trees, and grass, walking along familiar paths and drinking in the safety of darkness. There is plenty of grass left, and although it is drying along with the season, it is still nutritious.

In mid-June the sky dims from the smoke of the first wildfires started by the poachers. With nothing to stop them except the rivers, the fires sweep across the plains and hills, gobbling up the vegetation that would feed the entire elephant population for months.

Forced by the fires to move on, Survivor and his group turn west and trek toward the scarp mountains. Many of the streams are now dry, so the elephants often walk on the parched riverbeds hemmed in by steep banks. Their large feet leave readily identifiable tracks in the sand.

One afternoon there is a rustling near a tree just above Survivor.

He whirls in alarm, lifting his trunk. One of the other elephants backs into him as they all lurch about in confusion, holding their trunks high to take in the scent. They watch for signs of men with guns. Then they turn and run along the streambed, their feet kicking up sprays of sand. But they are trapped by the banks and cannot escape. Eventually they find a gully and scramble to the top, their sides and rumps bumping one another. Survivor pauses briefly and looks back to see a small troop of baboons climbing into the lower branches of the tree where he had heard the noise. He stops. It's okay. This time.

When the elephants reach the rocky foothills, they often follow the well-worn paths their kind have used for generations. Along the way they feed on scrub mopane and small combretum trees. The trails continue over the mountains, winding around the steepest peaks and into deep ravines. The grass in the mountains is not so plentiful, nor is the water. The group feeds on small trees of the miombo forests, twisting each plant off at its base. They drink at clear springs and streams tucked away in the creases of the range.

On the other side of the small mountain, also walking an ancient trail, is the matriarch One Tusk and her family unit of females. Well over thirty years of age, she leads Misty, Mandy, and Marula — three young adult females — a three-year-old calf, and an infant. Halfway up the mountain they reach the meadow known as Elephant's Playground, where a few palm trees tower over a small stream. The elephants fan out and feed, staying within twenty yards of one another. Misty, who may be the daughter of One Tusk, accidentally backs into the matriarch, but neither of them moves. With their huge backsides lightly touching, they continue to pull up the grass and stuff it into their mouths. Often the females reach out their trunks to sniff each other's faces, or lean against their neighbor. The calf lies flat on the ground, sleeping near the front feet of his mother. Now and then she reaches down with her trunk and moves it along her baby's head.

Soon the three-year-old swaggers over to the small calf and plops down on his rump. The calf lifts his head and wiggles his bum out from under his playmate, who sinks to the ground. The babe staggers to his feet and the two youngsters entwine their trunks, gently pushing against each other. The calf turns away and runs through the grass, his ears and trunk flopping up and down. Within seconds the three-year-old catches up and lays his trunk over the calf's back. They face each other again and push their heads together in miniature sparring.

Abruptly the elephants stop feeding and playing, to listen. A rumbling sound drifts across the clearing from the north, and One Tusk's group returns the call. The temporal glands on the sides of their faces begin to seep, the liquid streaming down their cheeks. One Tusk gives a loud, short rumble and they walk quickly northward. The mother softly prods her infant with her trunk, and he follows the adults in a half-run.

In the trees beyond the meadow, Long Ear and her small family unit emerge at a trot from behind an outcropping of boulders. Their ears held out and rumbling loudly, they rush toward One Tusk and her group. The greeting elephants swarm together in a confusion of purring, twisting of trunks, and clanking of tusks. All of their faces are streaked with the temporal gland secretion. One Tusk and Long Ear wrap their trunks together and flap their ears vigorously; the others do the same, all the while rumbling loudly.

Long Ear, whose left ear has been torn off at the bottom, making her right ear look long, is the "child matriarch" of her group. She is only in her mid-twenties, not old or experienced enough to be a matriarch (in stable elephant populations, matriarchs can be as much as fifty or sixty years old). But the three older females in Long Ear's group were shot by poachers. Now she and the two other young females — one is probably her sister, one her daughter — roam together. They have no young. Last year one of them gave birth, but the small, squiggly baby died the next day, never having found the teat of her inexperienced mother. Sometimes Long Ear's family joins that of One Tusk, and they forage together. The two units make a "bond group"[2] and probably are all closely related.

Groups of female elephants are not haphazard formations that simply bump into one another in the bush. They are close-knit families of relatives whose kin lines are generations old. They communicate with a variety of vocalizations — rumbles, trumpets, screams — except that in North Luangwa they rarely trumpet, apparently afraid that they will betray themselves to poachers. Odors in the secretions of their temporal glands contain important social messages, but they may communicate most by touching. They usually stay within thirty yards of one another and often reach out their trunks to stroke, caress, or sniff their kin mate.

One Tusk gives a loud rumble and the two groups move a short distance into a thicket of miombo woodlands, where they calm down and stand napping in the midday heat. The elephants are quiet and still. Now and then a tail swishes at a fly; now and then a trunk is lifted and sniffs gently along the face of a sister.

In days gone by, the family units and independent males continued over the mountains to the plateau beyond, grazing the lush grass of the extensive glades and dambos. But now these areas are cultivated by man, and poaching is intense. So the elephants must remain in the mountains feeding on the small trees during the months of June, July, and August. Sometimes Survivor and his group come upon small family units of females. Occasionally they approach the females to feed nearby or to check if any of them are in estrus, but most of the time the males are on their own.

In September — the heart of the hot, dry season — Africa performs a miracle. Long before the first raindrop falls, many of the trees, large and small, burst into growth as green and tender as spring. While the grass is still parched by the fires or dried by the sun, the leaves of almost all the trees and scrubs choose this moment to unfold. The valley and mountains are covered with this new life that is so fresh and bright that it seems to glow. And once more the elephants begin to move.

Following many of the same paths down the mountains, Survivor's group and the family units walk back across the foothills toward the river valleys. They pass again through the belt of marula trees, but now there are no fruits. They feed instead on the abundant new leaves and seedpods of the mopane, combretum, and terminalia trees. Since the rains have not begun, many of the rivers and water holes are still dry. The elephants, who must drink every day, are forced to find water wherever they can. One Tusk and Long Ear move along the Mwaleshi floodplains; some elephants forage along the Mulandashi River; Survivor and his group stay in the area of the Lubonga.

In late October and early November, the legendary Luangwa storms build towering monuments of cloud in the sky. Windstorms and sandstorms slap and tease the valley, now trapped in a stifling heat. Some of the most spectacular lightning displays on earth flash across the silent savannas. Many of the new leaves have begun to wither and droop, as though their early burst of energy was too optimistic. All of life, both plant and animal, seems to pause as if waiting. Then in mid-November the first rain falls. Almost immediately the elephants, wherever they are — along the Mwaleshi, near the Lubonga, or still in the foothills — begin moving slowly toward the plains.

Survivor, followed by his four companions, crosses the Fitwa River near Mvumvwe Hill and walks east through the mopane forests. Once in a while they stop to feed, but mostly they keep moving. By the time they reach the plains, miles of young green grasses march across the savannas in endless parades. Survivor sees massive herds of fifteen hundred buffalo and several hundred zebras grazing the new grass, which is surging with more nutrient per volume than almost any plant in the valley. He watches other elephants walking onto the plains from the west, south, and north. Not all of them have migrated to the mountains; some have moved south and north along the Luangwa River. But now most of them — small groups like his own, solitary males, and family units of females — move out onto the expansive plains.

By mid-January about 80 percent of the North Luangwa elephant population has assembled on the grasslands. Even though three-quarters of them have been slaughtered by poachers in the last fifteen years, it is still incredible to see three thousand elephants strung out in herds along thirty miles of plains. One Tusk and Long Ear's females join other bond groups to form large aggregations. Perhaps the grass is too tempting or perhaps they feel safer in numbers, but the elephants leave the sanctuary of the tall grass and feed in the open. Almost like the old days, herds of a hundred elephants stroll gracefully through the grass in long gray lines.

One day, feeding on a soggy plain, Survivor sees a female elephant running at full speed away from several males on the other side of the savanna. Instantly he and his four companions run toward the commotion, their feet sloshing and sucking up the mud. When they arrive, eight young males in their twenties are pursuing the female, who is twisting and turning as nimbly as an elephant can, to escape. One male finally catches the exhausted female and, placing his trunk over her back, attempts to mount her. Another male rams him in the side with the top of his head, and the female dashes off again.

This chaotic scene is not necessarily the way elephants mate. Before poaching was so intense, when a female came into estrus she would make every effort to avoid the young males until the arrival of a musth male — a fully mature, sexually active male more than thirty years old. The two of them would form a consortship for three to four days, during which he would guard her from other males. The pair would mate occasionally and feed together in a relatively peaceful setting.[3]

But most of the musth males in North Luangwa have long ago been shot by poachers. Survivor has not seen one in several years; perhaps all of them are dead. Without a musth male to protect and mate her, the female has no choice but to succumb to these inexperienced bullies. During the next four days she is mated by five different males. She spends most of her time trying to escape them and rarely has a chance to feed. It is not certain that she will conceive under these conditions, and even if she does, it will not necessarily be by the best and strongest male.

Even though aggregations of elephants moving across the plains may resemble the great herds of yesteryear, they are not the same. An elephant's ivory grows during all its life; so does its wisdom. Most of the musth males and matriarchs are dead, and along with them much of the knowledge, experience, and memories of elephant society. This younger generation carries on in the tradition of the past as best it can, but the social system seems in large part to have died away with the numbers.

If the rains are heavy, the plains become waterlogged by February. Survivor's group moves westward to the fringes of the savannas. They make forays onto the plains as the rains allow, still feeding mainly on the lush grass and its nutty-tasting seeds. But almost with the last raindrop, the grasses dry and wither. By April, Survivor is on his way again toward the mountains. There is compensation for the drying grasses; soon the marula fruits will ripen and fall to the ground. And Survivor knows where the marula trees are.

10
Eye of the Dragon

MARK

> Late afternoon. Distant shouts.
> Young raw voices, male, floating
> In the heat. Are they angry, or
> Bored, or is it the heat shout
> ing through them?
> You forget where you are sometimes,
> Where you started from.
>
> —JOYCE CAROL OATES

○ ○ ○

WE SIT HIGH UP in our Unimog, in the early dry season of 1988, eyeing a pole bridge in front of us that sags across the deep stream cut like a wet spider's web. In the back of the Mog are bicycles, sleeping bags, mosquito nets, camping mattresses, boots, first-aid equipment, food, and other supplies for the men of the Nsansamina and Lufishi game scout camps.

This equipment is not coming a moment too soon. The scouts must start patrolling. Having wiped out most of the animals at the fringes of the park, the poachers are striking right at its center. North Luangwa is bleeding from the heart. Each volley of gunfire that we hear, and each cloud of vultures that we see, reminds us that the last of the elephants are dying.

By comparing our aerial wildlife censuses with one flown in 1973 by a team from the United Nations Food and Agricultural Organization, we estimate that poachers have already killed more than twelve thousand of the park's seventeen thousand elephants, about three of every four, and a thousand more are dying each year. Since 1973 between seventy-five thousand and one hundred thousand elephants have been poached in the Luangwa Valley as a whole; *that's roughly one for every word in this book.* Perhaps twenty thousand to thirty thousand elephants are left in Luangwa, and no more than five thousand in the North Park. At this rate they will all have perished in four to five years.

Before we can expect the Mano scouts to go after poachers armed with military weapons, we must equip them properly. We are hoping this Mog-load of supplies will help motivate them.

The Mog weighs more than six tons empty. Its load of tools, winching tackle, camping gear, and game scout supplies brings its total heft to almost eight tons. The poles that make up the floor of the bridge are no thicker than my calf; they span the stream, thirty feet across, bank to bank. A few smaller limbs laid crosswise on top will help distribute the truck's weight. Even so, nearly four tons will come to bear on the poles under the wheels on each side as we drive across. From my seat I can see through the bridge to the stream, eight feet below.

"If the Mog breaks through this pile of poles, we're going to have a tough time getting it out of the stream," I say, leaning my elbows on the steering wheel. "And if one side breaks through and not the other, it'll roll off and end up on its top in the water." Delia and I climb down from the cab and search for several hundred yards upstream and down for another way across, but there doesn't seem to be one.

With a stick from the woods I measure the distance between the Mog's two front wheels, and compare it with the width of the bridge. The truck will barely fit, and the two right wheels will bear fully on a single pole on the upstream side of the bridge. Meanwhile the left wheels will track back and forth between the outside pole and the one next to it on the downstream side.

I scramble down the steep bank and examine the underside of the bridge, looking for rot. The bark on the timbers disintegrated long ago and the wood is peppered with holes from sawdust beetles. Other than that they look fairly sound, though none of them appear strong enough to support the Mog. Nevertheless, we will have to give it a try. If we can't get these supplies to the scouts, there is no hope of protecting the elephants.

Delia signals me into alignment with the narrow bridge, then wades into the stream to keep her eye on the poles as the Mog's weight comes to bear on them. At the first sign that one is giving way, she is to wave me back, although there will probably be little warning before the truck breaks through.

I shift to low-low and creep forward at less than one mile per hour, watching out the window to align my right front wheel with the extreme right edge of the bridge. The heavy wheel finds the butt of the outside pole and drives it into the ground as the truck crawls forward.

Pow! Crackle! Snap! The poles complain as they bow under the weight. I stamp the clutch pedal down, hit the air brakes, and look down at Delia. Peering at the sagging underbelly of the bridge, her jaw rigid, she is waving me forward.

I open the door and jump down to look for myself. The truck's front wheels are already warping the poles badly, but they do not seem to be splitting yet. With the turbo diesel at dead idle, I let out the clutch and the Mog creeps forward.

As I reach the center of the bridge, more shots ring out from the overstressed wood. Ka-pow! The shattered end of a pole flies into the air and the Mog lurches to the left, swaying back and forth, up and down, on the bridge — which seems to be trying to catch its breath. I put my hand on the right door handle, ready to jump clear if the truck rolls left off the bridge. If it rolls right, toward the driver's side, I will have to stay inside.

"Stop! STOP!" Delia shrieks, waving her arms.

The Mog sways as though on a rope bridge. Its left front wheel has broken one pole and is forcing two adjacent ones apart. I sit quietly for a few seconds while the bridge settles down. Then, with Delia signaling, I switch the dashboard toggle to all-wheel drive, turn the steering wheel left, and reverse. Aided by traction from the other three, the left front wheel crawls slowly back up onto a pole. But now the right front tire is half off the right side of the bridge.

I see no sense in sitting at the center of the span waiting for the thing to collapse. I ease the Mog forward, its engine growling amid the gunshot sounds of the breaking bridge. As we teeter along the outside poles, it sounds as if we are driving over a bed of firecrackers. At last the truck's front wheels reach solid ground and, gunning the engine, I pull clear of the matchstick bridge. After their mauling by the Mog, the poles are even more of a jumble. We will have to rebuild parts of the bridge to get back to Mano. And someday soon we will have to make a proper crossing here.

We camp for the night in the cool, sweet brachystegia woodlands along the stream. Beneath a full moon we swim in the clear water, drifting with the current among moss-covered boulders. There are no crocs to worry about in this montane climate high above the valley — or hippos, for most have been hunted to extinction. We hang a mosquito net from the tailgate of the Mog and sleep with our heads in our backpacks to keep spotted hyenas from biting our faces.

The next morning we "mog" along a track that according to Island Zulu has lain unused for two decades. It isn't a track really, just a path of lesser resistance along which there are smaller trees, an occasional old stump, and slightly taller grasses than in the surrounding forest. Using the Mog and its bull-bar, we bulldoze brachystegias and julbennardias up to six inches thick, crowd past heavy branches, climb over logs, and cross more pole bridges. Although it is tough going, the temperature is pleasantly cool, with fog swirling through the trees and the sun showing through occasionally as a vague silver disk above us.

It is still early when we roll into the Nsansamina camp — little more than three small mud wattle and thatch houses set on a bare earthen clearing in the forest. The fog is lifting; the sun streams rich and golden through puffs of white cloud to the verdant forest below. Three scouts are sitting on squat, hand-carved stools around a small campfire. Its smoke curls up to the blue sky, like a gray rope climbing through the still morning air. One of the scouts is tending a steaming pot of sweet potatoes with a bright green banana leaf for a lid. The other two men are playing musical instruments — one, a thumb piano; the other, a sort of single-string guitar with a gourd base. Behind the men is their fowl's roost, a miniature thatched rondavel set on stilts with a ladder leading to the door. Rubbing sleep from his eyes, the fourth guard stumbles from one of the huts as I switch off the truck.

"Mashebukenye, Mukwai!" We shake hands with Patrick Mubuka, the Camp-in-Charge, and each of the three scouts. For the next few minutes we squat at their fire, inquiring about their health, that of their families, and any problems they might have. Their problem is survival. They have too little food, no medicine, no transportation, no backpacks or camping equipment, and very little money. They have two, maybe three, rounds of ammunition for two rifles that half-work, if they work at all.

"Sa kuno — come over here, please. We have some things for you." The scouts assemble next to the Mog as I climb aboard and begin tossing down boots, sleeping bags, camping mattresses, mosquito nets, first-aid supplies, and even bicycles, which came all the way from the United States. Instantly they are the best-equipped scouts in Zambia. None of the others have even a full camping kit. They clap their hands in thanks.

I am busy assembling a bicycle when a small boy with a big grin sprints past the Mog. Proudly stretched across his chest is a T-shirt with the menacing face of a bulldog and "Go, You Hairy Dogs!" stenciled on it. An instant Georgia fan! On his heels is another child in a shirt with bright red flowers and yellow designer pants decorated with flamingos. Squeals of laughter draw me to the fowl's roost, where Delia is surrounded by women and children. From a big cardboard box she is dispensing clothing, medical supplies, coloring books, and crayons.

The last thing out of the box is "Luangwa Lion," a puppet who tells the children he needs their help to conserve the animals of the valley. The lion explains that he and the other lions live together in communities, similar to villagers in a chiefdom. These communities of lions and other animals are becoming more and more rare, because many men are killing them. So few are left in Africa that people all over the world consider those in North Luangwa priceless natural treasures.

The lion tells them: your fathers have a very important job to do: they must protect all of us animals in the valley from poachers. Remember, you can shoot an animal only one time and then he is dead and gone forever. His meat and skin can be used only once.

But if you keep us alive, you can show us to tourists over and over again and each time they will pay to see us. We are worth more to you alive than dead.

As we are climbing into the Mog to find a campsite for the night, the middle-aged wife of one of the guards calls to me. She cannot speak English, so she takes me by the hand and tugs me toward one of the small huts nearby. At the doorway I duck under the thatch into the dark interior. Even before my eyes adjust to the gloom, I can hear death on the breath of her child. Calling to Delia to bring a flashlight, I kneel down beside the girl. She is perhaps twelve years old. As I reach out to put my hand on her forehead she draws back, her eyes round with fear.

"Mararia," her mother says matter of factly; then to the girl, "Owensee — doctor." And the girl lies back on her grass mat.

Delia arrives with a flashlight and our medical kit. I switch on the light and look into the girl's yellow eyes as she pants with the fever, her lips parched and cracked. I feel for her liver; it is like a lump of cork under her hot skin. The girl will be dead within hours unless we treat her now, although neither of us is a medical doctor.

"Delia, go to Patrick Mubuka. He's the only one who speaks English. Tell him to get the women to bring cool water and some cloths. We've got to bring her fever down right away or she isn't going to make it."

While waiting for the water, I dig out a syringe, a vial of soluble chloroquine hydrochloride, and some aspirin to break the fever. When Delia returns we put wet cloths on the girl's forehead, hold her up so that she can drink and take the aspirin, then I give her an injection of chloroquine.

"If this is chloroquine-resistant malaria, she's probably not going to come right. If it isn't, she has a chance," I say to no one in particular. I pat the girl's arm as we turn to leave, but she does not respond. I should give her some chloroquine pills, but we have run out of them. Before driving away I promise the mother, through Mubuka, that I will bring some more medicine soon.

The next morning we set off toward Old Lufishi — and run into a wall of thick brush only four hundred yards beyond Nsansamina. We've had enough of bush bashing, so we drive all the way back to Mukungule and hire fifteen ax men to clear a fifteen-mile track between the two camps and to build another stream crossing.

While the track is under construction, we drive back to Marula-Puku and return with medicine for the sick girl at Nsansamina. Nine days later she has recovered, the new route is open, and we continue our journey. At Lufishi we give out more sleeping bags, T-shirts, and prophecies from the lion puppet, then return to Marula-Puku to rest and resupply before visiting Mwansa Mabemba and Chilanga Luswa camps.

○ ○ ○

We have been away for the best part of three weeks, sponging off in cold streams and the Mwaleshi River as we drive camp to camp delivering equipment to game scouts and their families. Both of us are looking forward to a hot bath as soon as we get home. Along with the gear we hauled to Zambia, we brought a bathtub that I have recently mounted in rocks in the corner washroom of our bedroom cottage. This will be our first opportunity to use it. At the workshop I pull on the Mog's airbrakes, switch off, and while the guys unload our gear, Delia and I grab four kettles of hot water from the fire at the kitchen and head down the footpath to the bedroom.

I set my kettles aside, light two kerosene lamps, hand one to Delia, and open the door so that she can enter the dark cottage and bathe first. She shuffles around the stone wall to the washroom, feeling her way in the lantern's dim light. I have just closed the outside door when I hear the clatter of Delia's kettles on the floor, followed by a screech. Before I can react she sprints out of the washroom, nearly knocking me over.

"Mark! There's a lizard in the bathtub!" she quavers.

"Is that all? I thought you'd been bitten by a snake. What's the matter — you like lizards."

"I do," she says, "but this one is as long as the tub."

I switch on a flashlight from our dressing table and inch quietly around the wall into the washroom, aiming the beam at the bathtub. Two red, beady eyes glow above a huge, blunt reptilian snout. A blue, forked tongue flicks toward me like a bolt of lightning. The thing grasps the edge of the tub with scaly feet and lunges at me, hissing like a ruptured steam pipe, its long dragon's tail lashing about.

I am reversing at high speed when I bump into Delia, who is watching from the doorway. Safely back in the bedroom, I break out laughing. "Poor Boo." I try to be sympathetic. "Most women worry about finding cockroaches in their bathtubs. But you have a five-foot Nile monitor lizard nesting in yours. The tub is full of grass straw! I think it's Mona, the one who was hanging around while we built the cottage."

"I don't care who she is. How did she get in, and how are we going to get her out?"

We finally conclude that the mother-to-be must have crawled through the small window above the tub. I close the door to the washroom, go outside, and lower a tree limb through the window into the bathtub, so that she can crawl out again. But she doesn't, at least not right away. Lizards are cold-blooded animals, which means that their body temperature fluctuates with that of the air. It's mid-July, winter in Africa, and outside it's about 45°F., with a brittle wind blowing. She apparently has no intention of giving up her comfortable bathtub nest.

Armed with a broomstick, I stalk into the small washroom toward her, to see if I can coax her to leave. As soon as she sees me she begins hissing again and smacking, her tongue moving forward and back in her mouth. I slowly extend the broomstick, to see if she is bluffing. Quick as a wink she grabs the end with the teeth of a miniature *Tyrannosaurus rex,* almost biting it in two. Impressed, I back around the corner into the bedroom.

"Unless you've got a better idea, I think I'd rather bathe outside," I say to Delia. Half an hour later, we warm-blooded animals are shivering and swearing in the frigid wind as we splash water over ourselves from a plastic basin; Mona, the cold-blooded monitor lizard, is snug in our tub. The next morning she is gone, apparently to find a meal before returning to her nest. I remove the tree limb from the bathtub and close the window, feeling a little guilty.

A few days later, on a supply run to Mpika, we stop at park headquarters to meet with Warden Salama. But when we step into his office, a short, stout man with remarkably tiny ears and a large gap between his front teeth is sitting behind Mosi's desk. Grinning shyly, he introduces himself as Bornface Mulenga.

"I am the new warden," he says. "I'm afraid Mr. Salama has been transferred." We ask why, and he explains that since it is a departmental matter he cannot offer details, only that the Mfuwe scouts, from near Chipata in the southeast of Zambia, recently came into Mpika on a sting. They caught Mosi acting as a middleman, smuggling tons of tusks from the North Park to Lusaka. Delia and I exchange glances, amazed not only that the game warden has been charged with poaching but that he has not been fined or jailed, merely transferred to another post. With a corrupt warden at the helm, no wonder the scouts have not been patrolling, and have even been poaching themselves. It no longer seems strange that we have seldom seen a wild animal within ten miles of the Mano camp: most have been shot by scouts, or by poachers cooperating with scouts.

Mulenga seems eager, honest, and capable. He goes on to tell us that the department, in response to our support, has decided to upgrade the five scout camps along the park's western border and merge them into a single law-enforcement entity, the Mano Unit. The unit leader will be John Musangu, who according to Mulenga has a reputation for being tough on poachers at Mfuwe, his previous post. More men will be brought in, more houses will be built to accommodate them, and tracks will be opened to service the camps. Given that Zambia is hamstrung by one of the worst economies in the world, these are generous gestures. We promise Mulenga that we will help in any way that we can.

But the new warden follows this with bad news: "I have had to transfer Gaston Phiri," he says. "He was causing trouble at Mano, flirting with the other men's wives." We are surprised and disappointed. Although Phiri seldom if ever patrolled the national park, at least he occasionally took his men on sweeps through the villages to look for illegal firearms. He was one of the few scouts who showed any willingness or initiative in law enforcement.

We tell Mulenga that the scouts refuse to patrol unless they have at least six rifles per squad; so we have collected the few serviceable guns scattered among the five scout camps and concentrated them at Mano. He gives us four more firearms belonging to Mpika scouts, who never patrol anyway. Mano will now have thirteen rifles. By joining forces with men from Nsansamina and Lufishi, they will have enough manpower and rifles to field two patrols, with one armed scout left over to guard the main camp. After loading the rifles into the truck, we drive back to Mano.

As we give the scouts their guns, we announce new rewards for every poacher convicted and for each firearm and round of ammunition taken in the national park. If a patrol captures even five poachers, each scout will earn an extra month's pay. The money offered by the new warden to build houses for the scouts has curiously disappeared. So we hire poachers from Chishala and Mukungule to do the job.

"This is a very fine thing you have done for us, Mr. Owens. Ah, now you shall see us catch poachers!" exclaims Island Zulu as we shake hands with the scouts. Before we begin the three-hour drive back to Marula-Puku, Zulu leads me to his private sugarcane patch, where he cuts a very large stalk for us to chew during our journey. When we finally drive away from Mano, all the scouts and their children follow us to the river crossing. Standing on the far bank, they wave until we are lost among the hills and forests of the scarp. At last, now that we have equipped the scouts, improved their camp, given them guns and incentives, we feel we have a chance of taking the park back from the poachers.

○ ○ ○

A ring of fire like a dragon's eye leaps from the dark woodland below my port wing tip. I pull the plane into a hard left bank and shove its nose into a dive. As we near the blaze I can make out about thirty individual fires. It looks as if a small army is bivouacked at the edge of the woodland. Poachers with a camp that size will have sixty or seventy unarmed bearers and two or three riflemen, each armed with military weapons — Kalashnikov AK-47s, LMG-56s, G-3s, and others. They could easily shoot down the plane.

With me is Banda Chungwe, senior ranger at Mpika. We have been on an aerial reconnaissance of the park to plan roads and firebreaks. I have purposely delayed our return to the airstrip until the last few minutes of daylight, so that we can spot any meat-drying fires the poachers may be lighting along the river. And seeing poachers in action may light a fire under Chungwe. Although he is in charge of overall field operations, this meek and mild-mannered man has never ordered the scouts on a patrol or done anything to inspire or discipline them. According to them, until today he has never even visited their camps or the national park. They need his leadership badly.

I pull off the power and drop the plane's flaps, checking my altimeter and taking a compass bearing on the fires. Then I take Zulu Sierra down over a grassy swale below the canopy of the woodland. Flying ten feet above the ground, I track the trail of gray smoke from the dragon's eye. Just before the poachers' camp, I check back on the stick, nip up over the trees, and chop the power. The camp with its blazing fires is in front of us and a little to the right. I drop the starboard wing and ease on a bit of left rudder, side-slipping the Cessna for a better view of the camp below — and so that any gunfire will, I hope, go wide of its mark.

I can see several dozen men hunkered around the fires, and three large meat racks made of poles — one at least ten feet long and four feet wide. On these giant grills, huge slabs of meat are being dried over beds of glowing coals. Nearby lies the butchered carcass of an elephant. Its dismembered feet, trunk, and tail have been pulled away from its body.

"You sons of bitches!" I swear. The senior ranger says nothing.

Less than two seconds later, the camp is behind us. In the shadow of the escarpment darkness is falling quickly after the brief dusk, and our grass airstrip is not equipped with lights. I turn the knob above my head and a dim red glow illuminates my flight and engine instruments. I am beginning to get the itch on the bottom of my feet that comes whenever I am pushing things a bit too far in the plane. I pour on the power and head up the Mwaleshi to its confluence with the Lubonga, then follow it to the lights of Marula-Puku. If I do not look directly at the airstrip, I can barely make it out on the back of a ridge a mile northwest of camp. We have about two minutes of dusk left, just enough time to go straight in for a landing. I begin to relax a little.

The strip of fading gray grows larger in the plane's windshield. At three hundred feet I switch on the landing light again. At first it blinds me, but finally some faint greenery begins to register in its beam. The crowns of the trees off the end of the runway look like broccoli heads, growing larger and larger.

Two hundred feet, one hundred fifty, one hundred, fifty. As we soar over the end of the strip, I cut the power and bring the plane's nose up to flare for the landing. All at once, big green eyes reflect in the landing light. Just ahead, a herd of zebras is grazing in the middle of the runway. A puku scampers under the plane, inches from its main wheels.

Ramming in the throttle, I haul back on the control wheel. The stall warning bawls as Zulu Sierra staggers into the air, just clearing the backs of the cantering zebras. Biting my lip, I force the plane away from the ground, banking around for another try at a landing. But in the minute it has taken to perform this maneuver, my view of the strip has been lost to the night.

We are on a downwind leg to an invisible airstrip. I hold our heading for another two minutes, which at 80 mph should put us more than two and a half miles from the runway, then I make a descending turn for the final approach.

I check my watch: the same time and speed should get us back to the field. I force my hands to relax on the controls and continue my descent from one thousand feet above the ground.

Flying blind, I feel my way down slowly and carefully, leaning forward, straining to see the ground with my landing light. My feet are jumpy on the rudder pedals. Five hundred feet per minute, down. Down.

The "broccoli" trees flash below. I still cannot see the air field. I ply the rudders back and forth, swinging the plane and its landing light side to side, trying to pick up the strip.

Two parallel lines snake beneath us. Our track from the airstrip to camp! Lowering the nose, I hold the track in my light until the grassy surface of "Lubonga International" resolves out of the blackness. Pulling back on the throttle, I haul up on the flap lever. How sweet the rumble of the ground under my wheels!

After parking the plane, we climb into the Mog and race down the steep slopes to camp. Delia throws together some black coffee and peanut butter sandwiches, and fifteen minutes later Chungwe and I are in the Mog and battering up the track for Mano. I'm going to need every drop of the coffee, for I've been driving and flying since dawn, bringing the senior ranger to our camp for our two-hour survey flight. But I'm eager. With their new equipment and the senior ranger — second in command only to the warden — sitting next to me, the scouts will have no excuse for not coming on this operation. It is one of the best opportunities we've had to send a strong message to the poaching community.

At 10:30 P.M. we roll into Mano and stop before the new unit leader's squat house of burnt brick and metal sheeting. As soon as John Musangu emerges from the darkened interior of his n'saka, I tell him what we have seen and ask him to get his men ready to come with us. He pauses for a moment, drawing hard on a cigarette, then turns and shouts to the scouts in Chibemba. I wait for Chungwe to add something, but he leans against the Mog in silence. The scouts in the n'saka mill about, while others drift in from distant parts of the camp and begin yelling angrily at Musangu. Finally, he tells the senior ranger and me that they refuse to come unless our project pays them extra for each night they are on patrol. I ask the senior ranger to explain to them that patrols are part of their job, not an extra duty, and they are already being paid for them. Instead, he turns and walks around the truck.

Grumbling, the men glare at me, refusing to move. Nelson Mumba declares that it is too late at night to go after poachers and walks back toward his hut. Neither the unit leader nor the senior ranger orders him to return. Even though as a project director and honorary ranger I have full authority over the scouts, I am reluctant to pull rank on Chungwe.

I cannot understand the scouts' behavior. Maybe they are afraid. "Look, gentlemen," I say, "I've been tracking poachers from the air for a long time. By now the two or three riflemen will have split up, each taking maybe fifteen or twenty carriers with him to shoot more elephants. Most of the men you find at the carcasses will be unarmed; only one or two will have guns. I can land you no more than half a mile from them. And, hey, what about the reward? An extra month's pay for every five poachers you catch."

Finally, an hour and a half after we arrived, and with deliberate delay, Island Zulu, Tapa, and some others collect their new packs and climb into the back of the Mog. Shortly after midnight, with the scouts and their leader in the truck, we begin the rough run back to our camp. At 2:30 A.M. we stop at the airstrip. The scouts pour out of the back of the Mog and into a large tent we have set up for them. I ask Musangu to have the men ready to go by four-thirty. He nods, then disappears under the flap of the tent. Driving on to camp, I slip into bed beside Delia to try to catch a couple of hours sleep.

.But I can only lie on my back staring into the dark. At dawn I will try to airlift fourteen men in five round trips from camp to Serendipity Strip near the poachers. In the two and a half years since I last landed there, floodwaters will have littered the runway with ridges of silt, deadwood, trees, and rocks.

Delia and I argued about my making this run just a few hours earlier, when she was standing at the old wooden table in the kitchen boma, slicing bread for my sandwiches. When I told her I planned to airlift the scouts to Serendipity Strip, she stabbed her carving knife into the tabletop with a violent thonk.

"Damn it, Mark! If you go head to head against these poachers, it's only a matter of time before they begin shooting at you — at both of us! They could sabotage the plane, or ambush us in camp or anywhere along the track. We can't fight cutthroats like Chikilinti by ourselves!"

"Look, I am not going to sit by while these bastards blow away every elephant in the valley!" I jabbed a stick into the campfire.

"But landing at dawn on a gravel bar you haven't seen in two years? You'll kill yourself, and the scouts won't go after the poachers anyway. That's just not smart."

"I'm not going to make a habit of this," I said. "But if we don't do anything when elephants are killed, we might as well not be here. And the plane is our only quick-response tool." The next slice of bread Delia cut was about as thick as my neck, and so ended the argument.

I have barely fallen asleep when the alarm goes off. I roll over, choke the clock, and stare at its face. Four in the morning. I stumble into my clothes and out the door. As I pass the office, I grab my red "life bag" full of emergency food and survival gear, then hurry along the dark footpath toward the kitchen. Delia stands there bathed in a halo of yellow-orange firelight, cooking up whole-grain porridge, making sure that if I die this morning, at least I will be well fed. A few quick spoonfuls, a swig of stiff coffee, a hurried kiss — and I am on my way to the airstrip.

In the Mog I climb the steep side of the ridge below the airfield. Out my window to the east, the sky is sleeping in starlight, soon to be awakened by the dawn. And so are the game guards when I reach the airstrip.

"Good morning, gentlemen," I shout into the tent. "Let's go. The poachers are already on the move." They struggle to their feet, rubbing their eyes, stretching and yawning.

I circle Zulu Sierra, flashlight in hand, untying, unchocking, and checking her for flight. Pulling the hinge pins, I remove the door from the right side and all the seats but mine, so I can squeeze in as many scouts as possible.

"I'll take the three smallest scouts, their rifles and kits on the first trip," I shout to Musangu. "Four more should be ready to go by the time I get back, about twenty minutes after we take off." I will keep the plane as light as I can for the first landing, until I have checked out Serendipity Strip. Still rubbing sleep from their eyes, three scouts shuffle to the plane, shirttails out, boots untied and gaping. I turn back to the plane to do my final checks.

I pull the bolts on each of their rifles to check that they are unloaded, then board the three scouts, seating each on his pack and securing him to the floor with his seat belt.

I climb in, crank up, and begin warming up Zulu Sierra's engine. While waiting for the first light of dawn, I give the scouts their last instructions. "Okay guys, we'll fly low along the river, so that we won't be seen. When I have all of your group there, I'll fly over your heads to show you the way to the poachers. Follow the plane. Get going fast, because they will head for the scarp at first light. While you are moving up, I'll try to pin them down by circling over their camp."

As soon as the stars in the eastern sky begin to pale with the dawn, I take off and turn onto a heading of one five zero.

Seven minutes after takeoff we are slicing through puffs of mist hanging above the broad, shallow waters of the Mwaleshi River. The gravel crescent of Serendipity Strip lies just ahead. I pull off power and put down three notches of flap, going in low and slow, the grass heads clipping the main wheels as I look for anything that might trip us up on landing. The plane's controls feel mushy at such a low airspeed and I need plenty of throttle to keep from stalling into a premature touchdown.

Gripping the control yoke hard with my left hand, I slowly bring back the throttle. Zulu Sierra begins to sink. The grassy, uneven ground, littered with sticks, rocks, and buffalo dung, flashes underneath the wheels. The stall warning blares. The end of the short gravel bar looms ahead. I can't find a good spot to touch down, so I ram the throttle to the panel and haul the plane back into the air.

On my third pass over the area I finally see a clear way through the rubble on the ground. This time I bounce my wheels and the plane shudders. But they come free without any telltale grab that would indicate a soft surface. Once in Namibia I tried a similar trick, and when the wheels stuck in a soft pocket of sand the plane flipped on its nose, burying the prop and twisting it to a pretzel.

The next time around I ease the plane onto the grass. As soon as the wheels are down, Zulu Sierra bucks like a mule, her wishbone undercarriage flexing. I stand on her brakes and we slide to a stop with less than a hundred feet to spare before the riverbank. The three scouts laugh nervously and immediately crowd through the open door of the plane. I grab the first by his shoulder. "Don't walk forward or the prop will chop you to pieces." He nods his head and they are out.

Four trips later all the scouts are at Serendipity. Standing under a tree near the river, they wave cheerily as I fly over, heading for the spiral of vultures and the cloud of smoke that mark the poachers' camp little more than half a mile away. I come in low, dodging the big birds, and side-slipping the plane to avoid being shot. I cannot yet see the camp, but the sickly sweet odor of decaying meat — the honey of death — washes through the cockpit. And there it is, the rack — no, six racks, covered with thick slabs of brown meat — the fires, and the men, at least fifteen of them, naked to the waist, covered with gore.

Flashing over the camp, I yank Zulu Sierra around and drop to the grasstops, bearing down on a gaggle of eight to ten poachers who are running away. I lower my left wing, pointing it at them, holding a steep turn just above their heads. They flatten themselves to the ground and stay put. Still circling, I climb out of rifle range and switch on the wing-tip strobe lights, signaling to the scouts that I am over the poachers. Far below, a spiral of vultures lands on the cache of meat, devouring it in a frenzy.

For the next hour I orbit high and low over the poachers, waiting for the scouts to arrive. Finally, I have to break off and return to camp for fuel. After refueling, I write out messages describing the number and location of the poachers and stuff them in empty powdered-milk cans from the pantry. I add pebbles to each can for ballast and attach a long streamer of mutton cloth. Then I take off again and fly over the camps at Lufishi, Nsansamina, and Fulaza, dropping the tinned messages to the scouts there. The poachers will have to pass through or near those camps to get out of the park. It should be easy for the scouts to cut them off.

By the time I land back at Marula-Puku I have been flying for almost six hours. Numb with exhaustion, I wince as I calculate that I have just burned up two hundred dollars worth of fuel. But it will be worth it if the scouts can capture twenty or thirty poachers.

Others will think twice about shooting elephants in North Luangwa, and maybe some will accept the employment and protein alternatives that our project is offering them. For the first time I feel confident that we are about to make a serious dent in the poaching.

We have no radio contact with the scouts and thus have no idea how the operation is going. Four days later Mwamba and I are fixing a broken truck at the workshop. "Scouts," he says, pointing to a long line of men wending their way toward us along the river south of camp. I shake hands with each of the game guards as they arrive. With them are two old men and a twelve-year-old boy dressed in tattered rags, their heads hanging, handcuffs clamped to their wrists.

John Musangu steps forward. "We have captured these three men."

"This is all?" I ask. "These are only bearers. What about the riflemen?" I have already heard over the radio from the warden's office that the scouts from the other camps have managed to catch only a single bearer.

"They escaped," Musangu declares. He goes on to say that there were fifteen men and a rifleman in this particular group. But except for these three, they all got away. The operation has been a bust — except that the airplane and the vultures have denied the poachers their meat and ivory.

Island Zulu, the gabby old scout, spreads his arms and begins soaring about, purring like an airplane as he mimes the airlift; then, hunching over, he stalks through make-believe grass, parts it, aims his rifle, and fires a shot. Turning in circles, he feigns a tackle of one of the three poachers, now sitting on the ground, scowling and rolling their eyes in disgust. Finally, a twinkle in his eye, he predicts, "With ndeke, now poaching finished after one year!"

I drive the arresting officers and their captives to the magistrate's court in Mpika. The boy is not charged. Days later the two men captured in the operation are each fined the equivalent of thirteen dollars and are set free.

11

The Second Ivory Coast

MARK

> Yet, though the hope, the thrill, the zest
> are gone,
> Something keeps me fighting on!
>
> — BERTON BRALEY

○ ○ ○

"THE ONE THEY CALL Chikilinti talked of coming to this camp to kill you and Madam and to destroy the ndeke," Mwamba whispers as we stand under the marula trees.

"While on leave we were in a bar," Simbeye says, picking up the story, "near Mwamfushi Village, not far from Mpika. Since we are from Shiwa N'gandu, the people there did not know us — or that we work for you. We were there for some hours, standing near the counter, when we overheard four men talking." One of them, about forty-five years old and of medium build, was wearing a brown safari suit, his hair straightened, greased, and slicked back. He walked with a swagger as he moved about the bar. This was Chikilinti.

"Who were the other men?" I ask.

"Simu Chimba, Mpundu Katongo, and Bernard Mutondo," Simbeye continues, spearing a leaf with a twig. "This Chikilinti — the people say last year he went poaching for rhinoceros in the Zambesi Valley with his brother and some others. They ambushed game scouts from Zimbabwe. Chikilinti killed two of them, but the scouts caught his brother and dragged him behind a Land Rover through the mountains until he was dead. Chikilinti escaped by swimming across the Zambezi River back to Zambia. He now stays in Mwamfushi."

Shaking their hands, I thank Simbeye and Mwamba. They cannot know how much their loyalty means to me. They turn to go, but Mwamba hesitates, looking back at me. "And Sir, just before Christmas Bernard Mutondo killed a game guard and wounded three others at Nakanduku."

"Thank you; I'll be careful" is all I can think of to say.

○ ○ ○

By late 1988 nothing is working, at least not fast enough. In the past month alone, from the air I have found twenty poached elephants; and there were plenty I didn't find. We are losing the battle for North Luangwa. For more than two years we have done everything imaginable for the Mano scouts, and our rewards haven't changed them. They still go into the park only when we find poachers and fly the scouts right in on top of them. Even then they rarely arrest anyone. The idea of a long patrol is about as appealing to them as a bad case of malaria. We can only surmise that it is more advantageous to them to cooperate with the poachers than with us. Our work with the villagers doesn't seem to be having much effect either; many of those we've helped most are still poaching. Loyal, dedicated scouts are our only real weapon against poachers. But the ones at Mano are hopeless. It's time to try some different scouts and some different tactics.

Maybe scouts from Kanona, a game guard post about one hundred fifty miles south of Mpika, would be a better solution. Some are military trained, armed with AK-47s, and because they are so far from Mpika, perhaps they are less corrupt. But in order to use them efficiently, we need to know exactly when and where poachers are coming into the park. Only undercover agents can give us this information.

○ ○ ○

Bwalya Muchisa is the son of Kanga Muchisa, one of the most notorious poachers in Africa. Using an AK-47 — thousands of military weapons are floating around Zambia after Zimbabwe's war for independence — Kanga has shot more than a thousand elephants in Luangwa Valley, as well as uncounted numbers of rhinos. A year ago he was captured in South Luangwa Park, where Mfuwe scouts are very good, and is serving eighteen months in jail. Bwalya, determined to better his father's record, at age twenty-six has already killed sixty elephants. Recently, though, the Mfuwe scouts warned him that if he continues poaching they will see him in a cell next to his father's. We have heard that Bwalya is now in Lusaka looking for a legitimate job, and through a friend we have arranged to meet him there.

We drive to Kabalonga market, a row of shops made of concrete blocks and tin roofs. Out front a cobbler sits under a tree working on a four-foot pile of old shoes. As soon as we pull up in our truck, we are hustled by sleek young men like packs of jackals, hawking ivory necklaces and bracelets, malachite frogs and ashtrays, shiny rings, bangles, and beads. A short, well-dressed young man with a pock-marked face and nervous eyes approaches the truck as I step out. He introduces himself as Bwalya Muchisa. With him is Musakanya Mumba, a handsome twenty-two-year-old poacher, fine-featured, soft-spoken, and dressed in a T-shirt and slacks. Musakanya has hunted with Bwalya, using one of his guns, but he is willing to join us and can be trusted if we will give him a job — so he says. I am a little nervous about hiring poachers, and reluctant to take on two at once. But Bwalya says he cannot do the dangerous work of an informant alone. So they hop into the pickup and we drive a short distance to a friend's home, where we can talk without being seen by poachers at the market.

Sitting in an alcove of bushes in the front yard, I ask, "Why would you give up poaching to work for us?"

"Ah but Sir, you know the animals are finishing. There is no future in poaching anymore."

"Okay, but the information you give me will tell me whether I can trust you."

"Sir, you have nothing to fear from us. We are ready to help you in saving the animals," pledges Musakanya. "And I am from Mwamfushi Village, very near Mpika. Many of my friends are poachers. If you can offer employment to them, like me, many will turn in their guns and join us. I am sure of this. Poaching is hard and dangerous work."

I explain that as soon as Bwalya and Musakanya offer poachers jobs with the project in exchange for their guns, the whole community will immediately know that they are working for us. So I tell them to recruit other reliable informants who will remain under cover.

I also say that I will be very surprised if many of their friends turn in their guns for a job because, unlike Bwalya and Musakanya, they have not yet been threatened with arrest. But I give them three weeks to convince their cronies to do just that, and offer a thousand kwachas to each one who does. Three weeks from today we will meet at the hut where we stay in Mpika, and from there go to see those poachers who are ready to join us. I shake hands with Bwalya and Musakanya. We have agreed on their base salary, plus a handsome amount for every piece of information that leads me to one of the commercial poachers operating in the park.

"One last thing," I caution before we part. "Be careful. Because they know you're working for me, your friends may play along but then set you up to get hurt by one of the big operators."

"Ah no, this cannot happen," Bwalya says, both of them laughing. "We know these people and our villages too well. We can tell if they are serious."

At Marula-Puku, three weeks after our meeting in Lusaka, we receive a radio message from the operator at National Parks in Mpika: "Bwalya would like to buy that old camera of yours." Using the code we had agreed upon in Lusaka, Bwalya and Musakanya are asking us to meet them in Mpika that night.

Delia and I throw an overnight bag into the plane and fly to Mpika, where we pick up one of our trucks. At about seven-thirty in the evening a knock sounds at the door of our hut. I open it to find two bedraggled men, Bwalya and Musakanya. Quickly bringing them inside, we greet them with pats on the back. Their bleary eyes and sagging shoulders tell us at once that they have been working hard on their mission. We sit around the table as Delia hands them each a cup of strong, sweet tea and I ask what they have learned.

Bwalya tells us four poachers are ready to work for us. "But they won't come here," he says. "They are afraid of being arrested. They are waiting now in the bush near Mwamfushi Village. You must come alone with us to meet them. We must hurry, or they will become afraid and run away."

I agree; but as we are leaving, Delia grabs my arm, saying, "Mark, let's talk about this, please." I ask Bwalya and Musakanya to wait outside for a moment. As soon as the door is closed behind them, Delia hisses, "If you go with them, you're crazy. You don't even have a gun."

"They've done what we asked them to do; now I have to follow through. Anyway, what choice do I have? If these men really do turn in their guns and join us, maybe others will follow. We have to deal with them in good faith. If I'm not back in two hours, go to the police."

Minutes later Bwalya, Musakanya, and I are driving south from Mpika along the Great North Road. We have gone about two miles when Bwalya asks me to slow down. He stares out his window at the tall grass along the ditch bank.

"Stop! You've just passed it." I reverse, swinging the truck's headlights over the berm of the road until I can see a footpath leading into the bush. Dousing my lights, I ease the cruiser off the road, barely able to follow the path by the faint light of the new moon. Grass as tall as the truck's hood swishes along its sides.

We drive for perhaps half a mile in silence. A tree looms out of the darkness along the side of the track as Bwalya says, "Stop. Wait here."

He jerks open the door and the two men run off into the darkness beyond the tree. Two or three minutes pass, and in the dead silence the pulse in my ears makes me uneasy.

I unlatch my door, drop to the ground beside the truck, and crawl through the grass to some bushes twenty yards away. From here I can escape to the main road if this is a hit.

Several minutes later I hear footsteps on my right, headed for the truck. Someone whistles, and in the moonlight I can just make out six men milling around the Cruiser.

"Bwalya, Musakanya! Is that you?" I shout, keeping my head down.

"Eh, Mukwai."

"Okay, switch on the parking lights — the little knob on the lever by the steering wheel — and have the men stand in front with their hands on their heads, so I can see them."

"Ah but Sir, it's okay . . ."

"*Do* it, Bwalya!" After a minute the lights come on, and I can see all of them, including Bwalya and Musakanya, with their hands on their heads. I stand up and walk to the Cruiser.

Musakanya introduces me to the four newcomers, two of whom are sons of Chende Ende, the headman of Mwamfushi. The other two have worked as carriers for Chikilinti and other poachers in the village. They are no more than eighteen years old.

Bwalya asks me if I can take the four teenagers to our camp. "The people of Mwamfushi have beaten very badly some of those who are working with us," he explains. "Now these boys are very much fearing to go back there. Musakanya and myself, we are not afraid; we will stay in the village and continue to pass messages to you." I agree to take the youngsters with us, and tell them to be at our hut by ten o'clock the next morning.

We all sit in the back of the pickup as Bwalya, Musakanya, and the others describe the poaching in North Luangwa. Virtually everyone in Mpika District eats poached or "bush" meat, which is sold illegally in all the marketplaces and by scores of black marketers along the main road. A dealer, usually several dealers, pays a hunter up front for the numbers and kinds of animals they want killed, they agree on a secret rendez-vous near or inside the park, and then each dealer, or sometimes the hunter, hires fifteen to thirty bearers to stockpile mealie-meal.

The hunters, bearers, and often the dealers meet at the rendezvous, occasionally joining other hunting parties there, forming a combined force of up to one hundred forty. A gang this size may include as many as ten to fifteen riflemen, armed with everything from military weapons to muzzle-loaders homemade from Land Rover steering rods. The muzzle-loaders use a gunpowder of fertilizer mixed with diesel fuel, strikers made from the tips of matches, bark fiber as wadding, and balls of steel pounded into a roundish shape as bullets. The powder, balls, and wadding are carried in an animal-skin pouch slung from the shoulder with a strap. The hunters decide who hunts where, then each takes his party to that area, usually in search of elephants and buffalo, large-bodied animals that carry a lot of meat. This information confirms my observations from the air: these splinter groups, consisting of mostly unarmed men, could easily be captured even by poorly armed scouts, if only they would patrol.

As soon as a hunter kills an animal, he leaves it before vultures or smoke from meat-drying fires can attract my airplane. Often he doesn't even go to the animal he has shot, for fear of being caught with it. Some of the bearers stay behind to cut out the tusks, butcher the carcass, dry the meat, and carry it back to their village or to a truck waiting on some remote bush track outside the park. Meanwhile the hunter joins another group of bearers camped nearby, to kill again. When he has filled his contracts, he leaves the park along a route different from that taken by bearers.

In an average three-week poaching expedition, one of the Chende Ende brothers says, each hunter kills from three to fifteen elephants and a larger number of buffalo and smaller animals, such as impalas, puku, and warthogs. An active poacher makes from nine to twelve such trips in a year. In the village of Mwamfushi alone are at least a dozen commercial poachers. It is no longer a mystery why the North Park is losing a thousand elephants each year, why it has already lost more than 70 percent of its elephant population.

"Do they ever hunt rhinos anymore?" I ask.

"The rhinos were poached out years ago," Bwalya reports without emotion. "They were the first to go, because their horns are so valuable. I haven't seen a sign of one since 1982." The others nod agreement. Reports from the early 1970s had estimated the population at seventeen hundred to two thousand. Now there are no more than thirty to fifty in the entire valley, and maybe none.

"Do you think the game guards will ever be willing and able to stop this?" I ask.

"Sir," Bwalya snorts, "they are not serious people in this work. Many of them are friends with the worst poachers. They regularly drink beer with them, sell ammunition to them, tell them where to find elephants and buffalo. The poachers give them meat and money."

Sitting up on the edge of the pickup, Musakanya asks, "You know Patrick Mubuka, the Camp-in-Charge at Nsansamina? He killed two elephants just north of Marula-Puku last year. Another scout reported him to Warden Salama, but he is still Camp-in-Charge."

"Ah, but you know, Sir, it is not just the game guards. It goes much higher than them," Bwalya says, shaking his head.

I lean forward. "How high?"

"When you arrived in 1986," he continues, "two truckloads of dried meat were taken from the park to Lusaka every week, to the National Parks headquarters and to other officials."

"And ivories!" he exclaims. "They call Mpika the 'Second Ivory Coast.' I know about one truck loaded with 547 ivories, all taken from the North Park in some few months."

"What about the magistrate in Mpika? Is he straight?"

Bwalya grinned and shook his head. "As straight as a bull's prick, Sir. I have a friend, Patrick Chende Ende, a cousin to the headman of Mwamfushi. He was charged with poaching. The night before Patrick went to court, the magistrate drank beer with the Chende Ende family. They gave him one thousand kwachas [thirteen dollars]. Next day he fined Patrick two thousand kwachas instead of putting him in prison for a year, as the magistrate in Chipata does in cases like these." He goes on to tell me that Bernard Mutondo, the poacher who killed and wounded scouts just south of the park, was never even arrested. When later charged with another poaching offense, he was sentenced to only four months in prison. Mutondo used a gun belonging to a close friend of the magistrate; it was never confiscated, as is prescribed by law. In the midst of the elephant slaughter, instead of imprisoning poachers, the magistrate is fining them an average of thirteen dollars! And he confiscates only the most dilapidated muzzle-loaders, returning the better guns to the poachers to be used again and again. Twice Mfuwe scouts have even caught poachers using the magistrate's own gun.

"There is more," Musakanya offers. "A very strange thing. Often lately we have seen the new warden, Bornface Mulenga, drinking in Mpondo's Roadside Bar on the main road near the airstrip, that very one where Chikilinti, Simu Chimba, and the others are usually found."

"Okay, guys," I caution them, "don't let your imaginations run away with you. Mr. Mulenga is probably just conducting some of his own investigations. I think he's straight. He has to be straight."

"Sir, you cannot know the extent to this problem," Bwalya adds. "The police in Mpika, Isoka, Chinsali, and the officers at the armory in Tazara, they all give weapons to the poachers. And the army — I know a soldier who brings AK-47s and ammunition from the barracks in Kabwe for poaching in the valley. He comes to Mpika once each month in an IFA [military] truck and takes meat and tusks back with him. And much more ammunitions are coming from the munitions factory near Kanona. You can't believe it."

But I can believe it. Officers from Zambia's Anticorruption Commission have told me they estimate that one hundred fifty to two hundred military weapons are being used for poaching in the Mpika area, many of them from official armories. Yet since we have been in North Luangwa, to our knowledge not one of these weapons has ever been confiscated from a poacher by local authorities.

Then Musakanya tells me that Mpundu Katongo left four days ago to hunt on the Mulandashi River. And even now, Bernard Mutondo is somewhere along the Mwaleshi shooting elephants and buffalo. "If you fly the Shatangala route through the mountains into the valley, you shall see their carriers bringing meat and ivories back to Mwamfushi," he says. In the beam of my flashlight, Musakanya and Bwalya sketch a map showing six major footpaths leading from villages west of the scarp, through the mountains of the Muchinga, and into the park.

"How are we going to stop this?" I groan in despair.

"Sir," Bwalya says, "it is too big. You will not stop it."

"We will. With your help we can and we will. The world is going to change for these poachers."

12
A Zebra with No Stripes

DELIA

> But for such errant thoughts on an equally errant zebra
> . . . I might have seen a little sooner.
>
> — BERYL MARKHAM

○ ○ ○

SIMBEYE, MWAMBA, KASOKOLA — the Bembas who have worked for us through the years — smile every morning no matter what the night has left in its wake. If we need a sentinel, they shoulder a rifle; if we need a carpenter, they lift a saw; if we need bread, they build a fire. They are as steady and solid as the Muchinga Escarpment that guards the valley.

Together we dug up three thousand stumps for the airstrip, side by side we collected thousands of rocks for the cottages, step by step we hiked to untracked valleys. But now that the camp is long ago complete, I cannot step out of the cottage without one of them rushing forward to take from my arms anything I carry. I tell them that I am getting fat with all this assistance, let alone from the fresh bread they bake in the black pot.

Not once have they refused a request, even if it meant climbing to the far reaches of a marula tree to cut down a dangerous limb, or hiking for days to deliver food to the ungrateful game guards. Unarmed, Simbeye has run after an armed poacher and tackled him to the ground. Unasked, Mwamba has brought me flowers. And Kasokola has carried my heavy backpack for the last mile of many hikes.

They know that we love to hear about the wildlife, so whenever we return to camp from a trip, they describe in detail the wonders we have missed. Very early on, we realized that the longer we were away, the more fantastic the stories would be. We would like to add some of their observations to our records, but we can't quite be sure of their accuracy.

Mwamba once told us in great detail about a leopard's killing a puku on the beach, and a crocodile's flying from the water to take the puku for himself. This episode could well have happened, and I started to write it in our "Leopard Observations" file. But at the same time Evans Mukuka, our educational officer, wrote in a long report that he had watched rhinos grazing near the airstrip. When I questioned him about it, he said of course there are no rhinos; everyone knows they have all been shot by poachers. But knowing that we would like to read about rhinos near the airstrip, he added them to his report. And so I did not record the leopard and crocodile incident. Still, we enjoy the stories and look forward to hearing them when we return to camp.

Kasokola, deciding that I need a cook, brings his elder brother, Mumanga, back to camp with him after his leave. Mumanga, a slim, jolly man of forty, brightens our kitchen boma daily with a freshly baked pie or cake. With so much more baking going on, Mumanga decides that he needs an assistant, so I hire Davies Chanda from Mukungule to help with the cooking and other camp chores. Chanda, twenty years old, would rather be in the army than in a kitchen and he marches around camp in stiff-legged military fashion, saluting me whenever I pass by.

This morning very early, Chanda and I leave Marula-Puku for the long drive up the scarp to Mukungule for the grand opening of the Wildlife Shop. Although Mukungule is a fairly large village, it has had no store whatsoever. Anyone who wanted to buy a bar of soap, a bit of salt, or a matchstick had to walk two days to Mpika. When the Wildlife Club that we sponsor came up with the idea of opening a shop, we agreed to purchase the first stock of goods, to help with transport, and to lend them enough capital to get started. Months later, after endless delays in obtaining their trading license, the shop — a small, neat mud hut with clipped thatch roof — is ready for its official opening.

The shop is one of several improvements we have helped bring to Mukungule. The North Luangwa Grinding Mill now grinds maize for the villagers for a small fee, and a weekly farmers' market offers a place for people to sell their produce. The Women's Club sews children's clothes that will be sold in the Wildlife Shop. We visit the school every month to teach both children and adults the value of wildlife.

Chanda and I reach the foothills of the scarp just as the sun greets the golden grasses, which stretch for miles over rocky knolls. Before us looms the solid shoulder of the Muchinga Escarpment, challenging our departure from the valley. A small herd of zebras emerge from the mopane scrub and canter slowly along the track. As I stop the truck to watch, they pause to look back at us. Bold black-and-white stripes against a golden backdrop — they merge into the spindly trees and disappear.

Rambling over small boulders and through dry streambeds, we drive on. A few miles later Chanda says, "Madam, you saw the zebra with no stripes?"

"What, Chanda? What are you talking about?"

"In the herd we saw, Madam, there was a zebra with no stripes."

My eyebrows lift. I saw the zebras and they all looked normal to me. I smile. "Well now, tell me, Chanda, if a zebra has no stripes, is he black, or is he white?"

"I do not know about every zebra with no stripes, but this one, she is a she and she is black."

"Oh, I see. Perhaps she was standing in the shadows and she looked black."

"No, Madam, I have even seen her before. She has no stripes."

"Fine, Chanda, that's interesting. Maybe someday I will see her. Now, please, can you help me decide what to say in my speech to the people of Mukungule at the opening. Even after all of our help, they're still poaching." Together we write my speech as we bounce over the scarp.

When we tire of talking and speech writing, my mind picks up where my mouth left off, and I think. This imaginary zebra with no stripes has made me think of the elephants in the valley who have no tusks. We have seen more and more of them. Tuskless elephants occur throughout Africa. But Mark and I wonder if there is not a greater percentage of them in this population due to the heavy poaching pressure on those with tusks. Since the tuskless ones are less likely to be shot, they have a better chance of surviving to reproduce and to pass the genes for tusklessness to their offspring. We must make an aerial count of them.

I ask Chanda what he thinks of the tuskless elephants. "Madam, as you yourself have seen, we tribesmen of the Bemba and Bisa always carry axes. As a small boy, we carry a small ax; as a big man, we carry a big ax. You can always know the size of a Bemba by the size of his ax. A man must never go into the forest without his ax, for if the way becomes too thick, he cannot pass or he must depend on his friends to cut the way. A Bemba without his ax is not a big man. That must be what the other elephants think of an elephant without tusks."

○ ○ ○

The Mukungule Wildlife Shop is draped with a wide yellow ribbon, and buckets of wildflowers sit by the door. Dozens of villagers — adults and children — have gathered in the freshly swept yard. The district governor, who has come from Mpika for the ceremony, gives a speech honoring the game guards; Chief Mukungule with his ancient eyes asks his subjects to stop poaching; and a young student of thirteen delivers the most moving speech of the day, declaring that wildlife is the best chance the villagers have for a bright future. The ribbon is cut, and people buy soap and matches. Life is just a bit easier in Mukungule because of the Wildlife Club. Are we one step closer to winning over the people, or will they continue to poach? Chanda and I, exhausted by all the merriment, drive back down the scarp.

The miombo forests of the Muchinga Escarpment are so thick that we can rarely see the valley below. But at one point the trees stand apart, offering a spectacular view of the sprawling Luangwa Valley all the way to the Machinje Hills in the distance. When we reach this spot, I exclaim — as I always do — at its beauty. "Yes," says Chanda, "at this place you can see as far as you can. When your eyes touch the other side, they are no longer in Zambia."

By the time we reach the foothills, the sun is as low in the west as it had been in the east on our ascent. I can almost imagine that instead of the sun's having moved, someone has turned the valley around in the opposite direction. The grass is just as golden, the sky just as soft; we have missed the hard, bleached colors of midday. "Now, Chanda, if you see this zebra with no stripes you must tell me." I know that the chances of seeing the same zebra herd eight hours later — stripes or not — are extremely remote. But he misses the teasing in my voice and cranes his neck this way and that, searching for the black zebra.

Seconds later, "There she is, Madam."

"Where?" I jam on the brakes, the truck skidding to the side, and look where Chanda is pointing. In full view at the edge of the mopane trees, only twenty yards from us, is a large female zebra. Her face, neck, and body are the color of dark charcoal with only a faint shadow of stripes. Beside her is a small foal with a perfect black-and-white pattern.

Chanda is grinning from ear to ear. "You did not believe me, did you, Madam? But here is a zebra with no stripes."

"You are right! Chanda, you are right! She has no stripes. At least, she has fewer stripes."

The female turns and faces us head on. With this stance her stripes fade away completely. "Madam, is a zebra still a zebra, if she has no stripes?"

"Yes, Chanda, she and all zebras have the genes for many combinations, but in nature usually the stripes prevail because they have advantages in the wild. Like camouflage, for example."

"Well, Madam, that may be so. But for myself, I just don't know what the world is doing, to make elephants with no tusks and zebras with no stripes."

13
Chikilinti Juju

MARK

> In my rudyard-kipling-simple years I read
> Of mid-jungle where the elephants go to die.
> Old bulls know, and rather than death by herd,
> Wait alone, and add to the fabulous ivory.
>
> —JOHN HOLMES, "The Thrifty Elephant"

○ ○ ○

KASOKOLA AND I MIX a sludge of diesel fuel and sand in a pail, then spoon it into Nespray powdered-milk tins. Each is equipped with a twist of diesel-soaked rag, which will serve as a wick for the homemade flare pot.

At the airstrip, after dark, we remove their lids and set out our lighted flares at hundred-yard intervals along both sides of the runway. I park the Land Cruiser so that its headlights will play across the end of the strip. Before going to the plane I plug a spotlight into the cigarette lighter socket. The light will serve as a beacon to help us find the airstrip in the dark. Musakanya has radioed us that Chikilinti, armed with four brand-new AKs, is somewhere in the park with an army of other hunters and bearers. For several nights we have been flying to look for his fires.

It is early 1989, and for a while now I have been keeping two guards posted on Foxtrot Zulu Sierra. Poachers would relish a chance to strafe or burn it, or at least chop it to bits with their pangas, or machetes. To further guard against this, I have evoked several of my own brands of juju. Some time ago I mounted solar lights on poles set in opposite corners of the plane's boma, each with an infrared beam fixed on the aircraft. Whenever anyone approaches, breaking one of the beams, the lights switch on automatically and suddenly the plane is brightly lit, almost jumping out of the darkness — as if by magic. One day I convinced the game scouts that Zulu Sierra cannot be hit by bullets — by drawing my pistol and shooting at it with blanks. No holes. It must be juju. Another day I took one of the scouts flying and homed on one of our radio-collared lionesses across miles of wilderness; I even talked to her over the plane's radio — or so it seemed. The scout didn't know about homing on radio transmitters and I didn't tell him. The word about my juju has spread quickly. It may work for a while.

Now, as I untie and check the plane, I tell the guards to make sure the flares stay lit. Pulling its hinge pins, I remove the door from the right-hand side of the Cessna so that Kasokola can have a better view of the landscape; then we taxi to the end of the strip and begin our takeoff run. There is something unearthly, surreal, and primal about accelerating to take flight at night with the door off: the rushing wind, the roar of the engine, the vibration, and the lines of flickering yellow flares speeding past.

I pull back the yoke and point Zulu Sierra's nose at the waning, lopsided moon as we take to a starry sky. The wheels lose contact with the earth and their rumble and vibration cease. We seem to glide through a liquid combination of nightness and moon day; through another time-space dimension where neither night nor day prevails; where their elements are equally mixed like two pigments on an artist's pallet, blended to yield an altogether more beautiful hue. This hue, combined with the cool, humid night air, makes for a flying medium that is languid, moist, and dense, like the water in a blue-black pool. We are not flying so much as sailing through this celestial pool, and I can almost imagine that the stars are white waterlilies, or points of phosphor drifting by.

Fifteen minutes later our dream-like flight has led us down the Lubonga to the Mwaleshi, then up the Lufwashi. As far as I can see, Africa is asleep. Even the hills and mountains of the scarp are recumbent in the darkness. I bank the plane across the shadowy face of Chinchendu Hill, then back toward the Mwaleshi River. Like a silvery snake, the moonlit waters gradually resolve out of the night. Minutes later, Kasokola's faint voice finds its way through the roar of the wind and the engine into my earphones.

"Fires! There!" He points. At a thousand feet above the ground we are nearing a gap in the ridge through which the Loukokwa River flows on its way to the Luangwa. As we pass over it, I look down into the rough amphitheater that the river has carved out of the ridge. Like a giant hearth, the fifty-foot walls glow orange from dozens of campfires. Another dragon's eye.

I pull back the throttle and take two notches of flap for a descending turn that will head us back past the encampment at a lower height. This time I clearly see several tents set up among the trees along the river. Only Chikilinti and his friends are affluent enough, and bold enough, to shelter in expensive, conspicuous tents.

"Can you see meat racks?" I shout.

"No."

"Then we've caught them in time. We'll have to get the game guards down here early." Tomorrow the hunters will split up, set up several camps in the area, and start shooting elephants. I bank the plane toward camp and a short night of fitful sleep.

Up before dawn the next morning, I send a truck for the paramilitary scouts at Kanona, as planned. On their way through Mpika they will pick up Bwalya and Musakanya, who will guide the patrol and tell me how well the scouts conduct themselves. This crack unit will be armed with their AKs, so going after one of these bands of poachers should be no big deal; they'll give a fitting reception to Chikilinti's group.

Then, knowing it is probably useless but determined to do everything I can, I fly to all the camps around the park, dropping powdered-milk tins with notes telling the scouts to intercept any poachers fleeing from our operation on the Loukokwa River. All of this flitting about the countryside dropping tin cans is still necessary only because National Parks has not, in more than eighteen months, arranged licenses for the radios we bought for the camps. And the same is true for the sixty-one guns that were ready to be shipped from the States two years ago.

Late the next afternoon, squatting on its axles, our truck returns from Kanona loaded with scouts. The next morning I airlift them to an emergency airstrip an hour's walk from the poachers' camp. When they are assembled and ready to go, I tell them how happy we are to have their help, and that it should be easy to find at least one of the several poaching bands that have splintered off from the large group I spotted two nights ago. Shaking their hands, I give the group a small radio and send them off. Bwalya and Musakanya, eager as two young hunting dogs, are in the lead.

As the scouts begin moving toward the poachers' camp, I take off, flying in the same direction to show them the way. They need only follow the plane. I am hoping that we will be in time to stop the poachers before they kill any elephants. But I have flown only three miles when I run into three thick spirals of vultures, and looking down I can see the carcass of a freshly killed elephant at the base of each. Tucked up under the trees near the carcasses are clusters of big racks covered with slabs of smoking meat. The cabin of the plane is immediately saturated with the familiar sweet smell that hangs cloyingly in the back of my throat.

Dodging vultures, I take the plane down and discover two more slaughtered elephants lying within a few yards of each other. Three tents and four flysheets are set up under a tree surrounded by a thicket, and scattered around the camp are jerry cans, pots, pans, axes, ropes, and other gear. Ten to fifteen men are hiding in the thicket with a mountain of red meat at least five feet high and six feet in diameter.

"Chikilinti, Simu Chimba, Bernard Mutondo, and Mpundu Katongo." I grind the names of the worst poachers in the district between my teeth. This time the scouts, real scouts, are right here!

Some of the poachers begin running when they see the plane. I circle over them, very low, pinning them to the ground. After a few passes I break off and fly back to where we have just left the scouts, not a minute and a half away. Over and over I call on the radio, but they do not answer me. I scribble a note on a pad: "Found poachers with five freshly killed elephants approximately three and a half miles southwest of you. Will pin them down with airplane and continue circling with wing down to show you their position until you arrive. Come as fast as you can." I tear off the sheet, tie a white mutton-cloth streamer to it, and drop it to the scouts. When they pick it up and wave to me, I head back to the poachers' camp.

Once again I come in low and slow, trying to see details of the camping equipment or anything that might lead us to these poachers if they escape back to Mpika. The encampment is concealed well, in a small forest of stunted mopane trees. Except for the smoke and the vultures, I might never have found it.

I am passing over the last elephant when a man in a red shirt steps out from behind a tree and shoulders a stubby AK-47. I kick hard left rudder, and the plane skids sideways through the air. Looking out my window, I see his shoulder jerk from the recoil and a puff of gray smoke bursts from the muzzle. Suddenly I am very aware that he is shooting bullets with steel jackets — at my flying biscuit tin with its thin aluminum skin.

I am over him and gone before he can fire more than a couple of rounds. For a minute or more I circle away from the poachers, dizzy with the blood pounding in my ears. The scouts should be there in about an hour, but if the poachers start pulling out now, the scouts will have a hard time tracking them in the thick brush. I have to keep them pinned down. My hands damp on the control wheel, I bank for the camp again, skimming the treetops so Red Shirt will have no more than a second to see me and get off a shot. I keep my speed low, so that if I hit one of the vultures turning above the carcasses there may be enough left of the plane to try a forced landing. I once saw the remains of a twin-engine Aerocommander that had run into a vulture. The big bird had blasted through the windshield like a cannonball of feathers, killing the pilot and copilot instantly, then continued through the cabin, destroying its interior. The remains of the vulture, a blob of red meat the size of a baseball, were later found in the tail cone of what had been an aircraft.

I kick the rudder pedals left and right, zigzagging as I head into the vultures and smoke. A bird is coming straight at me, craning its head and flapping furiously to get out of the way. I pull off power and jink to the right. As the roar of the engine subsides, I hear the pop-pop-pop of gunshots through my open side window.

I circle back and this time fall in with the glide pattern of the wheeling vultures, spiraling with them, holding a steep left turn thirty feet above the main camp. But there is Red Shirt behind a tree, pointing his rifle at me again. To put some distance between us, I spiral up high with the vultures. At fifteen hundred feet, with my wing-tip strobe lights flashing, I circle, waiting for the game guards. It has been more than an hour since I dropped my note to them. They surely can see the plane, and they must hear the shooting.

Another hour passes, two, two and a half. Still no sign of the scouts. I fly back in their direction but I can't spot them. Dodging vultures, aching with fatigue, I continue circling over the poachers until my fuel gauges nudge empty. And then I head back to Marula-Puku, certain that the scouts will arrive soon.

They never do, of course. They never come. Days later they show up at Marula-Puku, asking to be taken back to Kanona. They found only one dead elephant, they say, did not see the airplane, heard no shots, and did not find poachers or any signs of them.

The next morning, after the scouts have gone back to Kanona, Bwalya and Musakanya tell me a different story. The scouts joined the poachers, whom they know well, and spent an enjoyable evening eating elephant meat around the fire.

I write yet another report to the National Parks and Wildlife Services, but do not receive a reply, and again nothing is done.

14
The Eagle

MARK

I am the eagle
I live in high places
In rocky cathedrals
Way up in the sky.

I am the hawk
There's blood on my feathers
But time is still turning
They soon will be dry.

—JOHN DENVER

○ ○ ○

MWAMFUSHI VILLAGE: eleven-thirty at night, a week after the busted operation with the Kanona scouts. Musakanya and his wife have been asleep on the floor of their mud and thatch home since about nine. Gunshots shatter the darkness outside. Chips of mud and splinters of wood rain down on them. Throwing his body across his wife to protect her, Musakanya holds her down as she screams. More shots. Bullets punch through the walls, kicking out puffs of dust and clods of dry dirt. Musakanya crawls to the door in time to hear angry shouts and receding footsteps.

Neither Musakanya nor his wife is killed, fortunately, but sooner or later someone will be. The poachers have also shot up the home of the Mwamfushi headman, who is encouraging his villagers to stop poaching; and they have poisoned, not fatally, Jealous Mvula and two of our other men. Clearly, they are upping the ante. If they can do it, so can I. But I will have to do it alone. I've had it with scouts.

At dawn I lift off from the camp strip and fly along the Mulandashi River, following one of the poachers' footpaths that Musakanya and Bwalya sketched for me. The poachers have hit this area hard, because it is miles from our camp. In this poachers' shooting gallery, nearly all the elephants and buffalo have been wiped out in the previous four or five years.

Several times lately, when I have discovered poachers from the air, I have chased them with the airplane until they ran away, abandoning their meat and ivory to vultures and hyenas. It is expensive for a hunter to mount a three-week expedition into the park, and if operating in North Luangwa becomes unprofitable, the poachers will give it up. If I can't get them locked up, maybe I can at least bankrupt them.

Staying low so that any poachers in the valley ahead will not hear the plane, I follow the broad footpath. Banking left and right — watching for vultures, smoke, and meat racks — I fly along the trail through the hills to the large baobab at the confluence of the Kabale and Mulandashi.

Just as I begin to turn away from the tree, something on a broad sandbar along the Mulandashi catches my eye. Leveling the plane, I see two men run across the bar, each carrying an elephant's tusks on his shoulder. Other men sprint beside them, lugging baskets of meat.

I point the nose of the Cessna at the two men with the tusks as they dash across the dry riverbed, heading for thick bushes along the shore. They drop the tusks, turn, and race for a stand of tall grass. I put the plane down "on the deck," my wheels skimming just above the sand.

The poachers glance over their shoulders at the plane bearing down on them, their legs pumping hard, sand skipping from their feet. When my left main wheel is just behind one of them, he looks right at me, and I can see him wondering desperately, and much too slowly, which way to dive. At the last instant I nick back on the controls and the wheel misses his head by inches. I look back to see him plunge headlong into a devil's thornbush at the river's edge.

The other men have wriggled into the tall grass patch on the sandbar. I think it needs mowing. On this pass my Hartzell propeller from Piqua, Ohio, chops the tall stems into confetti. The prop blasts it over the poachers, who are lying face down, hands over their heads. As I pull up and away, I switch the plane's ignition quickly off and on. A tremendous backfire explodes from the exhaust pipe. I haul Zulu Sierra around for another pass, and another, burping her again and again.

For half an hour I make repeated passes over the poachers, reinforcing their terror, extracting from them a price for killing in the park. Then I make a show of landing, rolling the plane's wheels along the sandbar, to make them think I am going to stop and try to arrest them. But if I drop too much speed in this loose sand, I will indeed land — without a hope of taking off again. I will be stuck on this sandbar, unarmed in the midst of a gang of poachers who hate me now even more than they did before. So I abandon my pretense at law enforcement and head back to camp.

Even without any arrests, my air patrols begin to have an impact on the poachers. For several weeks I fly almost every day, diving on poachers along the Mulandashi, Luangwa, Mwaleshi, and other rivers. Musakanya tells me that many of the men from Mwamfushi are refusing to work as carriers, so the hunters are forced to hire from villages farther from their base around Mpika. More often now they have to wait until late afternoon to shoot, drying their meat at night to avoid being discovered from the air. And whenever they hear the sound of the airplane, they quickly cover their fires or put them out with buckets of river water. Other poachers are setting up their meat racks in the cover of hills where I haven't been flying. These air patrols are the only thing protecting the park, so often I fly until midnight and then get up at three to fly again.

Delia is more supportive of these antipoaching flights than of my "suicide runs" to pin down poachers for scouts who never show up. "Finally, something is working," she says, "even if just a little." Still, the park is losing elephants at the rate of five hundred a year — too many, too fast. We don't have long to save the rest. And Zulu Sierra and I aren't going to be able to work our juju on the poachers for much longer. Soon they will realize that the plane can't really harm them. We need help. And at last we are going to get it.

In October 1989, in a warm room in a snowy land far from the shimmering savannas of Africa, seventy-six nations of CITES (the United Nations Convention for International Trade in Endangered Species) vote to list the African elephant as an endangered species (see Appendix B). In so doing they forbid trade in ivory and all other elephant parts, and provide the last hope for earth's largest land mammal.

15
Moon Shadow

DELIA

The only paradise we ever need — if only we had the eyes to see.

— EDWARD ABBEY, speaking of the earth

○ ○ ○

I AM ALONE IN CAMP. Mark is flying an antipoaching patrol and all the Bembas are working on the track between camp and the airstrip. In our stone and thatch office cottage, I analyze more survey data — calculating how many buffalo, impalas, kudu still remain in North Luangwa. I can hear the Lillian lovebirds whistling as they fly from tree to tree, feasting on the ripe marula fruits.

Weary of numbers, I walk to the river's edge and sit cross-legged with Nature for a while. Across the water, far away at the next bend, I see a tall gray bush moving. Then an elephant, also tall and gray, steps from behind it. It is the first elephant I have seen from Marula-Puku. In exactly four seconds he disappears in the tall grass. We have worked three and a half years for those four seconds. It has been worth it.

When Mark returns, we walk to riverbank and I point out where the elephant had been. To our astonishment two others appear at that moment, in the same spot, and wander along the river. All at once it seems that there are elephants everywhere. The next morning Mwamba runs to the office cottage to show us five elephants feeding on the high bank behind the workshop. They are the surviving members of Camp Group — and at last they have accepted us enough to feed within sight of camp. When the Bembas walk to the airstrip, they see three other elephants feeding on the tall grass of the distant hills. They have finally come home to the Lubonga.

A few days later I am alone in the office cottage again, still working on the game census figures. At first I am only faintly aware of the sound. Then I lift my head and listen. It is an odd noise — whaap, whaap, whaap — like someone beating a blanket. I try to work again. Whaap, whaap! I look out of the window but see nothing unusual. Too curious to work, I step out of the cottage and look around. The sound is coming from the other side of the river. I look toward the tall grass some forty yards from camp, and I gasp.

There, standing in full view, is Survivor, the elephant with the hole in his left ear. Apparently relaxed and unafraid, he wraps his trunk around the base of a thick clump of grass, pulls it up by the roots, swings it high over his back, and pounds it on the ground. Whaap, whaap, whaap! Dirt falls from the roots; he sticks the cleaned grass into his mouth and chomps.

I do not budge, sure that if he sees me he will run away. I have been watching him feed for twenty minutes when I hear the truck coming. If Mark races into camp the way he usually does, it will frighten Survivor. I ease along the wall of the cottage and creep toward the road, watching the elephant carefully. Surely he can see me, but he shows no sign of alarm. Once I am around the corner and out of his sight, I race through the grass toward the approaching truck.

When Mark sees me running toward him, waving my arms, he stops the truck and leaps out, shouting, "What's wrong?"

"You're not going to believe it! Follow me." We tiptoe behind the cottage, around the corner, and into the open doorway. Standing just inside the cottage, we watch Survivor feed. He is not a large elephant, but at this moment he seems enormous — he represents hope, success, and a glimpse of Luangwa as it should be.

Eventually, confident that the elephant does not feel threatened, we walk slowly to the riverbank and stand near a marula tree. After some time, Survivor lifts his trunk and walks directly toward us on the far bank. He stops at the river's edge, only twenty yards away, and raises his trunk, taking in our scent. It is an elephant handshake — a welcome, across an invisible line, into the natural world. I feel the honor of the moment deep in my heart.

o o o

We long to follow lions across moonlit savannas, to rise at dawn to see where zebras feed, to count infant elephants standing beneath their mothers' bellies. But the antipoaching battle has devoured our time, energy, resources, even our spirit, since we arrived in North Luangwa. We know that even important scientific observations are a luxury in this place at this time. How can we observe the social behavior of lions when elephants are literally dying at our feet?

Yet at this moment there is a respite; elephant poaching has declined. It is now April 1990, and in the last seven months Mark has seen only five dead elephants from the air. We are convinced that his antipoaching flights and the CITES ban on ivory are working. The price of ivory has plummeted from one hundred fifty to five dollars per pound, and 90 percent of the world's legal ivory markets (plus some illegal routes) have dried up.

Six African nations, however — Botswana, Zimbabwe, Mozambique, South Africa, Malawi, and Zambia — have filed reservations against the ban, and this allows them to export ivory legally or to sell it within their borders. It is appalling to us that Zambia, where in only fifteen years poachers have killed 115,000 of 160,000 elephants, has refused to join the ban. Since there is no legal elephant hunting or culling in Zambia, all of the ivory in this country is from poached elephants. The southern African nations have formed their own cartel for trading ivory, and we are afraid that soon new local markets within this region will replace the international ones that disappeared with the ban. But at least for the moment there is a strange peace in the field.

So we feel that we can steal a few days to go lion watching. Soaring over the valley, we search for the big cats.

o o o

The lion glares into the eyes of his unlikely opponent — a Nile crocodile, whose pupils are as thin and cold as an ice pick. The giant jaws and ragged teeth of the two animals are locked into opposite ends of the glistening raw flesh of a dead waterbuck. The massive tail of the croc, plated with dragon armor, is coiled to launch the reptile forward in a flash. The leg and shoulder muscles of the lion ripple. Each of them has the strength and power of a small truck. Neither moves. The rest of the Serendipity Pride — three females, four large cubs, and another male — watch nearby, their ears turned back in apparent annoyance at this reptilian intrusion.

Mark pulls the plane around once more in a tight turn, as we watch the standoff on the beach below. We have never seen a lion and a crocodile challenge each other in this way. We fly back to the airstrip, grab our camping gear, and jump into the truck to get a closer look.

The Luangwa and its tributaries have one of the densest populations of crocodiles in Africa. During the rainy season many of the crocs migrate up the tributaries, returning to the Luangwa in the dry season when the streams dry up. A few crocs — such as this one on the sandbar of the Mwaleshi — stay in the shallow tributaries year round.

After the long drive from camp along the Mwaleshi, we park the truck under some trees that will make a good campsite, and hurry on foot to the riverbank.

"That's where they were, I'm sure." I point to a large sandbar on the other side of the Mwaleshi. From this side of the river there is no trace of a struggle between the lion and the crocodile, but we recognize the sandbar by its proximity to the bend in the river.

We wade into the clear, shallow water, heading for a smaller sandbar, covered in grass, that juts into the main channel. As our feet splash through the water, we both turn our heads this way and that, searching the sandy bottom for signs of a crocodile.

As I step up onto the sand, slightly ahead of Mark, I scan the deeper water on the other side of the bar. The river is faster here, and murkier, so it is difficult to see the bottom. But as I squint into the current, a curious pattern of reptilian scales takes shape, lying motionless only a yard from my feet. "Mark! He's right here!" I bend over, staring down at the coiled form.

Mark grabs my shoulder and pulls me back into the shallow current. "Delia, you can't just stand there watching a crocodile! He can fling himself out of there in a flash."

We back up, walk downstream for fifty yards, and cross to the large sandbar on the far shore where the skeleton of the waterbuck lies twisted on the beach. Kneeling, we study the lion tracks, carved deeply in the moist sand. They tell us that the lionesses grabbed the waterbuck as it stepped out of the tall grass of the floodplain and dragged it across the sandbar. Apparently, all of the lions fed for some time; we saw from the air that the females were quite full, and the tracks tell the same story. Then the lionesses left the carcass, probably chased off by the males. Soon after, the croc rushed in from the river and snatched one end of the kill. He was able to scavenge some of the spoils, but it was obvious that he did not drive the lions off; if he had, he would have dragged the carcass into the river or to his lair.

There are still many mysteries. Why did the other pride mates, the three lionesses and the male, lie basking in the sun while one male challenged the crocodile? Usually when other scavengers, such as spotted hyenas, vultures, or jackals, approach a fresh lion kill, the pride will chase them off. If the hyenas vastly outnumber the lions, the cats may retreat, but this was only one croc. His tough armor, lightning speed, and very capable jaws presumably give him license enough to feed with lions.

By watching Serendipity and her pride mates on earlier occasions, we have already learned that the Mwaleshi lions often hunt along the steep riverbanks where the prey species come down to drink. Thus their kills are accessible to the crocodiles. Furthermore, the Mwaleshi is so shallow that there are not many fish for the crocs to eat. To survive here they must be resourceful — even to the point of stealing meat from lions. Could scavenging from lions be a major source of food for these crocs? We will have to search for other lion-croc interactions to see how common such incidents are — and who usually wins.

The warm sands and cold bones yield no more clues, so we

wade back across the river, retracing our wide semicircle around the crocodile. After setting up camp on the banks of the Mwaleshi, we bathe in a very shallow area, taking more care than usual to check for predators.

Just after dawn, when the river looks like a ribbon of sunrise, the lions roar. We wiggle out of our sleeping bags, take a compass bearing on their position, and set off in that direction on foot. It is much more difficult to follow lions in Luangwa than it was in the Kalahari. In the desert, once we had a good compass bearing on lions, nothing stood in our way except rolling dunes; but here the land is crisscrossed with steep river cuts, dry streambeds, wet streambeds, rivers, lagoons, and eroded craters. At times we have spotted a lion only three hundred yards away and been unable to drive to it.

As we walk along the Mwaleshi, we come upon a herd of buffalo meandering toward the river. Creeping behind bushes and through the tall grass, we observe them from thirty yards away. Next we surprise a hippo wallowing in a shrinking lagoon. He whirls around and challenges Mark with a gaping mouth and squared-off teeth, while I scurry up a high bank to safety. We hear an elephant trumpeting and see the spoor of a mother and a tiny infant disappearing into the woodlands. There are no sounds or sights of man; it is a safari into old Africa.

The lions do not roar again, so we continue on the same bearing. When the noon sun is bleached to a blazing white, we see vultures circling over the river's edge and find them feeding on a dead bushbuck. We walk closer, our attention focused on the scrambling vultures.

A low growl erupts from the bushes. We swing around and two large male lions explode from the undergrowth, toward the river. Fifteen yards away they whirl around to face us. It is the two males from Serendipity Pride. We have made the mistake you cannot make with lions — we have crowded their space.

We stop in our tracks. They are in an aggressive stance, their heads and massive shoulders pulled to full height. One growls again through closed teeth, as they stare at us with piercing eyes.

There is nothing we can do but stand here; if we run, they will almost certainly charge. The male on the right raises his lips, exposing his canines in a snarl, then they both trot away, grunting loudly as they go. The entire encounter has lasted only ten seconds, but it has drained me. Mark and I lean against each other for a moment, and when we regain our legs, walk down to the beach to inspect the dead bushbuck. Although there are no signs of a crocodile, it is one more example of Mwaleshi carnivores making their kills near the river, where they could easily be confronted by crocs.

After several more long walks in search of lions, we decide to radio collar at least one of the Serendipity Pride members so that we can find them more easily. After dark we play tapes of lion and hyena vocalizations over loudspeakers near an open floodplain. Within thirty seconds, ten spotted hyenas are galloping toward the speakers, and ten minutes later the pride arrives. We want to dart Serendipity herself, but as they walk by the truck in single file, Mark has a better shot at one of the smaller females. He darts her. When the syringe stings her flank, she whirls around and trots toward the river. If she crosses the Mwaleshi before the drug takes effect, we will be unable to follow and collar her. Just at the water's edge she sways and stumbles, and finally succumbs.

As I watch the other lions with the spotlight, Mark walks up to her and nudges her gently with his foot to ensure that she is properly sedated, then I move the truck closer. As we begin to collar her, the other lions lie watching in a rough semicircle forty yards away. Shining the spotlight around every few minutes, I keep an eye on them; but the spotlight bulb burns out. Unbelievably, the backup spotlight also blows. We have to keep tabs on the curious, undarted lions with the weak beam of our flashlight as we collar, ear tag, and weigh the lioness.

Finally we finish and name her Kora, after the beloved Kenya bush country of George Adamson, who was murdered by Somali ivory poachers. These poachers cross into Kenya, shoot elephants, and smuggle the tusks back to Somalia, which is heavily involved in the illegal exportation of ivory. Adamson had attempted for years to defend the Kora Reserve against these pirates, but eventually they shot him to death and he became yet another victim of the ivory trade.

The next morning, by listening to Kora's signal, we find that the pride has crossed the river. Carrying the antenna, radio receiver, and rifle, we wade across the Mwaleshi, following the beep-beep-beep of her collar. On the other side, the grass is so high that even when we part it with our arms we still can see only two feet ahead. The needle on the amp meter goes into the red, indicating that we are very close to the lions, but all we can see are grass stems and blue sky. We listen for the sounds of lions walking in the grass. Nothing. Mark motions me forward, but I point behind us, suggesting that we retreat. Mark shakes his head, and we walk on slowly, parting the grass, trying to see ahead, listening.

The signal remains strong and constant as we go forward. The lions must be staying just ahead of us, moving in the same direction at the same speed. Quiet as we try to be, we know they can hear us coming. Again I suggest a retreat. Whispering, I say that we can't see them in this tall grass anyway, and we might stumble upon them unexpectedly and frighten them. I don't mention that I am already scared silly, and that this scheme is just plain foolish. "Just a few more minutes," Mark whispers. We stalk on through the grass for another ten minutes before giving up and heading back to our little camp on the Mwaleshi.

The next day we walk the beach, following the lion tracks and scanning for vultures, but we cannot find the pride or pick up the signal. Tomorrow we must return to Marula-Puku to continue the antipoaching and village programs. But as soon as time allows, we will return with the airplane, find the radio-collared lioness, and observe the pride in more detail.

As we are breaking camp at dawn, we see a swarm of vultures across the river on the same sandbar where we first saw Serendipity Pride and the croc. Pulling and tearing on a puku carcass, the vultures glare with beady eyes as we wade the river. When we step onto the sandbar, they lift off in a flurry of flapping wings.

The vultures have not been here long, and the story of the kill is still etched in the sand: the lions killed their prey on the sandbar, and once again the crocodile rushed from the river to grab a share.

"This croc's really got something going," Mark says, as he inspects the remains of the puku.

"And there he is." I point to the river's edge, where the croc is lying in shallow water, his massive back rising above the surface, his flat head held up, mouth open, exposing a row of jagged, uneven teeth. He looks incongruously as if he is grinning. Mark steps slowly toward him, and I follow a few steps behind. The croc doesn't budge at our approach; he obviously owns this beach. When Mark is ten yards away, the croc hisses and snaps, warning him not to come any closer. And I remind Mark of his words: "You can't just stand there watching a crocodile."

As we turn to leave, we see a cyclone of black smoke rising in the south. The poachers are back in the park. Our short days of lion watching are over.

○ ○ ○

The wide, unfamiliar waters of the Mutinondo River spread before me. The only other time I have seen this river, it was a raging torrent, sweeping past with driftwood on its bow. Now its clear waters lap gently at grassy shores and its current whispers quietly over polished stones.

"Well, it looks okay to me. What do you think, Marie?"

Marie Hill, a Texan, and her husband, Harvey, live in Mpika, where he is the representative for the Canadian Wheat Project. Marie has volunteered to coordinate our conservation education program, which has grown too large for Mark and me to handle from camp.

"Yeah, it looks okay to me, too," Marie drawls.

"Let's go for it." I ease the front tires into the river and start across. We're on our way to Nabwalya, one of the picturesque villages in the Luangwa Valley, to begin our village and school programs. Many of the poaching expeditions into the park begin in Nabwalya; it is essential to win the people there over to our side.

To get this far I have had to drive up the scarp to Mpika to pick up Marie, and down the scarp on another track south of the park. Nabwalya is completely cut off during the rainy season, and not many trucks reach the village at any time of year. My Toyota is overflowing with medicines for the clinic, materials for the school, emergency protein rations for the hungry, our gear — an array of duffel bags, sleeping bags, camera cases, food boxes — and a watermelon for the chief. Balancing on top of this load are our educational assistant, the village medical officer, a schoolteacher, and the Nabwalya mail carrier, who usually has to walk for four days to reach the village from Mpika.

The river is shallow and easy to ford, and although the rest of the track is grueling at times, we make it to the village by four in the afternoon. The first thing we must do is pay our respects to the chief, so we send a runner ahead to announce our arrival. After we drive across an abandoned field, we find him and his headmen waiting for us in his n'saka. Nabwalya is young for a chief, alert, articulate, and progressive. He welcomes us warmly in perfect English, and we pass out our gifts — *International Wildlife* magazines and the watermelon. After a few moments of polite greetings, we ask for permission to begin our programs in his village, and he says that he has been waiting for us.

"Of course, you will stay in the 'guest palace,' " the chief says. "We have made a very nice guest palace for the tourists when they come. My headman will show you the way."

The new guest area is indeed a palace: two large bungalows, a n'saka, and a latrine, all made of woven grass and reeds. The roofs, doors, and windows of each structure have been trimmed with decorative spirals of grass. The charming encampment is perched on the high bank of the wide Munyamadzi River, just outside the village. A group of hippos have already begun their night song as we start to unpack. I am enchanted with the guest palace, but a little worried about how soon Chief Nabwalya expects the tourists to start coming.

The first camper to rise is usually rewarded, and the next morning is no exception. As I stoke last night's coals at 4:45 A.M., I hear the swish, swish of hippo feet in shallow water. Below me, just as the river turns a bright orange from dawn, a hippo strolls past, silhouetted against the shimmering water. In the faint light I can see the outlines of thatched huts and the smoke from a few cooking fires. It is a rare moment of people and wildlife together in harmony.

It is also the last moment of peace we have for four days. Marie, Mukuka (our assistant), and I present our conservation slide show to one hundred fifty villagers packed into the mud-brick schoolhouse. At our prompting, Chief Nabwalya explains to his people that many of their problems will be solved if the village can make money from tourism, but it will happen only if the poachers stop shooting the wildlife in North Luangwa.

With many of the curious villagers in tow, we deliver medicines to the clinic and talk with the medical officer about his problems. The first thing we notice is that all the patients are lying on reed mats on the floor, while the rusty hospital beds are stacked in a corner draped with spiderwebs. The medic tells us that poachers have stolen the bolts from the beds to make bullets. Never missing a chance to deliver our message, we point out to the patients that the poachers are their enemies and that we will get more bolts for the beds.

Next we inspect the airstrip, which is under construction by laborers we had hired earlier. When it is complete, the Flying Doctor can land and the village will not be so isolated during the rains.

Sunlight beams through holes in the walls of the schoolroom. Standing at the front, Marie and I encourage the children to draw posters asking the poachers not to kill the animals near their village. We wait for the children to color on the white paper we've given them, but unlike the students in the other villages, the Nabwalya children only stare at the page.

"Why aren't they drawing?" I whisper to the teacher.

"They have never had their own sheet of clean, white paper," he whispers back. "They are afraid to spoil it."

After we promise the children that we will bring more paper for them, they slowly begin to draw. A little girl sketches a hippo with ten babies under the caption, "Please Mr. Poacher Do Not Shoot the Hippo She Has Many Children." Later, walking along the well-worn footpaths, we and the children post their pictures throughout the village on trees and stumps.

On visiting the game guards of Nabwalya, we discover that they have never mounted a patrol in North Luangwa because they would have to cross several rivers with many crocodiles. When I point out that the poachers cross the rivers, they tell me that crocs do not attack criminals. They agree to patrol the park if we buy a small banana boat for them. Before leaving their camp, we give out T-shirts to all the game guards' children.

Steaming campfire coffee and hippos silhouetted against the dawn begin the last morning. The sun is especially welcome, because the village drummers have celebrated a wedding all night and only now end their rowdy beat. Exhausted, Marie, Mukuka, and I cook toast and oatmeal over the fire. We still face breaking camp and driving up the scarp. As I struggle toward the truck with a large food box, I hear a familiar sound drifting in from the distance. Our plane. None of the others have heard it.

I rush to the riverbank and wait. I know Mark; he will soar along the river course, just above the water and below treetop level, until he finds me. He knows me, too, and has guessed that I am camped somewhere along the river.

In seconds the plane appears just above the water, almost level with our grass palace. Marie and I wave frantically. Mark holds a note from the window, signaling that he will drop it on the next pass. I run to a clearing behind the camp and watch him circle back, figuring it is a shopping list for Mpika or some other errand he wants me to run before returning to camp. As the plane soars past, Mark flings the note, tied to string and a rock, out the window. I tear it open and read: "Greetings, my love. Come home to me. You have been away too long. I have a special surprise for you. Love, M." True, there is a short shopping list below, but the love part comes first. I hold the paper high in the air, signaling to Mark that I have received his message. He waggles his wings and flies south toward camp. "It's a love letter," I say to Marie. "He flew all this way to bring me a love letter. I've got to get back to camp!"

Two days of hard scarp driving makes my shoulder muscles

burn. But I pull into camp late in the afternoon of the second day. Mark welcomes me with a bear hug.

"Where's my surprise?" I smile.

Mark can barely contain himself. He pulls me along to the porch of our bedroom cottage, tells me to sit down, and hands me a glass of cool wine. "Okay, we wait here. The surprise is coming." As we chat quietly, Mark keeps glancing at his watch and then toward the tall grass bordering camp.

Minutes later, he touches my arm and motions for me to stop talking. He points behind me to the edge of camp. "There, there is your surprise."

I turn and see an elephant — Survivor — only forty yards away. He lifts his trunk and holds it high, taking in the amalgamation of camp scents. I squeeze Mark's hand, but otherwise we are still. "Just wait," Mark whispers, "just wait."

Survivor takes one step forward, then stops and lifts his trunk again. He raises his right front foot as if to step, then pauses and swings it back and forth. For long minutes he dangles his foot and lifts his trunk, then quite suddenly walks toward us with no further hesitation. He marches right into camp and begins feeding on the marula fruits behind the office cottage. Twenty-five yards from us, he feels along the ground with his dexterous trunk, finds a fruit, pops it into his mouth, and chews with loud slurping noises. Now and then he gently swings his entire head in our direction, but otherwise he does us the honor of ignoring us completely. He feeds for thirty minutes; just before dark, he walks away quietly along the same path he had followed into camp.

Mark tells me excitedly that Survivor has been coming into camp every evening since I have been gone. That this kind of acceptance can happen so soon, in the midst of such a slaughter of his kind by our kind, is all the proof we need that our project may work. It is stimulus enough to keep us going.

Survivor continues to come to camp every day, not just in the evening but anytime. Mornings he ambles up to the kitchen boma and feeds ten yards from the campfire. He forages between the office and bedroom cottages, and once he walks within four yards of us, as we stand quietly on the porch of the bedroom cottage — so close he could touch us with his trunk. No longer do we have to freeze in his presence. There is an unwritten truce — as long as we move quietly and slowly around camp, he pays us no mind. Simbeye, Mwamba, and Kasokola are as taken with Survivor as we are, and often I see them standing quietly at the workshop, watching him feed.

The truce is broken only once. One morning Mark hurries down the path toward the office cottage, his head down. As he steps around the cottage, he looks up to see Survivor's knee only six yards from him. The elephant, caught by surprise, draws up his trunk and flaps his ears, making loud blowing noises as he steps backward. Pivoting around, he runs twenty yards before swinging to face Mark again. Mark resists the urge to flee in the opposite direction and stands quietly. After a few minutes of ear flapping, Survivor calms down and feeds again.

○ ○ ○

The annual inspection of the airplane is due, so Mark has to fly to Johannesburg to have it serviced. Unfortunately, he will be away for more than three weeks. I stay behind to continue our work and to watch Survivor. Occasionally the guys and I see him and his four companions roaming the hills between the airstrip and camp. All of them have become accustomed to us and do not run away — but only Survivor comes into camp.

Elephants can move through the bush as quietly as kittens, but when they feed, they make a noisy racket as they strip leaves from a branch or topple small trees. Whether I'm working at the solar-powered computer, building the fire, or reading, I know where Survivor is by his loud slurps. At night he drifts through the sleeping camp like a large moon shadow. Lying in bed, I am lulled to sleep by the stirring wind, his soft footfalls, and the rustling leaves — the song of Survivor.

One night as he forages in front of the cottage, I cannot sleep, or perhaps do not want to. I get up and ease the door open. The half-moon winks through the marula leaves as Survivor feeds beneath the tree ten yards from where I stand. Inching forward, watching his every move, I step onto the stone veranda and slowly sit on the doorstep. Gracefully he turns to face me, lifting his trunk to take in my scent. He immediately relaxes, lowering his trunk and sniffing loudly for another fruit.

Ten yards from an elephant. Sitting down and looking up at an elephant. He covers the world. Even in this soft light I can see the deep wrinkles and folds in his skin. They look like the craters and valleys of the moon.

Slowly rocking back and forth, he picks up the fruits, sometimes extending his trunk in my direction. Gradually he makes his way around the corner of the cottage, until I am sitting in the moonlight watching his huge backside and his tail. Even that is enough. When at last he disappears into the shadows, I return to bed and sleep.

It is, of course, the marula fruits that keep him coming. In early May thousands of them carpet camp, releasing a sweet scent into the soft air. But by late June most of them have been eaten by Survivor and the Lillian lovebirds. Once the fruits are finished, he will migrate to the scarp mountains. I wonder, in spite of his name, if he will survive another season. Every morning I poke around under the bushes, under the solar panels, in all the hard-to-reach places, pulling the fruits out into the open where he can find them.

Survivor is already coming into camp less often, maybe every other day instead of daily. Only rarely do I see him and the four others feeding on the tall grass and short bushes of the hillsides.

Now the marula fruits in camp are nearly gone. At night I sit at the window watching the moon cast eerie shapes across the grass. But the large moon shadow and the soft song for which I wait come no more.

16

One Tusk

MARK

I am the wind.
I am legend.
I am history.
I come and go. My tracks
are washed away in certain places.
I am the one who wanders, the one
who speaks, the one who watches . . .
the one who teaches, the one who goes . . .
the one who weeps, the one who knows . . .
who knows the wilderness.

— PAULA GUNN ALLEN

○ ○ ○

WHERE THE LUBONGA meets the scarp, One Tusk carefully picks her way down a steep ravine, stepping gingerly over sharp gravel on the path, her massive body swaying rhythmically, almost as though she is on tiptoe. Her single tusk, more than three feet long, seems to touch the side of the stream cut as she looks back at her family. They include Misty, her eighteen-year-old daughter, and Mandy and Marula, two younger adult females. One infant and a three-year-old calf follow closely, watching their footing as they maneuver down the slope.

The matriarch has passed this way many times before, as her ancestors did. Each time she pauses, as she did earlier today, to smell and fondle with her trunk the bones of the recent dead. But now instead of thousands of elephants, only small, isolated groups move silently, nervously, through the dying forests toward the Lubonga River.

The winter sun, dull and bloated from the smoke of dry-season wildfires, sags into the distant hills. One Tusk will take her small family to drink at the river only after dark, when the poachers have camped for the night.

Staccato bursts of gunfire thunder through the canyon. Several bullets slap One Tusk in quick succession. She staggers back, raising her trunk and screaming a warning, eyes white with fear, blood streaming from small holes in her neck and shoulder. She screams again, a pink froth foaming from her mouth. Three more blasts shatter her skull. Sinking to her knees, as though in prayer, she slides in that position all the way to the bottom of the bank. The calves run to their fallen matriarch, wailing in confusion. Their mothers turn to face the gunmen.

One of the shooters steps boldly to the top of the bank in full view of the terrified elephants. Shrieking, ears back, trunks raised, Misty, Mandy, and Marula charge up the slope toward him. More shots ring out. Two puffs of dust explode from Mandy's chest. She screams, sits on her haunches, then rolls back down the hill in a tangle of legs, trunk, and tail. Misty and Marula break off their charge and stampede out of the ravine, the calves huddled close to their flanks. They run for more than a mile, to a meadow below the scarp where there are dense thickets, and a stream from which to drink. Without One Tusk's leadership, they mill about in utter confusion.

The beleaguered elephants press together, turning circles, their trunks raised, sniffing the air. Over and over they entwine their trunks and reach out to touch faces, apparently reassuring themselves that the others are still there, and are all right. The mothers reach down with their trunks, pressing the calf and infant close to their sides, caressing their faces, necks, and shoulders.

After they have calmed themselves, Misty, Marula, and their young walk farther east, away from the point of attack. Then they turn back and spend the night huddled together just a few hundred yards from where One Tusk and Mandy were shot.

The next morning, rumbling loudly and holding their trunks high, their temporal glands streaming, they walk to where One Tusk and Mandy lie sprawled in a great reddish-brown stain made by their body fluids. The faces, feet, tails, and trunks have been hacked off the slain elephants, and they are buried beneath a seething pile of hissing vultures, which have fouled the gray and bloating bodies with white streaks of excrement. Swarms of maggot flies have already begun laying their eggs in the rotting flesh.

Leading the others, hesitating after each step, her trunk raised, flapping her ears, Misty cautiously approaches the mutilated corpse that just hours ago was One Tusk. She and the others assemble around it, their trunks extended, smelling every inch. Then Misty nudges it with her front foot and tusks. The others join in, as if willing their slain matriarch to get up and live again. After a long while Misty walks to the severed trunk, picks it up with her own, holds it for a moment, and then puts it down, her cheeks wet from her weeping temporal glands.

After smelling and fondling their dead for nearly two hours, Misty and Marula begin ripping up tufts of grass, breaking twigs from trees, and scuffing up piles of gravel with their feet. The younger elephants join in as they cover the corpses with this debris. The burial takes the rest of the morning, and when they are finished, the elephants stand quietly, their trunks hanging down for several minutes. Then Marula leads them away. Misty returns to her slain mother, puts her trunk on her back, and stands for nearly two minutes. Finally she turns to follow the others.

She catches up to the little group and assumes the lead. Walking at a determined pace, they all head northwest toward the tall peak of Molombwe Hill, which is set behind the chain of hills that forms the leading edge of the scarp. Below it is Elephant's Playground, where they last saw Long Ear and her family unit. Rumbling constantly, temporal glands streaming, they follow the paths used by their relatives as they cross the hills and vales along the foot of the Muchinga. Often they stop to listen, and to smell, circling with their trunks raised high, testing the breeze. The elephants have hardly fed for two days, and the two youngsters are especially hungry and tired.

On the morning of the third day Misty, Marula, and the others are nearing Elephant's Playground when they hear a rumble ahead. Running along the slope at the edge of the swale, they see Long Ear's group watching them, trunks raised. Misty runs faster, as Long Ear and her two young daughters rush to meet them. The trumpeting, rumbling, and clacking together of their tusks echo to the hills as the two groups entwine in greeting. Pushing together, milling in a tight compaction of gray bodies, over and over they touch one another's faces with their trunks. Long Ear keeps looking east, as though expecting One Tusk and Mandy to appear. Misty walks into Long Ear's side and stands there, her face buried in the loose and wrinkled skin.

Eventually the elephants calm down, but they continue rumbling softly and touching one another. Both groups have lost their matriarch — and with her, access to the immense wisdom acquired from her ancestors and from her decades of roaming the valley. Young, inexperienced, relentlessly pursued, these orphans of the poaching war will stay together, raising their young as best they can. They move off now, deeper into the hills, touching often.

○ ○ ○

Harassing the poachers with the plane is no longer working. I had flown over One Tusk and her family just an hour before she and Mandy were killed. The poachers certainly saw the plane, but it didn't frighten them anymore. They have figured out that I can't land except on an airstrip or a sandbar. The next morning, drawn by smoke from a fire the killers set on their way out of the park, I fly again and find the dead One Tusk and Mandy, their family milling around them.

Flying a patrol along the Mwaleshi four days later, I see two elephants grazing near the river. On my way back to camp an hour and a half later, I discover their tuskless carcasses. Landing along the river, I hike to the spot, where I record their age and sex and look for any evidence — a shirt, a boot track, rifle cartridges, a piece of camping gear — that might lead us to the poachers. Then, afraid they may still be in the area and attack the plane, I run back and take off for camp.

I am two hours overdue by the time I get back to Marula-Puku. Delia meets me at the workshop, her face pale with worry. "Mark, where have you been? I was just about to call out a search."

"I've been out counting dead elephants, where else!" Slamming the door of the truck, I stomp off to the kitchen for a cup of black coffee. For some time I have been living out of my coffee cup, drinking a brew so strong it is like a thin syrup. The caffeine gives me the kick and the courage to do what I have to do, but increasingly it is running my brain and my mouth. My fuse is very short.

Poachers have invaded large areas of the park, including the sanctuary around our camp, which until now I have been able to defend with the airplane. The region has become a war zone. From the air one morning I discover six dead elephants, faces chopped off, tusks removed, on the Lubonga near its confluence with Mwaleshi. Two days later a freshly set bush fire leads me to another two carcasses on the Lufwashi near Chinchendu Hill. The next day three more are slaughtered along the Mwaleshi River at the north side of Chinchendu. And then three more north of Marula-Puku — killed by Patrick Mubuka, the officer in charge of the Nsansamina game scout camp.

I am flying night and day, spotting poachers, diving on them with the plane, and airlifting scouts when they will come. But the killing is totally out of control and escalating. Delia and I cannot go on like this for much longer, and neither can the elephants. But we have at least solved a mystery: we have found the fabled elephant graveyard. It is Zambia.

On long night flights, droning along in the darkness while searching out poachers' fires, I find myself staring into the plane's black windscreen, the faint red glow from the instruments reflecting back at me, trying to figure out why the poaching has so suddenly escalated. Even though it is not as bad as it was before the ivory ban was enacted, it has exploded recently and I don't understand why.

One morning a few weeks after the killing of One Tusk and Mandy, I am standing next to our Mog at the Mpika marketplace. Local people are coming and going to the cubicles and stands that sell potatoes, mealie-meal, cabbages, dried fish, and black-market cooking oil, sugar, and tobacco. Kasokola is inside doing the buying while I guard the truck. I feel a little uneasy, as though every poacher in the district is watching me. After about twenty minutes a Zambian man dressed in light gray slacks, an argyle knit shirt, leather shoes, and sunglasses slopes toward me across the dry and dusty ground.

"Mapalanye," I greet him in Chibemba.

"Good morning. How are you?" He is slightly unsteady and smells strongly of beer.

He studies the Frankfurt Zoological Society logo and the North Luangwa Conservation Project lettering on the side of the Mog. Aloud he misreads, " 'North Luangwa Construction Project.' So you work in construction. Where?"

"Down in the valley." I wave east, toward Luangwa. "I'm in road construction."

"I see." Pause. "You want to buy something, maybe?"

"Depends what you're selling."

"Aaaanything! Anything you want." He holds out his arms. "You want ivories, I have ivories; you want lion skins, I got lion skins; elephant foots and tails; zebras, leopards, anything." He leans close to me, lowering his voice as some women come by selling a basketful of dried fish. "I even got rhino horns. You interested?"

"Well, I don't know. I'd have to see the goods first. Where are you getting all this stuff?"

"I know people with a safari company. My merchandise mostly comes from Fulaza Village, near North Luangwa. They organize the hunters that side, some from Mpika, some from Fulaza, then transport the ivory and skins to Mpika."

We step aside as Kasokola and another man lug a bag of beans by its ears to the back of the truck and throw it in. "How much do you have to pay a hunter to shoot an elephant?"

"For now, not so much. Only about a thousand kwachas." That's a little over ten dollars — for an elephant.

He tells me that a good hunter can earn as much as fifty thousand kwachas in three weeks in the bush, and up to half a million in a year. The illegal ivory is transported to Lusaka in army trucks or in civilian vehicles, hidden in spare tires, bags of mealie-meal, drums, or buried at the bottom of heavy loads. In Lusaka the ivory takes various routes out of the country. Some of the tusks are cut up in dozens of illegal "chop shops" and smuggled in small pieces to Swaziland aboard Swazi Airlines. Or a government contact is paid to launder it with official documentation, and it is shipped with legal ivory through Botswana and Zimbabwe to South Africa. From there some of it is carved and sold as crafts; the rest is marketed to dealers in China, North Korea, and other non-African countries that refuse to observe the ban on trading ivory.

"This ban is troublesome," the dealer complains. "For now it has made ivory too cheap. We survive by selling to dealers in countries still trading." He refers, of course, to South Africa, Zimbabwe, Botswana, Mozambique, Malawi, Angola, and Zambia, which refuse to observe the moratorium. "But we hope this will not last. Countries will vote again soon. So we are shooting elephants and burying ivories, waiting for America, Europe, and Japan to refuse this foolish ban." He leans against the Mog, his hands in his pockets.

"What if all countries stop trading ivory?" I ask.

"Ah, but then there will be no market at all and my business will be finished. I will have to go farming. Come, Big Man. Let us do some business. What you want and how much?"

"Right. Let's see some of your goods." Gary Simutendu spells his name for me and tells me how to get to his house. I promise to stop by in a day or two. Instead, I head straight for Bornface Mulenga, the warden. He tells me Simutendu is no longer dealing, that I should just forget what he said. Instead, I fly to Lusaka to talk to Paul Russell and Norbert Mumba at the Anticorruption Commission. Months later they will break up several dozen illegal ivory-processing factories in Lusaka and indict a Chinese diplomat and three senior administrative officers in the Department of National Parks for smuggling ivory to Swaziland and China.

Simutendu, drunk as he was, told me all I need to know about how to save the elephants of Luangwa: it will be impossible without a total, long-term, worldwide ban on trading ivory and other elephant parts. We will do everything we can to convince Zambia and other nations to join the ban, but until they do it will be up to us to get rid of poachers like Chikilinti.

One of our newly recruited agents is an ex-poacher who has hunted with Chikilinti many times. Several days after my encounter with Gary Simutendu, we set up this informant with money for beer, four rounds of shotgun ammunition, and the story that he has been jumped by scouts while on his way into the park to poach. We send him to Mpika. Finding Chikilinti at a bar in Tazara, he buys him beer after beer until he is drunk. Then he slips away to the warden's office, asking that he send scouts to arrest the poacher. Two scouts hurry to Chikilinti — and warn him that he is about to be apprehended. Immediately he melts into the crowded street, and we have lost our best chance at nailing the godfather of all poachers.

○ ○ ○

Perched in our canvas chairs high above the murmuring Lubonga, we watch the thunderheads tumbling and growling in the bruised sky above the stony rubble of the riverbed. The butter-colored light of the setting sun comes and goes between the clouds, bringing out the brilliant green of the young grasses springing up in the sandbars along the floodplain. The puku are sprinkled like flakes of red cinnamon through the grasses, and now and then a flock of snow-white egrets or a yellow-billed stork soars past, flowing with the river course.

The color seeps from the sky, and dusk settles over the riverbed community. A flock of guinea fowl rails plaintively to our right; a fish jumps in the pool below our feet, and the puku and waterbuck take tentative steps toward the river for a drink. Pennant-winged nightjars, wispy phantoms of the twilight, trill as they sail above and around us, so close that their wings almost touch our faces. The darkness deepens, and the soft forms of the antelope slowly dissolve into the gray stones across the water.

An elephant's life is worth about ten dollars.

We can talk of nothing else. So mostly we don't talk. There is a time to quit, and this is it. We must give up; giving up is survival. Delia leans her head back, looking up at the sky, and when she speaks her voice is far away and very tired. "I can't remember when we last looked for shooting stars. Let's go home for a rest," she pleads. And I agree, it's time to get away for a while.

Several days later, leaving the guys in charge of Marula-Puku, we drive to Lusaka. Two hours before our flight to the States, we get a radio message from Marula-Puku: gunshots have been heard all around. Poachers are killing elephants within a few hundred yards of camp. The director of National Parks agrees to send paramilitary scouts to protect the camp while we are away.

In Atlanta, only two weeks after arriving, I take an urgent phone call from Marie Hill in Mpika. Late last night, she tells me, the home of another of our informants was raked with AK fire; some nights before that, still others were beaten; and Mathews Phiri, a trusted scout whom we brought from Livingstone in southern Zambia to work undercover in Mpika, is sick in the hospital after being poisoned. We tell Marie to have Musakanya call in all the undercover agents until we get back.

We needed to get away, but it seems eight thousand miles is not far enough.

A few days later Delia and I are in a lounge at Atlanta's Hartfield Airport, waiting for a flight to Charlottesville, Virginia. Returning to our table with her drink, Delia staggers and clutches her chest. Before I can jump up to help her she collapses into her chair, spilling her drink over the table, her face twisted in pain, her breathing ragged and shallow. I run from the lounge to the boarding gate nearby, and the attendants call for the airport's paramedic team. Within two minutes they are setting up a portable electrocardiogram machine in the lounge and stabilizing Delia so that we can get her to a specialist.

In the cardiologist's office the doctor warns her: "Your body is trying to tell you something. I can prescribe some drugs — beta blockers — but the main thing is that you're going to have to change your lifestyle in order to minimize stress." Delia looks out the window and laughs.

17
The Eye of the Storm

MARK

The storm clouds come rolling in, and night is down upon us with a poison wind . . . We have all but lost.

— JIM BARNES

○ ○ ○

"ENCOUNTERED A GROUP of one hundred plus poachers moving down Mwaleshi. Group had twelve weapons including automatic military rifles. Surrounded our porters, but released them later. Appealed to Chanjuzi [scouts] for help but they were incapable of raising more than one weapon with four rounds and no mealie-meal. Please assist with antipoaching. As Mulandashi River now unsafe for walks must fly with you to find alternative areas so won't have to cancel rest of safari season . . ."

The radio crackles with this urgent telex message from Iain MacDonald. Months earlier he set up a reed and thatch camp on a lagoon near the Mulandashi-Luangwa confluence and organized photographic walking safaris, the first full-time tour operation in North Luangwa. We are anxious for him to succeed.

After three weeks in the United States we are back at Marula-Puku. In spite of our talk about quitting, we have never seriously considered it. We cannot abandon the park and its elephants. The problem with Delia's heart is a faulty valve, its performance made more inefficient by stress; but as long as poachers are attacking the park and game scouts refuse to work, our lives will never be peaceful. So we have come back armed with beta blockers and a new determination.

At the airstrip on the night of Iain's message, Kasokola, two guards, and I set out our milk-tin flare pots. We have just lit the last one when a big thunderhead begins grumbling southwest off the airstrip, between us and Chinchendu Hill. Kasokola and I wait in the plane for forty-five minutes, hoping the storm will move on, but it just sits there. After another fifteen minutes, the thunder and lightning start to fade and I decide to take off.

I taxi to the west end of the strip, run my power checks, take a last look at the sky — and decide to wait again. I can see the black cancroid mass of a broader storm system moving in with the thunderhead. Although the sky to the north is generally clear, I don't want to take off and then not be able to see the horizon properly, especially if the storm moves north again. My plane's vacuum pump is broken, so the artificial horizon and gyrocompass are useless. My radar altimeter, which would give my exact height above ground, doesn't work either; and with the changing barometric pressure associated with the storm, my pressure altimeter will be very unreliable. Some days ago I managed at last to fix my airspeed indicator: Cedric, a crafty mouse who was living in the plane, had chewed through the line from the Pitot head to the pressure canister under the instrument panel.

It is still almost pitch black, but I think I see dawn growing under the sleepy eyelid of the eastern sky. "Do you see it, Kasokola?" Yes, he thinks he does. I'm going for it. If we wait any longer we will have a hard time spotting Chikilinti's fires after daybreak. For this is Chikilinti, all right; I know by now that any poaching group this large will have been organized by him.

Almost as soon as Zulu Sierra's wheels leave the ground, I'm sure I have made a mistake. There is no sign of dawn and I can barely make out the horizon to the east. All other corners of the sky are pitch black. If the storm envelops us, I will be forced to fly on instruments, and the ones I need most are not working. I am flying out of the realm of reasonable risk and into the realm of stupidity. As we pass over camp I turn the plane around, intending to get back on the ground as quickly as possible. The new beacon beams at the east end of the strip, but the west end has already been swallowed up by dark clouds and heavy rain. The downpour has drowned six of the nine flares, leaving the south side of the runway in total darkness and only three flares and the beacon on the north side.

"Mark, are you there?" Delia is calling over the radio. "It's really blowing hard down here. Do you read me?"

"Roger, Boo, it looks a little nasty to the south, so I'm coming down right now. Over."

But for some reason Delia cannot hear my transmission. "Mark! Do you read me? *Do you read me, Mark?*"

"Roger, I am coming down right away."

"Mark, I repeat, there's a bad storm moving in. *Do you read me?*"

"No time to talk now, love. I'll see you when I get down."

"Mark, I cannot read you. Are you okay? Answer me, please . . . Oh God . . ."

A giant fist of wind slams into the plane, flipping it on its right side. Rolling the controls to the left, I try to steady it. Maybe I should buzz camp, to let Delia know I haven't gone down. No time. Two, maybe three, minutes is all I have to get back on the ground before the entire strip is buried in cloud and rain. I shove the control wheel forward, diving toward the runway. At the same time I reach behind my head to turn up the red instrument panel light so I can see the altimeter unwind. Whatever else, I must not go below 2300 hundred feet. If I do, we're dead; for I have previously calculated the airstrip's elevation at 2296 — where soft sky turns to hard ground.

Descending through 2900 feet, I turn on my landing light. But the rain pitches the beam back at my face, a white sheet that totally blinds me. I quickly switch off the light and steepen my dive for the friendly, mesmerizing beacon, pulsing like a firefly at the end of the strip.

Then the spluttering flares and the beacon are gone. The storm is shouldering its way up the airstrip toward me. Pulling the nose of the plane up a bit, I slow our rate of descent while trying to find the beacon or flare-path. I glance at my altimeter again. Its white needle is nearly touching 2300! My God, we're almost on the ground! But where is it? I can't see a thing.

Rain and hail hammer the fuselage like buckshot, and my windshield is black. I fumble for the landing light switch. Suddenly the beacon reappears out of a paunch of cloud, beaming cheerily atop its twelve-foot pole — in front of my right wing. I throw the control wheel over, lifting the wing, and pull it back to bring us out of the dive. With my finger I stab the switch. The powerful beam of light cuts through the darkness.

And there is a tree . . . right in front of me . . . not fifty yards away. We are below its crown, within ten feet of the ground. Without a lighted flare path I have misjudged not only our height but also our alignment with the airstrip. We are landing crabwise at about a thirty-degree angle to the strip. Traveling at a speed of seventy knots, in exactly 1.27 seconds we are going to hit the tree.

I ease the controls back and shove the throttle forward. The engine roars and the plane surges, as if someone has booted her in the backside saying, "Come on, baby; now is the time to show us you can fly." She points her nose bravely at the storm, and as she claws her way up, her landing light lifts. The tree disappears from view.

I grit my teeth, listening to the tearing sound as some part of the plane rips through the tree. But we are still flying. Later I will find shrubbery caught in the left main wheel, and green stains on the undercarriage.

Now I can see nothing, and Zulu Sierra is bobbing and jerking. Wrestling with the control wheel, I watch the turn and slip indicator, trying to keep its miniature wings level so that we won't spin out and crash. This instrument was never meant for flying blind, but it's all I've got. "Keep climbing! And don't overcontrol! Get away from the ground!" my mind shouts at me.

The racket of the rain drumming on the skin of the plane becomes a dull roar. Through the windows all I can see is the blackest black I've ever seen: no flares, no beacons, no moon or stars. But minutes earlier the sky to the north was clear. Careful not to overcontrol and spin out, I push right rudder, ease on a little bank, and begin a very gradual northward turn from my southwest heading.

For several minutes I fly through air like lumpy ink, feeling my way out of the black belly of the storm. Finally I see a faint amber glow in the windshield — the beacon on the airstrip. Damn! I'm diving into the ground again! No . . . I force myself to believe my altimeter. It shows 4000 feet and climbing. Anyway, flying north, the light should be behind us. Looking around, I see the beacon through the right rear window. It is reflecting in the windshield. We have flown out of the storm. A string of yellow flares is growing along each side of the airstrip. The guys, God bless them, are busy trying to get us home.

I circle in the clear air for several minutes while the storm drenches the runway and moves on. Then I turn back and land on the soggy strip, the plane's main wheels spraying the underside of its wings with mud and water. I taxi Zulu Sierra to her boma, switch off, and slide from my seat. As the guys tie her down and pick up the flares, I stand alone on the brow of the hill, sucking in the sweet, wet air, listening to the last grumbles of the dying storm. I've had enough; finding Chikilinti can wait for better weather. Before heading down to camp, I give each of the guards a pat on the back and a fat bonus.

Delia is sitting on the bed of our stone and thatch cottage, crying in the dark. I switch on the solar light and try to hold her. But she pushes me away.

"Mark, I thought you were dead! I actually thought you were dead! There were no trucks here and my radio wasn't working, so there was nothing I could do about it. And this happens night after night! Do you know how that feels? Do you care?"

Turning to the window, I part the curtains and watch the heavy clouds turn silver above the rising sun. "I'm sorry, Boo. I just don't know what else to do. You know my flying is the only thing standing between the poachers and the elephants."

"Yes, but I'm not sure this is worth dying for anymore. If your dying would change anything, then maybe it would be. But it won't. And I don't want you to die for nothing! I want to stop the poaching as much as you do, but you've crossed over the line, and I can't go on like this. I just can't. I know you can't change; you're doing what you believe is right, and I respect you for that. You'll keep after the poachers until you either drive them out or fly into the ground trying. But I cannot sit here night after night, day after day, waiting to see if you make it back, knowing that someday you won't, waiting for that moment."

I look at Delia sitting on our bed, her face swollen from crying, her eyes shut tight. Taking her in my arms again, I try to squeeze the poison out of her. But there is this thing between us now, this difference in how much risk we should take to rid the valley of poachers. I can no longer get as close to her. She is slipping away from me.

"And so, I am leaving," she says, shoving me off again. And I am suddenly more afraid than I was of the storm.

"Look, Boo, we can work this out . . . ," I try again.

"No," she interrupts. "I'm going to the Luangwa River to build a little camp of my own, a place where I can radio track Bouncer and his pride; do something more constructive than sit around waiting for you to kill yourself."

"That's fine," I say firmly. "But it's a long way from here to the Luangwa. Your portable radio won't reach camp from there, and you won't have anyone to drive you out if something goes wrong. What happens if poachers attack your camp? Or if you are bitten by a snake, get malaria, or sleeping sickness? There won't be anyone to treat you or get you out."

"Don't talk to me about risks! It won't be half as risky as flying through treetops at night with people shooting at you, or taking off in a thunderstorm without any instruments."

"Okay, I know, but those are necessary and . . ."

"So are the risks I'll be taking!" she counters. "I have to find a life of my own, so that if something happens to you I'll have some reason for living. Can you understand that?"

Looking at her face, drawn and haggard under the harsh glare from the light over the bed, I can see her aging before my eyes. I cannot remember the last time we laughed, really laughed, together.

"I understand, Boo. Do it if you have to." I have to let her go now, or lose her forever.

The next morning I take off again, to fly a patrol over the northern sector of the park. When I get back to camp, one of our trucks is gone and the kitchen and the office are closed up. Delia has already packed and gone. As I head down the footpath through camp, Marula-Puku seems hollow, empty of spirit, deserted. That night as I get into bed, I discover her note propped against my pillow.

> Dear Mark,
> I love you. Maybe if we survive this, we can start over.
> Love, Delia

The next morning I'm off on a three-hour flight to Lusaka, to have our airplane inspected. Halfway through the journey a strange sickness comes over me: I am feverish; my arms are suddenly as heavy as lead; and my heart is pounding. I'm not fit to fly and should land, but there is no serviceable airstrip much closer than Lusaka. I take Zulu Sierra down to a thousand feet above ground, so that I can make a quick forced landing if I begin to black out.

Dizzy, my vision blurry, I somehow make it to Lusaka, where I rest at a friend's home for more than two weeks. Every time I decide to fly back to camp, I change my mind because I am too ill.

One morning Musakanya shows up with an urgent message: Chikilinti, Simu Chimba, Mpundu Katongo, and some others have headed into the park for poaching. But this time their targets are not elephants and buffalo: they intend killing Delia and me. Not knowing whom in Mpika to trust with this information, Musakanya has hopped the mail bus to Lusaka to deliver his message in person.

The director of National Parks immediately orders trusted scouts from the Southern Province to Mpika and into the park to secure our camp. Musakanya will go back with them. But it will take two days before they can get there. Meanwhile, Delia is on her own at the river all the way across the park. Even after they arrive at Marula-Puku the scouts would not be likely to go to her, and anyway there will not be enough of them to cover camp and the airstrip and protect her. To find Delia the poachers have only to follow her truck's spoor through the bush to her camp. She will be an easy and satisfying target for them.

Still dizzy and weak, I take off in the plane headed for camp. I feel okay until about an hour and a half into the flight, a little more than halfway there. Then my head begins spinning, my vision blurs, and sweat breaks out on my forehead. I force myself to relax, closing my eyes for seconds at a time, and I just keep flying. Over and over I imagine Delia camped alone on the Luangwa, unaware that poachers may be coming to kill her. For the first time I can understand the fear she has lived with, watching me fly off to engage the same poachers over and over.

Nearly three hours after takeoff I fly low over Marula-Puku. Banking over the airstrip I notice a foxhole that the scouts must have dug near my avgas dump. Neither Delia nor her truck are in sight. I firewall the plane's throttle to get full power and head for the Luangwa to find her camp. Fifteen minutes later the river's broad sandbars and pools of hippos flash under the plane. Rolling steeply to my left, I drop between the rows of tall trees that line its bank and fly upstream just above the water. She must be here somewhere . . . Damn her for going off on her own at a time like this!

I spot her khaki tent with its brown flysheet, tucked under a grove of ebony trees on a tall bank above the river. But there is no truck in sight, and no Delia.

"Brown Hyena, Brown Hyena, this is Sand Panther," I call over the radio, using our call signs from the Kalahari. "Do you read me, Boo?" Flying back and forth over her camp, I call again and again. But she doesn't answer. I hope she has her radio.

I try the radio again: "Delia, if you can hear me, listen carefully. Poachers have come into the park to kill us. Stay at your camp and I will be there later tonight." With little daylight left, my heart heavy with worry, I follow her truck's spoor toward Marula-Puku, hoping to spot her somewhere along the way.

A minute later my radio crackles to life. "Sand Panther, this is Brown Hyena. Mark, is that you? I've been away from camp doing some survey work. Over."

"Roger, love. Now listen . . ." And I tell her of the poachers and my plan to drive out tonight to escort her back to Marula-Puku.

"Negative. There's more work to do here. I have my pistol, five rounds of ammunition and I have a game guard with me. I don't need you to come rescue me. See you at Marula-Puku on the weekend." Nothing I say changes her mind, so I head for Marula-

Puku. Later we will learn from Mpundu Katongo and Bernard Mutondo themselves that they, Chikilinti, and Simu Chimba left Mwamfushi on foot one night, each armed with an AK-47. Three days later, at four in the afternoon, they crossed the truck track two miles west of Marula-Puku. They walked a little farther, then camped for the night on a small stream between two hills.

At sunrise the next morning they made their way through the bush and up the back side of the hill above camp. With Chikilinti in the lead, they crawled to the edge of the bank and peered down on the stone cottages. The cottage on their right, where the trucks were parked, was closest to them.

They watched me walk along a footpath and into a building near a campfire. For the next fifteen minutes they could hear me talking on the radio. Then they saw me come out and begin walking toward the building where the trucks were parked.

The four men crawled along the steep bank until they came to a stream cut, then scrambled down to the cover of the tall grass below. From there they watched as I walked into the workshop with three of our men. They crawled forward through the grass until they were within seventy-five yards of the trucks. There they waited, lying side by side in prone shooting positions, fingers on their triggers.

When I stepped from the building, they quickly sighted along their weapons at me. "Wait!" whispered Chikilinti. A game scout with a rifle slung over his shoulder was talking to me, then another stepped into view. Raising his head and leaning slightly to the right so he could see past the trucks, Chikilinti saw five more game scouts sitting around a campfire. Their berets and AKs told him they were special paramilitary scouts, not his game-guard friends from Mpika and Kanona. Their presence was totally unexpected.

I climbed into the Land Cruiser and drove away from the cottages toward the hill where the plane was kept. The poachers backed away from the edge of the camp and quickly retreated up the bank. They could not risk attacking with the scouts present. Under cover of the tall grass and bushes, they ran for the airstrip.

The poachers crossed a stream, then climbed through mopane scrub to the crest of the next ridge. From the peak of a termite mound fifty yards off the runway, Chikilinti could see me and our two guards fueling the plane. A rifle was leaning against the tail of the plane and I had a pistol in a holster on my hip. The Bembas were unarmed. Chikilinti and his men crawled through the tall grass to a point directly across the airstrip from the plane and only sixty yards from it. Flattening himself to the ground, he pointed at something. Simu Chimba wriggled up beside his leader and looked along his finger. Just twenty yards behind the plane, a head covered with branches peered out of a hole in the ground near a stack of avgas drums. The stubby muzzle of an AK was visible over the small mound of dirt. Looking carefully, they discovered several other scouts dug in around the strip and three more walking out of the guard house toward me.

Withdrawing through the scrub brush, the poachers turned and hiked as fast as they could back to Mwamfushi, pausing only briefly at sandy river crossings or dusty game trails to brush out their tracks with small mopane branches, in case they were being followed. Later, in hiding near the village, they sipped beer from a good mash and made plans to attack the bwana's camp after the game guards had gone back to their posts.

18
Nyama Zamara

DELIA

> I make all my rounds
> without leaving a trace
> and sit by the water
> the breeze in my face;
> The future is distant
> yet triumph is near
> I notice the sounds
> only spirits can hear.
>
> — SETH RICHARDSON

○ ○ ○

I MAKE MY OWN CAMP on the Luangwa River; the Bembas call it Delia Camp. It is tucked in a *Combretum* thicket under the dark, embracing arms of an ebony tree, overlooking a broad bend in the river. So many massive trees line the torn riverbank — eroded during the rains by raging floods — that my small grass hut and tent are completely hidden. A sprawling white beach fifty yards wide reaches toward the water. Crooked snags and the remains of entire trees — swept away by the torrential rains — lie like fallen monuments in the now-forgiving current, which laps gently at hippo ears.

This land is wild land. Deep ravines, jagged tributaries, and lush oxbows are lost in green forests draped with intertwining vines. Powerful roots of the strangling figs smother towering trees. This is not the open savanna I have seen; it is what I thought Africa was all along.

It has been no easy task to reach this spot. Days of breaking trail and mending tires have brought me once again to a rugged paradise. I have come to see if what we are fighting for still exists; have we become so immersed in the battle that we do not realize it is already lost? I have come to see if Africa is still here.

It is. Hundreds of hippos — the river lords — laze, yawn, and sleep just beyond my beach. Puku, warthogs, and impalas graze on the far shore. On one walk I see zebras, kudu, waterbucks, buffalo, and eland. One morning a large male lion walks into my camp, and the next day a leopard saunters along the same path. I can hear baboons somewhere behind me, scampering and foraging their way through the forest. And a Goliath heron glides by on slow, silver wings.

With the help of the Bembas I build a small grass hut on the riverbank, overlooking the beach. It is a frame of deadwood logs tied together with strips of bark and covered with a slanting thatch roof. One end is enclosed with neat grass walls, where I hang baskets, pots, and pans. The tin trunks of supplies are stacked against the walls, and grass mats cover the ground. The other end is open like a veranda with a sweeping view of the river. Here I have my table and chair for working and eating. I always return from a hike with a bird feather, porcupine quill, or snail shell, which I stick into the grass walls until my little hut looks more like the nest of a bower bird than a house.

Hippo paths go around both sides of my tent. At first this seems like a good idea — to be close to where the hippos walk. But I have to stretch the guy ropes across their paths, and when I lie down to sleep on my mat, I worry about what would happen if a hippo tripped over the rope. Glad that Mark is not here to laugh at me, I wriggle out of my sleeping bag and remove the ropes. I would rather risk the collapse of the tent from an unlikely windstorm than a ton of mad hippo stumbling over the cord.

My friend the moon is here, casting his warm illumination on the river bends. With ease I watch the hippos at night as they leave the river and wander along the beaches toward the grasslands and lagoons. Although some males have territories along the river and forage there every night, none of the hippos — including the territorial males — use the same paths every night. In fact, they do not sleep in the same part of the river by day.

Before sunrise one morning, when the river and banks are shrouded in fog, I watch an enormous female hippo waddle across the beach with her tiny calf. When their young are born, females separate from the group and tend their infants in secluded reed beds for several months. This female appears to be returning to her group with her youngster, which bobbles around the beach like a rubber toy. But when they reach the water's edge, the baby halts. The mother looks at the calf and I can almost hear her saying, "There's something I forgot to tell you. We don't live on the beach; we live in the water."

Curious to see how a baby hippo gets into the river for the first time, I creep through the grass to get a closer look. The mother eases into the current, until her legs are half submerged, then looks back at her young. He follows, but is soon completely under water except for his head. The mother lies in the shallow water with the baby bobbing next to her. Later, when the sun is hotter, the mother pulls herself into the deeper current, and her offspring floats with his head resting upon her titanic nose.

While walking one cool July morning only a few days after setting up my camp, I discover a lagoon that stretches into a maze of clear waterways, so thick with life that the surface seems to breathe. Almost every inch of the still water is covered with bright green lilies and "Nile lettuce." The lagoon is only a half-mile from camp, but so well hidden in the forest that I do not see it until I am twenty yards away. If I had been more clever, though, I would have known it was here by watching the ducks and geese fly over my camp every morning in this direction. After they have roosted all night in the cold air, their bellies are nearly empty and they waste no time flying directly to the pools, where a buffet breakfast floats on gentle waves. In the evening — their bellies full — they fly back to their roosts on a more leisurely course, following the river bends, as though taking the scenic route home.

Stepping silently through the undergrowth, I walk almost every day to the lagoon and am never disappointed. Crocodiles slither from the banks into the emerald shallows, where a few hippos lift lily-covered snouts to peer at me. Hundreds of ducks, geese, storks, plovers, herons, eagles, coots, owls, lily-trotters, and hornbills wade, waddle, feed, and call in a natural aviary. Nile monitor lizards — more than five feet long — splash into the water and take refuge under the weeds. Puku, waterbuck, impalas, and buffalo nibble succulent morsels in the sunken glades interlacing the lagoon. Once I come so close to a female bushbuck and her fawn that I can see the sunset in her eyes.

This is not a swamp, oozing with decomposing matter; the water is as clear as a glacial lake — except, of course, where a thousand webbed feet have stirred up the bottom. The morning grows tall and hot, and the surrounding mopane forests are dry. I want to sidle up to the lagoon's edge, put my toes into the coolness, and slide into the pure water. I imagine that my hair would drift among the lilies and that all my troubles would dissolve. But the jagged ridge of a crocodile's tail glides slowly back and forth, just below the lily pads, reminding me that this is not my lagoon. Still, I cannot resist tiptoeing a bit closer and leaning over to touch the water. Stiff-necked and poised to spring, I must look like an impala approaching cautiously to drink. Yet I am held back from the peace and comfort of the lagoon by a strong fear; it is not my reflection that I see in the water, but the reflection of Africa beyond me.

The lagoon has no name. In fact, I cannot find it on my twenty-year-old map, so perhaps it is only recently born of the river. I ask Kasokola and Mwamba, who are with me, to help me think of a beautiful African name for it. After a few days they suggest "Nyama Zamara." Liking the sound of the phrase, I ask where it comes from and what it means.

"It is in the language of the Senga tribe from Malawi," Kasokola tells me. "It means, 'The game is finished.' "

I am taken aback. "But that is a horrible name for such a beautiful lagoon."

"It does not mean that the game is finished in this place," Kasokola explains. "But once a poacher was caught here, and on his clothes he had written the words, 'Nyama Zamara,' so that is what the lagoon must be called."

Reluctantly I accept the name, but add, "Please, you must help me make sure that the wildlife is never finished here. We must make this pledge." And they agree.

For despite the abundance of wildlife, poaching is a serious problem here, as elsewhere in the park. We find twisted wire snares on the game trails just outside camp, and a tree blind poised over the lagoon, where a sniper must have taken his pick of the gentle creatures who came to drink. One of the reasons I have come is to establish a game guard camp, the first inside the national park.

Of course, we could have sent the game guards on their own, or with our staff, to set up a post here. The main reason I am here is that at least for now, I can no longer live with Mark in base camp, which has become the command center for antipoaching operations. Hordes of green-clad game guards file through on their way to forced patrols. Mark flies them to remote airstrips, packs them off toward poachers' camps, drops supplies to them from the air — yet only rarely do they return with poachers. The last time he supplied them from the air, risking his life as he flew right over the treetops, it turned out that all they wanted were cigarettes. Over and over he puts himself in extreme danger for these men, but it is obvious that they are not going to do their jobs. I beg him to try something different — for example, hiring carriers to supply the game guards, or even training our own scouts. He believes strongly, though, that it is the game guards who must ultimately protect the park, so we must do whatever it takes to get them working.

When Mark flies dangerous night missions — in and out of storms — searching for poachers' campfires, I am the one responsible for organizing an air search if he does not return. Still, when I ask him when he expects to be back, already racked with stress he snaps that he has no idea. To make things worse, the radio is very unreliable. Sometimes I can hear him relay his position, then suddenly, as he is talking, the radio goes dead. Pacing back and forth under the marula trees in the middle of the night, I don't know whether he has crashed or not, until I hear the drone of the plane sometimes hours later. To get away from this madness, I stay busy with the village work and the education programs. But it is not enough, and finally I decide to set up my own camp to protect this one corner of the wilderness.

I know that our strong love is somewhere just below the surface, but I also know that love cannot survive unless it can grow. I can't afford to let myself feel too much for Mark, for tomorrow he may be dead. We have to find a way to face this struggle together, or we may come out apart on the other side — if we come out at all.

The game guards' field camp is almost a mile north of my camp. Since they will not have to walk all the way from Mano into the park, I hope they will patrol more often. They are supposed to use their tent and food stores as a base from which to conduct four- or five-day antipoaching patrols throughout the area. But whenever I drop by, I find them lounging around the camp. I give them pep talks and cigarettes; there is no improvement.

If I wake up early enough, at about five o'clock, and look out of the tent window, I can see the hippos strolling across the beach on their way back to the river. If I sleep too late, all I see are ears and noses in the current. It has become a game with me. As soon as I open my eyes, I scramble out of my sleeping bag, unzip the tent door, and count the hippos.

One morning I hear thumping on the beach as an animal runs across the sand. Hurriedly I step out of the door and find myself face to face with a lioness. She has loped up the hippo path and stands only five yards from me. Sleek and golden, she twitches her tail ever so slightly and looks me over. Then she looks back at the beach, where two other lionesses and four cubs saunter toward us. Without even a glance at me, the others walk up the hippo path past my tent and into the mopane forest.

Pulling on my clothes, I rush to the tent where Mwamba, Kasokola, and a game guard are sleeping. Calling softly, I ask them to come quickly to follow the lions.

Walking along the hippo path, we soon catch up and trail the lions, staying about one hundred fifty yards behind. The females move purposefully, as though they know exactly where they are going; the cubs roll and tumble behind their mothers, playing chase through the grass. Before we reach the edge of the trees, the females stop and look ahead. Standing in a small grassy clearing is a large male lion with a full golden mane. As I look through my binoculars I see that he wears a radio collar; it is Bouncer. It has been more than a year since we've seen him. Because of the poaching war, we haven't been able to study the lions as we had wanted.

The females rush to Bouncer and greet him with long, sensuous rubs. Lifting his tail, he scent-marks a bush. Then they settle into a deep *Combretum* thicket to spend the day in the shade. We humans return to my little camp for breakfast. The vegetation is too thick, the terrain too rough to follow the pride in the truck, and I do not feel safe following them at night on foot. But each morning and evening I search for them and make observations on their prey choice and habitat movements.

Now that it is the dry season, they have moved away from the plains and spend most of their time in the woodlands near the Luangwa. One morning I watch the females hunt a warthog; another morning they stalk a puku. But mostly they kill buffalo, one of which is large enough to feed the whole pride for several days.

The days are cool now, and one day the lionesses and their cubs spend the entire morning sunning themselves on the beach. Soon a female puku and her fawn walk across the sand toward the river. She apparently wants to drink, but seeing the lions she stops about fifty yards away. For a few moments she looks back and forth from the water to the lions, and ultimately lies down with her fawn right where she is. Watching from my camp, I wish so much that I could stroll across the sand and join the ladies on the beach.

The breeze blows strongly against my face, and as I stand alone on the riverbank, I feel as though I am being interviewed by the wind. How can we hold on to the old, wild Africa? When the elephants are safe, can we go back to our lives of lion watching?

I long to return to studying the animals, sinking into Nature and learning her ways. There are always more wonders to uncover. Discover them quickly, before they go — is that where we are? In the Kalahari, Mark and I discovered the second largest wildebeest migration in Africa. No one else saw it except the sun; a few years later it was gone. Will anything save the elephants? Will the rain bring back the desert? Will the desert bring back the wildebeest, or have they all marched on to a world — a time — that was and will not be again? Somewhere, is there a dusty plain where wildebeest still dance?

The wind rises and slaps my hair, but I do not have the answers.

The Africa I speak of is still here, but it is in little pockets — in small corners of the continent — hiding.

○ ○ ○

Driving back and forth between Mpika and the Luangwa, I divide my time in the dry season of 1990 between our work in the villages — that we now call the Community Service and Conservation Education Programs — and my studies at the river. We have expanded our programs to ten target villages that are near the park and have many poachers. These projects have grown so much that we have taken on a full-time employee, Max Saili, and two volunteers from Texas, Tom and Wanda Canon. I still believe that the only way to save the elephants in the long term is to convince the people in the area that they are worth saving.

On one of my trips back to base camp to resupply, Mark and I walk along the Lubonga, trading war stories about the game guards. He has not had time to visit my camp, and the only chance we have to see each other is when I come to Marula-Puku for supplies. There is still a strain between us and we operate more or less in our own realms, our personal lives on hold.

Mark lags behind me, which is so unusual that I turn around to see if he is all right. He walks slowly, his head down, the .375 rifle slung loosely over his right shoulder.

"Are you okay?"

"I feel a little weird." Beads of sweat glisten on his forehead. "Need some food. Gotta get to camp, some food." He starts to sway and stumble.

Rushing to him, I grab the rifle. "First, you've got to sit down." I push him gently to the ground. He sits hard and then falls backward. His right arm flings out straight, his head lurches back, and he slumps into unconsciousness.

"Oh God! Mark, is it your heart? Tell me what's wrong!" His eyes are open, staring blankly. I grab his clammy wrist and feel for his pulse. It is strong. His breathing seems normal but his lips are blue. Mark has had mild trouble with his blood sugar for years, but can usually control it by eating properly and avoiding too much caffeine. Lately, however, he has been drinking cup after cup of strong black coffee with sugar to stay awake for his hours of night flying. Since his sickness in Lusaka he has been lethargic, barely able to keep going. I have begged him to see a doctor, but he has refused, saying that if anything serious were found, he might be grounded, and that his flying is our only weapon against the poachers.

Now he lies totally unconscious, legs and arms splayed across the ground. I try to stay calm, to think. I have to get some glucose into him. I run the five hundred yards to camp, screaming for Simbeye to get the truck. In the kitchen boma I mix powdered milk, water, and honey into a canteen. My hands shake, and white powder and goo spill all over. What seems like hours later, all the guys are in the back of the truck and we race out to where Mark lies.

I stare deep into his vacant eyes, which seem pale and lifeless. If I try to give him the honey mixture now, he will choke. Since it is Sunday, there is no radio schedule until tomorrow morning — no way to call for help, and a six- or seven-hour drive to the clinic. It has been twenty minutes since he collapsed.

Slowly he blinks. He moves his head. I put my face directly over his.

"Mark, can you see me?" He twists his head around, his eyes full of fear.

"What happened? Where am I?"

"It's okay. You fainted. I mixed some milk and honey for you. Can you drink it?"

"I think so." But before I can get the canteen to his lips, he passes out again, staring straight ahead with empty eyes for another ten minutes.

Again he tries to look around him. "Boo, where am I? Did I crash the plane?"

"No, Mark," I say softly. "It's okay. You're right outside camp. Remember, we were walking."

"Oh, I see." He faints again. For fifteen more minutes he slides into and out of consciousness.

Kasokola and I lift him by the shoulders, until he is slumped against me. When he wakes again, I murmur, "Here, drink this."

He sips the milk laced with swirls of honey. Leaning heavily against me, he is able to get five or six swallows down. He rests with eyes closed.

"I feel better," he whispers. I push the canteen to his lips and he drinks again. "Where am I? Is anybody else hurt?"

I explain again, holding him tightly in my arms. "It's all right, everything is all right."

After ten minutes he is able to sit up by himself, and is already joking with the guys, who stare from the back of the truck with deep concern on their faces, like so many masks. "I just had too many beers," he cracks, "what's all the fuss about?" But they do not laugh. To see a strong man in such a state is not funny.

I call softly to Kasokola and Simbeye, and we lift Mark into the back of the truck and lay him down. I drive him to the bedroom cottage, and they help me get him into bed. Kasokola asks if he can bring more milk and honey, and I say, "Yes, please."

When they are gone, I whisper, "Mark we can't go on like this. We have to do something different. We have to get some help."

"You're right, Boo, we will. I promise."

But the next morning — only fifteen hours after passing out, and in spite of everything I say — Mark flies another antipoaching flight. Feeling that I can no longer reach him, I return to my river camp.

19
Close Encounters

MARK

The elephant moves slowly to protect its vast brain,
With which it hears subsonic sound,
And in which it carries the topology,
The resonances and reverberations,
Of a continent.

— HEATHCOTE WILLIAMS

○ ○ ○

I HAVE JUST FALLEN ASLEEP when I am awakened by the sounds of harsh breathing, heavy footsteps, and grass being ripped from the ground somewhere near my head. Wafting through the window is a sweaty, bovine odor mixed with the sweet pungence of marula fruits. Sliding slowly out of bed, I press my face to the flyscreen. Six Cape buffalo loom in the darkness, one of them an arm's length away, its stomach churning like an old-fashioned Maytag. Moving along the cottage, the old bull rakes his horns against the stone wall, making a clacking sound. I am lulled to sleep knowing that in some small way we have been successful.

○ ○ ○

When we first stood on the high bluff looking down on Marula-Puku, we didn't know it had once been a poachers' camp. But we soon found abandoned meat racks and ashes beneath the marula trees. Poaching had conditioned the animals along the Lubonga to fear humans. After we arrived and began defending them, it took only a few months for the animals to grow accustomed to their new sanctuary. Soon puku, impalas, wildebeest, buffalo, and waterbuck grazed across the river from us, then around camp, and finally among our cottages at night after we had gone to bed. Mornings we would hurry outside to see how the shrubbery had been rearranged during the night.

For some reason the warthogs seem more shy than the buffalo and other animals. With faces like uprooted tree stumps — all knobs and nodules — they have a right to be shy. But during the dry season of 1990 a boar, a sow, and three piglets begin feeding across the river from camp, usually in the late afternoon. On their front knees, they root for tubers along the far bank, occasionally splashing through the rocky drift upstream from camp, all in a line, their tails stiff as pokers and straight up like lightning rods. Whenever they reach the edge of camp, they stop to watch us for a while, then trot off in the opposite direction, still afraid of us after all this time.

One afternoon in late August, Survivor comes into camp again on his way to the mountains. There are no marula fruits now, but he feeds on the new leaves and seeds of the *Combretum* trees. The six buffalo still graze along the bedroom cottage each night until morning, but otherwise Survivor has camp all to himself.

Right on schedule, he strolls into camp along the track. Jogging close at his heels, as if they were his miniature cousins, are the members of the warthog family. The gray, wrinkled pigs trot in the footsteps of the gray, wrinkled elephant. As Survivor stops to feed on some small shrubs, the warthogs fan out to root tubers, shoots, and bulbs. They never venture more than twenty feet or so from their towering companion, and when he finally ambles out of camp, the warthogs jog in a line behind him, down the track and out of sight. If only Delia could have been here to see this procession.

Soon Survivor is coming every day with his entourage, and as I walk along the footpaths between the kitchen boma and the office cottage, the pigs pay no attention to me and keep on rooting.

○ ○ ○

One evening Luke Daka, permanent secretary to the minister of tourism, and Akim Mwenya, deputy director of national parks, are sitting with me on the riverbank at camp. Over the years Delia and I have met with numerous officials in Lusaka to describe the poaching and corruption, and have invited them to visit the project. Daka and Mwenya are the first to come.

"Look! An elephant!" He points across the river as Survivor strolls to the water's edge. Jumping up from his chair, he exclaims, "I can't believe it. I am Zambian, but this is the first time I've ever seen an elephant in the wilderness."

"That's Survivor. If you can imagine it, there used to be seventeen thousand elephants in North Luangwa. Now, because of poaching, maybe a thousand or two are left."

"That's awful," he says. "Of course, you have told me at our meetings in Lusaka, but I didn't imagine it was so bad."

"It's bad all right. When I next see you in Lusaka, Survivor may be dead — unless you can help us." I tell him again about the apathy and corruption among the game scouts and officials in Mpika. By the time I finish, Daka's face is sagging. He promises to do what he can.

The next morning, after Daka and Mwenya leave, Survivor is back in camp. The poaching is still bad, and I should be flying. Delia is right, though — I need a day off. So I gather up my daypack, field notes, and binoculars, intending to follow my favorite elephant, record his behavior, and see where he will lead me. I'll have to do this surreptitiously, because Survivor still does not like people to approach him; he prefers to make the advances.

He leaves camp by way of our outhouse, where I fall in behind him. I stay far enough back that I can keep his tall rump in sight without his seeing me, and stay downwind so that he won't be able to smell me. He crosses the stream cut next to camp, climbs a steep bank, and wanders through an expanse of *Combretum fragrans,* casually wrapping his trunk around an eight-foot bush and decapitating it as he passes. He doubles back to our track, crosses it, and descends the old false bank of the Lubonga, where the river used to run, there to stand in a deep glade under a huge marula tree. I close to within thirty yards of him, sit with my back against another tree, and we doze together until midafternoon.

At about three-thirty he leads me along the river, past the airstrip ridge and onto a floodplain near Khaya Stream. The grass here is more than eight feet tall. Since I can no longer see him, I follow his rustling sounds.

Other elephant paths intersect this one now, so I quicken my pace, afraid that he has taken one of the trails to the side and is about to lose me. I pause to kneel at a pile of dung and an elephant's track at the junction of two paths. The grass in the track is flattened to the ground, but a few stems are beginning to rise as I watch. I poke my finger into one of the balls of dung; it is very warm. He has just passed. I stand and hurry on.

Suddenly the air reverberates with a deep rumble, like thunder far away. There is Survivor, less than ten yards ahead, curling his trunk high above the grasses like a periscope. Other deep rumbles sound. And now I hear the grass rustling from several directions. Other elephants are coming toward us. Afraid to retreat, I sidestep off the trail into a shallow mud hole and squat down. The massive crown of a bull elephant, ears flapping, feet swishing in the grass, cruises by so close I can see his eyelashes. He is like a giant combine harvester in a field of tall wheat. Reaching Survivor, he lowers his head and the two bulls briefly push at each other. Several other bulls arrive, milling about Survivor for a minute, their trunks touching the streams of temporal gland secretions that flow from the sides of his head, behind and below his eyes. The elephants remind me of humans, shedding tears of welcome. Then Survivor leads them off toward Khaya Stream two hundred yards ahead. I follow.

Nearer the stream the grass mostly gives way to tall *Khaya nyasica* and *Trichelia emetica* trees, which stand on a high bank above the streambed. The elephants follow the trail through a deep cut in the bank and disappear. Creeping closer, I hear the sound of splashing water. Anxious to see what is going on, I crawl into a clump of grass on the bank and ease forward, my chin on the ground, until I can see over the edge.

Below, the elephants have assembled around a pool at the edge of the sandy streambed. A ledge of rock running across the stream provides a shallow basin that collects water trickling from a natural spring halfway up the bank. They stand shoulder to shoulder around the basin, drawing up water, raising their heads and curling their trunks into their mouths to drink. Their thirst slaked, they squirt water over their own backs, and onto one another. It is an elephants' spa.

Finished with their bath, they walk five yards to a dust wallow near an enormous ebony tree that grows horizontally about six feet above the ground. With the tips of their trunks they gather a quart of the gray powder at a time, flinging it over their backs and between their legs until a great cloud rises against the red sun of late afternoon. Then, one by one, they file past the "Scratching Tree," each leaning against it at a spot rubbed shiny smooth, heaving his bulk up and down against its bark, his eyelids heavy.

For the next half-hour, they stand around in the spa, heads hanging, trunks resting on the ground. My neck tires of holding up my head, so I rest my chin on my hand. But in moving I dislodge a pebble that rolls down the bank into the streambed near Survivor. Jerking his head up, eyes wide, the bull elephant pivots toward me. His trunk is up and air blasts from his mouth. Aroused, the others spin around, prepared to flee. Lying motionless, my face in full view, I feel like a Peeping Tom. Survivor walks slowly toward me, his trunk snaked out. Before I can react, the tip of his trunk is snuffling through the grass, inches away from my right foot. The tall bank stops his advance, but he keeps reaching for me, his trunk fully extended, patting around in the grass, as though looking for my foot. We stare into each other's eyes for long seconds. I think he knew I was here all along — just another guy in the locker room.

Curiously, Survivor takes a bite out of the bank, withdraws his trunk, turns and walks back to the others, dropping the grass and soil from his mouth along the way. Alert, but apparently no longer afraid, the elephants file into the long grass beyond the stream, Survivor in the lead.

The shadows are long, so I follow an elephant trail along the Lubonga on my way back to camp. Not far from the elephants' spa, the path leads to the edge of the Lubonga, where the river cuts into a low hill on the opposite bank. Directly across from me a bull buffalo is grazing the grass on a shelf fifteen feet above the water. Immediately beyond him the hill rises steeply away from the river. I am so close to him, no more than thirty yards, that I am amazed he has not seen me. Raising my field glasses to watch him, I immediately realize why he has not: his left eye is bluish-white and stares sightlessly into space. His hide is covered with old scars, his ears have been shredded by thorns, his tail has been stumped — probably by lions or hyenas — and over the years the African bush has worn the tips of his horns to polished black stubs. He has been well used — almost used up.

Still unaware of me, he continues to graze, moving on a diagonal toward the sheer edge of the tall bank — and in the direction of his blind eye. Step by step he grazes closer. Finally he puts his left front hoof within six inches of the edge and a slab of the bank crumbles under him. The sixteen-hundred-pound buffalo pitches over the side, feet flailing, into the shallow river below.

Heaving his bulk onto his hooves with surprising agility, puffing like a steam engine, the old buff swings around and charges the bank, trying to get back up on his ledge. Scrambling halfway up, he loses his footing and rolls into the river again, spray flying. He tries again, with the same result. And again. Each time becoming more frantic — and more pitiful.

But before I can feel very sorry for him, the buff spins to face me. Standing with his front legs splayed, he swings his head from right to left, taking in his options with his one good eye: obovatum thickets to his right, another bank to his left, and one behind him. I am his path of least resistance; I might as well have cornered him in a back alley. Somehow the water between us has given me a false sense of security. But here the river is inches deep, as he is about to demonstrate.

Bellowing and snorting, he charges through the river, fountains of water erupting from his feet and crashing around his body. About fifteen feet behind me is a dead tree with a limb at eight feet above the ground. I whirl and run for it, the bull's hooves thumping hollow on the ground behind me. Praying that it will hold me, I jump for the limb, hauling myself up and out of reach as the buffalo charges past and out of sight beyond a thicket. For several minutes I perch there, catching my breath. When I am sure he's gone I jump down, smiling to myself, and head for camp — glad that Delia did not see me running for the tree. She probably would have shot me in the back.

20

The Last Season

MARK

. . . an old dream
Of something better coming soon
for each Survivor.

— L. E. SISSMAN

○ ○ ○

I AM WALKING PAST the big marula tree near the center of camp when Mumanga's "pssst" stops me in my tracks. Looking up, I see a bull elephant watching me from forty yards away. I back up to the wall of the office, and after hesitating for several minutes, the elephant walks slowly to the kitchen. He stands ten feet from the fire where Mumanga is cooking, searching with his trunk through the dried leaves for fruits, curling one after another up into his mouth, his ears flapping back and forth. I walk closer, until I can see the hole in his left ear. It is Survivor.

At first Mumanga stays rooted to his spot beside the stove. But as Survivor moves even closer, he slowly retreats, backing up until his heels strike the step to the kitchen door and he sits down with a plop. Our wood stove and cooking area is covered with a large thatched roof, which gives some shelter against the sun and rain — but not against elephants. Apparently deciding he needs some roughage to go with his fruit, Survivor snakes his trunk to the thatch, pulls out a great plug, and stuffs it into his mouth. The poles supporting the heavy roof stagger, crack, and groan until I think the entire structure will collapse. And so does Mumanga, who darts into the tile-roofed kitchen cottage. Fortunately Survivor does not care for the taste of the coarse dry thatch; he spits it out and picks up another fruit, feeding around the kitchen and workshop until after dark. Then he shambles away from camp through the long grass, like a massive gray boulder rolling through the moonlight, his great round feet leaving tracks across my life.

When I get up for breakfast, one side of the thatched roof of the open kitchen boma is sitting on the ground; the other is perched on top of the smashed stove. Weakened by Survivor's assault, the poles supporting the roof have collapsed during the night — with a little help from termites. Delia will have a surprise when she gets back from her camp on the river.

Later that morning I fly to Mpika to talk with Warden Mulenga about the Mano scouts, who still seldom go on patrol — except when they want some meat. Shuffling her papers and grinning shyly, Mulenga's secretary tells me he is out for the day. Her reaction tells me he is "out" drinking at ten o'clock in the morning. I drive to the British Aid Compound, pick up our mail, and am about to leave for the airstrip when a man named Banda Njouhou, one of the warden's senior staff, catches up with me and leads me to a quiet corner of the compound, where we sit under a tree.

Looking about nervously, he begins. "Mark, the warden is not only warning poachers of patrols, he is poaching himself." On weekends Mulenga is taking trucks donated to National Parks by USAID (United States Agency for International Development) and driving to the game management areas, where he orders scouts to shoot buffalo and other animals. Then he hauls the bush meat back to Mpika and he, his wife, and two scouts sell it from his home, at the market, at two bars, even at the banks.

"The warden uses the Mano Unit's ammunition and gasoline rations for poaching," Banda goes on, "and he sells their mealie-meal rations. He is also trading in animal skins." Patrick Muchu, the Fulaza unit leader, and some of his scouts are shooting cheetahs, leopards, lions, zebras, and other animals, whose skins Mulenga sells on the black market through a senior parks official in Lusaka. He and the official transfer scouts who are Mulenga's cousins to areas around the North Park, to help him poach. And they send away good scouts like Gaston Phiri.

"What can we do about this?" I ask Banda.

"We could catch him at a roadblock some night when he is returning to Mpika with his truck full of meat."

"Yes, and what scouts or police can we trust to arrest him? And if they arrest him, what do you think the magistrate will do? He poaches too, you know."

He holds up both hands. "Yes, I know these problems very well. I don't know what you can do. I can do nothing; these are my bosses."

As we walk back to his truck, I thank him for coming to me with his information.

Almost as soon as he drives away, another truck pulls up and stops near me. Two men get out and introduce themselves as officers from the Anticorruption Commission. One of the men, small, with a round face, frowns. "I am afraid someone has charged you with buying black-market military weapons." The other man, slightly taller, with a thin, haggard face, looks silently at me.

"What? Who says so?"

"Do you know Bwalya Muchisa?" asks the round-faced man.

"Bwalya accused me of this? Where did you see him?" He went to visit his family almost two months ago and I've been wondering what has happened to him.

"He's in Lusaka. He's been caught with a new black-market AK, and he told a minister you gave him the money to buy it. Look, we know about your good work, but I'm sure you understand that some very important people are dealing in ivory and don't like what you are doing to stop it. This minister may be one of them. He wants you out of here very much."

Sitting at the table in our hut, I write six pages of testimony, saying that Bwalya must have bought the AK for poaching, and when he was caught with it, he came up with the story that I had given him the money to buy it. Since his father is one of Zambia's most infamous and successful commercial poachers, he probably has connections to this minister, connections Bwalya has exploited to try to save himself. Or maybe the minister is out to get me. If so, he must have found out that Bwalya worked for me, learned that he had been caught with an AK, and is trying to use this information to get me thrown in jail or out of the country. Later I would learn from my informants that the whole time Bwalya was working for us, he was keeping an AK-47 and lending it to poachers. As soon as I hand over my finished statement, the officers stand to leave.

"I would advise you to get a lawyer," the round-faced man says. "We'll be in touch. Please notify us if you intend leaving the country." We shake hands and they drive away.

Back at camp, I pack and fly to Lusaka to meet with a lawyer, who tells me that until I am arrested, there is nothing he can do. I brief the American ambassador and the British high commissioner in case I need their help, and then fly to Mpika. There I ask friends to radio us if they hear that the police or military are headed for Marula-Puku. Back at camp again, I refuel the plane and keep it on standby for a quick takeoff.

○ ○ ○

During September of 1990 Survivor continues to visit our camp, often bringing with him another elephant we call Cheers. One morning, when Delia has come to Marula-Puku to resupply, we are walking along our footpath to the kitchen for breakfast, the golden sunlight spilling into camp through the marula trees. "Mark, look, across the river." Delia points to a group of five elephants feeding near the staff camp. One is Survivor. We watch him pull up big bunches of long grass, then beat the roots against his foot to dislodge the dirt before stuffing them into this mouth. Sparrow weavers hop on the ground near our feet, chirping loudly, and a family of warthogs kneel on the riverbank upstream, rooting for food. It is one of those cool, still mornings when Africa seems to be standing back from the mirror, admiring a last vestige of her fading beauty.

BWA! A gunshot cracks from across the river and echoes off the high bank behind camp.

Delia spins toward me, half crouching, the color draining from her face.

"Oh God, no! Mark, they're shooting Survivor! Do something!"

BWA! BWA! BWA!

"Get behind a tree!" I shout, pushing her toward the big marula next to our footpath and sprinting for the office. I grab the rifle and shotgun from the corner near the bookcase, and strap on my pistol.

"Kasokola! Simbeye! Get to the truck!" I bellow through the office window. I jerk open the cupboard door, claw ammunition from the shelves, and stuff it into my pockets.

BWA! BWA! BWA! BWA! BWA! BWA! Six more shots thunder from across the river. The hundred-fifty-yard dash to the truck leaves my legs rubbery.

"Do you have your revolver?" I ask Delia as I climb into the Land Cruiser.

"Yes! Just go!" She dumps two more boxes of ammo into my lap.

With Kasokola and Simbeye in the back of the pickup, holding on tightly, we race the quarter-mile to the staff camp, driving across the Lubonga, spray and rocks flying. As we near their camp I lean on the horn and whistle for the guys to come. "Let's go! Let's go!" But they are already running for the truck before it stops.

I hand Mwamba the shotgun and Kasokola the .375, then spill ammo for each gun onto the seat of the truck and scoop it into their hands.

"Where did the shots come from?" I ask. I am afraid I already know, but the echo from the high banks along the river has made it hard for me to be sure.

"That side!" Mwamba points directly at the spot where Delia and I had seen Survivor feeding from our camp. I look at these young men. They are workers, not fighters. Only two of them are armed. The other six are carrying hoes, shovels, pickax handles. "You don't have to come with me," I tell them. "These poachers have AKs. It'll be dangerous." None of them walks away. "I won't think less of any of you for staying here. This isn't your job." Still they stand there.

"Right," I say. "Let's go! Kasokola, Mwamba; help me cover the river while the unarmed men cross!"

No such order prevails. Mwamba and Kasokola immediately

leave me and swarm across the river with the others. I lag behind, training my pistol on the opposite bank. We are sitting ducks as we struggle through the current.

"You guys with the guns, stay up front!" I whisper harshly. We are in the tall grass and brush on the opposite bank, and may run into the poachers at any time. Once at the top of the ridge, we sweep upstream along the river, looking for human footprints going to or from Survivor, or his tracks accompanied by blood spoor — drops of crimson in the dust that may warn us he has been wounded rather than killed. With this sweep I am hoping to keep the poachers from taking cover in the thick *Combretum fragrans* scrub, and to flush them out into the open riverbed. I curse their gall, shooting an elephant within sight of our camp. Then a thought strikes me: maybe they wanted to be seen.

"Nsingo!" I grab the arm of one of our new workers. "Is anyone in camp with Delia?"

"No."

"Then you get back there as fast as you can, in case the poachers attack the camp. Mwamba! You, Simbeye, Chende Ende, and Muchemwu carry on with the sweep. Kasokola and I will go with the others to look for Survivor. If you come across the poachers, don't wait for them to shoot first."

My team scours the riverbank east of where I'd seen Survivor. The tall grass along the river, and the dense brush and hard ground back from it, make the search difficult and dangerous. We will be lucky to get out of this without someone's getting shot, or trampled by a wounded elephant. I soon lose contact with Kasokola and the rest of my group. I hope they will not contact Mwamba and the others and open fire on one another.

After half an hour I still have not found any sign of Survivor or the poachers, and I am growing more and more worried that the shots may have been a decoy and that the poachers are in camp now. Giving up the search, I wade back across the river and run to the truck.

As soon as I pull into camp I see Delia, her revolver strapped to her hip, and Nsingo — but no poachers. Thank God, no poachers. I try to convince her to come with me in the plane to look for

Survivor. But she insists that someone must guard camp, and Nsingo has never seen a revolver before.

"Be careful!" I warn as I jump into the truck.

"Be careful yourself. I'll stand by on the radio."

When I am airborne, Delia gives me a rough bearing from camp to where the shots had been fired. Heading in that direction, I have only flown a few seconds when I see the body of an elephant, its tusks hacked off, lying in a deep sandy stream cut just a little beyond where we had been looking. Vultures are already spiraling down to the carcass, and I cannot tell if it is Survivor. Mwamba and his group are within fifty yards of the dead elephant and walking quickly toward it. I stick my arm out the window and motion them back toward camp. The poachers have fled and there is nothing more they can do here. Better to have them in position to defend Marula-Puku if necessary.

After checking with Delia on the radio, I fly to Mpika to get some of the new scouts who recently arrived. I can only hope that they have not yet been corrupted, but in any case there is nothing else I can do. They are my only hope of capturing these poachers.

Leaving the scouts on the airstrip at Marula-Puku, Kasokola and I take off at four-thirty in the afternoon to look for the poachers. After shooting Survivor they will have headed for Mpika by the most direct route that provides them with cover and water — along the Mwaleshi River. We have flown along the river for only fifteen minutes when we spot their camp near the scarp. I circle some distance away, pretending to be interested in another area. A few minutes later, looking through binoculars, I see some familiar green tents and flysheets. I know immediately who owns them: Chikilinti, Chanda Seven, Mpundu Katongo, and Bernard Mutondo.

I fly back to our airstrip on the Lubonga, land, and then take off again with Brighton Mulomba, the scout leader, to show him the camp and the most direct way to get there. From a distance we can see a column of smoke with vultures circling around it. The poachers have killed another elephant and apparently are feeling secure enough to take the time to dry its meat. I can drive the scouts to a point only a two-hour hike from the poachers, who will be virtually trapped by the valley's steep walls. It will be hard not to catch at least some of them.

Back on the ground I give Mulomba and his troops a pep talk. As soon as I have finished, the group leader announces, "Ah, but you see, my fellow officers and I have decided that we are not due to go on patrol for some time yet."

"But this is an emergency," I explain, "not a regular patrol, and according to the regulations you are bound to take action against these poachers."

"Yes, but anyway we are needing salt and . . ." Resisting a powerful urge to draw my pistol, I turn and walk away.

○ ○ ○

Back at camp Delia tells me that she saw Survivor running as the shots were being fired. She believes he may have been only wounded, or may have escaped unharmed. But in the past I have often found the carcasses of other elephants several miles from where they were shot, and Survivor was surrounded by the gunfire. He must have been hit by at least some of the bullets. If they have not killed him outright, he will surely die of his wounds.

We hike across the river to the carcass. Sprawled in the sand of the dry streambed, it is already bloated, rotting, blown with maggots, the juices of its decay fertilizing the soil. It has been so mutilated, first by the poachers and then by scavengers, that at first we cannot make an identification. It is a male about his size, however, and I finally conclude that it must be Survivor. But Delia cannot accept it.

"Mark, we can't see his left ear. We don't *know* it's Survivor." She bites her lip and turns away.

I cannot delude myself that he is still alive. To me he has become another statistic in the war against poachers. All hope of saving this valley and its wildlife seems to have died with him. For our own sakes, for our sanity, we must at last recognize that there is a time to quit, a time to admit that nothing more can be done.

But I have not yet played my last card.

21
Cherry Bombs

MARK

Why not go out on a limb? Isn't that where the fruit is?
— RENEE LOCKS AND JOSEPH MCHUGH

○ ○ ○

AT SUNSET THE SAME DAY, Kasokola and I take off and fly low-level north along the Lubonga toward the scarp. By using the mountains to cover our approach, we hope to surprise the poachers who shot Survivor.

I have removed the door from Kasokola's side and turned his seat around so that he can see out easily. Cradled across his lap is a twelve-gauge shotgun tied to his wrist with a bootlace, so that the slipstream will not tear the weapon from his hands. The gun is loaded with cracker shells, each of which will project a cherry-bomb firecracker to a hundred yards, where it will explode with a blinding flash and a very loud bang. Cherry bombs are virtually harmless, but Chikilinti won't know that.

At the scarp I climb the plane into the mountains, dodging peaks and hopping over ridges, staying low to keep the poachers from hearing the plane until the last minute. It is almost dark by the time we reach the headwaters of the Mwaleshi River, a few miles upstream and a thousand feet in elevation above their campsite. I pull back the plane's throttle, lower my left wing, and sideslip into the deep river gorge. Sheer, dark canyon walls loom close on either side of us. I drop flaps to slow Zulu Sierra and bank steeply right and left, hauling the plane through hairpin turns as we descend through the gorge.

By the time we come out of the scarp into the Mwaleshi's narrow valley below, the moon has risen, two days from full and halfway up the eastern sky. Now each of the water holes, rivers, and flooded dambos twinkles with moonlight as we pass; occasionally my heart jumps, but the twinkle is silver — not the flickering, sallow yellow of a poacher's fire.

We have just begun to fly along the foothills of the scarp, approaching one of the Mwaleshi's tributary streams when Kasokola leans out of the open doorway and shouts, "Poachers — fire! There!" He points to a large circle of flames near the river. I bank the plane and push its nose into a shallow dive that will end up over the camp.

Kasokola picks up the spotlight. I warn him not to use it for more than a couple of seconds, just long enough to see the meat racks and confirm that this is the poachers' camp. The light will make the plane an easy target. "Eh, Mukwai — yes, sir." I glance over to see him grinning. He wants Chikilinti as badly as I do. "And don't shine the light inside the plane," I yell in his ear. "It will blind me."

I fly past the camp and turn on the landing light. When I can see the crowns of the trees flashing just under the plane's wheels, I reset the altimeter to read our height above the ground around the poachers. I will use this reading as a minimum safety height to help keep us clear of the woodland while making passes over the camp. Banking steeply, I turn back toward the fires and ease off the throttle, cutting our speed to about 55 mph. As we come in over the camp I cross the controls, using heavy right rudder and left aileron. Foxtrot Zulu Sierra skids sideways through the air, turning around the encampment, the stall warning bawling like a sick goose. The rising heat from the fires below lifts and rocks the plane.

"Now, Kasokola!"

He thumbs the switch on the Black Max and the camp is instantly bathed in the 450,000-candlepower light. Steadying the plane, I lean over him and for a second take my eyes from my flying to look down.

Tents . . . fires . . . and meat racks — covered with huge slabs of meat, so large they can only be from elephants. And a pair of tusks is leaning against a tree near the fire, tusks the size of Survivor's.

A pencil-thin trace of white light flicks past my right wing, followed by a popping sound. Tracer bullets! "They're shooting at us! Fire into the trees and bushes; blast their tents if you can. Don't spare the ammunition." Kasokola puts down the spotlight and grabs the shotgun as I pull the plane up away from the trees and begin turning back again. "Okay, get ready!"

Even with her lights switched off, to the poachers on the ground Zulu Sierra must look like a huge bat flitting about the moonlit sky — a nice fat target. And after our two passes, they must be getting the hang of tracking us with their rifles. I circle to the side of camp away from the moon so we won't present quite such a strong silhouette. Then I drop to the minimum safety height that will keep us clear of the trees, hoping to pass over the camp so quickly they won't have time to get off a shot, at least an accurate one. The dim shadows of trees are skimming by just under the plane's wheels, and then the meat fires are below us. I throttle back, kick right rudder and corkscrew the plane above the poacher's camp. A tracer streaks past, and another, much closer.

"Fire!"

And Kasokola answers: pfsst-pfsst-pfsst-pfsst-pfsst! From its barrel the twelve-gauge issues a trail of red and orange sparks as each cherry bomb arcs into the night.

BOOM-BOOM-BOOM-BOOM! Great thunderflashes of light and sound rock the poachers' camp. Kasokola's face is strobe lit as he cackles with laughter, unable to believe that he has caused all this ruckus. BOOM! The last cherry bomb lands in the campfire. Sparks and fiery traces of burning wood rocket through the camp and into the trees like Roman candles going off. One of Chikilinti's tents starts to burn, set alight by the scattered embers of the campfire.

"Happy Fourth of July, bastards!" I shout. Then, "Reload!" I yell to Kasokola as I haul Zulu Sierra through a tight turn. This time we come in fifty feet higher, spreading our cherry bombs over a broader area, hoping to catch the scattering poachers. I jink and sideslip the plane, avoiding their tracers. Kasokola reloads four more times, shooting up the camp again and again until there is no more return fire.

Thinking the poachers may have split up earlier, I climb to a thousand feet above the ground and see another campfire, about two miles downstream. I push Zulu Sierra into a dive and Kasokola switches on the spotlight. A circle of men with guns is sitting around the fire, near a large empty meat rack. They have not yet killed.

I haul the plane through another tight turn. Back over the second camp, I can see the poachers still sitting close to their fire, so confident that they haven't bothered to take cover. Kasokola puts the first cherry bomb at their feet. KABOOM! At the explosion the poachers throw themselves to the ground, crawling into the bushes. On the next pass we shower them with more cherry bombs and move on down the valley, blasting other poachers in their camps on the Lufwashi, Luangwa, and Mulandashi rivers. We stay out long into the night, until clouds began covering the moon and we have to head home.

After sunrise the next morning, Kasokola and I fly to Chikilinti's campsite of the night before. All that remains are the charred and smoldering shreds of his tent and a pile of squabbling vultures.

22

Scouts on the Prowl

DELIA

You never feel it
till it's over —
the relief
at having survived
and the new sun
rising calmly as ever
before your eyes. It's
morning.

— PAULA GUNN ALLEN

○ ○ ○

WE SEE NO POACHED ELEPHANTS in North Luangwa for three months. For four months. For five months. By February 1991 Long Ear's and Misty's group of elephants and other family units stroll onto the floodplains, feeding in the open on the blond grasses. Occasionally families come together, forming aggregations of up to two hundred sixty elephants.

One evening Long Ear's group ventures down to the river's edge before sunset. The calf and the youngster — now five years old — gallop through the Mwaleshi, sending sprays of water into the air. Their mothers bathe nearby; but then, caught in some new spirit, they too run in circles through the shallow river. Chasing one another, adults and young alike frolic and romp — something they have not done in a long time. A natural wildness slips back into the valley.

Still receiving coded messages from Musakanya, Mark flies night and day. He greets every poaching band that enters the park with his special cherries, even before they can set up their camps. Musakanya sends word that the poachers are having trouble hiring bearers, because they are afraid of the plane and its explosive bombs. The carriers start trickling into our small office in Mpika, asking us for work. We hire them with money we have raised in the States.* It is as simple as this: Mark chases them out of the park with the plane; I greet them on the top of the scarp with a job.

○ ○ ○

Bumping along the bush track one afternoon, I drive across the valley toward Marula-Puku from my river camp. The track takes me through the dusty plains that are spotted with buffalo and through the forest where kudu hide. Earlier Mark radioed from the airplane, asking me to come by camp to talk about something important. When I reach the Lubonga, I stop in the tall grass and walk to the river's edge, where the water tumbles over a small rock shelf and creates a natural whirlpool. I bathe in the sparkling current and change into a fresh blouse and jeans. Sitting on the rocks, I brush my hair in the sun. I drive the truck across the river and down the track into camp, where I park under the marula trees.

As always, Kasokola and Mwamba rush out from the workshop to shake my hand warmly, and Mumanga, the cook, and Chanda, his assistant, run from the kitchen to welcome me back. But Mark is flying a patrol and won't return until much later. Swallowing my disappointment, I plan a special dinner for us. Mumanga, who thinks Mark and I never eat enough, pitches in.

Most of the open kitchen area has been without a roof since Survivor tried to eat it. The little wood stove, whose legs collapsed under the roof, is now set on blocks under a small, round, thatched roof. In no time Mumanga has the fire going. Smoke belches from the tall chimney with its cocked tin hat.

"Mumanga, you make a cake, okay? I'll bake a tuna pie — Mark's favorite. Chanda, please set the table in the little din-

* The Owens Foundation for Wildlife Conservation, which depends on donations from the public, supports our work. Tax-deductible contributions may be made to the foundation at Box 53396, Atlanta, Georgia 30355. We send periodic newsletters to contributors. Our other major sponsor is the Frankfurt Zoological Society of Germany, 6 Alfred-Brehm Platz, Frankfurt am Main 1, Germany.

ing cottage. Mark and I haven't had a real dinner together in months."

As we dash around the kitchen, up to our elbows in pastry and batter, Chanda and Mumanga tell me about the wildlife they have seen near camp. The zebra without stripes grazes across the river every so often, and the small herd of buffalo come into camp every morning.

Late in the afternoon the plane zooms over us as Mark approaches the airstrip. Everything is ready: Mumanga is icing the cake, the pie is baking, the table in the dining cottage is laid with candles and pottery dishes.

His eyes bloodshot, his face drawn, Mark steps out of the truck at the workshop. He hugs me briefly, and before we have taken two steps he announces that he must go straight back to the airstrip. Musakanya has passed the word that poachers may be heading into the park from the north, to a hilly area where Mark does not fly often.

Standing in the n'saka, Mark wolfs down a peanut butter sandwich and chases it with thick black coffee. I don't mention the special dinner I have made, or suggest that he take a rest, because I know he won't listen. According to the doctors in Lusaka, his collapse was brought on by stress and fatigue, by parasites and a virus, and by too much caffeine. All the same, he has ignored the warnings to slow down.

Sitting on the low stone wall of the n'saka, Mark drinks more coffee as we talk. The cherry bombs have cleared the park of poachers more effectively than we could have imagined, but we know this cannot last. Sooner or later the poachers will realize that the firecrackers are harmless; sooner or later Mark will be shot down or arrested by a corrupt official.

We have to try again to get the game guards to do their jobs. Our last hope, we have decided, is to find a tough, committed Zambian to serve as their unit leader. The encouragement, motivation, and leadership that the Mano scouts so desperately need should not come from us, but from one of them. We need a Zambian as crazed about elephants as we are.

Only two men can help us: Luke Daka and Akim Mwenya.

Together they are in charge of all the scouts, wardens, and administrators of National Parks. It was Daka who fell in love with Survivor when he met him at our camp. We will fly to Lusaka in a few days to meet with them again.

Mark, not noticing the pie or cake in the kitchen boma, quickly kisses me good-bye and drives back to the airstrip. So that I won't hurt Mumanga's feelings, I follow through with the evening meal, sitting at the table alone, eating a dinner meant for two. As the sun sets, I hear the plane take off in the distance and disappear among the hills of the scarp. I have never felt so lonely. After dinner I pack fresh supplies for my camp, give some cake and pie to Mumanga and Chanda, and ask them to keep the rest warm for Mark's return. Then I climb into my truck for the three-hour drive to the Luangwa. The half-moon will be my companion.

○ ○ ○

Acrid smells and shrill city noises filter through the open windows of Electra House, office of the Ministry of Tourism in Lusaka. Mark and I sit at a conference table with nine men from the Zambian government: Luke Daka, permanent secretary of the ministry, the director and the deputy director of National Parks and Wildlife Services, several other high-level officials from that department, and a few representatives of the Anticorruption Commission whom we have invited. We have explained the poaching problems to all of these men many times during meetings in Lusaka. But never have we met all together.

"Mr. Daka," Mark begins, "you will remember Survivor, the elephant who came to our camp when you were there. I'm afraid I have to tell you that poachers came to Marula-Puku and shot into his group, killing at least one elephant. We believe it was Survivor."

Daka frowns. "No! That's terrible!"

"It gets worse. I found the poachers' camp from the air," Mark went on, "but the game guards refused to go after them."

"This is outrageous! How can game guards refuse to take action in such an emergency?" Several men squirm in their seats.

"Sir, this is just the beginning." Mark talks for twenty minutes, telling about the radio and gun licenses not being granted, about scouts seldom patrolling, about corruption in Mpika, about National Parks officers — including the warden — who deal in ivory, skins, and meat. He describes how he has been shot at again and again while aiding the scouts, and how an official has accused him of buying black-market military weapons.

"But," Daka stammers, "this is ludicrous. Who has made these charges against you? And why two years to get radio licenses — they should be ready in two or three days." He glares at the men around him.

"We believe," Mark continues, "that people with poaching interests in North Luangwa are trying to block everything we do. They want to keep us from getting firearms and radios so the scouts can't protect the park."

Mark pauses to let the message sink in. "Sir, North Luangwa is one of the most beautiful parks in Africa — one that could, along with South Luangwa, bring millions of dollars into Zambia through tourism. But I can only say that we cannot go on like this. We have to know that this government is going to support us, or at least not undermine us."

Daka stares at the table, twisting the pen in his hand. "Mark, Delia," he finally says, "after being at your camp, I can see that your project is the only hope for this park. We WILL support you in every way."

Mark and I have heard this before; we are skeptical. But then Akim Mwenya continues, leveling his eyes at his junior officers from National Parks, "Tomorrow I want someone from the department to fly to Ndola to get these radio licenses. I also want the licenses to bring these guns into the country right away, so that the scouts can be armed properly. And new personnel should be sent to the Mano Unit."

The director offers to immediately send twenty scouts with special military training to Mano and build a new camp for them. North Luangwa will be given top priority.

"Sir, I would like to make one more request," Mark interjects. "The unit desperately needs a dynamic new leader. Please send us the best man you have."

We thank them all, especially Mr. Daka, but after four years of false hopes and disappointments we leave feeling more anxious than optimistic.

"Wonder how many hours they'll give us to pack up and get out of their country," Mark jokes as we step out onto the street. Walking through the jostling crowd, I do not laugh.

○ ○ ○

Up before dawn, I count the hippos from my camp before driving up the scarp mountains to meet Mark near Mano. Since our meeting in Lusaka a few weeks ago, three senior government officials have been suspended, pending investigation of charges that they were smuggling ivory to Swaziland. Our radio licenses have been approved and fresh scouts assigned to North Luangwa. A new unit leader has arrived in Mano, and Mark and I are to meet him today.

Driving along different tracks, Mark and I pull up at the Mwaleshi River near Mano at about the same time. We climb out of our trucks to inspect the new pole bridge we had built with local labor, then drive along the new Mano-to-Mukungule road to the recently completed airstrip. To our astonishment, a squadron of game guards dressed in full uniform marches double time along the strip toward us. They halt, turn smartly in place, honor us with a crisp military salute, then march off again. At the head of their column is a lanky, young Zambian wearing a proud smile. Incredulous, Mark and I look at each other. Can this be the Mano scouts drilling?

In Mark's truck we drive to the main camp. The children swarm around us as we step down from the Cruiser, then ask us to wait in the crumbling n'saka while they fetch the new unit leader. Ten of them race off to get him, while the other children ask for stories from the Luangwa Lion puppet. Mano still looks more like a refugee camp than an official game scout unit headquarters. The cracked walls of the old huts have simply been plastered with new mud that will soon crack in the sun.

Ten minutes later, the children dash back across the field ahead of the young man and the column of scouts. He orders his drill team to about-face, they march back down the field, and he dismisses them. Sweating heavily from the march, but crisp in his new green uniform, he walks briskly toward us. I stare at him. This is it, as far as I am concerned. If this man cannot bring Mano Unit under control, the project will be forced to recruit its own scouts. If that doesn't work, we will find another wilderness to save.

His handshake is firm and he looks me straight in the eye, his gaze steady and confident as he introduces himself. "I'm Kotela Mukendwa. I've heard all about you. We have much to discuss. Please sit down."

As Mark and I brief Kotela on the poaching in North Luangwa and our problems with the scouts, he nods his head knowingly. He intends to turn these undisciplined guards into a crack military-style unit, he says. We promise whatever he needs within reason to get started; if he does the job, we will consider requests beyond reason.

Talking so fast we can hardly understand him, Kotela presents a neatly prepared list of his needs: use of a truck to capture known poachers in the villages, fuel, more guns, ammo, and food for patrol. He will drill the men every day, instruct them in military tactics, order them to be dressed and ready for patrol at all times. He has sketched in detail his plans for an office, jail, armory, and storage complex for Mano. Almost dazed by his competence and determination, we agree to get him virtually everything on his list.

Mark stands, offering Kotela his hand. "Let's do it!" And he smiles his first real smile in a long while.

○ ○ ○

Mark and I set up a little camp near the waterfall, across the Mwaleshi River from the scout camp, so that we can help Kotela as much as possible. Using our trucks and funds for fuel and food, he provisions Mano with supplies and lectures the men on patrol tactics. He hires informants and prepares the scouts to go on village sweeps, in which they will raid poachers' homes in the middle of the night and arrest them. Meanwhile, we install new solar-powered radios at the various scout camps, organize farmers to grow food for the scouts, and in general try to improve their living conditions. Using money we have raised in the United

States, we purchase two new tractors and trailers to supply the camps, and a grader to make better roads and airstrips for the budding tourist industry.

An old man from a nearby village knows how to make proper adobe houses, so we hire him to build new cottages for the scouts and their families. Using beautiful earth shades of rust, red, brown, and green, the scouts' wives paint the new mud houses with striking geometric patterns. We hire a crew of sixty villagers to improve the track into the park.

The special military-trained scouts promised by the director show up and settle into the new houses. Every dawn Kotela can be heard barking orders as he drills them on the airstrip. Looking neat in their new uniforms, the scouts salute their officers smartly. The old beer pot — formerly the center of activity — has disappeared. Mano Camp, the once-dreary den for bedraggled scouts, is pulsing with new energy.

We hire two English lads, Ian Spincer and Edward North, who are fresh out of the University of Reading. They are unsuspecting and ready for anything, so we station them at Mano to help Kotela organize camp logistics and a law-enforcement program. Ian, a graduate in agriculture, begins a farm at Mano that produces vegetables, rabbits, and poultry for the scouts and their families. He installs a mill to grind their corn for mealie-meal, and supervises the delivery of all foodstuffs to the remote camps by tractor and trailer. Edward sets up a firearm training program for the scouts, issuing the new guns we have imported from the States. Both he and Ian patrol with them, evaluating their field performance. We purchase more camping equipment and a truck for the scouts, and Simbeye moves to Mano as their official driver. He is also in charge of training an auxiliary force of local villagers who will aid the scouts.

Kotela, Ian, and Edward organize the unit into seven squads and devise regular schedules for patrols into the park. They employ a regiment of porters — most of whom previously worked for the poachers — to carry food and supplies to scouts in the park. Now the men can patrol for as long as three weeks, covering much larger areas, without Mark's having to fly dangerous resupply missions. For the first time ever, there are at least some scouts in North Luangwa National Park at all times. Mark creates special units for those who perform well, and they are issued extra equipment — new guns, jungle knives, binoculars, compasses.

Everything is in place; but we have yet to capture poachers.

One afternoon, after supervising the road crew all day, Mark and I drive into the main camp at about four in the afternoon. The place seems deserted, and then we see that all the wives, children, and men of Mano are standing around the n'saka. The scouts have returned from their first village sweep, and the n'saka is crowded with fourteen meat poachers, a pile of illegal guns stacked against a tree outside.

The sweep continues for four more days. The scouts raid villages all night — bursting into poachers' huts while they sleep — and drive back to Mano in the morning, their truck loaded with suspects and illegal guns. The poachers have acted with impunity for so long that they are caught off guard. Moving swiftly, Kotela and his men capture dozens before the word gets out that the scouts are back in business.

The old game guards, like Island Zulu and Tapa, walk taller now and salute us with pride. No longer full of excuses and complaints, they tell us wildly exaggerated tales of capturing notorious poachers. Nelson Mumba, still wearing his red bandana and refusing to patrol, and Patrick Mubuka, the scout who shot elephants in the park, are put in the back of a truck, driven to Mpika, and dumped at the warden's door, never to return to Mano.

While Kotela and his scouts patrol the park and raid the villages, Mark continues to terrorize the poachers from the air. Suddenly Mano has become the number one unit in Zambia, capturing more poachers than any other.

The five camps of Mano Unit are only effective on the western border of the park. To protect its northern flank, we send Edward North to assist the scouts and villagers of Fulaza. We hire an Alaskan bush pilot, Larry Campbell, to rebuild the scout camp in Nabwalya, south of the park, as well as to solve some of the problems in the village.

Dramatic as the changes are, they are just a beginning. Although Kotela is having great success rounding up many of the commercial meat poachers, most of the big ivory poachers in villages like Mwamfushi are still eluding the scouts with their reputed powers of invisible juju. The park covers twenty-four hundred square miles, and only twelve game guards patrol at a time. Experienced men such as Chikilinti and Chanda Seven have little trouble avoiding them. Mark chases them out of the park, but they come right back. The scouts capture one; the magistrate lets him go. Somehow we have to get these men of Mwamfushi Village.

23
Mwamfushi Village

DELIA

Dear Directors
North Luangwa Conservation Project

My name is Steven Nsofwa and I am thirteen years old and I student at Mukungule Primary School. Please, I wanting thank Madam and Sir for the things you have done for our village. Now since you are coming the maize mill makes our mealie-meal, the shop sells our soap, the school now has a map of the world. We the students love to play the games about the elephants and draw pictures of the lions. When we grow up we will chase the poachers from our village so that there will always be the animals in the rivers. For now we are not too big to chase them. Please we want to thank you.

Yours,
STEVEN NSOFWA

○ ○ ○

DODGING DEEP GULLIES and ruts, Mark steers the truck toward Mwamfushi Village. On the seat between us are Mark's leather flight bag and my briefcase. In Mark's flight bag — jammed among the aeronautical maps and papers — is his 9-mm pistol; in my satchel is a .38 caliber revolver. As we drive along, we scan the tall, waving grass along the track, searching for any sign of an ambush.

We have been warned not to go to Mwamfushi. Even Kotela tells us it is too dangerous. The men in this village have tried to kill us, they've shot at Musakanya's house with automatic weapons, and they have poisoned Jealous and several other people who work for us. But if we can't stop the poachers of Mwamfushi, there is no hope for saving the elephants of North Luangwa. We have sent word to the headman of Mwamfushi that we would like to meet with his villagers this Saturday morning at the schoolhouse. We are gambling that the poachers won't risk attacking us in broad daylight, with other people around.

Stopping along the way at scattered huts and bomas, we pick up Chief Chikwanda and his retainers. Also with us is Max Saili, who is in charge of our project's work in the villages. When we drive up to the clay-brick school, our pickup splattered with mud and loaded with dust-coated officialdom, thirty villagers are waiting in the barren schoolyard. A few old men, dressed in patched trousers and ragged shirts, shake our hands; but most people just stare. Clutching our cases tightly, we make our way through the crowd.

As we enter the schoolroom, Mark discreetly points to a man who is a big buffalo poacher. None of the ivory poachers — Chanda Seven, Chikilinti, Bernard Mutondo, Simu Chimba, or Mpundu Katongo — have come, but I am glad this man is here; if he will exchange his weapon for a job, that will set an example for others to follow. Saili, Mark, and I sit in chairs that have been arranged at the front of the room; the villagers sit on the students' benches. We all stand as Saili leads us in the singing of Zambia's national anthem. Its soft, mournful melody drifts out of the cracked windows and across the untended fields.

Standing to give the opening speech, Honorable Chief Chikwanda is wearing a T-shirt we have given him earlier. The print of a large elephant adorns the back, and whenever he repeats the word "elephant" in his speech — which is very often indeed — he whirls around, swaying back and forth, presenting the dancing elephant to his audience. Shouting and strutting like an evangelistic preacher, he reminds his people over and over that wildlife is a valuable resource, that it is the heritage of his people, and that poachers are sacrificing their children's future. He ends with a stern warning that poaching in his chiefdom must cease immediately. It is quite a performance, but it would be much more impressive if everyone in the room did not know that Chikwanda himself has been charged with elephant poaching more than once. At this very moment, in fact, he is appealing one of his convictions.

Saili introduces us, and as we speak he translates after every few sentences. We begin by explaining that we are not here to arrest anybody; that if, by chance, any poachers are present (we know that probably 85 percent of the people here are involved), we will give them jobs if they turn in their weapons. We know they are poaching because they need food and work, and we are here to help them find alternatives. It is a long, halting business with Saili translating, but finally we exhaust our supply of convincing and worn-out statements. There are murmurs of approval from some of the older, toothless crowd, but several of the younger men argue heatedly among themselves.

A youth in a faded pink shirt stands up and says in English, "This what you say may be a good thing, but there are many men in this village — not myself, of course (laughter) — who have to poach. You maybe to hire some of them, but you cannot hire us all. There are plenty." Several people nod or shout in agreement.

Another young man, no more than sixteen, raises his hand. "A friend I have who carry for the poachers. What will he do if poachers go from this place?"

An elder stands. "That is what the Owenses are saying, they will help us find other work."

"What are you saying, old man?" shouts the man in pink. "It is you who gives your daughters to the poachers for some little meat!" The room erupts as men shake their fists and shout at one another in Chibemba. One elder stomps out of the room. Raising his hands and speaking Chibemba, Saili eventually restores order.

When the crowd is calm, Mark speaks again. "We know this will not be easy. But your whole village depends on poaching, which is a crime. Your own children are told to be carriers, which is illegal and dangerous. And you know better than I that if you continue shooting the animals they will all be finished. Think about how far your father had to walk before finding an elephant, buffalo, or hippo to shoot. Your grandfathers and fathers could get meat right around your village; now you must walk forty or fifty miles to find any animals. Gentlemen, there are so many people and so few animals now, that they cannot feed you anymore. If you keep killing them, soon they will be gone. So you must find ways to make money by keeping them alive. And we are here to help." Saili translates.

Again a murmur of discontent rattles around the room. Mark and I look at each other, disappointed; things are not going as we'd hoped.

Then Mark points to the buffalo poacher in the back of the room. "I'll start with this man. I know you, I have seen you in the park. I'll give you a good job right now. Come and see us after the meeting." The crowd erupts in laughter. The man grins at his friends, but says nothing.

After forty-five minutes of shouting and arguments, I pass around paper and pens and ask those interested in working for us to write down their names and skills. A few young men walk hurriedly from the room, probably nervous about revealing their identities. But most of those who can write scribble their names, and the names of their illiterate friends.

Seven of the men — including the man in the pink shirt — claim to be trained carpenters. They are out of work because the tools from their cooperative were stolen and they cannot afford new ones. One man is a tailor; several know how to make and lay bricks; two are licensed drivers. The village is full of men who, if given a chance, could earn an honest living. Mark and I whisper quietly together, making some quick decisions.

"We'll start right now to help your village," I say. "First, we'll lend you cash to buy the tools, wood, and hardware necessary to open a carpentry shop. When you are making furniture and bringing in money, you can gradually repay us, so that we can help others."

"But remember," Mark interrupts, "this is not a gift. In exchange, you must stop poaching and you must chase the big poachers from your village. Do you agree?"

Almost everyone, including the man in the pink shirt, nods.

"Also," Mark adds, "we'll hire a labor crew to rebuild the road between your village and Mpika. Musakanya, who was once a poacher from your village but who now works for us, will be the supervisor." Before he has finished speaking, men are scrambling around Musakanya, asking to be chosen for the crew.

We invite them to apply for loans to start other cottage industries — cobbler shops, peanut presses for making cooking oil —

but caution that we cannot grant everyone a loan. Priority will be given to the businesses that employ the most people or produce food or some essential community service.

By now it is well after lunch. Almost no one has left the schoolroom and many others have come in. Exhausted, we close the meeting with another singing of the national anthem and make our way through the crowd of people pressing around us to ask for help. A small woman, dressed in a red chitenge, grabs my arm. "Madam," she says, "you have forgotten the women."

I stare at her for a moment, feeling embarrassed. "I promise, I haven't forgotten you. It's just that the men do the poaching, so we've offered them jobs first."

"You do not understand," she continues. "The women are very dangerous in this village. They do all the work — farming, house building, cooking, washing — while the men sit under the trees. So it is the women who say to their husbands, 'Why don't you go to the park and get some bush meat?' It is the women who tell their children to leave school to work as carriers for the poachers."

I have not heard this before, but I can see the truth in it. "How can we help?" I ask. Standing in the dusty schoolyard, surrounded by chattering villagers, scampering children, and the ubiquitous scratching chickens, the women and I make a deal to set up a sewing shop for them.

When at last we reach our truck, still surrounded by would-be converts, I see the buffalo poacher walking quickly around the school toward the fields. He has not come to us for a job. This saddens me, but I feel that otherwise the meeting has been a huge success.

Not wanting to lose momentum, we immediately send Tom and Wanda Canon, our project volunteers, to Lusaka to buy carpentry tools, a manual sewing machine, a grinding mill, and tools for the road crew.

A few weeks after our first meeting we drive back to Mwamfushi with Tom, Wanda, and Saili. Eighty men and women are crammed into the schoolhouse, chattering excitedly as they wait for us. Small children line the walls outside, chinning up to poke their faces through the windows. The villagers clap, sing, and ululate a high-pitched, spiritual melody as we present the sewing machine to the women and the tools to the men. We clap along, then open a discussion about other industries that can be started in the village and how poaching can be stopped.

While Saili is translating, a young man slips through the doorway into the schoolroom and hands Mark a scrap of paper. He reads it, grins, and hands it to me. Scribbled in a wavery block print are the words, "I want to joine yu. I give my weapon. Please to met me in shed behind the school before you going. Cum alone." It is signed "Chanda Seven."

○ ○ ○

"Mark, you can't just walk out there by yourself," I whisper. The meeting is finished and almost everyone has filed outside. We are standing alone in a corner of the schoolroom.

"I'll be careful."

In the schoolyard Saili, the Canons, and I continue talking to the villagers. Meanwhile Mark, his hand in his flight bag, disappears around the corner of the school, heading for a crumbling mud-brick shed that stands on the edge of a maize patch. A wooden door dangles on one hinge, hiding the dark interior. Mark stands against the wall, listening for sounds from inside, then kicks the door open, and peers in. Gradually his eyes adjust to the darkness, and the outline of a man takes form. He is standing in the shadows behind a crude counter, his hands on its top. Near his fingers — a twitch away — lies an AK-47.

"You are Chanda Seven?" Mark asks, his eyes riveted on the rifle. "What do you want?"

"I'll give you my weapon if you give me work."

"The first thing you must do is step back from the counter." Chanda Seven moves deeper into the gloom. Mark steps quickly inside, takes the rifle by its barrel, and leans it against the wall.

"I can give you a job. But how do I know I can trust you? You have tried to kill me and my wife, you have shot many elephants, you have shot at Musakanya's house, you have poisoned Jealous."

"I do not know how you can trust a man such as me. It can be only that I give you my weapon. Then I am unarmed."

"It is not enough to give me your weapon. You might come to work for me, learn our routine, then lead other poachers to kill me. To work for me, you must first prove I can trust you. Help me capture the other poachers from Mwamfushi — Simu Chimba, Chikilinti, Mpundu Katongo, and Bernard Mutondo — and I will give you a very good job. You must find out when and where they plan to poach, and send a message to me through Musakanya. Do you agree?"

"Eh, Mukwai, yes."

Mark puts the AK in a gunnysack and shakes hands with one of the most notorious poachers in Mwamfushi. Walking back across the crowded schoolyard, Mark gives me a thumbs-up salute.

I smile. One of the big guys taken — without a shot fired, without a dangerous night flight.

24
Sharing the Same Season

DELIA

The struggle for any dream
is always worth the effort,
for in the struggle lies its strength,
    and fulfillment
    toward the changing seasons
    of ourselves.

— WALTER RINDER

○ ○ ○

IN MAY 1991 the marula fruits lie on the ground bursting with a honey-sweet fragrance, and my mind turns once again to Survivor. Did Mpundu Katongo, Chanda Seven, and Chikilinti kill him or did he escape? Am I foolish to hope that he will wander into camp on his return from the plains? Mark continues to fly antipoaching patrols and count elephants; I spend most of the time at my river camp, encouraging scouts, or working in Mwamfushi. But I never drive through the hills near Marula-Puku without thinking of Survivor, without searching the ridges and valleys for an elephant with small tusks and a hole in his left ear.

One afternoon a few weeks after our visit to Mwamfushi, I am sitting on the red, dusty ground with the children of Mano, drawing pictures of elephants. The surrounding forest trills with the songs of lovebirds and wild parrots, and the encampment hums with the steady sounds of the women cooking and washing outside their mud huts. The drone of an engine drifts through the trees: Mark is grading the Mano airstrip with one of the new tractors.

A plume of dust rising behind it, Mano's truck roars into camp with ten scouts in the back, singing and holding their thumbs up. We have never heard the scouts sing before; the children and I jump up and run to meet them. A ragged, dusty man sits in the back of the truck, handcuffed, his head hanging.

"We have captured Simu Chimba, Madam! Look how small he is! A big poacher like this, how can he be so small?"

"Well done!" I congratulate them, thinking, "Two down, three to go."

○ ○ ○

With Mark patrolling in the air, the scouts and our team busy on the ground, we haven't seen a poached elephant in eight months. Our work to win over the people of Mwamfushi continues, although in a painfully halting way. Everything needed to supply the budding cottage industries, from sewing needles to hacksaw blades, must be trucked all the way from Lusaka or imported from abroad. But already there is a change in the village; it seems to whistle. Musakanya and his road crew have built a broad, smooth track from Mpika to the Mwamfushi; the mill is grinding mealie-meal; the sewing shop is manufacturing new uniforms for the game guards; the carpenters have produced a desk. One person talks of making candles, another of making soap, a third of developing a fish farm. We have started a conservation education program in the school, and posters of elephants, lions, and leopards — courtesy of the Dallas Zoo — give splashes of pride and color to the clay-brick walls.

With a new sense of authority and hope, the people of the village have been spying on Chikilinti, Mpundu Katongo, Simu Chimba, and the other commercial poachers, and reporting their plans to Musakanya. By harassing them with insults and threats, the Mwamfushi vigilantes have forced the poachers out of the village into the bush, where they hide out in grass hovels, afraid even to have a campfire at night. Their power over the villagers has been broken. Chanda Seven and Musakanya, the two ex-poachers now working for us in Mwamfushi, are shining examples for the unconverted. Both have supervisory positions — Musakanya with the road crew, Chanda Seven on a farm — and are pulling down good salaries without breaking the law.

One lazy afternoon, while all of Africa is nodding in the heat, Mpundu Katongo wanders down from the hills toward Chanda Seven's hut. He is planning a major poaching expedition into North Luangwa and hopes to persuade Chanda Seven to join him. Mpundu has heard all the nonsense about fish farms and grinding mills, but does not believe any of it will pay as well as poaching. Although he is short, he is very strong; and unlike some of the other poachers he is not frightened by the villagers.

Chanda Seven sees his old friend across the field and invites him into his mud-wattle hut for beer. They shake hands in the neatly swept yard, and Chanda Seven steps aside, allowing his guest into the hut. As they duck through the tiny doorway, Chanda shoves Katongo against the far wall, jumps back outside, and locks the door. Katongo shouts and bangs on the puny door, threatening to break out. Grabbing an ax, Chanda Seven swears he will chop Mpundu into tiny bits and feed him to the hyenas if he tries to escape. Drawn to the commotion, vigilantes armed with hoes and rakes race through the maize patches to help Seven contain his captive, shouting insults at him through the door of the hut.

When Musakanya sees what has happened, he runs five miles to Mpika to inform the game guards. It takes some doing to convince the Mpika scouts to come, but eventually, using one of our trucks, they drive to Mwamfushi and arrest Mpundu Katongo and take him to Mpika. Early the next day, even before we have heard of the arrest, Max Saili radios us to say that he has heard the warden is going to release Katongo.

"Oh no he's not!" Mark shouts over the mike. "Don't let anything happen! I'll be in Mpika in thirty minutes." Mark jumps into the plane and flies to Mpika, where Saili meets him at the airstrip. No doubt a bribe has changed hands, but this time it won't work.

At ten o'clock in the morning Mark roars up to Mpondo's Roadside Bar and jams on the brakes, a cloud of dust swirling behind him. He marches inside the ramshackle building and looks around the dimly lit room. Warden Mulenga is sitting alone at a table with eight empty beer bottles. He glances in Mark's direction and then stares blearily at the wall.

"I heard you're going to release Mpundu Katongo?" Mark demands.

"Insufficient evidence," the warden slurs.

"You know this man is a poacher. If you don't have enough evidence, we do. If you release him, I'm going to make a big stink at the ministry."

The drunken warden, mumbling something unintelligible, tears a scrap from a brown paper bag and scribbles his authorization for Katongo to be taken to Mano for questioning. He agrees not to drop the charges against Katongo as long as we hire him. Mpundu will be in custody of Kotela and the Mano scouts.

"Thanks, warden, have another beer." Mark slaps some kwacha notes on the table and walks out.

Handcuffed and guarded by two scouts, the poacher is lifted into the plane. Mark flies him to Mano airstrip, where the scouts and I meet him. They swarm around the plane, and when Mpundu is handed down to them, they march off toward camp, pushing and shoving the shackled captive. Once in the n'saka the scouts hold Mpundu down on the ground and paint blue and yellow lines on his face — a juju that removes all power from the poacher. Hands and feet bound, he sits in the center of the n'saka while the scouts, wives, and children take turns humiliating him. One scout demands that Mpundu act like a chicken. Hobbling around the camp, he scratches the dust with his bare feet and flaps his arms as best he can. Every few steps he topples over and falls hard to the ground, and everyone laughs.

When the scouts at last tire of the ritual, Kotela tells us that we can interview the prisoner. We set up the video camera and I stare into the eyes of Mpundu Katongo. He is a short, stocky man with a bulldog's face. Stripped of his juju, he sits quietly staring into the dirt and confesses that he has shot more than seventy-five elephants, hundreds of buffalo, and too many puku to count. Speaking clearly to the camera, he admits shooting at the airplane with semiautomatic weapons on many occasions. In vivid detail he describes how he and the others planned to attack our camp but abandoned the scheme when they saw the game guards. He tells us that it was he, Chanda Seven, and Chikilinti who shot the elephants near Marula-Puku.

We bring Katongo's family to Mano and give them a house. We hire him to lead the scouts on patrols, using his knowledge of routes and hunting areas to help them ambush and apprehend other poachers. Later we also hire Bernard Mutondo, the poacher who killed a game scout and wounded three others south of the park and nevertheless was released by the magistrate. Now three of the five men who tried to kill us are on our payroll.

○ ○ ○

Stepping quietly through the undergrowth, I walk away from Nyama Zamara lagoon toward my river camp. A large male water-buck, standing in the tall grass, swings his head in my direction. I don't move. He looks at me for a moment, then continues to graze. I walk on toward the beach, where sixty hippos are sprawled on the damp sand.

Unexpectedly I hear the sound of our airplane to the south; Mark must be patrolling the Mwaleshi River. As always when I hear the plane, I take the walkie-talkie from my backpack and switch it on in case he calls me. Although he often patrols in this area, he has never visited my camp. The drone of the engine grows louder.

"Brown Hyena, this is Sand Panther." Mark's voice crackles over the radio. "Do you read me?"

I can see the plane swooping low above the trees at the river's bend. "Roger, Sand Panther. Go ahead."

"Hi, Boo! Want some company for dinner tonight?"

"Roger, Sand Panther. That'll be fine. As long as you understand that dinner at my camp is a jacket-and-tie affair," I joke. "And don't forget the chocolates."

"Of course," Mark laughs over the air. "I'll fly back late this afternoon. Please pick me up at the airstrip on the plains where we darted Bouncer."

"Roger. See you then. Brown Hyena clear." I zip the radio into my backpack and run through the trees toward camp, avoiding the beach so that I won't frighten the hippos. What in the world will I cook for dinner?

In my little grass hut I fling open the blue storage trunks and rummage through the tins looking for something special. I decide on packaged onion soup, pasta with canned mushroom and cheese sauce, green beans, and cookies. I set the table with a chitenge patterned with swirls of greens, blues, and reds, candles set in snail shells, and yellow enamel cups and plates. At the edge of camp I pick tiny blue wildflowers and place them on the table in an empty peanut butter jar. Apparently sensing my excitement, the baboons scramble into the ebony tree over the hut and lean from the branches to watch me.

Folding a sheet of paper in half and decorating it with sketches of hippos and crocodiles, I write out a menu for the evening:

Appetizer
Smoked oysters Zamara
Soup
Luangwa onion soup with garlic croutons
Entrée
Lagoon pasta with mushrooms and cheese
Green beans Lubonga
Dessert
Moon cookies

I have no decent clothes at my bush camp. Determined to look as spiffy as possible, I make a skirt of another chitenge and wear it with a white blouse, sandals, and my favorite Bushman earrings. In the late afternoon I drive to the grass airstrip on a flat open plain about four miles from the river. During the twenty-minute trip I pass herds of wildebeests, zebras, and buffalo grazing along the track. I am a mile from the strip when Mark swoops down in the plane right above the truck. Perfect timing. He will land just before I arrive.

By the time I turn onto the dusty strip, the plane is parked at the far end. But driving toward it, I cannot see my pilot. Strange — he should be out of the plane by now, tying it down for the night. Driving closer, I am more and more puzzled; the plane stands deserted. I park next to it, step out, and look around.

Suddenly Mark struts from behind the fuselage where he has been hiding. Below the belt he is dressed as usual — khaki shorts, bush socks, and desert boots. But above the waist he is wearing a smart blue blazer, a white dress shirt, and a tie. A wiry bunch of wildflowers hides his devilish grin, and a bottle of champagne is tucked under his arm.

"Bonjour, madame. Sand Panther at your service," he says with a sweeping bow.

On the bank overlooking the beach, we nibble smoked oysters and sip champagne, watching the sun and the hippos sink into the broad river. Later, with moonlight streaming on the white sand, the hippos stagger from the water and stroll just below our dinnertable perched on the edge of the bank. My little grass hut glows with soft candle and lantern light. Whispering and laughing softly, we search the sky for shooting stars — and count six.

Later, on our bedrolls in the tent, I snatch up my pillow and look for chocolates. A long time ago it was Mark's favorite hiding place for special surprises, including chocolates. But there is nothing. Hiding my disappointment, I slide between the sheets and he pulls me close — laughing. Then my feet touch something at the far end of the covers.

"Mark, what have you done now?" Peeling back the blanket, I discover chocolate bars — twenty-five of them — lined up at the tips of my toes.

○ ○ ○

It is the dry season again. The grasses are tired now, having made seeds in every imaginable shape and array. They lie on their sides, resting their heads near the ground. Eventually the wildfires will consume them, sending their last drops of life to the clouds, which in turn will rain down on the saplings of distant hills. Or, if the fires do not come, the grasses will return to the soil, giving their souls to new hopeful seeds. Either way, we will see them again. Even the colors are weary, having burned themselves out with brilliant golds and reds, then fading to the pale hue of straw. Life is taking a breather, and the year itself must rest.

It is the dry season again. It comes every year. But I know now that the life-giving rains will return. Just as there is an end to winter, there is an end to drought. The secret is to *live* in every season. The Kalahari taught me this, and like the desert I want to sing in the dry season and dance in the rains.

Since the poachers were stopped before they could set their wildfires, for once there is grass for the animals to eat, long into the dry season. Meandering lines of elephants drift across the valley floor, feeding on the savannas. In former years, by March or April they would have fled into the protective hills of the scarp, abandoning the superior forage of the valley grasses for the fibrous bark of trees in the miombo woodlands. But now Long Ear, Misty, Marula, and their young feed along the open floodplains of the Mwaleshi, where the tall elephant grass waves in the gentle breeze.

At the airstrip one morning, Kasokola and Mwamba, who are guarding the plane, tell us they have seen two elephants in the small valley near Khaya Stream below the hill. One, they say, has tusks; one does not. For the next few days we look for them but see nothing. Several mornings later, we are passing Hippo Pool on our way back to camp when a bull elephant without tusks appears in the tall grass near the bank. It is Cheers. Every day after that we find him feeding on the long grasses across the Lubonga near camp, or on fruits near the airstrip; but he will not come closer. Always there is another elephant with him, standing deep in the trees, so that we can never get a good look at him. Like a gray shadow, he always slips silently away.

Late one afternoon, sitting quietly by the river, Mark and I hear a rustling on the far bank. Slowly, an elephant plods from the tall reeds of a dambo on the other side and stands looking at the marula trees behind us. I put my hands to my face in disbelief. The elephant has tusks as long as Mark's arms and a tiny hole in his left ear. It is Survivor.

For several minutes he watches us with eyes that have seen too much. He lifts his trunk high into the air in our direction. But we are not fooled; this is not a greeting. It is the marula fruits that he smells and the marula fruits that he wants, not contact with us. He is not thanking us for being here, or blaming us for not doing a better job of protecting him. He just wants to eat these fruits, wander these hills, and live with his own kind. It is not too much for his kind to ask, or for our kind to give.

He gives us a wide berth as he passes on the far bank, not coming nearly as close to us as he did last year. He lumbers to the river, touching the water with his trunk, lifting it to his mouth. He stands for long moments, looking at us, then glides silently along the sandbar. It is said that elephants do not forget; perhaps they do forgive.

"What are we going to do now?" Mark whispers to me.

"What do you mean?"

"You've always said we'd go home when the elephants could come to the river and drink in peace."

I look along the Lubonga, where it gently sweeps through the high banks and rocky shoals. Five puku lie in the cool sand near a pair of Egyptian geese.

And I answer, "We are home."

EPILOGUE

Return to Deception Valley

DELIA

The land has been hurt. Misuse is not to be
excused, and its ill effects will long be felt.
But nature will not be eliminated, even here.
Rain, moss, and time apply their healing bandage,
and the injured land at last recovers.
Nature is evergreen, after all.

— ROBERT MICHAEL PYLE

○ ○ ○

DURING ALL OUR YEARS in Luangwa we never forgot the Kalahari. Whenever we saw the Serendipity Pride, we thought of the desert lions; whenever it rained at Marula-Puku, we wondered if East Dune was still dry; whenever there was a full moon, we longed for Deception Valley.

In 1988, while we were in North Luangwa, we received a letter reporting that a special commission in Botswana had decided the fate of the Central Kalahari Game Reserve. Among the alternatives it had discussed was dissolving the lower two-thirds of the reserve so that it could be used for commercial cattle ranching. In the end, under scrutiny by international conservation agencies, the commission voted to keep the entire reserve intact. In addition, it adopted many of the environmental recommendations we had made before all the controversy. These included taking down certain fences to open a corridor for migratory species such as wildebeests and hartebeests. Of course, by then most of the wildebeest population — more than a quarter of a million animals, as well as tens of thousands of other desert antelope — had perished. But perhaps if good rains return to the Kalahari, this harsh but resilient land will once again provide the miles of golden grass necessary to bring back these populations. Man has dealt the Kalahari a staggering blow, but deserts know all about rebirth.

Inasmuch as our Prohibited Immigrant status had been reversed, once the decision was made to save the reserve, nothing could keep us away from the moody dunes and ancient river valleys that had been our home for seven years. We planned an expedition to clean up our campsite, to remove every trace of our having lived there; to search for the lions we had radio collared before our deportation; and to say a proper good-bye to the Kalahari.

As we had done in 1985, Mark flew our plane from Gaborone and I drove to Deception Valley through the thorn country. In 1988 the drought that had gripped the desert since 1979 still had its hold on the land. The heavy clay soils of the ancient riverbed had been reduced to a sickly dry powder from the years of angry sun and tireless winds. As I drove across Deception and around Acacia Point, billows of pale dust rose behind the truck. Not a single gnarled scrub or tortured blade of grass had survived. Even the grass stubbles were long since buried under a layer of time.

Mark was standing by the plane, parked in the dilapidated boma we built years ago to keep the Blue Pride lions from chewing the tires. He walked out to greet me and we sat on the dry riverbed near our old camp and homestead. To the north was Acacia Point, Mid-Pan Water Hole, Eagle Island, Cheetah Hill, and North Dune; to the south, Bush Island, Tree Island, and Jackal Island in South Bay — all as familiar today as they were years ago. The Kalahari's face was ashen with drought, sandblasted, wrinkled, and lifeless from the harsh wind. I wondered if she had noticed a similar change in us; for we too had endured a long dry spell.

After a while we walked into what was left of our camp. The *Ziziphus mucronata* and *Acacia tortillas* trees had managed to produce leaves, but they were gray and withered. As I stepped into the barren tree island, a Marico flycatcher swooped past my head and landed on a branch five feet away. He chirped urgently, wings trembling at his sides as he begged for food. Surely this was one of the flycatchers we had known before. I ran to the cool box, tore off a piece of cheese, and held it out to him. He took it as if we had fed him only yesterday.

After we had been deported, friends had removed our tents, but the kitchen boma with its ragged thatch roof was still standing. The "hyena table" — built six feet off the ground to keep the brown hyenas from our pots and pans — remained beneath the acacia tree. The bath boma and a few stick tables lay in various stages of termite consumption. Tomorrow we would clean it all up, stack it into a huge pile, and burn it.

Late in the afternoon we dug up a bottle of Nederburg Cabernet Sauvignon that was still buried in our "wine cellar" beneath the ziziphus tree. We replaced it with a new bottle and a note in a jar, thinking that someday we might pass this way again. Then, sitting crosslegged on the riverbed, just a few yards from where our water drums once stood, we watched the sun disappear beyond the dunes. Sipping wine from tin mugs, we listened to the click-click-click of barking geckos and the mournful, wavering cries of a jackal somewhere beyond the dunes.

The next morning Mark was determined to search for the lions we had radio collared in 1985 on our initial return to the Kalahari, just weeks before we were deported. I didn't want to discourage him, but my own feeling was that there was very little chance of ever finding them. It had been two and a half years since we had darted and collared eight of them, including Happy, whom we had known for years, and Sunrise and Sage, her younger pridemates. Since our departure the lions must have scattered for thousands of square miles, searching for prey in the far reaches of the desert. But how could we not try to find them? We mounted the antennas under the wings, and Mark took off as he had hundreds of times, to search for lions in the dunes.

I stayed behind and began the grueling task of taking down the kitchen and bath bomas, the airplane fence, and the tables. I hacked away with an ax and dragged poles and grass to a large pit. The heat around me was intense, something you could almost reach out and touch. As I worked, I wondered how we had endured this for so many years. Sometimes I could hear the drone of the plane, as Mark flew on and on — north, south, east, and west on imaginary grid lines across the sky. When he landed for a lunch of nuts and fruit, his face was red with heat, grim and determined. All morning he had heard nothing through his earphones except static and phantom signals. He tried for hours again that afternoon, and landed just before sunset, shrugging his shoulders. Nothing.

The next morning he took off and flew until noon, landed to refuel, and took off again. I burned poles and cleared rubbish. I was beginning to think that hauling heavy logs through the heat while Mark waffled around in the cooler altitudes was a lousy arrangement. Then I heard the plane making a beeline for camp. It landed. Mark jumped out and ran toward me, shouting, "I've found them! You're not going to believe it. I've found seven of the eight lions! And Happy is just beyond East Dune."

As though we had never been away, we found ourselves once again in the truck, trundling over the dune faces, toward the beep-beep-beep of a lion's radio signal. This time my throat knotted, not from thirst but from the laboring of my heart. "Are you sure you saw her? Maybe she slipped her collar. Or maybe she's dead."

"Hang on, Boo. You'll see."

The dune grasses, bleached blond by the sun, rattled with drought as they swayed gently in the midday heat. The sun's rays beat straight down, making a desert without shadows. Mark stopped the truck and pointed ahead. Three lionesses sleeping under an acacia bush slowly raised their heads, panting as they peered at us. Two were very young, and we did not recognize them. But the other had a vaguely familiar face and wore a tattered radio collar. She stood, her eyes wide. It was Happy, now thirteen years old — ancient for a Kalahari lioness. We had sat with her for hundreds of hours, followed her across star-lit dunes, and even slept near her on the desert sands on several occasions. We had found Happy on our first return to the Kalahari in 1985, and here she was again.

She staggered to her feet and walked slowly toward us, her ribs jutting out in dark lines under skin like parchment, her belly high and tight to her sagging spine. She was old and she was starving. She stumbled, then hesitated, swaying, her strength dissipated in the waves of midday heat. She started forward again and came to within ten feet of the truck. I thought for a moment that she might chew the tires, as she and the other Blue Pride lionesses had done so often before. Instead, she looked at us with soft, golden eyes whose lack of fear told us all we needed to know about whether or not she recognized us. If only we could ask her, "Where's Blue? Whatever happened to Moffet? Are these your cubs?" But years had gone by, and the answers were forever lost in the desert.

She walked around the truck, nearly touching its rear bumper with her side, and rested again in the patchy shade of a few scrawny branches. We stayed with the lionesses all afternoon and that evening watched them try unsuccessfully to kill a large male gemsbok. The effort exhausted them and they stood panting, their shrunken bellies heaving. They were a pitiful trio: Happy too old to hunt well anymore, the young ones too inexperienced. Born in a land that only rarely offers water and is stingy even with shade, they stood like three spindly monuments to survival. We left them at sunset, feeling the way the Kalahari always makes us feel; intrigued by her wonders, sobered by her harshness, saddened by her finality.

The next morning we drove across East Dune and found Happy one final time. She was with three older females as well as the two younger ones: the Blue Pride members, unnamed, unknown, but enduring. Tucked under an *Acacia mellifera* bush was a freshly killed gemsbok. All of the lions' bellies, including Happy's, were full.

Animals know about greetings: long-separated lions rush to one another, rubbing heads and bodies together in reunion; brown hyenas smell one another's necks and tails; jackals sniff noses. But do animals know about good-bye, I wondered as we drove away from Happy for the last time. I held her eyes with mine until her tawny face faded into the straw-colored grasses of the Kalahari. We knew we would not see her again; she would never survive another dry season. But at least she was surrounded by her pride in a reserve that was secure.

We returned to North Luangwa to continue our programs there, and on landing at the airstrip we were told by the guys that a lioness had been visiting their camp every evening. Several nights later we found her near the strip, where we darted her. And as always we weighed, collared, and named her. She is small, not very strong, but she is still here. She is Hope.

Postscript

DELIA

WHEN WE BEGAN our project in 1986, the elephants of North Luangwa National Park were being poached at the rate of one thousand each year. By the end of 1991 that number had been reduced to twelve.

On January 16, 1992, David Chile of Mwamfushi Village, one of the scholarship students of our North Luangwa Conservation Project, presented newly elected President Frederick Chiluba with a petition signed by three thousand Zambians requesting that their government observe the ivory ban. Many other organizations and individuals in Zambia — the David Shepard Foundation and the Species Protection Division are but two examples — participated in the effort to convince the Zambian government to join the ban. On Save the Elephant Day, organized by Wanda and Tom Canon, students all over Zambia and in the United States sang a special song they had written about the elephants. The singing was coordinated so that it lasted for five hours across Africa and America. The song was heard.

In a press statement on February 7, 1992, President Chiluba's government announced that it would join and fully support the international ban on ivory trade: "After reviewing evidence of a disastrous decline of the country's elephant population under the previous government, [the new government] has announced a radical change in Zambia's elephant policy . . . Zambia effectively is opposed to the resumption of international trading in elephant products." The new minister of tourism went on to request that other African nations still trading in ivory follow Zambia's lead, and he invited their cooperation and coordination in establishing measures that would ensure the conservation of their collective wildlife resources. Finally: "On Friday, 14th February 1992, the

Minister has arranged for a ceremonial burning of ivory seized by National Parks and Wildlife Services and other Zambian agencies from poachers and smugglers."

○ ○ ○

The North Luangwa Conservation Project (NLCP) is now housed in a smart office in Mpika. Evans Mukuka, our current education officer, visits ten schools a month, presenting slide shows about wildlife and conservation to the children. These programs, which first began on the red, dusty clay of Chishala Village, now reach twelve thousand students in thirty schools, in villages that once were notorious for poaching. Our scholarship program sponsors a student from each village to attend the University of Zambia.

Recently Mukuka held a wildlife quiz competition among the sixth-graders of the Mpika area schools. Teams from each school answered a battery of questions about the wildlife of North Luangwa — and the children of Mwamfushi won!

With the assistance of the Canons, Max Saili, Ian Spincer, and Edward North, our village programs help people find new jobs, start cottage industries, and grow more protein. In all, the NLCP has created more than two hundred jobs for local men and women, many of whom were once involved with poaching.

In much of Mpika District, for many years there were no butcher shops or other places to buy domestic meat. So the Bemba people, who have a long history of subsistence hunting and a keen desire for meat, were poaching wild animals to extinction. As a way of discouraging subsistence and commercial meat poaching, the project loaned enough cash to a Zambian businessman in Mpika to open a butcher shop. He brings cattle up by train from the Southern Province, butchers it, and sells beef at a lower price than that charged by black marketers who sell poached meat. A sign on the side of his butchery urges, SAVE WILDLIFE: BUY BEEF, NOT BUSH MEAT.

Confronted by the American ambassador, the official who had swallowed Bwalya Muchisa's story and charged Mark with buying black-market military rifles backed down. Bwalya has disappeared.

The Anticorruption Commission has formed a Species Protection Division (SPD), which is charged with looking into official corruption related to poaching. Periodically, SPD officers come to Mpika to investigate officials who collaborate with poachers. In 1991 they arrested Mpika's chief of police, the police station commander and an armory officer at Tazara, and two tribal chiefs. In early 1992 Warden Mulenga was discharged and Isaac Longwe, a very capable and trustworthy man, was made acting warden.

In spite of the progress, we cannot yet claim that North Luangwa is secure. Corruption is still unbridled, although under President Chiluba's administration we have renewed hope that it will diminish. Poaching continues, though it is much reduced. The police released Simu Chimba, the "little" big poacher captured by the Mano scouts; but later he was killed in the Zambezi Valley — by a charging elephant. Chikilinti eludes the scouts with his powers of invisible juju; these days, however, he poaches more often in the game management areas outside the park.

Pressured by former warden Mulenga to join his corrupt activities, Kotela — who so transformed the Mano Unit — requested a transfer to another post. We will be sad to lose him, as ultimately the protection and development of the park depend on him and his countrymen. It is up to them, not us, to make it work.

In October 1991 the new democratic government in Zambia, the MMD (Movement for Multiparty Democracy), was voted into office by an overwhelming majority — in a free and fair election monitored by former U.S. President Jimmy Carter. President Chiluba's administration is committed to the conservation of Zambia's natural resources, including its wildlife, and is supportive of a free-market system that welcomes visitors to Zambia. Many of the high-level officials of the previous one-party system who were heavily involved in poaching have been voted out of office, and the new government is addressing the widespread problems of corruption and exploitation. Poaching is so institutionalized that it will take some time before the administration can stamp it out. Nevertheless, Zambia has an opportunity to start over, and to demonstrate that man and wildlife can live side by side for the benefit of both.

The country will need strong support in this quest for a truly effective national conservation program.

Until substantial benefits can be realized from tourism and other wildlife-related industries, the North Luangwa Conservation Project must continue to find ways of fostering an economic bond between the park's animal communities and nearby villages, which might otherwise destroy the wildlife. Unfortunately, if our project and its community services were to disappear tomorrow, poaching would again threaten the park. The short-term advantages to the villagers eventually must be replaced by sustainable benefits that come directly from the park.

Tourism may be the answer, but it must be designed so that it does not disrupt the ecosystem. We have strongly recommended that it be limited to old-fashioned walking safaris. Everything is ready: the park has been secured from commercial poachers, the tour camps are set up, and there will soon be an official way to return money from tourism to the Bemba and Bisa people. All that remains is for tourists to come.

They have started. Two small companies have established walking safaris in the park. Their visitors do not have to ride in radio-controlled minibuses and elbow their way through crowds to see lions on a kill. Each person who comes and walks in the real Africa helps save elephants by making living wild animals valuable to the local people.

○ ○ ○

In the meantime Mark and I will continue in North Luangwa, assisting the government in its responsibility to secure, manage, and develop the park for the benefit of people and wildlife.

Simbeye, Mwamba, and Kasokola, who joined us at the very beginning, are still with us and still smile every morning. They and the other members of our Zambian team are working with spirit and determination to save North Luangwa.

Bouncer and his pride continue to move from the plains in the wet season to the forest near Nyama Zamara lagoon in the dry season. The Serendipity Pride maintains its territory along the Mwaleshi and tries to avoid a certain crocodile. Mona, the monitor lizard, has abandoned our bathtub and made a new nest in the side of the riverbank nearby.

Sometimes Survivor and Cheers come by our camp as they migrate to and from the mountains. On rare occasions Survivor ventures into our camp at night to feed on the marula fruits. He walks as softly as before, slurps the fruits as loudly as ever, and lulls us to sleep with his song.

APPENDIX A

Fences and Kalahari Wildlife

○ ○ ○

In the Kalahari Desert, fences are blocking antelope migrations and extinguishing wildlife populations. The fences are being erected (a) to control foot-and-mouth disease (FMD) and (b) to enclose large commercial cattle ranches.

Foot-and-Mouth Disease Quarantine

In some cases fences constructed for this purpose run for hundreds of miles across the savanna. They were built along the southern, western, northern, and part of the eastern boundary of the Central Kalahari Game Reserve, blocking antelope migrations to and from the Botetle River and Lake Xau, the only natural watering points for animals during drought.

These fences divide Botswana into quarantine sections, so that in the event of an FMD outbreak diseased cattle can be isolated, theoretically preventing spread of the infection to another sector. Another purpose of the fences is to segregate wildlife populations suspected of harboring the disease from domestic stock.

After years of research in the Kalahari we questioned the efficacy of these fences for several reasons:

1. No FMD virus has ever been found in Kalahari wildlife.[1]
2. During FMD outbreaks the virus often spreads from one quarantine area to another, irrespective of the fences — which therefore do not seem to be effective barriers. Furthermore, in Europe FMD virus has been carried in damp soil on the feet of birds and rodents, on the wheels of vehicles, or even in the air.[2] Posts and wire cannot contain the movement of such vectors, and so the disease spreads across the fences.
3. It has never been proved that wild ungulates can transmit FMD to domestic stock.[3]

In spite of the fact that the fences do not control FMD, since they were erected in the early 1950s nine major desert antelope die-offs have occurred, similar to the one we witnessed near Lake Xau. In at least five consecutive years, beginning in 1979, massive extinctions of migratory wildebeests were recorded at Lake Xau (the drought and the DeBeers diamond mine had pumped the lake dry) by the two of us and by Doug Williamson, who manned our Deception Valley camp from 1981 to 1984. Rick Lamba, a film producer, also witnessed the tragedy and made a documentary about it entitled "Frightened Wilderness." The film was aired on the Turner networks and shown on Capitol Hill. The numbers of animals perishing at Xau each year varied from fifteen thousand to sixty thousand, but eventually more than a quarter of a million wildebeests died.

But the dying wildebeests at Lake Xau were only part of the story. Sixty miles south, up to ten thousand red hartebeests were dying each year, along with uncounted numbers of gemsbok, giraffes, springbok, and other desert antelope. They piled up and died against fences that kept them from water. In total since the 1950s, the fences have killed more than a million wild ungulates, and additional numbers of carnivores that depend on them as prey.

The fences, although merely the front line of exploitation, provided hard evidence that cattle-development money was decimating wildlife populations. Tractors pulling wagons loaded with armed men regularly patrolled the fences; any wild animal that came near was shot. Thousands did, and they were killed. One of the original owners of Safari South (Pty), a safari hunting company based in Maun, has a photograph of a pile of antelope bones "as large as a two-story house" taken near the northern end of the Makalamabedi fence line. According to a range ecologist for Botswana's Department of National Parks, these patrol crews made a business of marketing in Gaborone — the capital — meat and skins from animals killed along the fences. He reported seeing a mass grave full of hundreds of fresh carcasses on one of the government's experimental farms.

By any standard, these man-induced mortalities represent one of the worst wildlife disasters of this century — one that could have been avoided entirely.

Enclosure of Large Commercial Ranches

Beginning in the 1970s, wealthy private cattle ranchers, including some of the major political figures in Botswana, were given low-interest loans from the World Bank to develop huge ranches in Kalahari wilderness areas. They built fences, drilled wells, raised cattle — and blocked antelope migrations, killing tens of thousands.

Typically these ranches were profitable for about five years. Then the wells, which were drawing water from fossil (unrechargeable) aquifers, dried up; the semiarid savannas were overgrazed to scrub and dust. Before the ranchers could repay the loans, they were forced to abandon their ranches and move on to "develop" the next enormous plot of wilderness — with another loan from the World Bank. This high-finance version of slash-and-burn agriculture left in its wake sterile wastelands covered with coils of fence wire and piles of bleached skeletons, the remains of tens of thousands of antelope whose migrations to water had been blocked.

It was only a matter of time before these commercial ranchers began to run short of land. When they did, they proposed dissolving the Central Kalahari Game Reserve, the second or third largest wildlife protectorate on earth, so that they could use it for additional cattle ranches.

After destroying tens of thousands of square miles of wilderness habitat in the name of development, the ranchers never repaid any of the World Bank's loans. Even so, the Bank was about to finance another major cattle-development scheme in Botswana when an international outcry stopped it. The United States, which provides about 20 percent of the Bank's budget, balked at funding any more such projects in equatorial Africa without proper environmental controls.

Botswana's commercial cattle industry has been profitable in the short term only because the European Community (EC) countries have paid 60 percent above the world price for Botswana beef and have guaranteed to import as much as the ranchers could produce. But only 3 percent of Botswana's households are getting two thirds of the profits from the industry. Meanwhile, the Common Market countries were paying exorbitant sums to keep frozen a 720,000-metric-ton surplus of beef. Eventually, to reduce the surplus, much of the beef would be sold to Russia for 10 percent of the cost to produce it. Furthermore, the EC rebated to Botswana's commercial ranchers 91 percent of the tariff charged for access to its market. Lavish low-interest development loans by the World Bank, coupled with high returns from the EC, created a powerful incentive for ranchers-cum-politicians in Botswana. They cashed in by developing huge ranching blocks in wilderness areas, regardless of the cost to the environment.

On our return to the Kalahari in 1987 we flew over the northeast quarter of the reserve. There we discovered hundreds of cattle and goats grazing up to twenty miles inside the reserve, where they were being watered by game scouts — at boreholes developed with EC money for migratory wildlife. The spread of cattle into the reserve had begun, which may be the reason we were ordered to leave the Kalahari.

In the end, however, as described in the text, the government of Botswana voted to keep the reserve intact and not develop it for cattle.

APPENDIX B

The Ivory Ban

○ ○ ○

Poaching of the African Elephant before 1989

From 1963 to 1989 poachers shot 86 percent of the elephants in Africa for their ivory, skin, tails, and feet. In one decade the population plummeted from 1,300,000 to 600,000 — less than half its former size. Seventy thousand elephants were shot every year to meet the world's demand for ivory. Ninety percent of the ivory entering the international market was from poached elephants. In other words, there was a 90 percent chance that an ivory bracelet in any jewelry or department store in the world was from a poached elephant. Illegal tusks were "laundered" by using false documents.

The elephant populations in twenty-one African nations declined significantly in the decade preceding the CITES ban. Zambia lost more than 80 percent of its elephants. In the Luangwa Valley alone, 100,000 elephants were shot in the period between 1973 and 1985. In North Luangwa National Park from 1975 to 1986, elephants were shot at the rate of 1000 per year. Tanzania lost 80 percent, Uganda 73 percent. In East Africa as a whole, 80 to 86 percent of the elephants were shot by poachers. In the fifteen years prior to the ban, Kenya lost 5000 elephants a year — 1095 a year in Tsavo Park alone.[1]

In 1986 the United Nations Convention for International Trade in Endangered Species (CITES) attempted to control the illegal ivory trade by requiring that import-export documents written in indelible ink accompany each tusk. This scheme failed completely. In some instances documents and marks were falsified; most of the time the procedure was ignored altogether. The poaching of elephants and the illegal ivory trade continued as before.

Most African nations did not have the resources to control elephant poaching. The price of raw ivory soared to more than $136 per pound. Corrupt government officials in many nations (including Zambia, Zimbabwe, Botswana, and South Africa)[2] participated in poaching to supplement their incomes. Governmental institutions — customs, the army, police, departments of National Parks, the judicial system — frequently were involved as well. In the majority of cases the real profit from poached elephants went into the hands of private individuals or to foreign nationals. The national treasuries of the African countries benefited very little.[3]

The CITES Ban

In early 1989, realizing that poaching was out of control and that their nations were losing a tremendous resource, eight African countries (Tanzania, Kenya, Somalia, Gambia, Zaire, Chad, Niger, and Zambia) agreed to support an international ban on the ivory trade, to begin in January 1990. In March 1989 the United States imposed an immediate ban on the importation of ivory. Canada, the EC, Switzerland, and the United Arab Emirates followed the U.S. lead.

On October 17, 1989, CITES voted (seventy-six nations to eleven) to list the African elephant on Appendix I, thereby declaring it an endangered species. The sale of all elephant parts was prohibited for two years as of January 1990.

The price of ivory paid to poachers plummeted to a hundredth of its former price: about $1.36 per pound. As a result, poaching decreased dramatically in many areas: Kenya, which had lost 5000 elephants a year, reported only 55 shot the year following the ban. In North Luangwa National Park we recorded only 12 dead elephants in 1990 (down from 1000 a year). In Selous, Tanzania, no fresh carcasses were observed. In general, poaching declined in East Africa by 80 percent. It also decreased in Chad, Gabon, Zaire, and Congo.[4]

These incredible results show that the CITES ivory ban was one of the most effective environmental policies ever adopted.

Resistance to the Ban

In spite of this unprecedented success, eight nations who stood to gain financially from the ivory trade filed reservations to the ban in 1989: China, Botswana, Zimbabwe, Mozambique, South Africa, Malawi, Zambia — which had changed its position — and Great Britain on behalf of Hong Kong (for six months).

Furthermore, South Africa, Botswana, Zimbabwe, Namibia, Malawi, Mozambique, and the previous government of Zambia moved to downlist the elephant from "endangered" status to "threatened" and to continue their ivory trade. With the exception of South Africa, these nations formed their own ivory cartel, the Southern African Center for Ivory Marketing treaty (SACIM).

In an extremely courageous move, the newly elected government of Zambia, under the MMD party, announced that it would change its position again and support the ban, and not sell the stockpile of ivory it had confiscated from poachers. On February 14, 1992, it staged a ceremonial burning of the illegal ivory. Also, China reversed its position and joined the ban.

The Southern African nations that refused to join the ban mounted an international campaign to convince the non-African nations of CITES that their position of down-listing the elephant was the correct one. Their arguments were flawed for the following reasons.

1. These nations are involved in the illegal ivory trade.

South Africa, one of the most outspoken of the nations resisting the ban, is one of the largest clearinghouses for illicit ivory on the African continent. Raw ivory entering and leaving South Africa for other countries in its customs union (Botswana, Swaziland, Namibia, Lesotho) does not require import or export permits. In addition, worked ivory can be imported to or exported from South Africa without permits. So the door is wide open for illegal ivory to be imported into the country, then exported anywhere in the world without documents.

Much of the illicit ivory from Zambia, including that from North Luangwa National Park, has been flown on Swazi-Air from Lusaka to Swaziland, then trucked to South Africa. Three top-level Zambian officials were suspended for participating in this smuggling ring.

Once the ivory is in South Africa, it can be freely sold or exported. Before the 1989 ban South Africa imported 15 tons of illegal ivory from Zaire, 12 tons from Angola, 10 tons from Zambia, 2 tons from Zimbabwe, and 1 ton each from Malawi and Mozambique.[5] And South Africa exported 40 tons of illegal ivory annually. A United Nations study concluded that "South Africa serves as a conduit for the illegal export of significant quantities of ivory . . . from neighboring states (including Angola, Botswana, Malawi, Mozambique, Zambia, and Zimbabwe)."[6]

In Angola, members of the National Union for the Total Independence of Angola (UNITA) killed 100,000 elephants to finance their war with the government. These tusks were exported to South Africa, where they entered the free market.[7] A photographer from *Time* magazine witnessed a huge machine shop run by UNITA in Angola, where dozens of lathes were being used to carve tusks into replicas of machine guns (personal communications). Two men arrested in South Africa in possession of 975 poached elephant tusks were not prosecuted.[8]

On February 25, 1992, the Environmental Investigation Agency of England reported that after two years of scrutiny it had determined that the South African Defense Force (SADF) and the Zimbabwe National Army had been involved in large-scale elephant poaching and ivory smuggling. Their report provided evidence that the SADF ran a major smuggling operation out of Angola and Mozambique.[9]

2. Claims that there are too many elephants in some areas are inaccurate or irrelevant.

Zimbabwe and Botswana declare that they have too many elephants and need to cull them to prevent habitat destruction. Too often when elephants appear to occur in high numbers, it is actually because they have been crowded into small areas by outside poaching pressures, or by loss of habitat from human development. If the poaching were eliminated or if elephants were allowed to inhabit a greater portion of their former ranges, they would no longer be overcrowded. With human populations growing more than 3 percent annually, people will take over more and more elephant habitat for development and conflicts will occur. But the CITES treaty does *not* prohibit the culling of elephants in areas where their densities are too high. Culling should be considered a last resort, but when necessary it can be done according to the CITES regulations. Culling does not cause poaching; selling the ivory and other parts from culled elephants does.

Too often in the past, governments have repeatedly and prematurely resorted to culling operations to control elephant densities. It would be far more appropriate for the central, southern, and east African nations to form an international policing agency similar to Interpol to deal with the illicit traffic in animal parts and to coordinate antipoaching law-enforcement operations.

3. These countries claim that they have controlled poaching and that by being denied a trade in elephants' parts they are being penalized for the lack of control in other nations. But poaching still continues in Zimbabwe and Botswana. According to the deputy director of Zimbabwe's Department of Wildlife, the number of elephants killed by poachers has increased 300 percent in recent years.[10] The department reported intensive organized elephant poaching in the Zambezi Valley and was granted

$104,500 from the United States to help control it. Elephant poaching occurs in Chobe Game Reserve in Botswana and Nigel Hunter, the deputy director of Wildlife and National Parks there, has stated that "he suspects that illegally-taken ivory from Botswana moves through South Africa."[11]

Because there is at present no way to verify the origin of elephant parts, any country that trades in them inevitably stimulates a massive illegal traffic within its own borders and across its borders with other countries. As the demand for illegal parts grows, more and more elephants are poached in neighboring countries to fill the market.

4. Claims that people should be able to benefit from elephants are not contradictory to the ban.

The countries resisting the ban state that local people and national treasuries should be able to benefit from elephants. But the ban does not prevent them from doing so. Wildlife tourism can generate as much income as the ivory trade. Kenya's living elephants bring in $20 million a year through tourism, which flows to many different people; money from poached elephants falls into only a few hands.

5. Some nations want to down-list the African elephant so that there can be an international trade in hides, feet, and tails, even if trade in ivory is prohibited.

Before the ban, the trade of elephant skins, feet, and tails was worth as much as the ivory trade in Zimbabwe and in South Africa. It matters little to the poacher whether he shoots an elephant for its ivory or its skin. As long as there is *any* market in *any* elephant parts, poaching will increase again.

Ban Reconsidered

In March 1992 the CITES delegates met in Japan to vote on whether or not to continue the ban. In spite of its success, the SACIM nations and South Africa wanted it reversed. Unbelievably, the delegation from the U.S. Fish and Wildlife Service considered joining these countries in their vote for a down-listing of the elephant. Apparently the U.S. delegates had accepted statements by the SACIM nations that they had the means to control such a trade, despite overwhelming evidence that they could not. Sixty American environmental and conservation groups, including our own, as well as many senators and congressmen, sent petitions to

President George Bush, asking that the United States support a continued moratorium. After weighing all the evidence, President Bush decided that this action was "the right thing to do." He instructed the U.S. delegation in Japan to vote accordingly, and other CITES member nations followed suit. In the end, the nations opposing the ban withdrew their proposal and the moratorium on the sale of all elephant parts was continued.

Conclusion

Opening a legal market for *any* elephant parts (ivory, skins, tails, feet) will reopen the illegal market. Under the present conditions of widespread corruption and lack of resources to protect elephants in the field, *the most effective way to save the African elephant is with a continued long-term, complete international moratorium on the sale of all elephant parts, including ivory.* The next time CITES meets (in 1994), the moratorium should be extended for at least ten years, not two. A longer period will prevent stockpiling of ivory by poachers and send a strong message to black-market dealers that the CITES nations are committed to saving the African elephant from extinction. It will also permit elephant populations to rebuild their numbers.

One final word: the ivory trade not only kills elephants but also leads to the deaths of people trying to protect them.

APPENDIX C

Large Mammals of North Luangwa National Park

○ ○ ○

Baboon, chacma	*Papio ursinus jubilaeus*
Bush pig	*Potamochoerus porcus*
Bushbuck	*Tragelaphus scriptus*
Cape buffalo	*Syncerus caffer*
Cheetah	*Acinonyx jubatus*
Duiker, common	*Sylvicapra grimmia*
Eland	*Taurotragus oryx*
Elephant	*Loxodonta africana*
Giraffe, Thornicroft's	*Giraffa camelopardalis thornicrofti*
Hartebeest, Lichtenstein's	*Alcelaphus lichtensteini*
Hippopotamus	*Hippopotamus amphibius*
Hyena, spotted	*Crocuta crocuta*
Impala	*Aepyceros melampus*
Kudu	*Tragelaphus strepsiceros*
Leopard	*Panthera pardus*
Lion	*Panthera leo*
Monkey, samonga	*Cercopithecus alboqularis*
Monkey, vervet	*Cercopithecus pygerythrus*
Oribi	*Ourebia ourebi*
Puku	*Kobus vardonii*
Reedbuck	*Redunca arundinum*
Roan antelope	*Hippotragus equinus*
Sable antelope	*Hippotragus niger*
Warthog	*Phacochoerus aethiopicus*
Waterbuck	*Kobus ellipsiprymnus*
Wild dog	*Lycaon pictus*
Wildebeest, Cookson	*Connochaetes taurinus cooksoni*
Zebra	*Equus burchelli*

Notes

Chapter 9

1. Cynthia Moss, *Elephant Memories* (New York: Random House, Fawcett Columbine, 1988).
2. Ibid.
3. Ibid.

Appendix A

1. R. S. Hedger, Foot and mouth disease, in *Infectious Diseases of Wild Mammals*, ed. John Davis et al. (Ames: Iowa State University Press, 1981).
2. Ibid.
3. J. B. Condy and R. S. Hedger, The survival of foot and mouth disease virus in African buffalo with nontransference of infection to domestic cattle, *Research in Veterinary Science* 39(3):181–84.

Appendix B

1. Comments of the Humane Society of the United States Regarding Proposals by Zimbabwe, Botswana, South Africa, Namibia, Malawi, and Zambia to Transfer Populations of the African Elephant from CITES Appendix I to II (Humane Society of the United States, January 30, 1992).
2. Ibid.
3. African Wildlife Foundation, personal communication.
4. Comments of the Humane Society.
5. *The Ivory Trade in Southern Africa*, CITES Document 7.22, Annex 2, 1990.
6. United Nations Environmental *Panel of Experts Report*, August 16, 1991.
7. Craig van Note, *Earth Island Journal*, 1988.

8. *Johannesburg Star*, November 19, 1989.
9. *Under Fire: Elephants in the Front Line* (London: *Environmental Investigation Agency, 1992).*
10. *New African*, June 1991.
11. Comments of the Humane Society.

Acknowledgments

We are extremely grateful for the conservation initiatives taken by Zambia's new government, and especially for the vision of Frederick Chiluba, its new, democratically elected president. For the first time, we dare to hope that solutions to wildlife and human development problems may be complementary and lasting. Our thanks to the government of Zambia and the Mpika District Council for allowing us to conduct the North Luangwa Conservation Project; to former U.S. ambassador to Zambia Paul Hare and U.S. Information Services officer Jan Zehner for their roles in securing this permission; and to their wives for opening their homes to us on many occasions. We are indebted to the current ambassador, Gordon Streeb, for adding his prestige and influence to the politics of conservation in Zambia, and we appreciate the hospitality he and Junie, his wife, have shown us.

To Andy and Caroline Anderson and Dick Houston in Lusaka, thanks for understanding what it means to come in from the bush. Also for their friendship and hospitality in Lusaka, we thank Julie and Alan van Edgmond, Mary Ann Epily, Marilyn Santin, and Mary, Ralph, and Astrid Krag-Olsen.

We owe special thanks to Luke Daka, permanent secretary to the minister of tourism; to Akim Mwenya, director of National Parks and Wildlife Services of Zambia; to Gilson Kaweche, also of NPWS; to Paul Russell, operations head of the Anticorruption Commission; and to Norbert Mumba, Clement Mwale, and Charles Lengalenga, chief investigative officers of the Species Protection Division for their help in breaking up organized poaching in the Mpika area. Our sincere appreciation to the government of Canada for donating a truck to our community service program.

Our heartfelt thanks to President George Bush, and First Lady Barbara Bush, for their time and consideration in listening to our message and acting decisively to ensure continuation of the CITES international ban on trading elephant parts. We are grateful also to Senator Bob Kasten, to Eva, his wife, and to Alex Echols, the senator's senior staffer; and to Congressman Mel Levine and staffer Jennifer Savage for their actions to guarantee that subsidies from the World Bank do not continue to destroy Kalahari wilderness, and again to ensure that the U.S. delegation to CITES voted to continue the ivory ban. Our sincere appreciation also to Marguerite Williams for her assistance in this regard, and for all the other ways she has helped us.

We are very grateful to the Friends of the Animals of the Frankfurt Zoological Society, and especially to Richard Faust, its president, and Ingrid Koberstein, his assistant, who since 1978 have been the major supporters of our projects and have provided everything from paperclips to airplanes. Frankfurt is a strong force for conservation in Africa, Asia, and South America.

We are equally indebted to the members of our own Owens Foundation for Wildlife Conservation, who have supported us financially, morally, and spiritually, especially in the expansion of our North Luangwa Conservation Project's law enforcement, village outreach/community service, and conservation education programs.

To Helen Cooper, Delia's sister and our foundation's executive director, and to Fred, her husband — thanks for being there with everything from direct contact with presidents to deft leadership, sage advice, fund raising, and the organization of our speaking tours. Nephew Jay Cooper is our computer consultant and all-around hack; thanks, Jaybird. Thanks also to Jay's brother, Derick, for letting us store our lion range plots on his bed and on the walls of his bedroom. Our warmest thanks to Bobby Dykes, Delia's twin brother, for managing our photographic library. Mary, his wife, is the assistant director of our foundation and acquires items as diverse as airplane engines and crayons. One way or another, she gets them to one of the most remote corners of Africa; even more miraculously, she accounts for their purchase and shipment in as many as five different currencies. At the same time, she heads our program of sister schools. Additional thanks go to Mark's brother, Mike, and Jan, his wife, for their care of photographic materials.

Leslie Keller-Howington donated the beautiful artwork for our foundation's logo and lecture brochures. We are also very grateful to Rick Richey for video editing and reproduction and to Channing Huser for her illustrations for the North Luangwa Conservation Project.

For months volunteer Marie Hill worked in Mpika and more remote villages to develop our conservation education program. Harvey Hill provided fresh ideas and material support. We are indebted to all of them. When our programs were fast growing into a regional development project, Tom and Wanda Canon, our volunteer project coordinators in Mpika, came along to add order, calm reassurance, and confidence to the entire effort. Even though the sun dims and the thatch on their roundhouse smolders whenever they switch on their mega-appliances, they have helped the project tremendously and we could not do without them. To Max Saili, our fine community service officer, and Evans Mukuka, our education officer, we extend deep gratitude for helping take the message of conservation to the people of Mpika District.

Ian Spincer and Edward North, who joined the project as young graduates from the University of Reading in England, have literally waded flood-swollen, croc-infested rivers to get reliable firsthand information on poaching and game-guard field performance. No risk has been too daunting, no challenge too great, no task too menial for them to tackle. And through it all they have helped restore our sense of humor.

Our thanks also to Christopher, Mark's son, who for three months in 1991 helped build tracks, drove trucks, and named Bouncer, the lion.

Very special thanks to Mick Slater, David and Jane Warwick, Dutch Gibson, Barbara Collinson, and to Glen Allison, Charlotte Harmon, Gracious Siyanga, Grace, Exilda Mungulbe, Patrick Enyus, Carl Berryman and all the staff of the District Development Services Project (Masdar; British Overseas Development Agency) in Mpika who have sheltered us in their homes, allowed us to use their communications equipment and post office space, and encouraged and supported us in ways too numerous to mention.

We are grateful to officers Isaac Longwe, Martin Mwanza, and Mukendwa Kotela for bringing diligence and integrity to the Mano game guard unit.

Steve Hall, of Wings of Eagles, Tampa, Florida, a renowned ferry pilot, flew our plane all the way from Atlanta to Marula-Puku camp. He often flies to Africa, and whenever he comes within a few hundred miles of Zambia, Steve soars in, his plane engorged with supplies for the North Luangwa Conservation Project. To a great guy in the sky, thanks, Steve — and fly safely.

Students, teachers, and parents from more than thirty American schools support conservation in Zambia by sending letters, art work, stories, and reports and by donating books and school supplies to their friends in the sister schools.

We applaud Judith Hawke, our Lusaka coordinator, for her efficiency and diligence in expediting the flow of permits and other bureaucratic paperwork as well as personnel, information, equipment, and supplies for the project.

We are grateful for donations of video equipment from the Sony Corporation, and from Bubba, the Zenith dealer in Portland; for computer equipment from Hewlett Packard South Africa and Kaypro of California; and especially to our close friend Jose Jardim for years of computer support and for helping us clean up our camp in Deception Valley. We are also indebted to Richard Ferris of Kodak South Africa for stocks of film, and for hospitality and friendship.

For their helpful comments on the manuscript we thank Bob Ivey, Dick Houston, Lee and Maureen Ewell, Jon Fisher, Barbara Frybarger, Barbara Brookes, and Helen Cooper. To dear friends Bob Ivey and Jill Bowman, thanks once again for allowing us to rattle around your home spoiling your cats while putting the finishing touches to the manuscript.

Special thanks to Harry Foster, our friend and editor at Houghton Mifflin, for his enthusiasm, encouragement, and tireless editing of countless drafts of the manuscript; to Vivian Wheeler for her assistance; and to Suzanne Gluck, our literary agent, for her interest and support.

Dave Erskine and Gordon Bennet of Johannesburg evacuated our camp after we were deported from Botswana. In Johannesburg, George and Penny Poole, and Nick and Sally, kindly allowed us to stay in their family's A-frame cottage for three months after our deportation, and to recuperate at their cottage on the South Coast. Our old friend Kevin Gill offered us his home, companionship, and invaluable assistance in identifying the trees of North Luangwa. Everard and Patsy Reed of Johannesburg invited us to share their beautiful farm near Mulders Drift during our initial writing of the manuscript.

Hank and Margaret McCamish, we thank you for that very special place in the valley of the deer, and for your faith and trust in us and our philosophy of helping the people and animals of wild Africa.

We feel a special sense of comradeship with our "guys" at Marula-Puku: Mutale Kasokola, Mumanga Kasokola, Chanda Mwamba, Chomba Simbeye, Evans Mulenga, Timothy Nsingo, and other members of the A-team who have labored hard and risked much to save North Luangwa. Without them the park surely would have been lost by now.

To Bill Campbell and Maryanne Vollers, thanks for all the memories under the African stars and for your never-ending efforts for conservation. Bill and Marion Hamilton, Joel Berger, and Carol Cunningham were always there when we needed them. We are grateful to Jim and

John Lipscomb, producers of "African Odyssey," for following us around the continent on a seemingly endless journey of abandoned campsites, which ended with the beginning of a new dream.

Thank you to Randy Jones and Jim Cole for creating our brochure and to Joe and Geri Naylor for their help in producing it.

To all of our friends and family mentioned above, and to any we may have omitted, thanks for being a special part of our lives — and for helping to save the elephants of North Luangwa.

The Owens Foundation for Wildlife Conservation is a charitable organization which currently sponsors Delia and Mark's North Luangwa Conservation Project in Zambia. The project is attempting to recover North Luangwa Park and the surrounding wilderness areas from commercial poachers by strengthening game guard law enforcement programs, by sponsoring conservation education, and by involving local villagers in benefits from the area's wildlife. The project plans to expand its model programs to protect other endangered habitats and animals in Africa. If you would like to help in this important work, you may make tax-deductible donations to:

The Owens Foundation for Wildlife Conservation
P.O. Box 53396
Atlanta, Georgia 30355

○ ○ ○

The authors are grateful for permission to quote from the following material: From "When We Looked Back" by William Stafford. Reprinted by permission. Copyright © 1959, 1987 The New Yorker Magazine, Inc. "Bivouac," from *Tickets for a Prayer Wheel.* Copyright © 1974 by Annie Dillard. Used by permission. "Heat," from *The Time Traveler,* by Joyce Carol Oates. Copyright © 1983, 1984, 1985, 1986, 1987, 1988, 1989 by The Ontario Review, Inc. Used by permission of the publisher, Dutton, an imprint of New American Library, a division of Penguin Books USA Inc. From "The Thrifty Elephant" by John Holmes. Reprinted by permission of Doris Holmes Eyges; © 1961, 1989 Doris Holmes Eyges. "The Eagle and the Hawk," by John Denver and Mike Taylor. Copyright © 1971 Cherry Lane Music Publishing Co., Inc. All rights reserved. Used by permission. "Sacagawea, Bird Woman" and "Something fragile, broken," from *Skin and Bones,* by Paula Gunn Allen. Copyright © 1988 by Paula Gunn Allen. Courtesy of West End Press. "Winter's End," from *A Season of Loss,* by Jim Barnes. Copyright © 1985 Purdue Research Foundation, West Lafayette, Indiana 47907. "Today I Am Docile" by Seth Richardson, from *Out of the Rain* by The Homeless of San Francisco. Copyright © 1988 by the St. Vincent de Paul Society. *Sacred Elephant* by Heathcote Williams. Copyright © 1989 by Heathcote Williams. Reprinted by permission of Harmony Books, a division of Crown Publishers, Inc. "Sweeney to Mrs. Porter in the Spring" by L. E. Sissman, in *Hello Darkness: Collected Poems* by L. E. Sissman, published by Little, Brown and Company. Poem by Walter Rinder from *Aura of Love.* Copyright © 1978 by Celestial Arts, Berkeley, California.

SECRETS of the SAVANNA

TWENTY-THREE YEARS
IN THE AFRICAN WILDERNESS
UNRAVELING THE
MYSTERIES OF ELEPHANTS
AND PEOPLE

MARK AND DELIA OWENS

TO BOB AND JILL
From guinea fowl pie in the Kalahari
to camping in the Luangwa bog,
thank you for everything.
Love always.

Visit our Web site: www.hmhbooks.com

Library of Congress Cataloging-in-Publication Data
Owens, Mark.
Secrets of the savanna: twenty-three years in the African wilderness
unraveling the mysteries of elephants and people / Mark and Delia Owens.
p. cm.
isbn-13: 978-0-395-89310-4
isbn-10: 0-395-89310-0

1. African elephant — Conservation — Luangwa River Valley (Zambia
and Mozambique) 2. African elephant — Effect of hunting on — Luangwa
River Valley (Zambia and Mozambique) 3. Nature conservation — Economic
aspects — Luangwa River Valley (Zambia and Mozambique)
4. Owens, Delia. 5. Owens, Mark. i. Owens, Delia. ii. Title.
ql737.p98o95 2006
599.67'4— dc22 2005023842

Printed in the United States of America

QUM 10 9 8 7 6 5 4 3 2 1

CONTENTS

FOREWORD

Not so far, relatively speaking, from where I spent the last years of my childhood in Zambia, there is a valley so rare and surprising in its beauty that once seen and heard and smelled, the sense of it stays with you always. Forever after, a tiny breath of it might come back to you in other places — say in a hint of dust in Italy or in the way the sun catches the land in Mexico — and you feel the tug of memory of that place. This valley is so rich with life that it seems entirely possible that Life itself started here, or at least that it congregated here in uncommon splendor and diversity. The landscape seems ideally suited to such majestic sights as herds of elephants casually fording a river or the philosophic stare of baboons at sunset. Perhaps that is why memory settles on the valley as a place of origin, as if we knew it in some other, wiser time.

But this valley — this template for what we might all have grown up with, or lived near, if we had not so carelessly eaten our way through our own wild lands long ago—was almost completely lost. When I was young, in the 1980s, North Luangwa National Park (for this is the valley of which I am speaking) was so rotten with heavily armed poachers and so corrupted with the blood money of elephants that anyone who ventured near it was considered foolhardy, if not downright stupid. Not only was the valley itself infested with armed gangs, but the villagers who lived in the land surrounding the park had been pressed into the service of the poachers — who were very often in the pay of powerful government officials and business people in the cities. Many thought that the valley was as good as gone.

But that was before Mark and Delia Owens happened upon the park and fell in love — illogically, incautiously — with a land so very nearly reaped of all its life that it had all but been left to die. This book is an account of the Owenses' years in that valley and with the people who live on its periphery. It is the story of how, together with the villagers and their chiefs, Mark and Delia gradually peeled away the dark years of elephant poaching and allowed both the valley and the settlements to flourish. In other words, the Owenses and the local people achieved what has been replicated in very few places in the world: a balance in which humans and wildlife have found strategies to coexist, not in some unsustainable primitive dream but in a viable, respectful way, with new ideas and resources building on the best of the old traditions. And in the process of saving the park, the Owenses found pieces of themselves in the sly, sometimes wickedly funny wisdom of the men and women with whom they worked. This book tells that story too.

However, as romantic as it sounds to hitch oneself to a dream and to attach oneself to an impossibly noble goal, the reality of years of gritty, flies-in-your-eyes, malarial loneliness in the name of love of land, humanitarianism, and science is not for anyone with less than a lion heart. I can't emphasize enough what courage and dedication — to say nothing of sheer stubborn passion — it must have taken for Mark and Delia Owens to rescue North Luangwa National Park while poachers and corrupt politicians and officials did everything they could to hurt them and derail their work and while even the land and the animals sometimes seemed ungrateful for their efforts. But with almost superhuman perseverance, the Owenses refused to give up until their goal of a valley without poachers had been achieved.

I recently returned to Zambia for a magazine assignment and spent time with Hammer Simwinga (the Owenses' protégé, a sort of agriculture extension officer for the region, and every bit the hero described in these pages), and I met some of the traditional birth attendants, beekeepers, farmers, fish farmers, and shopkeepers described here. The work that the Owenses instigated has outlived their time in the valley, and there can be no greater tribute than that. In the words of one villager, "You cannot separate the Owenses from this place. What they have done has changed our lives for the better." It is true, the Owenses cannot be separated from this place, which is ingrained in them forever.

—Alexandra Fuller

MARK

PROLOGUE

> One touch of Nature
> makes the whole world kin.
>
> — William Shakespeare

A heavy fog, thick and white, settled lower over the hills of Masailand in Kenya. I eased off the power and slowed down but pulled back on the cyclic stick, giving up altitude grudgingly. Our chopper's main rotor tore ragged chunks out of the cloud's underbelly and stirred great corkscrews of vapor that trailed behind us as we flew on. Fifty feet below us, malachite green hilltops dotted with flat-topped acacias and running giraffes — snapshots of Africa — flashed into view out of the white, then were lost to opacity. We flew on, while the fog squatted heavy on the hilltops, forcing us to skirt around and between them. But then the vapor began filling the valleys ahead; we were fast losing sight of the ground.

I keyed the intercom: "We've got to land while we still can; help me look for a place." Delia pressed her forehead to the cockpit window, scanning the terrain. Forested valleys and too steep hillsides all around: no place here.

To our right and slightly above us, a single rounded peak was still visible. But the clouds were already settling over it, like a goose on a nest. I banked hard right, pulled on some power, and climbed the slope. We popped onto the hilltop and planted our skids; even before the rotor wound to a stop, we could barely see beyond the blades.

Our camp in the remote northern Luangwa Valley of Zambia was still almost nine hundred miles and more than ten flying hours away. We would never make it before dark.

We unbuckled our safety harnesses, opened the doors, and stepped into the fragrant, misty air and into a surreal, palpable quiet. I have experienced such an utter absence of sound only among the old-growth Sitka spruce and hemlock forests of southeastern Alaska, where the wisps of moss clinging to tree trunks and branches and matting the forest floor absorb sound so completely that you can hear your pulse swishing in your ears with each heartbeat. Now, as Delia and I stood by the helicopter, we could see nothing beyond the ground immediately around us, could hear nothing but the occasional flinty *ping* of the chopper's cooling turbine.

Then, through particles of fog so thick they tickled our noses, came the merry, melodic, clear tinkle of little bells. At first they seemed far off, coming from everywhere at once. Then they grew louder, somewhere to our right, and we took several steps in that direction, yearning to discover the source of a melody that seemed to emanate from the heart of the hidden hills around us.

At first I thought I was imagining the faint crimson apparition, the red smudge that appeared in the fog. Then, like a distant memory gradually returning to consciousness, it gained form and definition, growing taller and still taller as it came toward us over the brow of the hill.

The Masai warrior, nearly seven feet tall, strode out of the swirling cloud, a red rubega cloth draped around his broad shoulders and large copper hoops dangling from his ears. His sharp, stern face was an ebony sculpture, and in his left hand he carried a long throwing spear with a broad blade.

"Jambo." He strode past us to our Bell Jet Ranger and began circling it, running his hands over its smooth, ivory-colored skin and Plexiglas windshield. "Tsk-ah!" He smiled and twiddled the ship's tail rotor back and forth as if it were one of his giant earrings, laughter rumbling deep in his chest.

Three women appeared carrying gourds and leading goats wearing necklaces of little bells. They stood back, gazing at the helicopter, chattering softly, their dark eyes wide with curiosity. Gradually a murmur of voices rose from all directions, and as the fog slowly thinned and began to lift, small groups of gaily dressed Masai streamed toward us across the green velvet hills. Soon they crowded around as I poured jerry cans of jet A-1 fuel into the chopper's tank, everyone trying to get at least a finger on the can so that they could help feed our strange bird.

After refueling, we stood waiting for the clouds to lift, surrounded by perhaps thirty or forty Masai. Delia begged a closer look at one of the beaded gourds — full of sour milk and ox blood — that a young girl carried around her neck on a strap of hide. Others showed us their bangles and bracelets, their spears and knives, apparently surprised that we should find these as interesting as they found our aircraft. Giggling shyly, one girl reached out and carefully lifted a lock of Delia's silky hair, massaging it gently between her fingertips. The cultural canyon that separated us was as wide as the Rift Valley, yet we felt a warm connection to these people, as though we had known them before, sometime in the distant past.

The fog lifted and the sun peeked through, bathing the green and golden hills with a buttery light. Reluctantly we bid goodbye to our new friends. Before starting the chopper's turbine, I led the warrior with the spear to the tail rotor, made spinning motions with my hands, and then drew my finger across my throat, to let him know what would happen should anyone get too close. He opened his long arms and, like a pelican gathering fish, stalked around the chopper, sweeping everyone back to the edges of the hilltop. We jumped in, lifted off, and then circled back to wave at the cheering crowd below, still standing around the space where the chopper had been. As I lowered its nose and we began speeding away, they closed in, still waving, and covered the spot — as if we had never been there.

Ten hours — and three countries — after the Masai, darkness fell, black and impenetrable under the solid layer of cloud that snuffed out sky light from above. Except for a stop to refuel in Dodoma, the capital city of Tanzania, and another on a remote plain in the southern part of that country, we had been flying continuously since leaving Nairobi, where our helicopter had passed its airworthiness inspection. Forty minutes earlier, the scattered lights of settlements west of Kasama, Zambia, had slipped away, leaving us alone with our worries about finding camp in this ink, our faces a Halloween green from the chopper's instrument lights. Somewhere, miles ahead beyond the mountains of the Muchinga Escarpment, in a five-thousand-square-mile tract of raw wilderness near the bottom of the Luangwa Valley, lay Marula-Puku, our bush camp, home, and conservation research base for the previous eight years.

With stars, with luck, and sometimes with the moon to light my way, I had often flown over wild Africa at night. It was always a beguiling experience, like swimming around in a womb with only faint flashes of nerve impulses and the lumps and bumps of a muscular landscape to lead me onward. But now I was extremely tired, and we were flying without navigational aids. My dead reckoning would have to be good.

Ahead, a jawbone of low mountains capped by clouds studded the rim of the Muchinga Escarpment, the western wall of the Great Rift, and I could not tell for sure whether the clouds were higher than the peaks. Before beginning our three-thousand-foot descent into the Luangwa Valley, we would have to fly east long enough to be certain we were beyond and clear of the Muchinga, while staying below the clouds. I dreaded the thought of blundering into the clouds in the dark; and if they were lying on the mountains, we would have no way to get through. My Global Positioning System (GPS) had burned out weeks before. Without it I had only the log of my time since leaving Kasama, my compass heading, our speed, and my altimeter to tell me whether we were safe. And I did not know if my message to light the milk-tin flares along the runway — sent by telephone from Nairobi to the United States, by fax back to Mpika, by radio to the main camp, and finally by truck to the airstrip — had been received and understood. If not, I would have to carefully descend until I could see the ground with the chopper's landing light, find the Lubonga River, then follow it north or south to camp. And finding the airstrip to land could be just as tricky.

Below and to our right I saw a scattering of yellow-orange lights, flickering, as though made by campfires.

"That should be Mano," I said to Delia, not absolutely sure it was. I had never seen the game scout camp from this high or from this direction in the dark. Something didn't feel quite right. But if I was correct, the mountains would be just beyond. The helicopter climbed higher, until wisps of cloud began breaking over her nose — and, I hoped, the jutting peaks were well below us. I imagined that I could feel them reaching up to gut the thin aluminum skin under our feet. "We must be high enough," I kept reassuring myself. But fatigue and darkness had planted a growing malignancy of doubt.

Leaving the cooking fires of Mano behind, we flew into the black void over the Luangwa Valley wilderness. The solid wall of darkness, and the lingering worry about flying into a mountain, so intimidated me that I suddenly and unconsciously reduced power and pulled up the nose, slowing us down to sixty knots instead of our usual cruising speed of one hundred. I picked up the lost air speed, tried to relax, and flew on.

"Where's camp? Shouldn't we see our lights by now?" Delia asked in a thin voice.

"Hang on; they'll be coming up anytime."

"So what are you going to do if there are no lights?"

In 1971, as young college students concerned about Africa's disappearing wildlife, we took temporary leave from our graduate programs and worked for two years at odd jobs to earn the money to field our own conservation research project on cheetahs. Early in 1974, one year after we married, we auctioned off all our belongings, bought one-way tickets, and flew to Johannesburg, South Africa. From there, over a period of several months, we found our way into the "Great

Thirst," Botswana's Central Kalahari Desert, and into Deception Valley, an ancient fossilized riverbed, where we set up a primitive camp in an island of thorn trees — and stayed for the next seven years.

Other than a few bands of roving Bushmen, we were the only two people in an area the size of Ireland; Maun, the nearest village, was more than a hundred miles away, so we often would not see other human beings for months. There was no rainfall for eight months each year, and droughts sometimes lasted for years. But the hardships of living in isolation, on a ration of little more than a gallon of water a day, every dry-season drop hauled to our camp in drums, were more than worth it. Most of the lions, leopards, brown hyenas, and other wildlife had never before encountered humans. They had never been chased by trucks, shot at, and in other ways abused by man, so they were naive and immediately curious about us — which often led to interesting close encounters.

Unable to afford a tent, we slept on the ground or in the back of our dilapidated Land Rover while observing the habits of black-backed jackals, brown hyenas, and lions. The latter two became our long-term research subjects because cheetahs were too rare and hard to find. At the beginning of our second year, a hunting company based in Maun gave us a faded, ripped cabin-style tent. Our first night in the tent we were sleeping on a thin piece of foam rubber when a *sssshhhhh*-ing sound and pressure on my feet awakened me. The night was moonless, but some light came through the mesh window near my head; I could see the silhouette of the wooded sand dune beyond our tree-island camp. A snake, no doubt a puff adder, seemed to be moving across my sleeping bag, its scales scraping along the nylon. I froze. The sound came again. The pressure began moving slowly up my leg. Carefully I reached behind my head for my flashlight. I would club the poisonous snake if it came near my face. But then came rumbles, squeaks, and heavy breathing — like something big digesting a heavy meal.

Resting on my back, I eased my head up and saw two black-maned Kalahari lions crouched at our feet, their noses roaming over our sleeping bags, their whiskers scratching the nylon like a scrub brush. I clamped my hand over Delia's mouth. Her eyes popped open as I whispered, "Lions — *in the tent!*"

We lay unmoving for a minute or two as the two male lions satisfied their curiosity. Then they withdrew and sauntered, one behind the other, along the footpath through our camp. We stood up, pulled on some clothes, and followed along behind as they strolled to our outdoor kitchen. They pulled down and tore open bags of cornmeal and onions we had hung in a tree for safekeeping and sniffed the spot where we had emptied some dishwater the night before. Then they sprayed urine on their favorite bush and lay down in the short grass just beyond our campfire. Delia and I sat quietly not ten feet from them and watched the sun rise over their shoulders.

During our seven years in the Kalahari, lions and brown hyenas sat at our campfire and smelled our hair, and the hyenas' cubs even nibbled our fingers as we took notes on their behavior; leopards hung out in the trees over our tent, and jackals stole meals off our table. Once while we were asleep on the savanna, a pride of lions lay down to rest in a circle around us, some of them an arm's length away.

We were with some two-year-old lions when, after a drought broke, they saw their first pool of standing water and took their first drink. We discovered that brown hyenas are very social rather than solitary, as had been thought, and that female clanmates, all relatives, faithfully adopt and rear the clan's orphans. We documented one of the largest antelope migrations in Africa — and learned that cattle fences built by the government with soft loans from the World Bank and trade subsidies from the European Union were blocking their migrations, killing hundreds of thousands of them, choking the life from one of the last great relatively intact ecosystems on the continent. When we wrote about this disaster in our first book, *Cry of the Kalahari*, the government of Botswana forced us to move on, though it rescinded the order a year later, after we had left.

In May 1986 I flew our Cessna 180 from Johannesburg to Lusaka,

Zambia, to begin looking for a new research site. But a week earlier the South African air force had bombed African National Council (ANC) bases around the city. Understandably, Zambian emotions were wound clock-spring tight with worries about a full-scale invasion. Government-issued posters and civil-defense radio and television announcements urged every citizen to be a "policeman" on the lookout for terrorists — all of whom were depicted as Caucasians because the country had been bombed by white-ruled South Africa. The U.S. State Department advised Americans not to enter Zambia, but we were anxious to find and settle in a new research site, so we had gone ahead with our plans anyway.

I landed in Lusaka, taxied to the terminal, and was locking up my plane when a squad of military police armed with AK-47s rushed up, grabbed my arms, and marched me to a small room in the terminal, where they began questioning me. At the time I didn't know that our newly purchased Cessna was the same model used by the South African air force for reconnaissance; it even had the same color scheme and bore a South African registration. The police held me for eight hours until they were sure I was not a spy, then released me.

I flew back to Johannesburg on a commercial flight, and Delia and I headed north with our trucks, towing a trailer and a shipping container loaded with gear needed to set up our new research project, at a site as yet unknown. A father-and-son film team from *National Geographic* followed us on our odyssey.

Shortly after we crossed the Zambezi River from Botswana into Zambia on the Kazangula ferry, we noticed two poles lying on opposite sides of the roadway. We had been warned about Zambia's notorious and often obscure roadblocks, so we stopped. But no one appeared, so we drove on. Twenty minutes later, I saw in my rearview mirror a large, battered East German army truck bristling with more than thirty soldiers and civilians, jeering and shaking their fists in the air as they drew up behind us. Lurching drunkenly from side to side, half on and half off the narrow road, the truck crowded beside me, its passengers shouting and waving AK-47s and bottles of beer from the back. One soldier aimed his rifle at me and forced me to stop. Then he jumped into the cab of my truck, jammed the muzzle of his weapon into my neck, and threatened to shoot me for running the "roadblock." His breath reeking of hops, he ordered me to turn around and drive back to the poles, where we were led to a small thatched hut hidden in the bushes. For more than an hour the soldiers questioned us, and all of our answers seemed to make them even more hostile. Then Delia remembered a photo we were carrying of our luncheon with President Kaunda, who had invited us to the state house while arranging our research permits earlier that year. I relaxed a little as she pulled it out of our file of papers.

Suddenly the men were very sober — and apologetic.

"Ah, you will — please — tell the president that we were only doing our job."

"Of course." And we were on our way again.

Numbed by the surreal roadblock incident, we drove on to Lusaka, which seemed as tense as a coiled snake. Even little children tugged at policemen to report our passing by. A lawless kind of martial law was in effect, and we couldn't get out of the city fast enough. On the long drive north on the Cape-to-Cairo Road from Lusaka to Mpika, we camped in darkness and hid our trucks in the bushes far off the road, sweeping away the tracks with tree branches so that bandits and military patrols would not find and follow them to our campsite. At more than a dozen roadblocks along the way, armed soldiers dressed in camouflage with helmets sprouting tree branches rifled through our belongings, demanded *nyama* (meat, usually from poached wild animals), and fingered their triggers, their eyes bloodshot, angry, and shifting. The air was gunpowder dry and seemed ready to explode.

A few years later, Zambians would begin yearning for a genuine democracy with a two-party system — and then demanding it, and in one of the most remarkable and benign political transformations in modern history, in 1992 they would hold their first free and fair presidential election since gaining independence from the colonial government three decades earlier. But the political atmosphere that greeted us in 1986, and in which we would work for the next decade, was much more ominous than it is today.

When we proposed working in North Luangwa National Park, officials told us that they had "written it off" because they lacked the resources to protect and manage it. Consequently, highly organized gangs of commercial poachers and ivory smugglers, sometimes in encampments of more than one hundred men, were slaughtering its wildlife with impunity.

We finally reached Mpika and found our way into the remote and ruggedly beautiful Luangwa Valley, near the northeast corner of Zambia. The North Luangwa National Park had been left undeveloped, its pristine wilderness a standard against which other parks in the country would be measured. It was largely undiscovered and little known to the outside world — except to poachers. We decided to continue our study of lions there.

As we packed mud on the walls of our first hut, gunfire broke out near our camp. We soon discovered that commercial poachers had wiped out all of the park's nearly two thousand black rhinoceros, that they had killed twelve thousand elephants for their tusks, and that they were still shooting one thousand elephants each year. Gangs numbering as many as 140 men were making regular forays into the national park and the wilderness around it. Two thirds of its area was largely depopulated of all animals larger than rabbits. Operating much like drug cartels, these poachers had virtually wiped out the wildlife in seventeen of Zambia's nineteen national parks.

It is difficult for Americans to fully comprehend the level of persistent instability in a country where people are always living on the edge because of political strife and shortages of even the most basic commodities, like firewood, water, and food. And that is why commercial poaching, which is motivated by greed, is such a crime, for it ultimately deprives people of the one renewable resource that can feed and clothe them and ensure their future when all else fails.

We drove to the local game scout camp for assistance but found only seven men there, who were supposed to protect the entire park. They lacked virtually everything they needed to patrol against poachers. At the time, in fact, many of the scouts in Zambia were poaching or taking payoffs from poachers just to survive.

Over the next ten years, with the help of generous sponsors from all over the world and a dedicated staff, we developed the North Luangwa Conservation Project (NLCP). The project brought to the area many more wildlife officers, who were equipped and supplied so they could do their jobs. And they did.

At the same time, we offered jobs to poachers, would-be poachers, and other villagers, provided loans and training for small business development and improved agriculture, trained village women in first aid and midwifery, provided basic medicines for clinics, offered conservation education programs and curricula for village schools, along with much more. In the beginning we focused this assistance on the fourteen villages in the area that were most involved with commercial poaching. At first we were met with suspicion and antipathy, but after four years of pilot projects, the fires of initiative and self-help began to flare among the people. Representatives from other villages began inviting NLCP to help them set up community development programs.

By the early 1990s, when this story begins, the United Nations had banned the international trade in ivory, devaluing it and making the alternatives to poaching offered by our project more attractive to villagers. Commercial poaching in North Luangwa was declining rapidly, but 93 percent of the elephants had been killed, and we did not know whether the population could ever recover. The ivory ban was to be reviewed every two years; if it was reversed, ivory poaching would intensify once again.

The success of the project brought its own ominous problems. Powerful people had made millions of dollars from poaching, and because we had helped put them out of business, they wanted to get rid of us. Their lackeys shot at our aircraft, sent assassins to our bush camp, and attempted to discredit us politically. The villagers, including many former poachers, had warned us that our adversaries had too much money at stake to give up, and it was only a matter of time before they would get us, one way or another.

On our long flight back from Nairobi this night in 1993, we could not know what lay ahead.

"Mark, there's a star!" Delia pointed through the windshield, and I studied the faint yellow light for a moment. It was directly ahead of us — but below where the horizon would be if we could see it. And it seemed to creep even lower as we flew onward.

"That's not a star — it's our beacon!" I exclaimed.

"But it's not flashing."

"We'll see the flash when we get closer." I tried to sound hopeful while resisting a strong urge to begin our long descent. I was still not absolutely certain that that single light, the only light for thousands of square miles, was coming from our airstrip.

As we flew nearer, we could see the solar-powered beacon winking like the light of a firefly, and I knew we had found our way home. A sun rose in my chest for all the people we had trusted to get that beacon lit. As we drew nearer, orange-red flares flickered to life on either side of the runway as Milfred, our assistant, ran along the airstrip lighting old powdered-milk cans filled with sand, rags, and diesel fuel.

I lowered the nose of the helicopter and began putting thousands of feet and miles of darkness behind us.

AUTHORS' NOTE

Zambia's current president, Levi Mwanawasa, has made unprecedented and commendable attempts to abolish corruption from the government of his country. He has made significant progress in this regard, and the people of Zambia and their wildlife have benefited. The corrupt officials named in this story were members of the previous two administrations. Acting with impunity, they were heavily involved with the poaching of elephants and the smuggling of ivory. They worked against us and others who tried to reduce poaching. In this narrative we have changed their names and their positions so that they cannot be identified. Many of them have been fired and/or jailed by the current government.

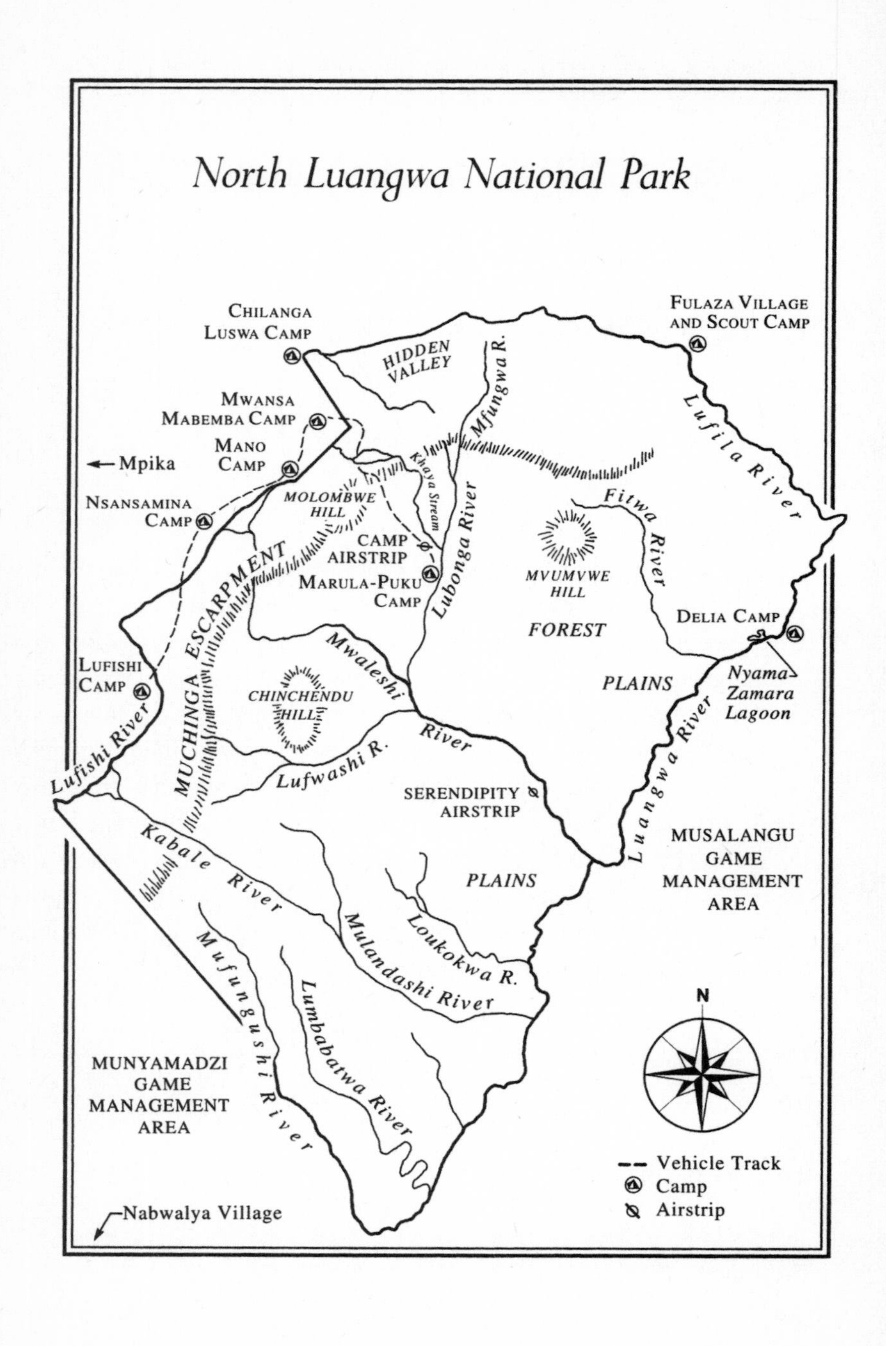
North Luangwa National Park
Chilanga Luswa Camp
Hidden Valley
Mfungwa R.
Fulaza Village and Scout Camp
Mwansa Mabemba Camp
Mano Camp
← Mpika
Nsansamina Camp
Khaya Stream
Molombwe Hill
Camp Airstrip
Marula-Puku Camp
Lubonga River
Lufila River
Fitwa River
Mvumvwe Hill
Forest
Delia Camp
Muchinga Escarpment
Lufishi Camp
Mwaleshi River
Chinchendu Hill
Plains
Nyama-Zamara Lagoon
Lufishi River
Lufwashi R.
Luangwa River
Serendipity Airstrip
Musalangu Game Management Area
Kabale River
Plains
Loukokwa R.
Mulandashi River
Mufungushi River
Lumbabatwa River
N
Munyamadzi Game Management Area
Vehicle Track
Camp
Airstrip
Nabwalya Village

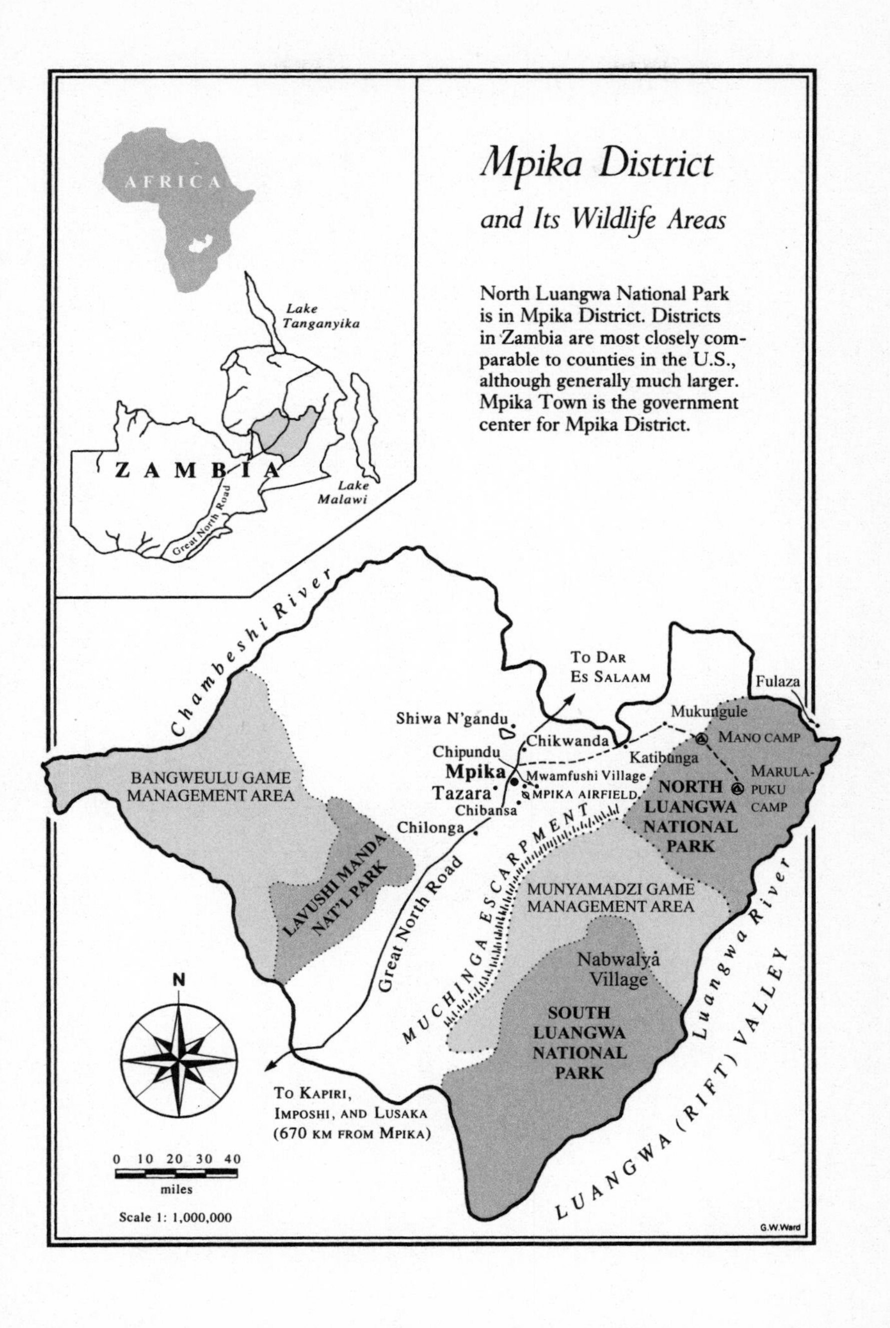

Mpika District
and Its Wildlife Areas
North Luangwa National Park is in Mpika District. Districts in Zambia are most closely comparable to counties in the U.S., although generally much larger. Mpika Town is the government center for Mpika District.
AFRICA
Lake Tanganyika
ZAMBIA
Lake Malawi
Great North Road
Chambeshi River
To Dar Es Salaam
Fulaza
Mukungule
Shiwa N'gandu
Chikwanda
Mano Camp
Chipundu
Katibunga
Mpika
Mwamfushi Village
Marula-Puku Camp
Tazara
Mpika Airfield
North Luangwa National Park
Chibansa
Chilonga
Bangweulu Game Management Area
Lavushi Manda Nat'l Park
Muchinga Escarpment
Munyamadzi Game Management Area
Luangwa River
Nabwalya Village
South Luangwa National Park
Luangwa (Rift) Valley
N
To Kapiri, Imposhi, and Lusaka (670 km from Mpika)
0 10 20 30 40
miles
Scale 1: 1,000,000
G.W.Ward

1 DELIA

GIFT

A gift into the world for whoever will accept it.

— RICHARD BACH

. . . there are conflicts of interest between male and female in courtship and mating.

— J. R. KREBS AND N. B. DAVIES

BETWEEN THE TREES of the forest, amid the thorny undergrowth, under tangles of twisted twigs is a space that is more color than place. It is a grayness painted by drooping limbs and distant branches that blur together and fade into nothingness. It is not a shadow but a pause in the landscape, rarely noticed because our eyes touch the trees, not the emptiness on either side of them. And elephants are the color of this space. As large as they are, elephants can disappear into these secret surroundings, dissolve into the background. When poachers slaughtered the elephants of North Luangwa, the few remaining survivors slipped into the understory. They were seldom seen and almost never heard because they rarely lifted their trunks to trumpet.

When we first came to the Luangwa Valley we could barely grab a glimpse through our binoculars of the elephants' broad, gray bottoms and thin tails before they tore into the thick brush and disappeared. As poaching decreased, a hushed peace settled over the valley, like the silence of fog folded among hills at the end of a rain. In 1991 fewer than ten elephants were shot in North Luangwa, down from a thousand killed illegally every year for a decade. It was an unexpected yet natural quiet, as if a waterfall had frozen in midsong in an ice storm, leaving the land humming with the soft sounds of life. And then, once again, the elephants began to trumpet.

Slowly, beginning with Survivor, then Long Tail, Cheers, Stumpie, and Turbo — the Camp Group — a few of the male elephants learned that they were safe near our camp, Marula-Puku, which we had built in a large grove of marula trees on a small river, the Lubonga, halfway between the massive mountains of the escarpment and the Luangwa River. The elephants came at all times of the year, not just when the marula fruits were ripe. Sometimes they turned their giant rumps to our thatched roof and scratched their thick hides on the rough grass, closing their eyes in what appeared to be the most blissful glee. Elephants can make a lot of noise while feeding, tearing down branches or pushing over medium-size trees, or they can feed as silently as kittens, munching on fruits for long moments.

One night, as Cheers fed on one side of our cottage and Long Tail on the other, both only a few yards from our bed made of reeds, they let forth with full vocalizations. Mark and I, shrouded in our mosquito net, sat up as the sounds shook us. A lion's roar pounds the chest like deep sounds reverberating in a barrel; an elephant's trumpet, especially after decades of being stifled, stills the heart.

In the years before they learned to trust us, they must have watched from the hillsides, remembering the fruits of the marula grove yet afraid to come near. But once they made up their minds that we were harmless, nothing we did seemed to bother them. No matter whether Mark flew the helicopter low over the treetops, or our trucks rumbled in and out, or we cooked popcorn on the open fire, the elephants came to camp. When we stepped out of our cottages, we had to remember to look carefully both ways, or we might walk into an elephant's knee.

That nearly happened one dark evening when Mark walked quickly out of our open, thatched dining *n'saka,* or gazebo, where we were eating a dinner of spicy beans by candlelight. He was headed toward our bedroom cottage to retrieve the mosquito repellent and, having his mind on other things, played his flashlight beam along the ground looking for snakes. He heard a loud *wooosh* and felt a rush of wind. Looking up, he saw an elephant's chin and trunk swishing wildly about against the stars. Cheers stumbled out of Mark's path, twisting and turning to avoid the small primate. Both man and elephant backpedaled twenty yards and stood gazing at each other. Cheers finally settled down. He lifted his trunk one last time, flicking dust in the flashlight beam, and ambled to the office cottage, where he fed on marula fruits, making loud slurping sounds.

The elephants were not always so amiable. On a soft afternoon when the sun was shining through a mist of rain, I was reading in the n'saka by the river. Cheers marched briskly and silently into camp and fed on fallen marula fruits next to the bedroom cottage some thirty yards away. For a while he and I, alone in camp, went about our work, only glancing at the other now and then. The occasional heavy drop of rain fell from the trees as the mist cleared, and a faint wisp of steam rose from Cheers's broad, warm back. The picture was too beautiful to keep only as a memory, so I decided to photograph him. To get a better view, I tiptoed out and stood under a fruit tree — not, as it turned out, a good place to stand in marula season. Suddenly Cheers turned and walked directly toward my tree. Within seconds he was only fifteen yards away. Surely he had seen me, but he came on purposefully, his massive body swaying, as though I weren't there. I was unsure whether to stand or run, but Cheers was not the least bit indecisive; this was his tree, his fruit. Flapping his ears wildly, he mock-charged me. I ran backward about ten yards, turned, and jumped off the steep bank into the river, where Ripples the crocodile lived.

Even as the poaching decreased, the small female groups — the remnants of those once large family units — were shyer than the males. Finally, after several years, one or two females with their young calves would feed on the tall grass across the river, not far from Long Tail or Survivor. But they never ventured into camp, just wandered nearby and stared at us from the bluff above our cottages. Their backs glistening with mud, the youngsters would splash in and out of the river and romp on the beach across from the n'saka.

TO KEEP OUT the African sun, we built our camp cottages with stone walls fourteen inches thick and roofed them with thatch about two feet deep. The huts stayed cave-cool even when the dry-season heat exceeded one hundred degrees. One afternoon, as I sat in the dim office cottage analyzing elephant footprint data on the solar-powered computer, a soft knock sounded on the door, and I looked up to see Patrick Mwamba, one of the first four Bemba tribesmen we had hired, years before, at the door. When he first came to us asking for work, the only tool he knew was his faithful ax; now he was our head mechanic and grader operator. Patrick is shy and gentle, with a fawnlike face.

"Dr. Delia, come see," he said. "There is a baby elephant. She is coming to us by the river."

I switched off the computer to save solar power and rushed to the doorway, where Patrick pointed to a small elephant trotting along the river's edge toward camp. Her tiny trunk jiggled about as she rambled along the sand. Suddenly she changed directions, galloped into the long grass, and reappeared upstream jogging in yet another direction, looking wildly around. Finally she halted and lifted her trunk, turning the end around like a periscope.

"Patrick, have you seen her mother — any other elephants?"

"No, madame, she is very much alone in this place."

An orphan. The park was sprinkled with these tiny survivors, youngsters who had watched every adult in their family mowed down by poachers. From the air we had seen infants standing by their fallen mothers or wandering around in aimless search for their families. Some died right there, waiting for their mothers to rise again. Some never found the herd. By the time we arrived at the site, the young elephants were usually gone or dead. Now one youngster had stumbled onto the shore opposite our camp and stood still, trunk hanging low, looking away as if we did not exist.

I could see Harrison Simbeye and Jackson Kasokola, our other assistants, and Mark watching the small elephant from behind the marula trees at the workshop. She wandered around the beach again for a few more minutes, then disappeared into the thick acacia brush. Without speaking and alert for crocodiles, the men and I forded the shallow river. We stood in a long line staring at the lonely prints in the sand.

Elephants grow throughout their lives, so their age can be determined by measuring the length of their hind footprints. The size of the prints suggested that this elephant was five years old. We named her Gift, after the recently deceased daughter of Tom Kotela, one of the Zambian game scout leaders. But we doubted if we would ever see her again.

There are two species of elephants in Africa. One, *Loxodonta cyclotis,* is the forest elephant found in Congo. Most of the others, including those of the Luangwa Valley, are *Loxodonta africana,* the savanna elephant.

Normally, when there is little or no poaching, female elephants live in family units whose matriarchal gene lines persist for generations. As is the case with many other social mammals, a female remains in her birth group all her life, so the group is made up of grandmothers, mothers, aunts, and sisters who feed, play, and raise their young together until they die. Males born into the group remain with the family only until their hormones send them off in search of unrelated females with whom to mate. Then they wander on their own or with a loose alliance of cronies, taking risks, fighting, or showing off to attract as many females as possible. So there are no adult males permanently attached to the family unit.

Female elephants touch often, rub backs and shoulders, gently tangling trunks. From their mothers and older relatives, the youngsters learn which plants to eat, where the waterholes are, and how to avoid predators. When an infant squeals, any of the female group members will run to the rescue. An elephant family is a fortress of females.

But little Gift was alone. She was old enough to be weaned, yet how could she survive without her family unit? Elephants rarely adopt orphans, and never nonrelatives.

The next day we spotted Long Tail and Cheers across the river, tearing up long grass and shoving it into their mouths with their trunks. Gift was forty yards away, feeding on shorter, tenderer grasses. From then on, whenever Long Tail, Cheers, or the other males wandered into camp, little Gift bounced along behind them. She looked minute next to them, a windup toy circling on her own in the background. In the absence of her family unit, and abandoning all normal elephant behavior, Gift had taken up residency near the Camp Group males.

For the most part, the males ignored her. At five, she was much too young to breed and, as is true of most male mammals, they had no other use for her. Before poaching was rampant in the Luangwa Valley, female elephants usually ovulated for the first time at fourteen years of age and delivered their first calf at sixteen. So, as the males roamed around in their habitual feeding patterns, first on the hillsides, then across the river in the long grass, the diminutive Gift stayed within sight of them but fed on her own. Sometimes she stepped gingerly up to one of the towering males and reached out her tiny trunk in greeting. Her mother, sisters, and aunts would have snaked their trunks out to hers and twisted them together. Her female family would have circled her, bumped heads, rubbed backs like affectionate tanks. Gift would have observed older mothers suckling their young and played with other infants, all the while learning the elephant alphabet. But the Camp Group males turned away from her, their huge backsides blocking her only chance at companionship. A cold shoulder from an elephant is a big rejection.

It would be an exaggeration to call any female elephant dainty. With their tree-trunk legs, thick ankles, and heavy shoulders — not to mention their less than elegant profiles — it's difficult to describe them as at all feminine. However, Gift came close to being ladylike, at least for an elephant. Perhaps it was just that compared to the males, she seemed so much more delicate in her feeding and lighter of foot. She had other little habits that reminded me of a young girl who had somehow found herself in a male world. One afternoon while feeding on a small tree, she broke off a branch covered with fresh, green leaves. Instead of eating the forage, she wandered around rather aimlessly for over thirty minutes carrying the branch in her trunk, as a girl might carry wildflowers in a spring meadow.

With no group, Gift had no playmates. More than a pastime, play with peers and elders is essential for forming lifelong bonds, perfecting trunk-eye coordination, and testing dominance. Gift had to play alone. Once she stepped into the flooded river and submerged herself completely. Rolling over and over, she splashed about, with a leg poking up here, her trunk there. Now and then she would burst out of the water like a breaching whale and dive underneath again.

Gift's special trademark was her jig. We often blundered into her when we rushed around camp. In a hurry to get to the plane for an elephant survey or to the office for binoculars or notebook, we would stride around a tree and come face to face with her. But she never charged us. If we got too close for her liking, she would trot away about five steps, stop, lift her tail slowly to the side, throw her head around dramatically, make a one-eighty turn, and trot back toward us. She would repeat this several times, as if dancing a jig. She also performed her dance for the massive buffaloes who fed in our camp and sometimes got in her way.

Gift was never a pet; we never fed her and certainly did not touch her. But she must have felt safe around us, because she lived nearby as though she had set up her own camp near ours. She sometimes stood near our cottages watching the small female families across the river, as the youngsters frolicked and the adults greeted one another with tangled trunks. We hoped that she would join them, that against all elephant tradition they would adopt her. But she never ventured near them. As she grew older, Gift wandered farther from camp during her feeding forays, and sometimes we would not see her for weeks, and then even for months. We always worried that she had been shot, and then she would show up at our camp again.

Whenever we flew over the valley, observing the elephant families from the air, taking notes on every detail of the groups, counting to see if their numbers were increasing, I always searched for Gift. I longed to see a little elephant among the others, one who would perhaps look up at us and dance her jig.

2 MARK

Poacher cum Miller

> That old law about "an eye for an eye" leaves everybody blind.
>
> — Martin Luther King, Jr.

Not long after Gift began coming to camp, I was flying the Cessna along the Lufila River, surveying elephant movements in the northern regions of the park. Whenever I flew I made a special effort to patrol the areas where Gift had last been seen, hoping to keep her safe from poachers.

The clipped voice of Tom Kotela, the unit leader of Mano, one of the five game scout camps responsible for securing North Luangwa, came through on my headset. He was relaying a message from "Spider," one of his informants: Mabu Kabutongo, one of the most determined and ruthless poachers still active in the area, had headed into the park along the Shatangalala poachers' route to kill elephants on the Mulandashi River. I rolled my eyes and groaned. I had hoped that those hard-core poachers who had refused the jobs and business opportunities spun off from our project had moved on to softer targets elsewhere. But apparently Kabutongo and a few others were still around, waiting for our project to fold and for the United Nations ivory ban to be lifted. Then they could get back to killing elephants full-time, with lots of big-league support.

For years some police, military, and other government civil servants in towns like Mpika had provided the poachers with guns, ammunition, and transport and had helped them smuggle ivory, skins, and even trophy heads south on trains and trucks to Lusaka and

South Africa; north to the port of Dar Es Salaam in Tanzania; and across Lake Tanganyika aboard the SS *Liemba* to Burundi and thence to Belgium. Our own network of informants and our contacts in Zambia's Anti-Corruption Commission told us that officials in virtually every branch of the government charged with protecting wildlife had been involved in profiting from the animals' demise, from game scouts to police, magistrates, military personnel, customs officials, departmental directors, government ministers, and others even higher up in the government. According to Paul Russell, then director of the Anti-Corruption Commission, the black market in wildlife parts was second only to the illicit drug trade as a secret source of revenue for the country. For a cut of the action, officials had laundered much of the contraband, providing documents to make the ivory and animal parts appear legal before passing them on to ships and aircraft, most bound for central Europe, Asia, and the Middle East.

Romance Musangu, a civil servant equivalent to the head of the U.S. Secret Service, was one of these officials. Later we would come face to face with him, but for now we knew him only as one of our informants described him — reluctantly, nervously, in secret meeting places, usually at night. Musangu was one of the "Big Boys from Lusaka," a man with the face and personality of an angry pit bull, who sat near the top of a tower of corruption. That tower was built with the body parts of wild animals and the wasted lives of people hooked on Mandrax and other drugs.

The local wildlife ranger Banda Famwila was one of Musangu's minions. A handsome, graying man with the refined, retiring air of a deacon, Famwila had for years been ordering his scouts to poach and to smuggle tusks, skins, and meat to his bosses in Lusaka. Tom Kotela told me that twice each week during the early 1980s two wildlife department trucks loaded with contraband from North Luangwa had traveled to Lusaka under cover of darkness. First the trucks stopped to offload some of the cargo at the ministry in Lusaka, then drove on to deliver meat to the Mundawanga Zoo, directly across the road from the Parks Department headquarters. Despite these regular deliveries of meat, the lions and other carnivores at the zoo had always looked more than half starved — because most of the meat was actually being delivered to Parks officials.

With cover from Banda Famwila, who kept the poachers informed of the game scout patrols' movements, Mabu Kabutongo had eluded Kotela and his scouts for years, once even hiding out for months in an abandoned termite mound. He had shot at my aircraft several times and had killed elephants very near our camp. On a circuit board with a tiny speaker, two wires, and a battery, Kabutongo had recently learned from a BBC radio report that the United Nations was considering relaxing its moratorium on the international trade in ivory. He and other poachers knew that the ban was voted on every two years and that it could be partially or wholly reversed at any time, allowing the legal sale of ivory, which could be used as a cover for an intensified illegal trade. If the ban was reversed or even weakened, the market price of elephant tusks would skyrocket. He and other ivory poachers would be back in business again. In the meantime they remained hopeful, and some, like Kabutongo, continued shooting elephants on speculation. Now that the scouts had blocked off most of the poachers' routes into the park from the west, he planned to mount operations from the villages of Nabwalya, to the south, and Fulaza, on the park's northern boundary.

"THE ELEPHANTS have been coming back nicely along the Mulandashi, sir," Tom said over the radio. "We must capture Kabutongo before he kills them. But it would take my scouts at least three days to get there on foot, and by then it would be too late. Maybe you can chopper them into position."

I sat back in my seat, exhausted. Just two nights earlier I had flown the scouts to intercept three corrupt policemen who for years had been supplying big-league poachers with weapons and ammunition from the police armory in Tazara, a railway settlement near

Mpika. The NLCP's support for wildlife law enforcement, along with our village outreach programs, had virtually put these police out of business. Armed with AK-47s and dressed like poachers, they had headed for our camp to "kill Owens and any scouts who get in the way." I had tried to intercept them by landing the scouts at night near their campfires in a deep ravine along the escarpment. The passage was so narrow that the chopper's main rotor had clipped tree limbs along the steep slopes. I had very nearly crashed. Badly shaken, I gave up and flew the scouts back to camp. The game warden told me later that before the corrupt police could get to our camp the next morning, they ran into a group of poachers dressed as scouts. In a shootout between policemen impersonating poachers, and poachers impersonating game scouts, one of the poachers had been wounded, and the cops had turned back to Tazara. Those hours of low-level night flying had left me haggard and raw. And now this.

"Copied, Tom, have them on standby at four o'clock tomorrow morning."

After a short night's sleep, I drove to our airstrip, where Milfred and I set out milk-tin flares along the runway. At 1:30 A.M. I took off in the Cessna to find Kabutongo and his bearers. The new moon hid behind a high layer of clouds; I could see only a hint of the sandbars along the rivers as I flew over. After I had been airborne for about twenty minutes, I put on my night-vision goggles and immediately picked up a hot spot of light from the poachers' campfires along the Mulandashi River northeast of Soma Hill. I climbed to eight thousand feet to avoid detection, and as I passed over the camp, I stored their latitude and longitude on the plane's global positioning instrument. The men did not snuff out their campfires, so I was pretty sure they had not heard the plane. I flew back to camp, preflight-checked the chopper, transferred the lat-long position of the poachers' camp to its GPS, catnapped for fifteen minutes, then took off for Mano to pick up the scouts.

Seven minutes after I landed at the Mano airstrip, Tom Kotela and Isaac Daka, Tom's stocky camp-in-charge and one of his most trusted officers, appeared out of the darkness leading two other scouts. They carried full packs so they could spend several days in the bush if needed, and they were armed with two rifles and two shotguns. We stuffed their gear in the cargo hold and took off. I slipped on my night-vision goggles again and began scanning the landscape — the image a grainy pea green in the starlight intensifier. Flying low-level along the forested foothills and ridges of the Muchinga Escarpment, I headed for the spot where the headwaters of the Mulandashi crept through the hills below the scarp and began their journey to the Luangwa, nearly twenty miles farther east. We were high above the valley floor — and still thirty miles from Kabutongo's poaching camp.

Minutes later, with dawn breaking, I slipped off my goggles and glanced at Kotela, sitting beside me, and then back at Daka, in the open doorway of the aft cabin, the cold wind rippling his crisp new uniform. Seven years earlier, on our first visit to Mano, Delia and I had found seven scouts dressed in rags seated around a frothing clay pot of beer. Only one looked up when we said hello, and the camp-in-charge, the man Isaac would eventually replace, scoffed when we told them that we hoped to start a conservation project in North Luangwa. Those seven men — armed with one working rifle and one round of ammunition — were the entire staff at the Mano Unit headquarters. The outlying camps had been abandoned, leaving a park the size of Delaware open to poaching. The scouts had no boots, uniforms, patrol food, medicines, or transportation; their mud-and-thatch houses were crumbling and leaky, they had not been paid in almost eight months, and their children did not have a school. They had not gone out on patrol for a year, maybe two — so long they could not remember for sure.

We would learn later that some of the scouts were poaching themselves; others were bartering their ammunition to poachers for meat. And even when they caught poachers, the magistrate would quickly release them for a small bribe.

One morning early in our third year I discovered more than a hundred poachers camped beside elephant carcasses on the Mulandashi River. They had kidnapped three tourists from one of the first walking safaris in the area. I flew in scouts from posts well beyond North Luangwa and landed them on a short gravel bar little more than a mile from the camp. We agreed that I would take off, fly over the poachers, and circle them while the scouts, following the airplane, would rush in to make the arrests. They never showed up. I circled over the poachers and dead elephants for almost two hours until, low on avgas, I was forced to go back to Marula-Puku. Later, I found out that the scouts had feasted on barbecued baby elephant trunk with the poachers, who had released the tourists earlier that day, warning them to stay out of the park.

Thankfully, those days were mostly behind us. Now more than sixty well-equipped scouts regularly patrolled North Luangwa. With the help of the project, the Zambian government, and the United Nations ivory ban, they had almost completely stamped out the poaching of elephants and other wildlife, at least for the time being, not only in the park but also in the areas around it. Almost. We still had Kabutongo and a few others to reckon with. And recently "Talky," one of our most reliable informants, a man who had formerly worked for the office of the president, had given me even more alarming news: Ranger Banda Famwila was moving corrupt scouts into the area and transferring good ones out to undermine the project and promote his operations. The warden confirmed this, but even though Famwila was his subordinate, he could not get his department to fire him or at least move him to another part of the country. He asked me to intervene, but when I did, I was met with icy hostility. Famwila's connections were too high up.

I was beginning to feel that permanently stemming the tide of poaching in North Luangwa was like trying to stamp out drug trafficking in an inner city. Talky had already warned me that certain officials, frustrated because the NLCP stood between them and their illicit interests, might move against us.

We joined the Mulandashi among the deep, fluted canyons of the scarp and began following it east, downslope toward the Luangwa. I watched the GPS count down the miles to the poachers' camp. Flying low and fast, we hugged the riverbank, hiding below its trees, stifling the slap of the rotor blade in brush and tall grass to cover our approach.

At three miles I warned the scouts to get ready.

At two-tenths of a mile I flew the chopper behind a hill at the river's edge, then snatched back its cyclic control and shot up out of the mist.

A column of smoke and vultures was rising into the air next to a waterhole where some poachers squatted around their morning campfires; others were still asleep in their bedrolls. I throttled up and we swept forward, flying fifty feet above the ground. Caught by surprise, men scattered from around meat racks and smoldering drying fires hidden under trees. One of them — Kabutongo — carried a rifle.

We dropped into a clearing beyond the camp, and as the skids kissed the ground the scouts jumped out. Seeing us land, the poachers broke and ran. I took off again and hovered in the sky a safe distance away while the scouts gave chase, rounding up one after another until they had captured three groups, each guarded by a single officer. The shooter was still out there somewhere — but so was Isaac, the scrappy five-foot-tall scout.

To my left, about two hundred yards away, I could see another clutch of poachers hiding in a thicket. Isaac was running toward them, his rifle pointed ahead of him, darting right, then left, going bush to bush, not sure where they were. Kabutongo raised his rifle as the "little-big scout" came nearer.

"Shooter at your two o'clock! Watch out!" I yelled into the mike. But Isaac had lowered his radio from his ear, and even at this distance the roar of the chopper had drowned out my transmission. He stalked closer, still uncertain which thicket held the poachers.

I lowered the chopper's nose, poured on full power, and rushed forward. In seconds I hauled the screaming aircraft to a hover with its skids not ten feet above the poachers' heads. The rotor's powerful downdraft sent a dust storm ripping through the thicket, thrashing its thorny branches. Kabutongo lowered his rifle and ducked down, covering his face with his forearm. Blinded, he staggered out of his cover just as Isaac arrived at a dead run. He hit the poacher with a right cross and chopped his arm with his rifle barrel, sending the shooter's weapon flying. In seconds Kabutongo was handcuffed.

Kabutongo had killed a waterbuck to black-market the meat, but the scouts captured him before he could poach any elephants. His failed expedition had cost him a firearm, money to pay the carriers, and a lot of credibility with men who might not be so eager to follow him into the bush again.

After the scouts had handcuffed the poachers for their march to the magistrate's court in Mpika, I landed nearby and switched off the chopper. Tom and Isaac questioned each man as to why he had joined Kabutongo's poaching expedition. Mulenga Mwengi, thirty years old and from Mwamfushi village, a former gateway into the park for poachers, was trying to support nine children. His three oldest had dropped out of school because he couldn't afford to pay for their education. Kabutongo and other commercial poachers, whom Mwengi referred to as "the big brothers from town," paid him little more than a lump of meat for his service as a carrier.

When we offered Mwengi honest work if he gave up poaching, he became the miller for his village, running the maize hammer mill installed by the project in Mwamfushi. We hired the other carriers to build a road into the national park.

After Tom and Isaac had finished interviewing Kabutongo's carriers, they turned to him. The rising sun was spilling its golden light onto the dusty hardpan and scrub brush near the waterhole where the handcuffed poacher sat watching us, shoulders back, head unbowed.

"You are a lucky man," Tom explained. "According to the laws of Zambia you would ordinarily go to jail. But if you like, the project will offer you a job as the maize miller at Mano Camp. So, what will it be?"

Kabutongo, his face covered with white dust, looked at me. The muscles of his square jaw softened, and his eyes seemed to brighten.

"I can be miller."

We immediately moved him and his family to Mano, built them a small home of bricks and thatch, and he began his new career. He nicknamed his wife Delia.

Later we received this note from Mulenga Mwengi:

> I was offered the job, which I grandly [gladly] accepted. Life changed so much . . . I started buying agriculture inputs from my salary and the project helped with other inputs like seeds and out let market for my products. I would say my life would never been like this, I have managed to send my children to school, a thing that I terribly failed in my poaching career.
>
> Mulenga Mwengi
> Maize Miller
> Mwamfushi Village

3 DELIA
Upside-Down Elephants

Like a crowd of kids . . .

—William Golding

One important variable affecting the development of aggressiveness is the type of mothering received by a young animal.

—James F. Wittenberger

Twenty years earlier, more than seventeen thousand elephants roamed North Luangwa, but in the early 1990s only about fifteen hundred remained. Now, instead of large aggregations of families moving through the valley, little pockets of survivors were tucked away in deep ravines and thick brush. We weren't sure whether enough adults of breeding age had survived to allow the herds to recover. To find out, we had to measure their feet; the age structure of the population would reveal what percentage could breed and whether or not the population was growing, stable, or declining.

I had decided to make the trek along the Lubonga River to the Mwaleshi River and on to the Luangwa, to measure elephant footprints in the sand. There were no roads or even primitive tracks near the rivers, so I would go on foot, a walk that would take six or seven days. Mark could not come along because he had to locate the elephant families every day by aircraft and support the village work.

I needed a tracker, someone who could distinguish one footprint from another, someone who knew where the elephants were foraging, which ravines they frequented. It occurred to me that Mabu

Kabutongo, the ex-poacher who was now the miller at Mano, would be an excellent choice. Who could read elephant tracks better than a former poacher? I sent a radio message asking him to come to Marula-Puku with carriers, and he agreed.

Mark was not enthusiastic about my plan. He pointed out that Kabutongo had shot at our airplane and was probably waiting for another chance to shoot elephants. I insisted that he had reformed, and I would have a game scout and three carriers with me. Mark finally gave in, saying he would fly over our position every day to check on us.

I had meant to depart at sunrise the next morning, but an hour later I stood at the edge of camp with piles of gear — big white bags of mealie meal, a string of pots tied together with blue plastic rope, tents, and backpacks — spread out in a circle. Kabutongo grew impatient as the porters circled their packs, insisting that they needed another man to share the load. "Tien, tien. Let's go, let's go," he kept saying.

Finally everyone shouldered their loads, adjusted straps and buckles, and balanced bags on their heads. Mark, a steaming cup of coffee in his hand, reminded me that whenever I heard the plane or chopper, I should radio my position. We marched single file out of camp with Kabutongo, armed and dressed in old fatigues, in the lead. I followed him, and the carriers, clad in an assortment of mismatched missionary hand-me-downs, their tin cups clanking against their packs, were strung out behind me. Francis, a game scout, outfitted smartly in his official uniform, provided recently by Prince Bernhard of the Netherlands, brought up the rear, his rifle slung over his shoulder with a piece of old rope. Grasshoppers flew up from the grass in front of us, spreading their wings and exposing their stunning red underwear.

Low, dirty clouds scudded just over our heads, masking the normally bright African sky. We passed the cook's camp, a squat mud hut under a huge marula tree, and I called goodbye to Mumanga

Kasokola, Jackson's brother. He stood next to the fire, waving a white dishcloth in farewell until we reached the first river bend, four hundred yards from camp. All I could see before I rounded the turn was his cloth flitting above the grass like a large butterfly.

The Lubonga River is born in lush miombo woodlands, a two-story forest with a wispy open canopy, high in the mountains of the Muchinga Escarpment. Its birth waters seep out of rocky, moss-covered crevasses and silent springs. As an infant, it meanders slowly through forgotten forests and small marshy plains, inviting other springs to join it along the way, growing in size and speed. The terrain becomes more broken as it approaches the three-thousand-foot drop of the escarpment, and there the small river picks up speed, tumbling over rocky outcroppings as startled, unnamed waterfalls and gushing through deep gorges smothered in ancient forests.

After running the mountains, the river takes a rest, slowing its pace through the foothills. Here the canyons are fewer and wider, and the Lubonga meanders gently through wooded foothills and small grassy glades of the valley. It wanders by our camp at this point — where we began to follow it — and continues to twist and turn through the riverine forests, finally losing its identity altogether as it flows into the wide, sweeping waters of the Mwaleshi. We headed downstream, following the Lubonga toward its confluence with the Mwaleshi.

Standing on the opposite shore, his rifle pointed toward the water, Kabutongo shouted to me, "Keep up, keep up," as I waded into a rocky shoal. The river is clear and shallow, giving one a false sense of security. But last year, as Charles Phiri, one of the workers, waded into a clear pool in the river near our camp, an enormous crocodile exploded from the calm water and grabbed his leg with jagged jaws. The twelve-foot reptile shook him violently, ripping his leg. Bornface Zulu, our airplane guard, grabbed Charles by the belt and pulled him free. As Charles heaved and struggled for breath on the beach, the crocodile lunged from the pool and grasped his torn and bloody leg again. Bornface ran for his rifle, which was leaning against a tree, stepped into the water, and shot the croc in the head. Although we flew Charles to Lusaka for the best medical care in Zambia, he later died from his injuries.

I never stepped into the river without thinking of Charles. Kabutongo shouted for us to bunch together while wading across, so I moved closer to the others, scanning back and forth for reptilian scales hiding in the current that lapped at our knees. Finally we reached the far shore and trundled onto the beach. Every half mile or so we had to cross the meandering river again, and each time Kabutongo urged us to stay together and walk quickly: "Tien! Tien!"

"More footy-prints." Kabutongo pointed to a line of prints crisscrossing the beach. I expected to find the tracks of only ten or fifteen elephants along the Lubonga, but by midmorning we had measured twenty sets.

I pulled the calipers, notebook, and pen from my pockets and squatted down to measure. By now we had a bit of a system going: the men would spread out across the beach and determine how many elephants were in the group, and I would follow along measuring one print of each. It was essential not to measure the same elephant twice, but because the elephants often milled around while drinking, bathing, and playing, it was difficult to tell their tracks apart. It looked as if a circus had been to the beach.

"No. You have already measured that one," Kabutongo said over my shoulder, as I knelt next to a print.

"How can you tell?"

"It is my work."

"I know, but please show me how." He pointed to the faint, squiggly lines in the sand created by the spongy bottom of the elephant's foot and, tracing them with his fingers, showed me how each was different, like a fingerprint. I had to study them for long minutes to see any difference, but it was obvious to Kabutongo.

At noon we dropped our packs to the ground under a *Trichilia emetica* tree at the confluence of the Mwaleshi and Lubonga rivers, a spot where Mark and I had lunched on our first day in North Luangwa six years before. We could see the rushing waters where the two rivers merged. The purple mountains of the scarp lay as a backdrop to the west. A campfire seemed to leap from Kabutongo's hands as he knelt in the clearing under the tree, and soon the men began cooking their lunch of *nshima* (cornmeal mush) and *kapenta* (small dried fish). I nibbled on crackers and peanut butter, and boiled water for tea in a pot on the edge of their fire. We chatted and laughed about the morning's work, very pleased with ourselves. Kabutongo seemed to relax, now that he had whipped us into an efficient unit.

At half past one we started off again, crossed the Lubonga for the last time, and followed the Mwaleshi, which is blessed with hundreds of wide sandy beaches and grassy floodplains. Many of the beaches were laced with long lines of elephant tracks, and we went about the backbreaking work of stooping to measure them. Taking our packs off and putting them on again at each set of tracks was tiresome, so we worked awkwardly with the packs on our backs. The clouds were gone now, and the heat seemed dense, like a curtain we had to push through to take a step.

As I knelt to measure a spoor, a large wasp hovered close to my wrist. Her brilliant blue, transparent wings were lined with black veins and reflected the stark light like colored foil. She landed and walked up and down my arm with dainty feet, then hovered just above my skin. She had powerful venom; we had watched others of her kind tranquilize mice and drag their immobilized prey into burrows for their young. I knew she wouldn't harm me; she was after my salty sweat, which to her must have been as refreshing as Gatorade. And I considered it an even trade, for the ambient air was so still and hot that the tiny breeze from her wings felt cool against my arm. I remained still, encouraging her to fan me. Finally she lifted off and flew toward the river, taking away the wind on her blue-black wings.

I stood and wiped my brow with my bandanna, thinking how nice it would be to actually *see* live elephants instead of just their "footy-prints."

Other species of wildlife were splashed everywhere across the wondrous, unscarred Mwaleshi floodplains. Waterbuck males strutted their stuff on sandbars, groups of cinnamon-colored puku grazed the short grasses, zebras pranced in lines along the beaches. Once, on the opposite shore, a herd of fifteen hundred buffalo jogged across the plain, stirring a plume of dust that blocked the sun. They plunged into the shallow river, splashing sprays of water, and as they emerged, they veered slightly and ran directly toward us. Kabutongo opened his arms like a mother hen herding her chicks and quickly moved us onto a bluff, where we could watch in safety.

By 4:30 my legs ached. Hiking through the burning sand was like walking against a strong current. Judging by the slowing progress of the men, I guessed they felt the same, though I was quite sure Kabutongo could walk all night. I began searching for a place to camp, ideally one with a wide, shady tree, a lovely view of the wilderness we had just embraced, a clean, safe place to bathe in the river, and a handy source of firewood. Often the camping place is the most memorable part of a day in the wild, and it sometimes seems my life is defined by a long trail of abandoned campfires.

Kabutongo and the others clearly had different criteria from mine. They unshouldered their packs in a small, rough clearing surrounded by tall, itchy grass with no view whatsoever, no shade trees, no firewood, and only a stagnant oxbow from which to draw water. I took one look at this unworthy spot, hefted my pack again, and told them they could stay there, but I was going back to the last group of trees we had passed, about three hundred yards upstream. There thick fig trees stood in a clearing by the sparkling, not-in-a-hurry current of the Mwaleshi. In the distance the soft body of the forested escarpment lay on its side to the west, and a zebra-spotted plain stretched to the east toward the rest of Africa.

"Wait, Dr. Delia, you cannot camp so far from us. It will be very dangerous," Kabutongo called after me.

"I'll be okay over here, don't worry." But soon he had the others lugging their packs toward my site, and we set about making camp. Someone wandered off for firewood, someone else for water. Scuffing the ground with my boots, I cleared a spot for my tent, and they a spot for theirs. A large clump of *Combretum obovatum* bushes, more gray, gnarled thorns than leaves, separated our respective sites, affording just a bit of privacy.

After the men went to the river to bathe, it was my turn. Although the rains had ended for the most part, the Mwaleshi was still murky from the wet-season runoff, making it impossible to see if the tail of a croc was coiled under the ripples. We had a rule that if you walked along the river for a hundred yards and could not see crocs through the clear water, it was okay to swim or bathe. But searching for crocs in this café au lait was pointless. Out of sight of my campmates, I undressed next to the current and slipped into the tepid water. I wanted to linger to soak up the coolness, but I jumped out to lather up, then plunged in once more to rinse quickly. I dried on the bank, feeling very clean but cheated; however, this was not the time or place to break the river rules.

I shared the men's campfire; the world could have shared their campfire. As usual, they dragged huge logs from far and near and started an enormous bonfire. The undercanopy of the tree was lit up in the yellow and red fire glow, and thousands of sparks sprayed into the air and mingled with the first timid stars of dusk. To cook their mealie meal they raked hot coals from the pyre and balanced a huge pot on top of the glowing embers. I stuck my tiny billy next to the coals to boil water for dehydrated soup. As we watched our steaming pots, all dented and scratched from miles of trail, and as the blushing sunset paled beyond the mountains, Kabutongo entertained us with stories about his poaching. He told us of a buffalo he had wounded, "but it did not die and it ran with me to the tree. But I was too fast because I had fewer legs and I climbed the tree in front of the buffalo.

And from there I was very safe until I shot the buffalo and finished him off." The other men listened with awe. I encouraged them to join in. I especially wanted Francis, the game scout, to feel as important as Kabutongo, but he was a shy, quiet man and did not want to boast about his experiences capturing poachers. Kabutongo carried the sunset.

As we stirred our pots, our slow movements around the fire cast giant, wavering shadows against the glowing tree. We ate in silence, and then I wished the men good night and moved over to my tent. I was so fatigued I could have fallen asleep instantly, but it wasn't even seven o'clock. If I slept this early, midnight would wake me stiff and sore. I dragged a small log from their woodpile, placed it in front of the pup tent door as a stool, and sat reading by candlelight. The stars were so bright in the black sky I felt I could reach up and touch them — even move them around. But who would want to rearrange Scorpio or disturb Orion's belt?

The frogs were louder than the lions, who called from the distant plains. By 7:40 the Southern Cross was fully on her side, and the arch of the Milky Way was holding up my tent. Fruit bats with beautiful fox faces swooped around me so close I could feel the wind of their wings on my face. The flicker from the candle distracted me, so I blew it out and put away my book. I would read the night instead. A different lion roared, closer. I felt alive, tucked into the earth.

I awoke at four and peeped out through my little tent window. A tide of clouds was flowing in so fast the moon seemed to be drowning. Struggling for a foothold, the predawn sky was heavy gray, with only a few weak streaks of gold far away. I lay on my camp mattress listening slowly to the guys as they began to stir. Rousing myself, I rolled up my sleeping bag and stuffed yesterday's clothes in my pack, then crawled from my pup tent like a caterpillar casting off a cocoon. The men, still half wrapped in their blankets around the fire, began to move about like giant worms.

I felt a bit tired and sore from yesterday's long walk but was "quite okay," as the Bembas say. No blisters on toes or heels.

For three days we walked along the Mwaleshi aging elephants, Mark now and then checking our position from the sky. We saw no elephants, only footy-prints. Once at night we heard their shrill trumpeting, and one afternoon they were so close in the thick bush we could feel and smell their huge bodies moving near us. Otherwise they kept their distance, and we studied them only by the stories they left in the sand. Our backs and knees ached from the constant stooping and kneeling with heavy packs, so on the third day we set up a base camp on a high bank overlooking the river and began doing day hikes from there.

One afternoon we saw a startling green lagoon blinking at us like an enormous eye from under the shadows of some ebony trees. The surface was so covered in life you could watch it breathe. On long, stiltlike legs, lily-trotters darted across water lily pads as large as elephant ears. Hadada ibis and spur-winged geese waddled along the shore eating tidbits. Five fat crocodiles as wide as kitchen tables lolled about in bright sun spots. We left the river beach and walked toward the lagoon to watch twelve hippos, their broad faces and tiny eyes peering at us from the water. One large male glided toward us, ducking his head now and then through the tangle of water plants floating on the surface. When he was thirty yards away he stood and threatened us with huge squared-off teeth and head rolls. I suppose he was trying to look fierce, but unbeknownst to him his head was draped with brilliant tendrils of green Nile lettuce and lovely water lilies, making him look more like a bridesmaid than a mad bull.

After five days we had aged almost two hundred elephants. In the heat of the day, when it was too hot to walk on the blazing sand, I sat in front of my tent and studied the data we had collected so far. In the 1970s, before heavy poaching, 50 percent of the female elephants had been of breeding age, that is, more than fifteen years old. Now only 8 percent were old enough to breed. Later on, after we had aged more than 60 percent of the population annually for six years, those preliminary figures were confirmed. Normally female elephants between the ages of twenty-five and forty are the most reproductively active, but very few of the old matriarchs were left. Besides being the most important players in elephant reproduction, the mature elephants are the storehouses for the collective knowledge of the herd. Such survival secrets had been shot and smuggled away with the ivory.

And, as with humans, adult elephants keep some sense of order and peace within their strongly bonded families. In elephant populations that have not been devastated by poachers, three quarters of the family units are led by a matriarch older than thirty years — a real grownup. Group members are seldom aggressive toward each other; even battles between gigantic males over courtship rights rarely end in serious injuries. In all social species, families designed by nature buffer youngsters against trauma and stresses that would otherwise lead to enhanced violence and poor maternal behavior in the next generation.

However, in North Luangwa a third of the family groups had no adult females older than fifteen years, because they had been shot. Nearly 10 percent of the groups were made up entirely of unsupervised, inexperienced, and unruly teenagers — some all females, some all males — roaming around on their own in an elephant version of *Lord of the Flies.* The social structure was scrambled. These disrupted families and unchaperoned gangs seemed vaguely familiar, not unlike some aspects of our own stressed species.

As a result of this change, the family units of North Luangwa were less cohesive and the adolescents were more aggressive than in populations that had not suffered from poaching. From the air we had seen young males chasing and harassing females far too young to breed. Enhanced aggression was seen elsewhere as well. In the absence of adult males, a small group of orphaned male elephants in Pilanesberg Game Reserve in South Africa went on a rampage and killed forty white rhinoceros. The killing spree stopped when mature bulls were introduced. The fractured groups of North Luangwa engaged in much less reaching out and twining of trunks; we seldom witnessed gentle touching. When families are dismantled, agonistic behavior increases; there is much less quality time at the beach. Based on what has been seen in other species, including our own, calves who had experienced the trauma of seeing their families killed were probably more likely to grow up to be aggressive. Children raised in wartorn neighborhoods are more likely to be violent than those raised in peaceful settings. Like the elephants, people do manage to survive in fragmented families, but society must endure the consequences of increased aggression and unruly gangs. We weren't sure whether man had more to learn from elephants or they from us.

The question was whether these abnormal groups of adolescent elephants would have the know-how to survive until they were old enough to reproduce. If not, the population would never recover. Amassing numbers is not the most important factor, as we, more than any other species on Earth, should know. Could these rogue teenage elephants put their social system back together? Could they ever return to a time and place where the most precious of accords — the basic family unit with its fundamental softness and security — was restored? When you lose the knack of hugging each other or twisting trunks together, how do you get it back again? Can society ever find peace once the family has fallen apart?

The columns of footprint measurements also presented a mystery. Most groups included more infants than adult females. How could this be? Even though a third of the families had no adult females, small infants still toddled next to the adolescents. Ivory poachers had left many orphans like Gift, but most of them had not been weaned from their mother's milk and thus had died. Elephants seldom adopt unweaned orphans. As inexplicable as the numbers seemed, it was certainly good news that twice as many infants had been born into the population in the past year as in the previous two years combined. Perhaps a recovery was beginning.

As the river swallowed the sun, I wandered to the sandy shore to bathe, as I did every night. Perhaps the coolness would wash away the muddle of numbers in my mind.

Just as I was testing the water with my toes, I heard the haunting shriek of an elephant trumpet. Another answered, and within seconds a chorus of elephant songs broke the silence. I grabbed my towel and soap and ran toward Kabutongo's camp. He had heard them too, and rushed toward me.

"They are just around the bend, madame. Let us go; we can see them." The other men followed as we walked quickly through the tall grass toward the river's wide bend downstream. We climbed a small bluff that overlooked the water and, peering from the thick bush, we could see twelve elephants milling about on the beach only forty yards below us. Two calves frolicked in the shallow current, while two adolescent females sprayed water over their own enormous backs. Subadult males pushed and shoved one another. A family of elephants just being elephants in an African river. Except that there were no old adults, and all the elephants were tuskless.

Every population of elephants has a small percentage, 2 to 5 percent, that never develop tusks. But in North Luangwa, since so many of the elephants with tusks had been shot, and those without tusks had lived to reproduce, the genes for tusklessness were spreading in the population. Thirty-eight percent were now tuskless. Having no tusks was definitely a disadvantage when it came to fighting and feeding, but it did help save the elephants from poachers.

We watched from our hiding place for twenty minutes. Kabutongo pointed out that one of the females had no tail. The men laughed at two young bulls fighting. Finally, Francis whispered that it was nearly dark and that we must get back to our camps. Reluctantly, I began to walk away, but Kabutongo grabbed my arm and pointed to a large bull foraging on the distant shore; he also had no tusks and, like one of the females, he was tailless. It was clear that Kabutongo did not want to leave the elephants and followed us only after Francis motioned urgently for him to come.

Around the campfire, Kabutongo helped me describe the elephant family in my notebook so that we could recognize them again.

He remembered characteristics about each one — a tear in the right ear, a medium-length tail, a jagged scar. I had definitely found a good elephant tracker.

After three days in our base camp, we packed up once more and walked downstream toward the confluence of the Mwaleshi and Luangwa rivers. As we neared the Luangwa, we approached the boundary of North Luangwa National Park. Although we could not see them from here, on the opposite shore were scattered villages, hunting and fishing camps, poachers. We encountered fewer and fewer elephant tracks as we neared the boundary. Wilderness on earth is now so confined that you can venture only so far into its heart before every step starts taking you away again. I could feel the shift, swinging like a compass in my chest.

In late afternoon we stood on a high bank overlooking the confluence of the two rivers, still somewhat swollen from the rains. At the height of the dry season, when some stretches of the Luangwa shrink to a mere channel, we had seen more than four hundred hippos packed nose to tail in this spot, but now, with the high waters, they were spread out in small groups of ten to twelve. As if luxuriating in the clean, rushing current, they were fully submerged except for their broad faces and tiny ears, which flicked continuously, sending sprays of droplets through the air. The men pitched their circle of pup tents farther inland in a small group of trees. I chose a camp very near the bank and, as darkness fell, I sat in front of my tent to watch the hippos waddle across the moonlit beaches. As they entered the water they made loud, hollow splashing sounds as if they were walking in big rubber boots.

Chief Mukungule, the oldest surviving chief in Zambia, had told us of the days when long, slow lines of several hundred elephants crossed the river. By sun or moon, they could be seen splashing through the wide, lazy Luangwa. The sounds of their giant feet against the current could be heard for a long distance, far around the river's bend.

Today elephants occasionally cross the river, but they know that poachers set up ambushes along the shore, so they usually cross under cover of darkness and, of course, in much smaller numbers. Even after spending years in Luangwa we had never seen this spectacle.

As I sat watching the glistening hippos emerge from the water, loud splashes broke the silence. I checked for lions with my flashlight, then crept through the silvery trees to the edge of the riverbank. Only fifty yards away a herd of fifteen elephants was slipping and sliding very clumsily down the steep, uneven bank. One youngster slid all the way down on his backside. Kicked free by huge feet, clods of mud rolled down the bank into the water. The elephants splashed into the river and in single file moved across it, their giant bodies swaying with an ancient rhythm. The night was lit brilliantly by the moon, and as they forded I saw their tails and trunks perfectly. They were all tuskless and two had no tails; it was the same herd we had watched bathe upstream. They reached the other side of the river and walked onto the flat beach.

The river was dancing with moonlight, yet the wet mud of the other side was black. When the deep gray elephants stepped onto the shore, they vanished into darkness. Even shielding my eyes against the bright moon, I could see nothing of them. But suddenly the perfect reflection of upside-down elephants, moving gracefully in a line, came into focus on the platinum river. Slowly and silently the inverted images floated on the sparkling current. The mirror river was so calm that every part of the elephants — the wiry tufts of their tails, the crooks of their trunks, their faces — was visible in detail. Stolen by the night, yet revealed by the moon's smile, these silent creatures drifted past my shore. Only the occasional ripple reminded me that they were mere reflections as they faded from magic into memory.

SUCH WONDERS COULD keep me following elephant footprints for days, but we had reached our destination, the Luangwa, and other duties called. The key to conserving the elephants lay in helping the villagers near the park. Within the next few days I was to drive across the wild, remote northern plains of North Luangwa to the village of Fulaza to discuss job opportunities with the people. Mark and I had gone there several times over the years. However, I had never driven there by myself, and since the trip included crossing several rivers crazed with floodwaters, I was a bit apprehensive about the journey. But first the elephant trackers and I had to get back to Marula-Puku.

Late the next afternoon, as the sun pounded down and the white beach blinded us and I began to hope we never found another elephant track to measure, the *whop-whop-whop* of the chopper drifted softly downwind. As Mark swooped in low, we waved and danced around the beach like the troop of primates we were — now to be airlifted home, avoiding the long trek back. To ferry us all, Mark would have to make two trips. He landed on a grassy knoll and handed out cold Cokes and chocolate bars — treats as rare as rain — as we talked furiously about our adventures and the success of the elephant tracking. Within minutes we had half of our gear stuffed into the aft compartment and were gliding over the beaches we had hiked. Along the Mwaleshi, not far from the orange-red bluff, the tuskless elephant family foraged in a thicket of riverine forest. They must have recrossed the river into the national park sometime during the night. I nodded a silent farewell and wished them well in their upside-down world.

4 DELIA

The Song of the Winterthorn

. . . passions will rock thee
As the storms rock the ravens on high.
— Percy Bysshe Shelley

Low, dark clouds with wispy bottoms skirted the treetops across the river from Marula-Puku, parting briefly to reveal the stars. One last flash of lightning mixed its eerie blue light with the golden moonlight, and the crack of thunder tumbled head over heels across the valley. Then, unbelievably, the sparrow weavers began to sing. These small birds, outfitted with startling patterns of black, white, and brown, had nested in the acacia trees of our Kalahari camp in Botswana years ago, and now this same species lived in our Luangwa camp. For more than fifteen years we had been awakened before dawn by their joyous chortles and throaty whistles. But now they were singing furiously at midnight. Perhaps they were bragging that they had survived the storm. Or maybe their nests had been blown out of the winterthorn tree, leaving them homeless in the night with nothing left to do but sing — that's the way a sparrow weaver would see it.

Earlier, during the rainy season, there had been other storms, hot and heavy like this one, leaving behind the signs of their passion — broken trees and flooded rivers. All that anger, all that energy spent, but not wasted. For they left behind wonders as well.

Every year at the end of the long dry season, every bit of scrub, every tree, bursts forth with pure, bright green. Even before the first storm, when the heat is still stifling, miles upon unbroken miles of shrubs unfold their tiny, curled shoots at once. The rivers may still be parched and choked with dry sand, but the huge trees spilling over their banks sprout new leaves seemingly overnight. With the first drops of rain, a flush of new grasses spreads across the savannas in a tide of fresh life. The only time of year when Africa is free of dust or mud, she swishes around in her new green dress for all to see. Every bush, every tree joins the parade except for one, the winterthorn.

In the midst of this celebration of new life and color, the winterthorn stands barren and leafless. A stranger to Africa will say, "Look at that huge tree; too bad it's dead." But the winterthorn, impervious to such insults, stretches its dry, delicate branches in a mighty arc across the sky, as if it knows its moment will come.

For all this green will pass too, of course. The last drop of rain is not the beginning of the dry season; the signs of the seasons are much more subtle. But you awake one morning in March or April — maybe even May — and find the dawn less soft, the air less gentle. You know, as the geese do, that the dry season is just around the river's bend. Clouds still form, and it may even rain again, a time or two, but the thunderheads have shrunk to puffy pillows floating over distant mountains.

When the plains and rivers dry up, the green trees wither and fade. At that moment, when it has the stage all to itself and life seems too hard to bear, the winterthorn begins to sing. At first only a whisper of green touches the tips of the thorny branches, but soon a rich, deep color spreads across the towering limbs. And then the stranger will ask, "What is that magnificent tree?"

Like Africa itself, the winterthorn dances in its own season.

SINCE THIS WAS early in the dry season, the time of the winterthorn, the midnight squall had been all wind and no rain. I awoke again at dawn. After an early breakfast of hot sorghum porridge and campfire toast, I set off in the truck for Fulaza village, whose mud-and-thatch huts hug the bank of the winding, clear waters of the Lufila River, the northern boundary of North Luangwa National Park. No roads went to Fulaza. Only a few worn trails snaked out of the village into the bush beyond; one of the main footpaths led into the park.

Riding beside me in the truck was Sugar, a Bemba man we had hired a year earlier to oversee our village programs. Sugar, like many of the tribesmen, had attended only a few grades of school in his small village. Then, holding tight to his brother's hand, he had traveled on an overcrowded bus to southern Zambia, which had more opportunities than the quiet and wild north. The pulsing capital of Lusaka was surrounded by vast farms, and there Sugar had learned the agricultural skills he was putting to use in his homeland by setting up projects in the tiny outposts scattered across Bembaland.

Fulaza was one of the fourteen villages where we had set up programs to help people find alternatives to poaching. The other villages had fish farms, sunflower-seed presses, soybean crops, grinding mills, and beekeepers. Men who were once notorious poachers now sold honey from beehives, raised rabbits and ducks, and reaped peanuts for protein. However, poachers coming into the park from the north were still shooting some of the few remaining elephants every year. Soon these small herds would be wiped out, and then what would the people who depended on poaching do? We wanted to give them options, at least. Villages like Fulaza were so isolated that the villagers could not go to visit the carpentry shops or fish farms in Chobela. They had no cash economy but shot elephants and traded the ivory and meat for mealie meal or cooking oil.

Sugar was short and stout, with round cheeks and smiling eyes. His real name was Musakanya Chatukwa; we nicknamed him Sugar because he put at least five or six teaspoons of it in every cup of tea.

"That was a strange storm last night, hey, Sugar?" I said.

"Yes, Delia, this weather is lost."

I drove through a stand of tall, prickly buffalo grass, and shifted the Land Cruiser into low gear to ford the Lubonga. The truck rocked gently over the rounded stones lining the stream bottom as the clear water flowed beneath us. I drove upstream several yards to avoid a waterfall that cascaded about three feet into a pool, where Ripples the crocodile sometimes hunted. As I drove onto the far bank, Sugar opened his leather briefcase — polished to a copper luster by his constant rubbing — and rummaged through his papers until he found his notes about Fulaza and studied the names of the villagers.

It would take five or six hours to drive the twenty-three miles on the dusty track across the park to the village. Mark and I had cut the track a few years earlier, a job that took days because we had to devise river crossings. Once we had four flat tires in less than an hour in a mean thicket of thorny brush. On the last night of track-making we worked long into dusk, and the full moon rose ahead of us. I stood in the bed of the truck and peered ahead into the thick bush, searching for the best course around fallen logs or holes. "Stay to the left of the moon," I called to Mark. Then, "Now drive straight toward the moon. Back left of the moon." Finally we reached the river, which seemed to flow into the mouth of night.

I hoped that Sugar could not tell that I was somewhat nervous about driving to Fulaza for the first time. When we reached the second crossing, I stopped the truck on a steep bank that descended about fifteen yards toward the water. The freak storm had apparently brought rain somewhere upstream, for the normally small river was in a mad and muddy mood. It was only about thirty feet wide and probably less than five feet deep, but it was in flood and flowing swiftly through the narrow ravine. I eased the truck down the pitch in low gear and drove slowly into the current. Within seconds the water seeped under the doors and around our feet. The front end of the truck went under the water, which reached halfway up the cab doors. The raised, snorkel-like air intake kept the truck from sucking water and stalling, but the engine hissed and moaned as the truck crept forward over the uneven bottom. As long as I did not get stuck and kept moving, we would be all right. I had watched Mark do this scores of times, but my heart thumped against my ribs as water sloshed around my ankles. Sugar stared ahead and did not say a word. He held his briefcase high against his chest.

In midstream the water flowed over the hood in a brown swirl. It seemed surreal to push the gas pedal, which was now under water, but the truck churned ahead, rocking and rolling. Finally, the front tires found purchase on the far shore and pulled us up the steep bank. Water poured from the cab and the bed of the truck. I looked at Sugar and grinned.

"This truck is a very powerful machine. It can even be a boat," he said.

ON ONE OF our previous visits, Isaiah, the one-eyed headman, standing outside of his grass hut, had told us that poaching was the only way the villagers could make a living. They wanted other jobs or opportunities but nothing else was available to them. So we had recruited a young Englishman, Edward North, to live in Fulaza and talk to the villagers about possibilities. Fresh from Reading University, Edward had set off one morning in a truck with a compass, a radio, and a few supplies to set up camp near the village. A few days later he radioed us to say he had built some grass huts under an enormous shade tree. He had no idea what kind of tree it was, but it offered deep, lush shade for more than thirty yards.

Edward moved quietly and shyly around the village, talking through an interpreter with one man or woman at a time about ways we could help them make a living. Sugar and I were on our way to a meeting he had set up with the villagers. We drove east across the park, cutting through several more steep river gorges, then turned north toward the Lufila River on an old colonial-era survey line. Dust swirling behind our truck, we crossed the Chimana plains, passing herds of zebra, impala, and Cookson wildebeest, which are blonder than the common blue wildebeest and are found only in the Luangwa Valley.

All wildebeests are curious and playful, and the ones on this lonely plain, perhaps because they rarely saw vehicles, seemed unable to contain their inquisitiveness. Each time they saw us driving across the dusty flats they trotted after us, tossing their heads. I played a game with them, as we often did. I stopped the truck when they were eighty or so yards away. Immediately, they applied their brakes, milling about and swinging their heads. I drove forward slowly, and again they cantered after us. I stopped, they stopped. Eventually, they were forty-five feet away, jogging after us like a string of circus ponies. When we had gone several miles in this strange parade, the wildebeests dropped out of formation. They galloped about in a small circle, shaking their heads, as if in farewell. We would see them in a few days on our return, when they would again escort us across their plain.

After a few more miles we saw no more wildlife; neither wart hog nor impala graced the savanna. There was lush grass, clear water, and nutritious forage, but no animals. Eden plundered. Although we were still deep inside the national park, these were the hunting grounds of Fulaza village. Wildebeest games behind us, Sugar and I drove on in silence.

"I worry that these people will never know this idea," Sugar said as we approached the waters of the Lufila, flowing gently through the tall papyrus.

"Panono, panono," I said. Kasokola, our camp cook, had taught me the expression, which means "little by little." He was always reminding me not to fret when a truck bringing supplies was three weeks late or when essential spare parts for the Cessna arrived eight months late and were the wrong specs. "Panono, panono," he would say.

I drove down a gentle grassy slope into the river. The bank on the other side was too steep and muddy to climb, so we slogged upstream through the clear current for about fifty yards to an old log. There I turned sharply and drove up the bank.

I followed Edward's directions along the small bush track and could soon see his enormous camp tree, the largest winterthorn I had ever seen. Edward strolled out, grinning broadly. He was obviously proud of his new camp. At the center was a tiny grass sleeping shack no more than twelve feet square. An even smaller hut held his supplies. Near the river he had made a reed n'saka with a mat floor. After a quick cup of tea in the n'saka, Edward, Sugar, and I drove to the village center for the meeting.

More than fifty villagers — mothers with infants wrapped tightly to their backs with bright *chitenje* cloths, strong young men toting axes, and bent old men and women in tattered clothes — waited on straw mats under a large fig tree. As we stepped down from the truck, four elders led by Isaiah greeted us. Isaiah, his blind eye staring into the bushes beyond me, shook my hand for a long moment and held on to it gently as he introduced the others. For three hours, with Sugar translating, we talked with the villagers about how they could support themselves in this remote and lovely spot. The farmers, who grew mostly corn and sorghum in small dry patches, said they could grow sunflowers if they had seeds, and if they had a press they could make cooking oil — a priceless commodity they referred to as *saladee* — which they had to travel at least five days by foot to obtain. The village needed a grinding mill, because crushing the maize by hand took hours of hard labor. A mill would provide an industry for at least one family. Several women wanted to be beekeepers.

Standing under the fig tree, the mud huts behind us, Sugar and I explained that the project would train them and lend them money for equipment. We explained that they would be required to pay back the loans. Free handouts have been a plague in Africa. The continent is littered with failed development projects that were too large in scope, too high-tech by design, and required no accountability. The result was broken-down tractors in dusty fields, dried rice paddies in ruined oases, sophisticated hospital equipment no one could repair in abandoned, wornout clinics. We assured them that no one had to participate; we were simply offering assistance to those who wanted it.

Sugar translated, going into long explanations complete with stories and parables. Sitting on the straw mats, faces fixed on Sugar, the villagers nodded their heads. They understood why they should pay back any loans.

After three hours the sun dipped below the branches of the fig tree. The rough drive from camp and the long discussions in the heat had made me weary. Just as we were about to close the meeting, an old woman with anxious dark eyes unfolded her bony frame in slow motion from the grass mats and spoke. Isaiah translated, "There is no school in this village for the children of us." Everyone nodded in agreement. One man said, "Our village will never find the world until we educate our children."

We did not have enough money in our budget to build a school, but as they leaned toward us waiting for our answer, I felt we couldn't disappoint them. Edward, Sugar, and I huddled together, and after a few minutes Sugar came up with a suggestion: the project would supply the materials and hire six villagers to make bricks, paying them with soap, cooking oil, and mealie meal. We would ask ADMADE, a government program that returned fees paid by trophy hunters to the villages, to pay for door and window frames. Later, when all the materials were assembled, we would hire a builder to supervise construction by the villagers. The people clapped, and several women swayed into a string dance that wound among the straw mats and blankets, leading us across the bush and sorghum patches to a small grove of trees not far from the main footpath. The village elders agreed that this was the right spot for the school.

"Madame, when do you think it will be finished?" Isaiah asked. Instinctively I looked at the sky and searched for clouds. When the rains came in three or four months, we would be unable to ferry supplies across the river.

"We must finish before the rains or a whole school year will be lost," I said, and he nodded.

We got busy right away. Edward and the elders chose six men — all of whom had been poachers — to make bricks from the local clay. When Sugar and I got back to Marula-Puku, I sent a truck to Fulaza with soap, cooking oil, and mealie meal for the brick makers. From his office in Mpika, Sugar arranged for a maize-grinding mill to be transported from Lusaka. Edward distributed sunflower seeds to the farmers and repaired the water pump for the small clinic staffed by a Zambian medical practitioner. The elders visited Edward at his camp and invited him to a wedding, then a funeral.

A FEW DAYS LATER Edward radioed to say that the brick makers had changed their minds about being paid in supplies. "They want to be paid in cash."

"Okay, Edward. I'll have to drive to Mpika for cash, then back to Fulaza. It may take a few days."

The next day I stood at the fuel station on the lonely stretch of the Great North Road, which transects the continent from the Cape of Good Hope to Cairo. To the east lay the Muchinga Mountains, whose lush forests spilled along the road and into the village.

"So, no diesel?" I asked.

"Yes, madame. The tanker trucks did not come from Lusaka, so there is no diesel. Maybe it will come tomorrow."

I had driven six hours over the mountains to the bank in Mpika village, but I could not drive back to camp or to Fulaza without more diesel. After staying the night with friends in Mpika, I went back to the station, where gumba music blared from the Dog Eat Dog Café.

"Sorry, madame. But we are sure tomorrow the tanker will come."

In the heart of the village the open market vibrated with colorful chitenje cloths that swayed on the hips of thin women toting baskets of golden mangos. Again loud music rang out from old ghetto blasters tended by young men. This time it was not tribal music but Western hits from the sixties like "I Want to Hold Your Hand." No matter what they were doing — selling cooking oil in Coke bottles or mending sandals — people tapped and clapped to the thumping beat, and I had a wild urge to break into a dance. Women squatted on straw mats, where carrots, cabbages, onions, and sweet potatoes were displayed in little piles. The odor of dried fish mixed with that of overcooked meat roasting over small pits. I bought two burlap bags of dried beans from a mother and daughter who had been up since dawn shelling them. The older woman grinned at me and insisted I take a small bundle of bananas for free.

Four days later the diesel tanker arrived. I filled the truck's tank plus several drums and drove back to Marula-Puku. The next morning I radioed Edward that I would drive to Fulaza that afternoon.

"Sorry, Delia, but the brick makers have deserted. Apparently they do not want to work now, even for wages. I'll let you know when I find replacements."

Edward found new brick makers, we paid them cash, and they began molding clay into blocks. Only a few bricks were fired before the rains started, and work on the school was delayed for another five months. Edward's time as a volunteer ended and he had to return to England. After the rains stopped, Mark and I drove to Fulaza to get construction going again. Progress was slow, and the school was not finished when the rains came once more.

Again I stood in Fulaza facing the headman. "When will we finish the school, madame? We must finish the school before the rains."

"This year, Isaiah. Surely this year before the rains."

Finally the bricks were finished, and one of our new volunteers, Alex Haynes, supervised construction. As promised, the villagers volunteered to do the labor as long as we donated soap, cooking oil, and food. The walls began to go up, but soon they ran out of cement and none was to be found in Mpika. It would have to come by train from Lusaka — maybe tomorrow, the shopkeeper said. Two months later it arrived, and we sent Moses Kunda off driving the tractor and trailer loaded with cement across the wildebeest plains to Fulaza. Moses had never forded the Lufila before, and he was supposed to wait at the river until villagers arrived to show him the crossing by the log. They would be able to hear the tractor coming for miles and would come to greet him. When Moses arrived at the river, he saw no villagers. The crossing looked easy to him, so he drove the tractor into the water and straight across to the other side instead of driving upstream to the log. Moses started up the far bank just as the villagers ran toward him through the papyrus waving their arms. The trailer stood nearly on its end as the tractor struggled up the muddy incline.

With a *whoosh,* one hundred bags of cement slid off the trailer and into the river. The brick makers knew about cement, but most of the villagers did not. They spread the contents of the soaked bags all over the ground in the sun to dry. And dry it did, making a huge, flat monument to the delayed school.

More cement was ordered, the rains came again, and then another dry season. A summer and a winter. Time and again the winterthorn where Edward had camped flushed green and turned barren. It became the tree of hope.

In the meantime the farmers planted sunflower seeds and sold their crop to the press operator, who sold cooking oil to the villagers or traded it for meat. Families raised chickens. The mill ground corn, so villagers no longer had to shoot wildlife in the park to barter for ground cornmeal. Farmers also grew soybeans and other protein-rich crops. The medical officer had a house, and the clinic was supplied.

One afternoon Mark and I flew the helicopter to Fulaza to return the mill engine, which had been repaired at camp. It was too large to fit inside the chopper, so Mark clipped it to the cargo line; it swung in gentle circles beneath us as we flew across the plains. Ahead we could see the mud huts, their thatched peaks sprouting among papyrus patches along the river. Herds of impala and puku grazed peacefully on the bank opposite the village. A family of wart hogs dug up roots on the riverbank, stirring up a plume of dust. The huts of Fulaza and the wild animals of North Luangwa stood within the same field of view, a sight I never thought I would see.

The villagers had been expecting the return of the engine for weeks. When they saw the chopper appear, the engine swinging below like prey in the clutches of a giant eagle, they swarmed from their huts and ran toward the millhouse. Scores of people dressed in bright yellow, red, and blue chitenje cloths streamed through the dusty green brush toward the village center. Mark hovered the chopper over the ground near the mill. Using the belly-mounted cargo mirror to see the load, he gently placed the engine on the ground. We landed beside the mill, and Mark helped the men restart the engine.

It took three and a half years, but finally the school in Fulaza village was complete. It stood near the river, its red mud bricks a rosy pink in the sun. Textbooks were sent from America, the Ministry of Education arranged for a teacher, and the children went to school.

After the opening celebration I said to Isaiah that we would be back next year, and he answered, "I know, madame. You will come with the winterthorn." Then he added, "How is it that you knew about our problems, that you did not come to arrest the poachers but to give them jobs?"

"There have been poachers in my family, too, Isaiah," I said. "In fact my grandpa was one."

5 DELIA
GRANDPA

Grandfather, . . .
Teach us love, compassion, and honor
That we may heal the earth
And heal each other.

—OJIBWAY PEOPLE OF CANADA

Destiny is made known silently.

—AGNES DE MILLE

ONE MORNING KASOKOLA was kneading bread dough under the thatched roof of the open kitchen *boma* (hut) while I picked weevils out of the mealie meal. He wanted to know where I had come from in America and why I had come to Africa. So I told him this story.

My grandfather, tall and handsome, with neatly combed white hair, sat behind the wheel of his Ford Fairlane in the summer of 1959. "Look here, HiDe, the gears are like an H. When you push the clutch plumb to the floor, you gotta ease the knob to the top here, up the left side of the H. Then let the clutch out thisaway, as you give 'er a little gas. Now give 'er a try. You can do it." I was ten years old, and as interested in pleasing Grandpa as driving, so I slid behind the steering wheel. Stalling and bucking, the Ford Fairlane lurched among the pecan trees as I honed my skills. Earth the color of dried blood stretched away toward crooked split-rail fences smothered in blackberry brambles as thick as fort walls and sweet-smelling honeysuckle. Hungry kudzu crawled across the nearby woods, consuming ancient oaks, lean-to shacks, even an abandoned barn. They say kudzu grows an inch an hour, so if you have nothing else to do — and some folks here can make that claim — you can watch it grow.

Gentle words and the occasional Baby Ruth candy bar encouraged me until I finally eased the Ford somewhat more smoothly over the red clay.

"Well, I declare, HiDe, you drive real good. Yessiree bobtail, you sure do." This was reward enough, but from his pocket he took a small white gold watch with rhinestones around its dainty oval face. My first timepiece, from the Kress five-and-dime, and now I could drive! I had surely grown up in a hurry.

My grandpa, Roy C. Johnson, had bought a small brick house on "plumb and nelly" street — "plumb out of town and nearly in the country" — on the edge of Americus, a small south Georgia town, in 1926, and he lived there with my grandma, Mary Belle, until she passed away, two days before their sixtieth wedding anniversary. Grandpa delivered the mail on Route 1 for forty-two years.

Grandpa hadn't always been a mail carrier. His grandfather and father had owned one of the largest plantations in Sumter County. Called Huntington, it stretched across the flat, fertile ground toward the Flint River. It was not a frilly estate, all columns and rose gardens, but a working plantation with expansive cotton fields, pecan groves, cattle herds, a milk and butter dairy, a brickyard, and a syrup factory fed by fields of sugar cane that marched between the pines.

But the Depression hauled off and kicked the South in the belly. Commodity prices wilted like dried tobacco leaves, and my great-grandfather could no longer pay the army of laborers required to pick and pack such a large plantation. Rows of cotton bales were left strewn across the fields like brilliant white coffins tied up with burlap, the soul of the old South interred within them. They waited for a market that never returned, and my great-grandfather died in debt. Grandpa, Mr. Roy, didn't have to pay off his father's bank loans, but he did. Every hot afternoon after delivering the mail, he and his brothers farmed for the bank until they paid off the debt. Then they sold the land, and Grandpa and Grandma moved to plumb and nelly street.

Most of the people on Route 1 were African Americans. They lived in unpainted wooden houses perched on rickety stacks of brick. Kneeling down, you could see under the house right to the other side. The dwellings may not have been brushed with store-bought paint, but they were colorful just the same, because thunderstorms splashed red mud onto the raw pine siding, mixing it with the orange rust that dribbled down from the corroded tin roofs. As Grandpa used to tell me, when you deliver mail to the same people for forty-two years you get to know them "real good": births, weddings, deaths, all the good times, all the hard times. Especially during the Depression, he got to know the people, and they got to know him.

Many a time, Grandpa told me, folks on Route 1 didn't have the money for a two-cent stamp. Grandpa would find an unstamped letter in the mailbox, and inside or under it would be postage: a single egg, a bundle of fresh turnip greens, or a brown paper bag of black-eyed peas, already shelled. He would supply the postage himself and either deliver the greens to another family who needed them or take them home to Grandma to fix for dinner, which was pronounced *dunnah,* and served at noon.

One item Grandpa refused to deliver. A few men on Route 1 made a living distilling corn liquor in the woods. Grandpa knew where all the stills were, but he never told the federal agents. One morning Grandpa found a big glass jug of moonshine hidden in the tall grass under one of the mailboxes. A rubber band around its neck held a note asking him to take it to a farm up the road. Turnip greens were one thing, but Grandpa worried that if someone saw him delivering moonshine, it wouldn't look too good for the U.S. Postal Service. He honked the horn of his Fairlane. Mr. Henry, a large black man in baggy bib overalls that were always too short for his long legs, came out, and Grandpa told him that maybe it wasn't such a good idea to leave moonshine right next to the road. Mr. Henry thanked

Grandpa for the advice and tried to give him another jug — this one for himself. Grandpa failed to mention whether he accepted it or not.

I lived with my family — Mama, Daddy, sister Helen, twin brother Bobby, and younger brother Lee — one hundred miles south of Huntington among the magnolias, plantations, cotton fields, and cattails of Thomasville, one of Georgia's southernmost towns. Ancient oaks adorned with wispy Spanish moss spread their limbs across wide avenues lined with antebellum mansions and flowering white dogwoods. The Big Oak, said to be four hundred years old, covered nearly an entire yard and was shored up with twisted steel cables, iron rods, and the unfailing love of the entire town.

My friend Libby Wine and I rode her quarter horses on the county's seemingly endless miles of winding back roads. We packed peanut butter and banana sandwiches in brown paper bags, which we tied to our saddles, and rode all day in the balmy breezes. One of her horses, a roan gelding named Strawberry, I considered my own. He never really belonged to me, but no one else rode him. He was the color of honey and had a thick mane and tail as blond as sunlight.

While riding along a creek in dense oak forest one morning, we discovered a nation of albino frogs, looking like delicate porcelain figurines in a fairy-tale forest. We thought the natural soggy debris of the creek — dead leaves, pine needles, and moss — was clogging the current and threatening these wondrous creatures. Day after day we rode the horses to the creek and, in a misguided conservation project, cleared the stream until it gurgled slightly faster over the rocks. (In fact, slower, meandering creeks provide richer habitats for wildlife. But Libby and I were in good company. Over the next twenty years the U.S. government would channelize streams, cement riverbanks, and drain wetlands, thereby destroying thousands of acres of prime habitat.) We told no one about the frogs for fear that men in white lab coats would come with nets and capture them in large jars for the Smithsonian Institution. Instead we kept their creek clean and watched until they dispersed throughout the clear water.

We were free to wander wherever the woods went. We found a

hawk's nest and shinnied up a nearby tree to watch the fluffy chicks. When the mother did not return, we crept quietly away, fearing that we had interfered with her brood-rearing chores. We never took anything, never collected bugs in bottles, and all we left behind were our footprints along with those of the deer in the soggy creek bottom.

One day a gunshot cracked through the bird songs and the pine-scented breeze. Like a posse, we galloped around a bend in the road and found a man standing next to a beat-up pickup, a shotgun bent over his arm. At his feet was a large bird, its blood-smeared wings spread across the red clay. When we asked why he had shot it, he said, "Because it was a buzzard." He then kicked it over and over in the dust until it flopped like an oil-soaked rag into the ditch. After he drove away, we buried the bird and marked the leaf-covered grave with a cross made of twisted twigs. We held a two-girl funeral, each saying a few words and a prayer "because it was a buzzard."

Maybe I didn't know it then, but the joy-sorrow of nature would never leave my heart again.

WE HEARD GROWNUPS talking about the Cuban missile crisis, and civil-defense-test horns blared periodically on the radio between Elvis songs. Yellow signs with black triangles popped up around town, each marking a fallout shelter. Mama stored cans of chili and beanie-weenies and jugs of water under the stairs, where Tammy always had her kittens. I asked her to please also stash cans of Puss 'n Boots for Tammy, and of course she did. For my parents, who had been through World War II — my dad as a navy pilot in the South Pacific, my mother on the home front making bandages — the threat of a nuclear bomb attack was dire.

One day long lines of camouflaged jeeps and trucks filled with soldiers began passing by the intersection of Monticello Road and the unpaved lane where we lived. Bobby and I stood at attention under the stop sign and saluted the soldiers going south to protect us, and they saluted back.

To me the biggest worry of the Cuban missile crisis was that our beanie-weenie supply might give out and we'd have to eat Tammy's Puss 'n Boots. But the war never came. When the soldiers motored back through town headed north, we took up our posts, but the saluting on both sides was less enthusiastic this time around. Sitting in the dirt, teasing doodlebugs with pine needles, we chatted with the neighborhood kids. It was then and there that Hank Pepin told me how babies are really made, which to me was a much more alarming prospect than any missile crisis.

GRANDMA SOMETIMES BAKED a plump caramel cake, wrapped it in foil, and sent it to us on the Trailways bus, where it rode on the floor next to the driver. But she and Grandpa visited us as often as they could, the Fairlane filled with sugar cookies, meringue pies, and corn on the cob. Knowing my love of horses, Grandpa often brought me toy ones made of plastic or wood. One autumn day he brought me a beautiful china horse, a golden brown palomino with rippling muscles and a waving blond mane. I named it Strawberry, though the resemblance to the real horse was a bit vague, and kept it close to my bed.

As far as Grandpa was concerned, one of the best things about being a rural mail carrier was finishing work about 1:30 every afternoon. He would sit down to Mary Belle's dinner of fried chicken, biscuits, gravy, butter beans, sliced tomatoes, corn off the cob, fried okra, and pecan pie or backbone stew, cornbread, turnip greens, sweet potatoes, black-eyed peas, and peach cobbler. "Pass me a hot 'un, HiDe," he would say, and I would pass the basket of hot biscuits that were as tall and light as clouds. Grandpa called me HiDe because when Bobby and I were babies, my mother would walk into our room and say, "Hi Bo. Hi De." So Bobby thought my name was HiDe, and called me that as soon as he could talk. Grandpa called me HiDe until the day he died.

After dinner Grandpa would take a nap in his reclining chair, since he had been up since four A.M. delivering the mail. The rest of the afternoon he was free: free to watch baseball in the spring, to make furniture in his garage during the winter, to go hunting and fishing all summer and autumn long.

Mr. Roy was the best man who ever lived on this earth, and I will argue that point with anybody, but he was not perfect. In fact, my grandfather was a poacher. He and Charles Jones, who was a banker and thus kept good hours, went hunting or fishing every day of every summer and fall and didn't pay too much mind to the limit of trout, quail, doves, or whatever their quarry. But catching fish and shooting birds were secondary to the thrill of outsmarting the game warden.

The warden didn't like to walk very far, so he could always be spotted driving his Ford pickup across the fields. This usually gave Grandpa and Mr. Jones plenty of time to run, hide, or dispose of the extra birds or fish. Once they climbed high in a big oak tree and sat watching as the warden ranted and raved below them when he found their cache of doves but couldn't find them. One day they illegally baited a whole field with corn and caught the game warden, who sat there all day waiting for them. Meanwhile they shot hundreds of doves that flew over an unbaited field a few miles down the road. Grandma cooked as many doves as she could in stews or pies and gave the rest away to the neighbors.

But the warden finally nailed Grandpa, and Ol' Dan was to blame. Grandpa swore that Ol' Dan was the best bird dog in the South; he would point quail and fetch ducks without a miss. Plenty of Georgia bird dogs can do that, but Ol' Dan was the only one who knew to bark at the game warden's truck, and *only* the game warden's truck.

One afternoon Grandpa and Mr. Jones shot about a hundred doves next to a small stream that runs down to the Flint River along the edge of a large, open field. They were just about to bag their birds and go home for the day when Ol' Dan gave a soft, short bark, warning that the game warden was coming. They looked up and saw the game warden's pickup rocking and rolling over the rough furrowed ground on the other side of the field. They were in the open, with no trees to climb and nowhere to run, so they started slinging the birds as fast as they could into thick blackberry bushes on the other side of the stream. They kept a few — a very few — over the limit, knowing the warden would be suspicious if he found them with the lawful quota. When the warden was close enough to see them clearly, Grandpa decided he still had too many, so he kicked a few into the stream.

The warden pulled up and strode over. Grandpa and Mr. Jones hailed him politely. He checked their licenses and shook his head as he counted the doves. "Looks like ya'll are a bit over the limit. But not too bad," he said.

As Grandpa pointed out some mallard ducks flying toward the Flint River, Ol' Dan pulled himself out of the stream with a dove in his mouth. He dropped it at Grandpa's feet, shook himself vigorously, ran across the stream, and retrieved another dove from the blackberry bushes.

"Well, well, what do we have here?" the game warden asked, as Ol' Dan retrieved bird after bird from across the stream. The old dog's enthusiasm cost Grandpa five dollars in fines, but it did give him another story to tell his grandchildren.

IT'S HARD TO KNOW which little things in life affect your decision to follow one course rather than another. There are probably hundreds of words and deeds — things you don't remember, or didn't think much about at the time — that make you turn one corner but not the next. I used to sit and listen to Grandpa's stories for hours. In later years, when he could no longer go hunting, he would shake his head and say, "There ain't as many birds as there used to be, HiDe." He would almost whisper, "There used to be so many doves they'd darken the sky when they flew over a cornfield. At dusk you could hear the ducks landin' on the river from half a mile away. You never heard so much squawkin' and carryin' on in your life. We didn't figure our shootin' would make a dent in 'em. But I reckon we did." He stopped short of saying the game warden was right all those years, but that's what he was admitting, and he felt bad, real bad. He told his tales to us and the "route folks" on their faded, weather-checked porches until the day he died. Almost every family in town, black and white, came to his funeral, and he was buried wearing his red vest.

Grandpa gave me a lot of things: my first wristwatch, a china horse with a glorious golden mane, and an apple tree from Sears Roebuck, because a fruit seed I had planted in the spring turned out to be a weed. But I think the best thing he gave me were his words, which started out as only stories, then became something more, one of the little things that changed my life and set me on a certain course.

6 DELIA

Any Time from Now

> Females generally put most of their reproductive effort into "parental effort" while males put most of theirs into "mating effort."
>
> — J. R. Krebs and N. B. Davies

As the dry season deepened, the elephants began to leave the valley for the lush browse of the mountains. Lines of the small families could be seen twisting through the ravines and gorges as they fed in the ancient forests. Mark airlifted six of the Mano Unit scouts, including Isaac Daka, into the rugged terrain to guard the elephants from any poachers who still trekked into the park to shoot them. The scouts hunkered in the bush along an old trail that was worn wide and bare from the days, only a few years earlier, when bands of more than one hundred men would march boldly into the park to kill for ivory.

Suddenly Daka pointed ahead. A pack of poachers, rifles slung over their shoulders, bundles on their backs, walked down the path single file toward the hidden scouts. Three of the carriers were balancing large white bags of mealie meal on their heads. Oddly, one of the poachers was outfitted with a sleeping bag, ground mat, and tent identical to those we had supplied to the scouts. With the poachers at thirty yards, the patrol leader squeezed the arm of his number-two man and pointed.

"Ah-way! But it is Mabu!" His bandy legs striding out, walking at a quick pace as always, Mabu Kabutongo, ivory poacher/miller/research assistant/tracker, who had helped me age elephants, a poacher once again, was leading the band of outlaws.

Stunned, the scouts half stood from behind the boulders and brush. Perhaps if Mabu had thought quickly enough, he could have waved warmly to the scouts and pretended to be bringing them a message from us. Instead he stopped suddenly, then slowly backed away, confirming that he was up to no good. Immediately the scouts felt betrayed. They had accepted Mabu into their camp, and he had repaid their trust, and ours, by pretending to go to the village for supplies, then organizing a poaching expedition from Mpika. He had even stolen their camping equipment.

The scouts shouted, "*Eway* — YOU! Just wait for us there!" At that the poachers scattered, running through the bushes like rabbits, each pursued by a scout. Mabu escaped, but his carrier and three others did not. Daka radioed Mark, and within thirty minutes he had helicoptered the scouts back to Mano with their prisoners. From there a squad of scouts drove to Mpika to turn in the poachers and to stake out Mabu's old grass hovel — the one he used before taking up residence in Mano — which was forty miles over the Muchinga Mountains from where he had been spotted. Mabu walked back out of the park all night, feeling his way along the rocky, darkened trails over the mountains. The next morning he crept through the outskirts of the village and entered his hut. Seconds later, on a signal, the scouts, shouting and firing rounds into the air, ran from the nearby bushes and surrounded the dwelling. Mabu surrendered — even he could not put up much of a defense from inside a grass hut.

Acting as his own counsel, Mabu tried to convince the magistrate that he had received a tip that poachers were headed into the park, borrowed a rifle from his grandfather — his own had been confiscated — gathered some of his friends as a posse, and headed into the park to apprehend the criminals. The old magistrate might have believed this story or accepted a bribe, but the new one did not. Knowing that these men were repeat offenders, he sentenced Mabu and the others to six months in jail for carrying illegal guns in North Luangwa.

Another ex-poacher gladly accepted the job as miller at Mano;

he and his family occupied the house we had constructed for Mabu. His accompanying me on my elephant walk had not helped his poaching; Mabu had known for years where the elephants lived. He must have been laughing at me as I scribbled the measurements in my notebook. We had helped many ex-poachers find jobs, and most of them were now fish farmers or carpenters. But Mabu had a reason for returning to poaching.

Field Commander Banda Famwila, who was based in Mpika, was still encouraging poachers to shoot wildlife illegally for large-scale commercial operations that smuggled illegal meat and ivory to high-level officials in Lusaka. Because of Famwila's lofty connections with Romance Musangu, he operated with impunity right under the nose of the game warden, the magistrate, and the other scouts. They could do nothing to stop him.

To make matters worse, it was still rumored that the Convention on International Trade in Endangered Species (CITES) ban on the international trade in ivory would be reversed or relaxed, allowing tusks to be sold once again. Before the ban, 90 percent of the ivory sold legally on the world market was from illegally shot elephants. No signatory nation to the CITES ban could sell or buy ivory unless the restrictions were lifted, but there was constant pressure on nations like Zambia, which supported the ban, to change their position.

The ivory ban had been one of the most successful environmental policies ever adopted. As a direct result of it, elephant poaching had decreased by 70 to 90 percent in most areas where illegal hunting had thrived. The ban also protected other wildlife, because when poachers ventured out on extended expeditions for elephants, they also killed buffaloes, wildebeests, impalas, and zebras for their meat and skins.

Less has been written about the human suffering resulting from the ivory trade. Since the 1800s, when long caravans of men from the north snaked their way into Africa's belly and enslaved men to carry ivory, the trade in "white gold" has led to the mistreatment and abuse of tribal people. More than a hundred years later, in the 1890s and 1990s, villages were still taken over by the "big men," powerful poachers and smugglers who abused women, forced children out of school to be porters, and paid men less than a dollar per expedition to shoot elephants. Because there were few other opportunities in these remote mud-and-thatch outposts, the poachers could tempt or force people to join this dirty, dangerous, illegal work. In the process, they stifled chances for legitimate development, keeping the villagers in stagnant backwaters of poverty and isolation.

The ivory ban changed all that. When nations could no longer sell or buy ivory, the price dropped dramatically. When it was no longer profitable for poachers to shoot for ivory, they left the villagers, as well as the elephants, alone.

But CITES was soon to vote again on the ban, and some nations were lobbying to sell ivory. Men like Musangu, Famwila, and Mabu were patient. Whispers of a new trade in ivory were incentive enough for these men to shoot elephants and stockpile the tusks. After all the progress that had been made against poaching, we worried that the situation would backslide.

NOW THAT MABU KABUTONGO had been caught poaching again, I had to find another elephant tracker. Bornface Zulu, the man who had rescued Charles after the crocodile attacked him, was an ex–game scout whom Mark had hired as a guard for the helicopter. Tall and thin, Bornface has a kind face and a nonstop willingness to please. He knew as much about elephants as Kabutongo and maybe more.

I asked him to assemble a tracking team, and the six men and I walked the wild and stirring rivers of Luangwa — the Lubonga, Lufila, Mwaleshi, and Mulandashi — aging elephants. As poetic and mysterious as their names, these rivers cascaded through secret forests in the mountains, then snaked across the wide, sprawling valley. Not once did we come across another human being as we explored them. Poaching had been reduced for several years in these remote areas, so the elephants were calmer, and we watched them forage in the trees or frolic in the rivers more frequently. Using natural markings, lengths of tails, and scars, I identified and number-coded as many elephants as possible before we measured the footprints.

Bornface always waited for me when I lagged behind instead of yelling for me to catch up, as Kabutongo had done, and he always walked by my side, rifle cocked, when we crossed the croc-laden rivers. The men were more at ease under his leadership, and we all consulted on campsites and river crossings. Bornface would walk all the way across a hot beach to identify a bird's nest or investigate an abandoned lion kill. He knew most of the trees by name and could describe in detail which plants an elephant family had been browsing in the forests.

One morning as we hiked a remote, narrow canyon of the upper Lubonga River, we came around a bend and suddenly found ourselves too close to a small female elephant. Alone in a grassy meadow between us and the rocky walls of the canyon, she was cornered, with nowhere to run. Even the gentlest creature can become aggressive when trapped. Instinctively, we halted. The elephant whirled around to face us and threw her trunk into the air. But then she turned away, pranced toward the wall for a few feet, lifted her tail to the side, and jogged slowly toward us, dancing a little jig.

"Ah, it is Gifty," Bornface said. We were miles from camp, but she seemed to recognize us. After shaking her head in our direction a few times, she calmed down and completely ignored us as she pulled grass from the riverbank. Standing quietly, we watched her for some time. It was nearly two years since we had first seen her, and we had often observed her either near camp or miles away. She was still completely alone. It unraveled my heart. When we finally left her, we gave her a wide berth by climbing up the canyon wall on the opposite side. As we continued north, I turned to look until her gray back disappeared in the long grass.

We followed the Lubonga toward Hidden Valley, a small, teardrop-shaped basin of spongy green meadows and meandering streams carved into the great scarp mountains. It is protected from the world by a fort of tall, rugged hills covered in thick forests of ancient trees and giant ferns. Steep, rocky ravines lace the hills like moats, warding off intruders. The only gate into this sanctuary is a steep canyon sliced through the rim of the lower escarpment by the river. We followed the river up through the dark gorge, climbing over huge boulders that blocked the way and wading through deep pools that reflected the towering walls around us. On a previous walk we had gotten to the very last pool of the canyon to find it guarded by a very large crocodile. Sheer rock walls, smothered with mosses and ferns, rose from the water on either side, so there was no way around the pool. Guardian of the valley, the croc lay on the surface, his eyes staring at us. We had had no choice but to turn around, hike back through the canyon, and spend an extra day climbing over the hills into the valley.

So on this trek, when we reached the last pool we leaned carefully over the edge to check for crocs. Our reflections were the only creatures staring back at us, so we waded through the pool and climbed the rocks on the other side. Before us lay the sun-splashed valley.

An enormous fig tree graced the entrance to the valley, and a smaller one stood about a hundred yards away. I said I would camp under the smaller tree; the men could pitch their tents under the larger one. I always wanted my own camp because the men liked to chat and laugh at night, whereas I wished to hear the owls and the hyenas. Besides, we all liked our privacy. The Bembas were extremely shy around women, and they would not come near my camp if they thought I was getting dressed. Even in our main camp I had to be careful about hanging my laundry; certain items were just not appropriate to fly in the wind.

Later, after dark, my pup tent set up, my forgettable meal cooked and eaten, I leaned against a big log, cocking my book at an odd angle so I could read by firelight. It was a great little camp. I had hung a kettle, a towel, and my clothes in the lower branches of the tree. My pack and boots fit in the fork of the trunk, just out of reach of the hyenas. The light from the men's huge campfire danced in the fig, the brilliant stars capping the scene. I was content reading one of my favorite books in one of my favorite places.

I heard a rustle in the grass to my right, maybe ten yards away. I lowered my book to my lap and peered in that direction. But the long grass stood like a wall on three sides of me, so I could not see very far. I began reading again.

I heard the sound once more — like a stick falling on duff — and jerked my head up. A lioness, her blond body shimmering in the light of my campfire, walked into the clearing just beyond my tent. Looking straight ahead, not in my direction, she sashayed through the shorter grass only twenty yards away, her tail forming a crook behind her. Clutching the pepper spray — my only weapon — I froze. She would probably satisfy her curiosity and then move on. I heard nothing for five minutes.

I went back to my book. The promotional spiel on its jacket stated that most readers were so touched by the story that they would always remember exactly where they were when they read it. I was sure that would be true for me.

Suddenly the grass crackled behind me — close. I stood up, shouted, and waved my arms. The lioness sprang away from me and trotted from the grass into the clearing. She stood, her head low, tail twitching, staring at me with a whole lot of attitude.

"Bornface!!! There's a lion over here!" I shouted.

Immediately, five flashlights swirled around in all directions as the men, silhouetted against the bonfire, rushed toward me. The lioness trotted into the tall grass as they approached, their flashlights illuminating her pale back.

But as soon as the men stood by my side, the lioness stepped boldly back into the clearing toward us, posture erect, tail lashing like a whip.

"Madame, this lioness may leave, but she will return any time from now."

"You're right, I can't stay here. Let's move my camp under your tree." The scouts moved toward the lioness, waving their arms, while the rest of us gathered up my gear. Two of the carriers toted the fully erect tent, billowing out like a sail, over to their fire. Bornface and I followed with armloads of pots, binoculars, clothes, and sleeping gear. Guarded by the scouts, the rest of the men went back for a last load and doused my fire with water, sending a plume of ash and steam into the night air. Within ten minutes my little camp was set up under the security of their huge fig tree. Without hesitation the lioness sauntered to my abandoned spot and sniffed around the extinguished campfire. Now and then she looked our way, ears back in annoyance that we had spoiled her game. But the six of us must have been a formidable sight against the large fire, for she finally disappeared into the tall grass.

I thanked the guys and wished them good night.

Five "good nights" echoed mine, and I slipped into my tent. I thought of reading by flashlight but instead lay very still. The men's soft laughter may have been at my expense, but I have never heard a more comforting sound in my life. Snuggled in my sleeping bag, the firelight glowing through the wall of my tent, I forgot about the calls of owls and hyenas for one night and drifted off to sleep to the music of their singsong voices.

The next morning, when I crawled out of my tent, Bornface was making tea by a small cook fire. The others milled about, folding bedding or stirring porridge. None of them looked directly at me or in the direction of my abandoned camp. Perhaps they were simply giving me my own space. I stretched and wished them good morning, which they all answered rather quietly. As I looked over the valley, whose muted colors waited impatiently for sunrise to give them life,

I noticed something flapping in the tree of my former camp. During our hasty retreat, we had obviously missed something. Dangling from a branch was my white, lacy bra, which, although very small indeed, somehow looked enormous in this setting. I sidled over, tore down the bright feminine banner, and discreetly stuffed it in my pocket.

BORNFACE AND I LEFT the others in camp that morning and hiked along the maze of streams that crisscrossed the marshy plains of Hidden Valley to look for elephant tracks. The day promised to be hot, so I wore shorts instead of long khaki pants. As we ventured northwest into the narrow part of the teardrop shape, the grass became very tall and razor sharp. In a half hour of breaking trail through the prickly weeds, my bare legs were cut to shreds, little beads of blood running down my calves. Then, as if they had been waiting for our arrival, the tsetse flies swarmed around our faces, and we had to apply fresh repellent every twenty minutes. Bornface cut branches for us to swat the tsetses. Nature so often turns out to be heat, flies, and saw grass.

Blue waxbills covered the ground like a pastel blanket, and paradise flycatchers flitted about the tall reeds, their long tail feathers flowing behind them like kite tails. Suddenly, breaking the silence, a hyena called with a voice as clear and sharp as a bell cut from crystal. We could not see him because of the papyrus, but from the direction of his yelp we knew he stood at the base of a canyon wall. A fraction of a second later his call echoed from the cliff and flowed through the meadow. It did not stop there. It bounced from canyon to cliff to rocky shoal all around us, over and over, filling the entire valley. It was unusual for a hyena to vocalize that late in the morning, but he called again and again as Bornface and I listened, entranced. Before one plaintive cry died away, the next one began, so there was a continuous rolling chorus of hyena song. In the end it seemed that he was as enchanted by his own voice drifting endlessly through the hills as we were. Or perhaps, being a social animal in a solitary state, the echoes made him feel, at least for a while, as if his clan surrounded him.

Just like that, nature can turn from heat, flies, and saw grass to paradise flycatchers and hyena sonatas.

Several days later, after aging the elephants of Hidden Valley — I always wore long pants now — we hiked higher into the mountains to find others. Like clues in a mystery novel, the footprint data had already revealed that the harassed female elephants of Luangwa had been reduced to groups of fewer than four elephants on average. The groups were odd assemblages, mostly adolescents and with too many infants.

And now we were learning more about the males. A male calf is snuggled, fed, and protected by his mother and the other females of his natal family unit until he is about fourteen; then his powerful instinct to reproduce sends him away in search of unrelated females. However, the young male usually has to wait a long time before he gains the right to copulate, because he must compete with the older males. In a normal population the males of thirty to sixty years — those mountainous "tuskers" with huge ivory — are the ones who usually mate with the females. The mere presence of a tusker decreases the aggressive and sexual behavior of a rogue teenage male and sends the upstart slinking into the bushes, his testosterone levels temporarily dropping to his socks. For a time the young male will lose all the physical characteristics advertising musth, or sexual readiness.

The females *choose* the mature tuskers for mating because their very survival demonstrates their genetic superiority. Genetically, young males may have what it takes to endure, the right stuff to thrive, but they have not had time to prove it yet. Why would a female risk so much of her time and energy — two years of gestation plus four years of maternal care — by allowing one of her few eggs to be fertilized with sperm from an untested male? The genes from such a male might be substandard, and she would pass this downmarket DNA to her offspring. Like almost all other female mammals on earth, female elephants look for successful males with whom to breed. There are always external signs to go by: large tusks, long antlers, deep croaks, rich territories — or big houses, expensive cars, higher degrees.

In a normal population estrous females will avoid young bulls, actually run away from them, and instead choose the mature males. But almost no large tuskers were left in North Luangwa. We had seen only one in ten years. The Camp Group males were barely twenty years old. In most populations of wild animals the sex ratio is even, with as many females as males. However, after the poaching in North Luangwa, the population of adult elephants was made up of 81 percent females and only 19 percent males. Since there were few older males to dampen the aggressive sexual advances of adolescent males, unruly gangs of inexperienced, untested males chased the estrous females and copulated with them. With so much social chaos on the surface, there was no telling how much genetic chaos — untested, possibly inferior DNA — was being introduced.

Of course, it isn't just young male elephants who try to prove themselves.

7 MARK
GULLYWHUMPER

For I have learned
To look on Nature, not as in the hour
of thoughtless youth;
but hearing oftentimes
the still, sad music of humanity.
— WILLIAM WORDSWORTH

ONE SUNDAY WHEN I was seven, Cousin Kent jumped from my uncle's car, the pockets of his bib overalls bulging with silver Blockbuster firecrackers, their green waxy fuses peeking out. Kent, my brother Mike, and I headed straight for the Gullywhumper — a small, spring-fed marsh in the creek bottom below our house. Choked with reeds and cattails, always too wet to plow, it was thought to be good for nothing — as all wetlands were in that day. But to the three of us it was a secret netherland of frogs, snakes, salamanders, skunks, minks, and other creatures hiding in its deep black, smelly mud, which regularly belched odoriferous natural gas. My fascination with nature began here, especially on spring and fall mornings when a dense fog stole silently among the cedar, poplar, and hickory trees guarding its mossy perimeter, their thick dark limbs outstretched in the mist, only their tops showing through.

No matter the season, whenever we weren't busy with chores or school, the Gullywhumper lured us, our eyes shining with excitement. In addition to our interest in the swamp's wildlife, we were captivated by the mystery of an eight-inch-diameter gas well casing drilled deep into its bowels. Whenever we put our ears to the pipe's opening we could hear mysterious hollow popping sounds as methane gas bubbled up through the water far, far below. The old well was a relic left from the bygone era when my great-grandparents had cooked and lighted their farmhouse with methane.

Mother forbade us to play in the Gullywhumper, worried that we might contract polio from its malodorous waters or sink in its quicksand. But whenever we could sneak away, my brother and I stalked barefoot through its depths, catching snakes, frogs, and salamanders and dropping pebbles down the gurgling pipe.

The Gullywhumper was our refuge from everything disagreeable about childhood: hoeing weeds, shucking corn, and picking strawberries. The tedium of these tasks not infrequently led to pitched battles between my brother and me on one side and Barbara and Anne, my two older sisters, on the other. We often peppered each other with overripe strawberries or other organic missiles before Mike and I went AWOL from the garden to our hideout in the Gullywhumper.

IN 1831 DANIEL SAEGER, my great-grandfather, built our rambling white clapboard farmhouse, with its white and gray porches of turned posts and lattice, on a knoll above Swan Creek in Fulton County, Ohio. In summer its foundation and clapboard sides stood deep in spicebush, honeysuckle, and ivy. Fluffy pillows of snow buttressed its flanks every winter. My parents moved into the old homestead in 1941, shortly before the Japanese bombed Pearl Harbor and after my grandparents had settled into the new home they had built a stone's throw away.

When the crops were in the ground, summer Sunday afternoons after church were for family get-togethers. Pontiacs, Plymouths, Fords, and Chevys carried my uncles, aunts, and cousins, each family with its own baskets of food, to my grandparents' driveway. Everyone piled out and spent the day eating, lolling on the front porch, and chewing over the weather, the state of our crops, the fall prospects for Fulton School's basketball team, President Truman's handling of the

Korean War, and other weighty subjects. We kids played kick-the-can and hide-and-seek, climbed the apple trees, and jumped off high beams into the granary's wheat bins, playing until dark. Then we caught night crawlers and salamanders in Maxwell House coffee tins or fireflies in Mason jars stuffed with grass to give the bugs some habitat. I can still smell the sweet, dank perfume of pollinating grasses, corn, and honeysuckle, hear the soft, easy laughter, the croaking of frogs, and the rhythmic creak of the porch swing's chains wearing, back and forth, back and forth, on its ceiling hooks, setting my life's rhythm as a coxswain sets the pace for his oarsmen.

AT THE BOG that fateful Sunday, our pockets stuffed with Blockbusters, Mike, Kent, and I rolled up our trousers and slogged barefoot through the black marsh mud to the standpipe of natural gas. We stood around it for a moment, convinced that the daring experiment we were about to conduct would blast us to the cutting edge of science.

I dug a firecracker and an Ohio Blue Tip sulfur match from my pocket, held the match at arm's length, scratched it on the side of the pipe, lit the fuse, and pitched the firecracker into the hole. Kent, Mike, and I bumped heads as we strained to follow the trail of orange sparks as it tumbled into the pipe's black depths.

BAA — WAAANG — WAANG — WAAANG! The Gullywhumper roared to life, a blue-orange flame shooting four feet straight up from the pipe. My eyelashes, eyebrows, and the hair above my forehead instantly burned to a crisp of black ash, and my lips were roasted like frankfurters on a grill. We staggered back and sat down in the mud, our heads rolling like bobble toys.

IN THE SPRING of my fifth year, Dad had hoisted me to his shoulders, saying, "Let's climb the windmill, Mark." Though I dreamed of flying, scaling the windmill balanced on my father's shoulders was not exactly what I had in mind.

"Dad — no! I don't want to go up." I wrapped my arms tightly around his head.

"Don't worry, you'll be all right, just hold on tight." He began climbing, and as we rose higher than the roof of our house, the fields beyond it came into view.

The narrow platform at the top, forty feet above the ground, was a plank no more than eighteen inches wide and bolted to the windmill's four steel legs just below their union at its peak. No railings or handholds, just a board barely wide enough for a seat. There Dad peeled me off his head, carefully sat down, put his arm around me, and eased me down beside him. Our legs dangled in the air as we looked out on a neat tapestry of cultivated fields — corn, oats, wheat, and hay — spread out for miles, a sea of grasses undulating in the summer breeze, their sweet perfume thick on the warm air. It seemed a world in miniature, quieter and more peaceful, more harmonious and less threatening. In the distance all around were the tiny barns and houses of neighboring farms, including those of my aunts and uncles; a quarter of a mile away, at the end of the sandy lane that ran through our fields, stood the maple-oak-hickory woods that was our family's small but beloved private nature preserve. The essence of everything I loved lay at my feet. *So this is what it's like to fly,* I thought.

"Take a good look, son," Dad said, almost to himself. "It won't stay this way for long." We sat up there for perhaps half an hour, and then we climbed down the way we had come up. But this time my arms were relaxed and I held on around his neck.

LATER THAT YEAR, on a hot September afternoon, tall dark thunderheads began piling up in the sky above the field where we were working. Dad, driving our model-A John Deere tractor, pulled a grain drill around and around the field near our woods, planting wheat. On a wagon hitched to the smaller model-B John Deere, which was parked along the edge of the field, I dragged heavy bags of seed and fertilizer from a stack, hauled them across the wooden deck to the back of the wagon, slit them open with my pocket knife, and stood by, ready to help whenever he stopped to top up the drill. It was heavy work for a five-year-old, but I was helping my dad.

As he wrestled a bag from the wagon to the drill, ripped it open, and began pouring it into the hopper, he paused to glance up at me on the wagon above him, his Dr. Grabow pipe clamped in his teeth, a white cloud of fertilizer dust around his head, his glasses, face, and cap chalky with chemicals and loamy dust. He winked as though he and I alone shared some secret conspiracy. And then, the bins full, he slammed the covers closed, stoked his pipe, climbed back on the tractor, and began his rounds again.

Circling the field, Dad looked up at the darkening sky. It was late in the season and he badly needed to finish the planting before the rain came. From overhearing conversations between Dad and Uncle Harold about the cost of fertilizer and seed grain, I knew that our struggling little farm could not afford to lose the contents of my wagon or the crop that would come from that field.

A gust of cold wind swept in from the northwest, flattening the clover on the ridge above us and sweeping windrows of dust from the freshly tilled soil. It slapped the wagon, ripping loose the tarpaulin that covered the seed and fertilizer. The tarp sailed away across the field and fencerows. Dad quickly turned and drove straight to the wagon. By the time he reached me, fat drops of rain had begun to pock the valuable seed and fertilizer.

"Mark!" he shouted as he jumped down. "Get on that tractor and drive it to the house — right now!"

"I — I don't know how, Dad!" Until then my brother and I had only ridden with him occasionally, turned around on the seat behind him, our legs and feet dangling through a gap at the bottom of the seat's back as he tilled the fields. A few times he had let me steer.

"Yes, you do! Now get on and drive!" He grabbed me under my arms, lifted me onto the platform behind the steering wheel of the model-B tractor, and started its motor. I put my hands on the big wheel, trying to remember how I had seen him drive. I advanced its throttle, put it into gear, and pushed the hand clutch forward. The machine lurched ahead, and by the time I reached the gate to the field, I had learned to steer — at least well enough to clear the posts. I learned how to brake before smashing through the barnyard gate, and by the time I reached the barn I was confident enough to drive my precious cargo under its shelter.

Dad was so pleased that soon afterward he began letting me drive the larger tractor alone to till entire fields. I was so small that I could not steer from the John Deere's seat, but instead stood on the small steel platform ahead of it, looking through the steering wheel's spokes as I drove. And I did not have the strength to engage or disengage its hand-clutch lever, which was almost as tall as I was. My father would drive with me to the field, put me behind the steering wheel, set the throttle, engage the clutch, and then, with his lips near my ear, shout that he would be back at noon to get me for lunch. If he didn't come, I was to simply switch off the ignition and walk to the house. He then jumped off and left me to drive around and around the fields for hours as I prepared them for planting, haying, or harvesting. I was a farmer at five.

WE HAD FINISHED the early morning milking, Dad and I, and we were walking in clover through the ridge field behind our big red barn, checking the young hay crop, a warm breeze in our faces. Bumblebees buzzed from one purple flower to another, their yellow and black bodies heavy with dew and pollen. Gradually, a deep-throated voice rose above the chorus of bees and blackbirds. It grew to a moan — and then a roar from the east. We turned to shield our eyes against the sun as a bright yellow airplane trimmed in black soared low above the barn, its wheels nearly clipping the lightning rods planted along the roof's peak. The craft dived at us, its propeller glinting in the sunlight, scattering flocks of blackbirds from around the field. Its wheels clipped through the clover, and I could see the pilot grinning as he headed straight for us. Dad and I dropped to our knees. At the last minute, the pilot pulled up and banked away, waving through his open side window.

"Well, I'll be damned, son. It's your uncle Kenneth."

Dad's younger brother circled the field again and landed. Before the plane's prop stopped turning he had run to Dad and hugged him, lifting his feet off the ground. Then, as we lay in the sun-warmed clover, he told us about the South Pacific island where he had hidden during the war, gathering intelligence on the movements of Japanese ships and planes; he talked about jungle rot and liberty and what he would do next with his life. Then he took off again and was gone for a long time from my memory. I don't remember if I knew then where he had come from, where he was going, or whose plane he was flying. But his brief visit, on his way home from the South Pacific, convinced me that someday I too would fly like the blackbirds from that field.

MOWING HAY WAS one of the most dangerous jobs on the farm. When the cutter bar, with its guides and sickle, got plugged up with wads of stems, the operator had to get off to pull them free. If the tractor rolled forward or if the driver stumbled or in any way touched the chattering sickle knife as it sliced back and forth in its guides, he could lose a hand or a foot and maybe bleed to death.

Dad was reluctant to let me mow hay, even though by the time I was seven I was regularly driving our tractors while pulling hay rakes, wagons, tilling equipment, and other pieces of machinery. But to make ends meet, he had begun chopping hay silage for neighbors, and he had even less time to tend to our own crops. So one morning we drove the tractor and mower to one of our hay fields, where he rode with me for a round or two. Then, after sternly reminding me never to get off the tractor without locking the brakes and shutting down the mower, and never to stand in front of the cutter bar, he left me alone. Mowing a swath of plants almost as wide as a country road with a single pass, I would quickly finish the field. A day or two later I'd rake the cut hay into windrows that would be ready for chopping.

But then I began noticing the pheasants, cottontails, quail, blackbirds, and meadowlarks running, leaping, and flying to escape. A cottontail mother waited a split second too long before jumping, and when I looked back I saw her lying behind the cutter bar, the stumps of her hind legs hemorrhaging blood into the green grass, her squirming, squealing babies and the remains of her nest strewn across the ground. Horrified, I stopped and quickly shut down the mower. I jumped off, ran to her, picked her up, and held her shivering body in my hands, her black eyes staring at me. I wanted to put her back together, remake her nest, and put the babies back in it. But I could not, of course, so I turned her head too far around, to help her die quickly. I laid her back in the clover and then stomped on each of her young. What else could I do? Then I stood by the big back wheel of the tractor and cried for what I had done and what I would have to keep doing. I climbed back on the tractor, pushed the clutch in, and kept mowing, cutting off heads and legs, destroying more nests — because my father needed me, because there was no other choice. But I learned something about myself that morning: I learned that I cared more than I had realized about wild living things.

At noon Dad walked across the field and stood watching me mow. When I looked at him he pretended to be spooning in food, his signal that it was time for lunch. We walked side by side the quarter mile to the house. Dad talked about Barney, the red-tailed hawk who, with the help of red foxes, controlled the numbers of field mice; about earthworms that aerated and fertilized the soil; about the Maumee Indians buried on our farm. In the washroom, just off our kitchen, we pumped water from the cistern, scrubbed our hands in an enamel basin, and took our places at the table, where Mother had spread platters of chicken-fried steak, sweet corn, mashed potatoes and gravy, green beans, salad, and apple pie — all from the farm.

Dad loved the violent storms that most often came on hot August afternoons. The wind and hail flattened our crops, tore shingles from our barn, and in other ways made life more interesting. One afternoon we were baling hay in the field behind the barn when the sky turned purple-black and the wind sprang to gale force. We quickly drove our load of hay into the barn and ran for the house. We shed our dripping clothes in the washroom and joined Mother and my sisters and brother in the kitchen. A bluish white bolt of lightning shot down the trunk of a big maple tree in our front yard, showering our porch and driveway with bark. A large limb thudded to the ground in a blizzard of leaves.

"Jim! That was really close!" Mother's voice quavered.

"Don't worry, lightning never strikes twice in the same place," Dad said. *GZZZZZZZ-BOOM!* This time the kitchen light switch exploded from the wall. Bits of plaster showered the room, leaving a cloud of white dust and gray smoke hanging around the light fixture.

"Kids! Follow me!" Mother ran into the dining room and stood next to our potbelly coal stove. We left Dad in the kitchen and joined her there, watching the trees in the front yard reel wildly in the wind and rain, their leaves shredded by golf-ball-size hail. Above the din of the storm I could hear Dad laughing from the kitchen. "What's so darned funny?" Mother shouted. "I thought lightning never struck twice in the same place."

"It doesn't," Dad said, entering the room. "That was a fluke."

GZZZZZZZZ-BOOM! The telephone in the corner of the dining room jumped off the wall and hung from smoldering wires.

Mother huddled close to the stove, holding out her arms and shouting, "Kids! Come here, take my hands!" Dad stood in the archway to the kitchen, his smile crooked. His eyebrows seemed at war over whether to move up in surprise or downward in concern, and his pipe jutted at an odd angle from his clenched jaws.

"All together now — let's sing!" Mother commanded, her voice thin and wavering. "N-nearer my God to thee, n-nearer to, to thee!"

As the storm began to slacken, Dad peered from one window

and then another, his pipe chuffing smoke. "Okay, kids." He rolled his eyes impishly. "Who's going to run to the woods with me!" With that he headed for the washroom, stripping down to his shorts as he went. Mike, Anne, and I immediately broke ranks from Mother and took off after him.

"Jim Owens," she scolded, "if you get those kids killed I will never forgive you!"

Dad ran through the back door into the storm, his laughter trailing behind him. We followed him as he skipped across the yard, our bare feet splashing in the chocolate water of the mud puddles. The hail and lightning had ceased for the most part, but sheets of raindrops stung our shoulders and eyes as we headed for the barnyard gate. Beyond it was the lane that led to our woods. Dad vaulted over the gate and, laughing and shouting, we sprinted after him down the lane into the dark, leafy sanctum of tall trees. As we ran along the paths Dad had cut through the undergrowth, rainwater poured through the canopy over our heads, coursing down the wagon tracks and across our toes.

We stopped to catch our breath in the heart of the woods, inhaling deeply of ozone, of the spirit of this tiny remnant of a vast deciduous forest and the Maumee Indians who had still lived there when my great-grandfather built our house. The Indians were gone soon after my grandfather Saeger was born, though we occasionally still unearthed their skeletons, bowls, and other artifacts from shallow graves when digging in our gravel pit. Most of these items were donated to a museum in Columbus. Dad spoke wistfully of the Indians and the great forest that had been their home. Even at an early age I had the sense that something profound had been lost, was still being lost, that there was not much left to lose and not much time to save what little remained.

ALL TOO SOON the seasons turned, the trees lost their leaves, and bitter winds blew in from the north and west, feeling their way through the cracks of our old farmhouse, its foundation buttressed with insulating bales of wheat straw to keep our water pipes from freezing. Without crops to plant or harvest, Mother and Dad had more time for us.

On dark and snowy winter evenings, in an age before TV, Mother read to us from *The Encyclopedia of Children's Stories* or opened the lid of our old grand piano and played "Bumble Boogie" or "The Mosquito Waltz." Sometimes she sent us into the yard to scoop fresh snow into a big bowl, and mixed it with eggs, vanilla, and sugar to make snow ice cream.

When we were a little older, Dad often lay on his belly, propped on his elbows before our coal stove, and read aloud to us from the works of Keats, Shelley, Frost, Byron, Poe, and other great poets. At the death of Annabel Lee, he cried unashamedly, wiping away his tears with a red bandanna. He recited from memory "The Cremation of Sam Magee," "The Rime of the Ancient Mariner," and Frost's "The Road Not Taken." When he read *Moby Dick,* his voice rose and fell as though with the sea's swells, until we could almost taste the salt air and hear the great whale spout. We sat rapt for hours, often until well past bedtime.

I shared one of the two upstairs bedrooms with my brother; my two older sisters shared the other. Before going to bed in our icy rooms, we dashed up the steps, grabbed our comforters and pillows, then took turns warming them on the potbelly stove, pulling them off, most of the time, just before they were scorched. After they had absorbed as much heat as they would hold, we wrapped our pillows in our comforters, bounded back upstairs to our frigid bedrooms, dived into bed, pulled our bedclothes over our heads, and then curled our bodies around our pillows, holding on to their warmth for as long as it lasted. Night storms often howled out of the west, rattling the windows and driving snow through cracks in the frames, leaving drifts inches deep on the floor and frost on the bedcovers. On many nights, long after I should have been asleep, I peered from beneath those covers to see, on our far bedroom wall, Sam Magee sitting on his funeral pyre, grinning at me in the darkness as the flames leaped and danced around him.

I often awoke in the middle of the night, stole from my bed, and tiptoed downstairs. As I opened the door to our dining room, the coal stove greeted me like some large friendly monster, its fiery eyes orange and flickering through their lenses of mica. I would sit for an hour or more, wrapped in my comforter, staring into those eyes, imagining the worlds in the books Mother and Dad read to us and wondering if I would ever see any of them. And then I quietly lowered the lid of our ebony grand piano, spread my comforter on its broad top, and slept there.

SNEAKING THROUGH the popcorn patch after getting singed by the Gullywhumper, Kent, Mike, and I couldn't see anyone sitting on the front porch of our grandparents' house, but the lights were on in our kitchen. Creeping closer, we could hear the murmur of voices and see the yellow light spilling through the doors and windows into the yard. Something didn't feel right. Why was everyone in *our* kitchen rather than on my grandparents' front porch? Their voices sounded tense, angry — with us? We hunched over, ran across the driveway, and hid in the clump of spicebush near the kitchen door. Through the window I could see Grandpa Saeger seated at one end of the table, his beefy fists in front of him, his thick, bushy eyebrows set in a scowl. Dad was in his place at the other end of the table, with Mother and our uncles and aunts shoulder to shoulder around it.

I heard Grandpa growl, "It's eminent domain. The lawyer says they can take our land for the highway and there's nothing we can do."

"It'll cut this farm in two!" Dad hammered his pipe on the ashtray, scattering flakes of charred tobacco on the table.

"I'm sorry, boys." Grandpa's voice was more tired than I had ever heard it. A heavy silence settled over the table; the fireflies in the yard seemed to dim, the crickets grew quiet. And then my aunts and uncles stood and filed out of our kitchen onto the porch and began calling for the kids. It was time to go home. I was already home, but for how much longer? I wondered.

ONE SUMMER DAY in my eighth year, my brother and I watched men with hardhats and yellow trucks tie orange ribbons in parallel lines through our cornfields. Not long after, our yards swarmed with neighbors and strangers, as all of our livestock and equipment were sold at auction. We still lived on the farm, but the right of way for the interstate had been staked through its heart. It left us with too few acres to make a living. The granaries where we kids had once jumped from the rafters into the wheat bins were now silent, hollow, and dusty.

Dad refused to apply for unemployment, although it would have paid more than his temporary job as a garage mechanic in a nearby town. At home he sat at the head of our table, quietly smoking his pipe and reading his paper. He played no more word games, read no more poetry. The rhyme and meter had been taken from our lives.

The next summer no corn grew in the field beyond the Gullywhumper, but the lines of orange survey ribbons were still there. Early on a morning in August, we awoke to a deep rumble from far across the fields. I ran to the windmill in our backyard, quickly scaled its forty feet, and stood on the platform at the top. With my hand shielding my eyes against the morning sun, I watched a phalanx of yellow bulldozers plow through our fields and our beloved woods, gutting our farm.

I heard a door slam below me and saw my father — a hardhat on his head and a lunch pail tucked under his arm — walking up the road toward the army of heavy equipment that was laying claim to our land. And to our way of life.

8 DELIA
No School for Gift

Come forth into the light of things. Let nature be your teacher.
—William Wordsworth

Gift stepped up to a small mopane tree. Six inches in diameter and twelve feet tall, it was not much more than a shrub. Lifting her trunk straight up like a stick, she placed it flat along the bark and then lurched forward, pushing all of her weight against the tree. She had watched Long Tail and Cheers stretch their thick trunks against the massive sides of marula trees that were four or five feet in diameter and fifty feet tall. As their great knees bent, they shoved the tree until marula fruits rained down all around them.

The dry mopane leaves rattled as Gift slammed the tree. The small crown shuddered as she pushed. Lowering her trunk, she stepped back and looked around on the ground, her small eyes hooded under long, gray lashes. But of course there were no fruits to be found because this was not a marula tree. Gift tried again, throwing her trunk into the branches and ramming her head into the bark. She stepped back and swept the end of her trunk along the ground, back and forth, searching for the sweet fruits. After several more tries she finally gave up and walked to a dry streambed, where she pulled up wilted grass stems and poked them in her mouth.

The valley was drying up. The short, succulent grasses of the floodplains that fed everybody from geese to elephants during the rainy season had withered and turned to dust. The dirt had cracked into a jigsaw puzzle of gray hardpan. Many of the elephants were leaving the valley, following ancient trails — some fifty feet wide and five feet deep from years of wear — that traversed the escarpment. The air was twenty degrees cooler in the mountains and held more moisture than that of the valley. The forests were thick with small edible trees, ripe seeds, and tasty shrubs. As long as they knew where to go, the elephants could find plenty to eat throughout the dry season. But there was no one to show Gift where to go.

The Camp Group males had dispersed with the last of the marula fruits. We had not seen them for several weeks, which was not unusual. They kept an odd schedule, coming and going in every season. After all, some females remained in the valley in the dry season, inhabiting the scattered woodlands and shrub-covered hillsides. So the males had to be flexible, hedging their bets to be close to as many females as possible. They wandered in the mountains, then returned to the valley, usually stopping by camp on their way.

Gift had not followed them, and now she was left completely alone to find nutritious fare among the leaves and grasses, which were shriveling more by the day. The undergrowth crackled under her feet like broken glass. Our camp was about halfway between the verdant mountains and the parched valley floor, so there was surely enough nutrition tucked away in acacia seeds, bark, and leaves to allow one small elephant to survive. And this was not her first dry season alone, so she must have learned something about living with a dwindling pantry. Still, the coming months would be raw and lean for an unschooled orphan.

I stood at the edge of camp with Kasokola and Patrick Mwamba, who had first seen Gift. We watched her move from one mopane shrub to the next as she shook them and then looked on the ground for fruits.

The elephant population in North Luangwa had now bottomed out at thirteen hundred. The poaching had almost stopped, but even though many infants were being born, the population was not increasing. This probably meant that some of the infants were not surviving. Certainly many of the orphans were not.

"I wish this elephant would go live with the mothers and babies," Kasokola said.

"That cannot be," Patrick replied. "She is from a different tribe, and they are no longer in this place."

The next morning Gift was gone. We could not find her anywhere near camp. An unlikely dry-season shawl of clouds wrapped itself around the cool shoulders of the mountains. I hoped that Gift was walking in that direction, into the food-filled forests, following an ancient trail once used by her fallen tribe.

9 DELIA
THE WOMEN OF KATIBUNGA

> Perhaps the healing of the world rests on just this sort of shift in our way of seeing, a coming to know that in our suffering and in our joy we are connected to one another with unbreakable and compelling human bonds.
>
> — RACHEL NAOMI REMEN

ONE MORNING NOT LONG AFTER Gift disappeared from camp, I headed up the back of the escarpment toward the village of Katibunga, where Dr. Philip Watt, known as PW, was teaching midwifery to the women. The Muchinga Mountains appear to have marched long ago to the rim of the Rift Valley. Some, it seems, halted at the precipice, leaning their giant shoulders over the edge, while others tumbled head over hills down the three-thousand-foot escarpment. Set off by tectonic forces, avalanches of entire mountains came to rest above the sinuous valley and along its deep gorges. Folded gently in the arms of the higher mountains, not far from the elephants' dry-season sanctuary, is a most unlikely forest of grand spruce and fir trees planted many years ago by a European priest. The deep green shadows of the exotic forest intermingle with the wispy, flat-topped woodlands of the rolling hills. These contrasting jungles embrace the tiny village of Katibunga, decked out in its own foliage of shiny banana leaves and sprawling fig trees. Like most of the villages of the Bemba and Bisa tribes, Katibunga is made up of mud-and-wattle huts, one to a family, scattered widely among the trees and connected by worn footpaths crisscrossing the red soil. Thick gray-blue smoke from the cook fires inside the huts filters through the shaggy thatched roofs, making them appear to be smoldering. Except for the old Catholic mission — a mosaic of low, misshapen rooms of crumbling bricks molded from the very clay on which it stands — the village looked much the same in the early 1990s as it had since its beginning, perhaps one hundred years ago.

As I drove alone from camp along the rugged bush track, I looked for elephants, especially Gift, through the soft mist that drifted like a bridal veil through the luscious forests. It was hard to believe that this moist world was only ten or so miles from the parched valley. At a crook in the trail I met Ronnie Hadley, a petite brunette on loan to our project from the Peace Corps. We drove our vehicles deeper into the woods to set up camp before going on to the village, which lay just over the hills. I laid out my pup tent on the soggy forest earth, matted with damp rotting leaves and worn-out mushrooms. Last night's dew dripped from the overhead thicket, leaving flower-shaped splat marks on my dusty tarpaulin. Ronnie erected her tent on the other side of our campfire — which so far was more smoke than flame.

In Katibunga we were to meet Dr. Watt, from Johns Hopkins University. PW, who grew up in my neighborhood in south Georgia, had volunteered to run our project's rural health care program in the villages. His wife, Alston Watt, had greatly expanded and improved the cottage industries.

The dilapidated bush hospital in the larger village of Mpika was the only clinic available to the Bemba and Bisa tribal people scattered through the forests that stretched for thousands of square miles near the park. For most villagers it was a three-day walk over rugged mountains to get to Mpika. The Bembas' traditional remedies — syrups of roots, berries, and owl parts, shaken with bones and mixed with ancient myths — were far more effective than Western physicians might imagine. We had seen these mysterious potions apparently cure diseases that were equally puzzling. Still, most of the Bembas, having been exposed to modern medicine, or at least having heard of it, longed for some of its magic, especially for their children. While never urging them to discard their own remedies, we offered them some of the new.

PW, Ronnie, and Grace NG'ambi, a Zambian registered nurse, were training two women from each village to be traditional birth attendants, or midwives. They would also learn AIDS prevention, basic first aid, and simple remedies such as rehydration to treat diarrhea. The Catholic priest of Katibunga had offered the mission as a dormitory and classroom for the course. Forty-eight women, wrapped in wildly colored chitenje cloths, had journeyed from all quarters of Bembaland on foot, by bicycle, and, from the most distant villages, by trucks that we had sent for them. Suckling babes were strapped to their mothers' backs or breasts with more brilliant cloths, and toddlers brought up the rear like a flock of waddling ducklings.

On sunny days for almost two months, PW, Ronnie, and Grace taught detailed lessons to the women seated on bamboo mats in the shade of the fig trees. Hand-drawn posters depicting sources of nutrition and clean water fluttered from low-lying branches. Other midwifery diagrams, of a more sensitive nature, were taped to walls inside the church, far from the eyes of village men. When it rained, red rivulets of mud gushed across the clay yard, chasing the lessons inside.

At night the women slept on straw pallets in the cozy, low-ceilinged chapel. There was hardly a minute during the night when an infant or child was not stirring, whimpering softly, or coughing. Mothers, half asleep, turned this way or that to offer a breast, pull up a blanket, or cuddle.

Most of these women had never been so far from their natal villages, certainly not for this long, and none of them had had any kind of schooling beyond third or fourth grade. More important, not one had been in a camp of only women, totally removed from their male-dominated worlds.

I had driven up to join the others for the last few days of the course and the graduation ceremony. When we reached the mission, the yard was a hive of activity: some women stirred huge pots of corn porridge over three fires, others swayed under the weight of water buckets balanced on their heads, a few shook out their colorful blankets, as children played with toys made of wire and sticks. They greeted us with a chorus of "Mopalayne" — "Hello."

Balanced on logs or boulders, we ate our porridge in upside-down red plastic Frisbees. Some well-meaning American had sent our project thousands of Frisbees to be handed out to the children as toys. But even though the Bembas are very good at playing soccer with their handmade balls, throwing Frisbees never caught on among them. However, the Frisbees made perfect dishes for porridge and mealie meal. All across Bembaland, around almost every campfire, folks could be seen eating out of red Frisbees. It was quite the thing.

We washed our Frisbees and teacups in large basins of steaming, soapy water and balanced them on the boulders to dry. At about this time PW arrived, having driven in from Mpika, and it was time for the lessons to begin.

PW, Grace, and Ronnie were concerned that the students had not completely mastered the details of female anatomy. Although they had reviewed charts and diagrams several times, some of the women remained confused about certain organs and their function. The teachers wanted to rehash this part of the curriculum, and knowing that the best way to teach the women was through song and dance, Grace had choreographed a special lesson. She asked us to sit on our mats in a semicircle around the yard.

Once we were settled, Grace directed six of the women to stand in the center of the circle. One tall, slender lady stood with her legs slightly parted and her upper arms held out, elbows bent, forearms and hands hanging down. Singing in ChiBemba, Grace explained that the woman's hands were the two ovaries, her head and torso were the uterus, and the space between her legs, the vagina. Next two other women, chanting and clapping, danced to the center and crouched down below the dangling ovaries. They were the eggs. "Each month,"

Grace sang, "the eggs grow," and with this the two women stood slightly, and the small audience cheered. "If there is no sperm from a man" (snickers at this unlikely scenario), "the eggs are discharged." The egg-dancers ducked between the legs of the center woman, rolled out onto the ground in a cloud of scarlet dust, and skipped away.

"The next month more eggs grow." The egg-dancers returned to their squatting position. "And if there is sperm . . ." — with a sweep of Grace's hands, three other dancers, trailing long cloths as sperm tails, rushed at the center woman and passed through her legs. The uterus smiled broadly. One sperm embraced an egg, the other two danced away. "One lucky sperm combines with the egg to make a baby." Loud cheers. "The baby grows in the uterus." The egg and sperm moved behind the torso. "And nine months later the baby is born through the vagina." Both dancers emerged, arms wrapped around each other, accompanied by squeals of joy. Shouts for an encore rang out, and the dancers took up their original positions. This time everyone sang along as another baby was conceived and born.

Grace told us that now all the women fully understood, and we could move on to the final lessons. During the last few days, PW had taught the new midwives as much as he could about abnormal births and how to deal with them. Each evening we and the other women cooked a supper of boiled chicken or fried fingerling fish on enormous bonfires that lit the undersides of the draping fig tree branches. Cross-legged around the fire, our faces warmed from the flames, we exchanged stories, mostly about the idiosyncrasies of men, which were amazingly similar in our vastly different cultures. Weary, Ronnie and I returned to our soggy pup tents in the weeping forest to sleep.

By the end of the week it was time for graduation. As many dignitaries as could be rounded up this far out in the bush had been invited to attend. All the appropriate chiefs were included, but only Chief Mukungule was able to make the trip. He arrived riding in the back of a project truck seated on his old DC10 aircraft-seat throne. He was joined by an official from the Department of Health, a doctor from the Mpika clinic, several members of the Mpika city council, and a representative from the Department of Labor. Sitting on a grandstand of planks balanced on boulders, the VIPs, relatives of the graduates, and villagers from all around waited for the ceremony to begin.

With a drumroll, the midwives jig-danced in single file out of the church, singing a song they had composed about their new jobs. Coming to a stop before the grandstand, they sang another song in English, thanking us for the lessons. Their angelic trilling voices lifted into the mountains, and I imagined them drifting forever as part of the mist. It was one of the most moving moments I ever had among these hills.

As PW called the name of each graduate, she sang and danced toward him, and he presented her with a certificate and a full medical bag.

Afterward as we nibbled on cookies and drank steaming sweetened tea, Ronnie whispered to me, "Delia, the women of Katibunga are giving a coming-of-age ceremony for several young girls about to reach puberty. They invited all the midwives, and they want us to come, too. Late this afternoon."

"What kind of ceremony? The Bembas don't practice circumcision."

"I'm not sure. They said they're going to teach the girls about sex and stuff. It's a traditional thing done only with women. The men aren't allowed anywhere near. They really want us to come."

THAT AFTERNOON, when Ronnie and I arrived at the mission, Grace ushered us quietly into one of the larger rooms, where we sat on grass mats laid on the floor along the walls. A few of the elder women from Katibunga, thin as dried grass stalks, filed into the room and stood before us, clapping and bowing in traditional Bemba greeting. As other village women arrived, all dressed in the colorful chitenges, they greeted the matriarchs and us in the same fashion.

Some of these women I had known for nearly a decade. There was old Mrs. Phiri, who had come asking for birth control pills after she had delivered seven babies and had had four miscarriages. There was Mary Chongo, who, because she had buried all five of her babies, had been deserted by her husband. Her ex–in-laws had arrived at her hut and carried away every pot, wooden spoon, blanket, or cloth that she owned. No other man would marry her. The project had loaned her money to buy a sewing machine so she could make and sell clothes.

After all the elders were seated on their mats, their thin legs sticking straight out, four young girls walked in and circled the room, bowing and clapping. They sat together, smiling shyly at each other. Then five women rushed into the room beating drums. They circled before us and, after several passes, squatted next to the door, the drums between their legs, and beat a rhythm that bid us all to sway and clap.

From outside we could hear a wavering chorus approaching, then a string of colorful performers, including some of the midwives, line-danced through the door and around the room. Hips and arms swaying, feet shuffling, voices trilling, they filled the room with soaring energy, sound, and spirit that bumped against the ceiling. When the opening dance was concluded, all the women sat down near the drummers except for Mrs. Phiri, who began a chant in ChiBemba. Grace whispered to Ronnie and me that Mrs. Phiri was explaining that a series of dances would follow, teaching the young girls all they needed to know about sex. That was the last thing Grace had to translate for the rest of the night.

Two dancers on opposite sides of the room swaggered to the center. One was a slender young woman dressed in a bright blouse with a chitenje wrapped and tied around her waist. The other dancer, a stouter, taller woman, had tied her chitenje in a tight knot wrapped around and around itself so that it protruded like an erect penis from her groin. Giggles and shrieks erupted all around the room.

The "man" and woman dancers circled each other, cooing and

pawing the air. The man chased the woman, and she playfully side-stepped him. He soon caught her tenderly; they embraced and dropped gently to the floor. The man touched and fondled the woman in all the appropriate places, and she reciprocated. Foreplay was slow and extended, careful and considerate. No how-to book could come close to competing with this explicit demonstration.

The mating dance was beautiful, like the union of two swans. Every conceivable position was performed for all to see. Apparently, one of the main objectives was to show a girl how to find pleasure while also giving it to her lover. I don't know about the young debutantes, but I learned a lot.

When these two dancers retired, finally collapsing into an exhausted heap, I thought the program was over. What more was there to learn? I was worn out. But they were only getting warmed up. A solitary dancer showed the young women how to find satisfaction when their men were away from home. Another taught the girls how to behave with their men during menstruation. There was a dance for cleanliness and one for cramping remedies. One dance revealed how to discreetly obtain birth control pills from the clinic; another, birth itself. The ovary, uterus, and vagina dance had been added to the portfolio. I thought of the stultifying sex education classes in American schools and of how even elephant matriarchs pass on some traditions to the young of their extended families more efficiently than we do.

Not all the dances were joyful. One swooning mother buried a dead infant. Another woman treated the wounds of a friend who had been beaten by her husband. During these poignant displays more dancers entered the stage and held hands, shielding the suffering women from approaching "men." The performance ended with all the dancers clinging together in a tight circle, chanting a melodic and tearful wail.

I felt as if a blanket were being wrapped tightly around us, pulling us together. From the youngest wide-eyed girl to the oldest seen-it-all great-grandmother, we shared an ancient pact formed eons before words were, way back when eye contact and body postures communicated more than sound bites. Overused terms like "sorority" and "sisterhood" would break into fragments of mere syllables under the weight of the oneness in this room. Ronnie and I may have been separated from these souls by oceans of cultural divides, by books they had never read and jets they had never flown, but in this place at this time, as our eyes met theirs, we were joined together, from the first woman on earth to the last, through unbroken chains of molecules like bright beads of color.

10 DELIA
MY TROOP

> Individuals in the middle of a flock, school, or herd may enjoy greater security than those at the edge.
>
> —J. R. KREBS AND N. B. DAVIES

KICKING A SPRAY of sand behind them, the young male baboons scampered onto the wide white sandbar that opened like a giant fan on the edge of the lazy Luangwa River. Enormous ebony trees, strangled by fig vines, leaned over the current, dipping their fingertips into the busy swirls and eddies. I was watching the baboons from the little straw camp I had built on the riverbank on the eastern boundary of the park. I often lived there alone, far removed from the bustle of our main camp.

Like kids let out of school, the baboons romped around, chasing one another in circles, over driftwood and uprooted trees left by flash floods. Two youngsters who had fallen behind slid down the steep bank on their backsides and galloped across the sand to catch the others. The adult females — some clutching small, dark infants below their bellies, some balancing older infants on their backs, all of them scanning the bush for predators — emerged from the deep forest and sauntered at a more leisurely pace onto the beach. Several adult males strutted along behind, swinging their heads and arching their backs to exaggerate their size, like a bunch of fullbacks barely able to contain their overstuffed egos and hazardous levels of testosterone. In all, the troop totaled more than 130 baboons scattered over several hundred square yards and moving out from the trees onto the shore.

Sitting under a *Trichilia* tree, a hardwood of such dark leaves and thick canopy that it offers one of the deepest shades on earth, I watched the baboons invade the beach for their afternoon drink and sunbath. To reach the sandbar the primates had to scamper, tumble, or slide down the steep bank on either side of my camp, so they passed all around me like a gray wave breaking on a shore.

My favorite group was the adolescent females. Sometimes these gangly teenagers joined the young males in their games of chase, but more often they sat in a loose circle near the adult females. Whenever possible they played with the infants, who occasionally wandered away from their watchful mothers. But their favorite pastime seemed to be just hanging out together, grooming one another with studied concentration, sunbathing on the beach, or having their own games of chase. I almost expected them to pull out colorful beach umbrellas, Sea and Ski suntan oil, and tumblers of iced tea garnished with mint sprigs.

But none of this behavior was idle. These females, like those of most social mammals, including lions, elephants, chimpanzees — and, in our past, humans — would remain in the same group all their lives. The bonds they formed at an early age were as strong as steel cables; only death would sever them. There were no signed agreements, but the contracts they sealed with their eyes would help them survive threats from leopards, lions, drought, and the aggressive males of their own species. They would not necessarily risk their own lives for one of their sorority sisters; they would always put themselves and their offspring first. And they would squabble with one another, competing for dominance, the best food, and the safest roosting branches. But living in a group brought its own set of benefits. If one mother saw a leopard and gave the alarm call, all had a better chance of escaping; if one found a special food source, each would have a chance to get a morsel. The more females there were in the group, the less likely it was that any individual mother or her offspring would be attacked by a dominant male — a real threat in many primate societies, including our own. It was an ancient club — watch out for number one, but stick together for all it's worth. The Junior League was camped on the beach.

At this moment two of the young females were grooming each other. At first they sat face to face, each picking through the other's hair, searching for parasites and grass seeds. But the warm sun seemed to have tranquilized one. Her head drooped to the side at an odd angle, her arms relaxed like wet noodles, her legs stretched out in front of her. Her troopmate moved her fingers gently through her hair in what must have been a most comforting and relaxing massage. It reminded me of another group of adolescent primates long ago.

"HERE'S TO'D YA! If I never see'd ya, I never know'd ya," we said in unison, as we clinked our tiny shot glasses filled with Coca-Cola spiked with drops of vanilla extract. Barbara Clark, identical twins Amanda and Margaret Walker, and I were sprawled on Barbara's four-poster bed like a bunch of throw pillows, with *Seventeen* magazines, dated June 1965, scattered among us. Her blue eyes swimming with mischief, Amanda announced that the plan was complete.

"Barbara, you tell your mama we'll spend the night at Deeya's, and we'll tell our mama the same thing. Deeya, you tell your mama you're staying at our house."

We met at 8:30 P.M. in the darkened backyard of an abandoned house. We jumped on our bikes and, taking our hands off the handlebars, interlaced our arms and rode side by side down the center of Junius Street under a dense canopy of sprawling oaks. We were not allowed to ride our bikes after dark, and as the sweetness of the balmy Georgia night blew through our long hair, a sense of freedom intoxicated us.

At the train station, eating homemade pie filled with fat, wine-colored blackberries, I told the others what Andy had told me: that one grave at the old cemetery had a windowpane over the guy's face. The man was afraid to be buried in a dark casket, so he had a window built right in it.

Ga-ahl-lee! Let's ride out there. We gotta see this.

We rode in a long line out the Old Coffee Road to Thomasville's ancient graveyard, where large magnolias and oaks reached protectively over the tombs. Tendrils of Spanish moss dangled almost to the ground, caressing the headstones with every breeze. Some of the flat granite slabs had cracked and buckled into weird shapes from the maze of oak roots growing beneath them. I imagined the roots wrapping their gnarled fingers around the coffins, strangling the occupants into a second death. We parked our bikes against the dilapidated wrought iron fence and pushed open the gate.

Huddled together, we moved among the graves. A wild Cherokee rose bush grew over the top of a marble crypt and tumbled down the other side. A night breeze stirred the rambling rose, which waved its blossom-laden branches over the tomb as if blessing the dead. At each grave we bent down and scraped the moss from the ancient granite, looking for a window with a skeleton peeping through.

"Look at this. 1819 to 1822. Just a baby."

"This is the oldest one yet, 1789 to 1846." The headstone of another mound was worn to a nub, the date long since washed away by rain and time.

One of the largest marble monuments stood near the center of the graveyard. It had a big base, at least five feet square, with a column rising from it. We stooped closer, trying to read the faint inscription. Suddenly Barbara grabbed our arms. About forty yards away a dark, hunched form moved from behind one headstone and darted to another. Screaming, we ran deeper into the cemetery, stumbling over stones and roots. We reached a magnolia tree, hid behind it, and looked back, panting and clutching one another. Through the shadows and waving moss, we saw two stooped figures moving among the graves, slowly but deliberately, in our direction.

"Oh, my gosh! We can't get to our bikes from here," Barbara gasped.

"Let's climb over the fence — run through the woods," Margaret whispered. We crawled over the wrought iron railings and tore through the trees until we could no longer see the graveyard.

"Stop! Listen," Amanda said. "Let's see if they're coming."

Our heavy breathing and the chirping of crickets were the only sounds in the night air. Then we heard the crunching of leaves under faint footsteps and the parting of branches in the brush as the forms moved toward us.

"Wait just a minute," Barbara declared. "Deeya, when did Andy tell you about this grave with a window?"

"This morning. He told me this morning. Why?"

"Because — that's Andy back there!" Barbara said. "And probably Murph or Troll. They knew we'd come out here."

"Let's circle back around real quiet, get behind them. We can play the same game."

Not making a sound, we crept back through the woods toward the cemetery and climbed the fence. We found their bikes not far from ours and squatted behind a nearby crumbling mausoleum. About ten minutes later we heard footsteps coming our way.

Just as they reached the mausoleum, we jumped up and shouted, "Boo!"

Andy staggered backward, roaring, "Aahhgg!" Troll made a loud "Eeeehhh!" We sat flat on the ground, laughing. In a few seconds Andy and Troll recovered and started laughing, too. We agreed it was a draw.

A short while later we said good night to the guys, not daring to tell them our plan for staying out all night.

Looking at our watches under a streetlight, we were stunned to find out that it was only 10:15.

"What in the world are we going to do now?" Margaret asked.

"Y'all better think of something — this was y'all's idea," Barbara said.

"Let's ride to my house," I suggested. "We can tell Mama we decided to stay there 'cause I bought some new records." We knew it didn't matter which home we chose. Like the elephants, we had a constellation of mothers.

"If we hurry we can watch *Twilight Zone*," Amanda said.

And so we did. Our hair rolled up in huge curlers, we piled onto the foldout sofa bed, arms and legs flung over one another, heads resting on stomachs, hips touching. Girls being girls on a sofa bed on a south Georgia summer evening. Rod Serling tried to frighten us with some weird and mysterious tale, but nothing he said compared with our adventures in the cemetery.

AFTER WATCHING the baboon troop scamper along the beach that morning, I walked back to my cozy camp of grass and thatch. I pulled a small table and a camp chair into the shade, and unloaded all my tree books, plant presses, and drying grasses, leaves, and seedpods onto the table. Every day that I wasn't going on an elephant walk, I worked at identifying the plants of North Luangwa.

As the baboon troop moved deeper into the trees, gathering seeds and fruits, their loud *wa-hoo*s and softer chatterings drifted toward me, imprinting a vague picture of their general location in my mind. I wasn't aware that I was keeping mental track of them until I noticed a young female stepping cautiously along a branch of my shade tree. She was alone, and the rest of her troop was quite far off, probably at the lagoon, almost a mile away. She seemed tiny, with thin arms, thin legs, and big eyes, as she gingerly moved one foot in front of the other down a branch that hung near the ground on the other side of my large tree.

I did not dare look directly into her eyes. That would constitute a threat and send her galloping away. So I looked all around her, passing my eyes briefly over her from time to time, then back to my reference books. I studied a weird seedpod, turning it over and over in my hand. It occurred to me that she could identify all of these damn plants if I could just ask her down for tea.

But she wasn't interested in the flora. She was focused on me. She stretched her neck out, taking me in, then bounded toward the safety of the tree trunk. A few seconds later she advanced again along the branch as it bobbed under her weight. Finally she sat on the limb, tail hanging down, and simply stared. I followed her cue and stole more frequent and direct glances, until we were more or less looking into each other's eyes.

The next morning she came again, venturing out alone, leaving her troop in the distance. Was that a daypack on her back? Binoculars around her neck? I half expected her to pull out a journal and start taking notes on my behavior.

"Okay," I said to her aloud. "It's a great life, but it's lonely. There can be many misfortunes when you leave your troop. Just so you know."

11 MARK
MOUNTAIN ELEPHANTS

If we listen attentively, we shall hear, amid the uproar . . .
a faint flutter of wings, the gentle stirring of life and hope.

—ALBERT CAMUS

TWICE EACH YEAR, once in the dry season and again during the rains, we flew through the hot, turbulent air over North Luangwa, counting elephants. Each time the numbers told the same sad story. Even though by 1994 poaching had declined dramatically, the population did not seem to be recovering.

Studies in East Africa have shown that elephant populations can bounce back quite quickly after drought, disease, and other natural disasters, increasing their numbers by up to 10 percent each year. Throughout their history as a species, elephants have adapted to the vagaries of their environment, which kill off the very young and old but leave most of the healthy individuals in their prime to survive and reproduce.

Unfortunately, poachers first target the most reproductively active elephants because they carry the largest tusks. Poaching had dealt a severe blow to the resilience of this population, and because female elephants deliver one or two calves only about every fourth or fifth year, any recovery was likely to take a long time. It would probably have to wait until some of the young males and females had grown older, gained experience, and reconstructed their fragmented and beleaguered society. Unless the North Luangwa elephants had a trick up their trunks.

To find out whether they did and to document the population

rebound that we hoped to see soon, we needed to have frequent close contact with a number of families as they roamed between the plateau above the valley to the floodplains along the Luangwa. Though we hated disturbing the elephants, equipping some of them with radio transmitters was the only way to keep track of them, and monitoring their movements twice each week would help us protect them from poachers and yield data on the greatly reduced but still ominous poaching problem.

"ELEPHANTS AT THREE O'CLOCK! About fifteen of them, headed down that ravine." I rolled the helicopter into a steep right turn, its main rotor slapping the air.

Mike Kock, a Zimbabwean animal-capture specialist, perched in the open doorway behind me, his darting rifle across his knee, the wind ripping through his red-blond hair. Delia sat on my left, a clipboard and data sheet, binoculars, and hand-held radio ready on her lap.

For several days we had been putting radio collars on elephants, but Mike was going home soon and we had not yet collared any in the mountains. In less than a minute we had descended to two hundred feet above the herd — high enough not to disturb them unduly — while we looked for a female without a calf. I chose the third cow from the back and kept my eye on her while climbing to five hundred feet, where I slowly circled at a distance, letting the elephants relax. Meanwhile Mike filled a syringe with etorphine, a morphine derivative one thousand times more potent than heroin. A single drop on your arm can put you to sleep forever, so he wore rubber gloves while preparing his syringe.

When Mike was ready, we returned to the herd and followed it down into the narrow, winding Lubonga River ravine, a jumble of sharp tree-covered ridges, sheer cliffs, and rounded peaks left by the water as it cut its way through the escarpment. The elephants immediately disappeared under thick riparian forest. We could not even see them, much less dart one. I banked right and left, following their well-worn trails and the clouds of dust rising from their huge feet through the canopy of trees. Now and then a gray, wrinkled rump and tail were briefly visible before they disappeared again in the dust and foliage. Swarms of tsetse flies and other insects launched from the foliage into the air as we swept over them. The canyon's sheer walls squeezed in on us until the rotor blades were slicing too close to the trees on either side.

"There they are — about three hundred yards ahead!" Delia shouted as I eased through a crack in the escarpment.

"Take your time," Mike said. "Let's just follow them at a distance until the ravine opens up a bit." To avoid stressing the elephants, I stayed back as far as I could and climbed to five hundred feet. Delia pointed through the windshield at a clearing about a mile ahead — a short, narrow floodplain along either side of the stream where the hills parted a bit.

The herd hardly seemed to notice us as we waffled in the sky, following slowly a quarter of a mile behind them as they headed through the trees toward the clearing. We would try to intercept them just before they emerged from the forest and then follow them onto the floodplain for Mike's shot.

At the right moment, and with the target cow near the back of the herd, I put the chopper into a steep dive, descending quickly so that we could deliver the dart and be gone in seconds. I leveled off at about ten feet above her back and slightly to her left, matched the speed of her trot, and tracked her into the opening. We were so low that Mike could have lowered himself onto her back from the skid. I could count every wrinkle as she curled her trunk and rolled her eye toward us.

"Tree! Dead ahead!" Delia shouted.

I snatched the collective lever, increasing power and pitch on the main rotor, and we lifted over a giant *Brachystegia longifolia* tree, its leaves shimmering in the chopper's downwash, my right skid skimming inches above its crown. With the clearing just ahead, I settled over the cow elephant again. In my periphery I could see Mike taking aim with his rifle.

"Clear ahead . . . clear ahead. Don't get any lower," Delia kept reporting.

I heard Mike's shot and saw the dart dangling from the elephant's hip as she broke away from the chopper. We immediately backed off to let her relax.

I relaxed a little too, sagging back in my seat as the chopper climbed.

We circled slowly in the sky for about ten minutes until she slowed, stumbled once, and then lay down. When she did, her yearling calf appeared at her side.

"Aw, man! Where'd he come from?" Mike groaned. The calf had been lagging behind its mother while we followed her; we thought it had belonged to another female.

I flew back to the bottom of the ravine, near the anesthetized cow elephant. Because of rocks and scrub brush, I could not land there, so I hovered about four feet above the ground while Mike jumped out and headed for his patient. Then Delia and I flew to the clearing some three hundred yards away and landed.

As soon as I shut down the chopper's turbine, Mike's voice came through on the radio in Delia's lap. "Get here as soon as you can. We need to process her within twenty minutes."

I grabbed Mike's darting kit with the antidote to the etorphine and followed Delia, running upslope through brush and trees until we found Mike and the elephant.

The cow sat on her haunches as if she had dozed off while reading a novel. Her calf, weighing perhaps 350 pounds, stood behind her, peeking his head out like a shy child behind his mother's skirt. Although she was immobile, we were sensitive to the fact that she could see, hear, and smell us. We approached slowly and whispered when we talked. We worked quickly, but I could not resist taking a few seconds to marvel at her soft, resinous eyes and to run my hands over her wrinkled gray skin with its own landscape of mountains and valleys. It was as tough as the bark of a tree hundreds of years old, yet I could not help thinking how fragile and vulnerable she was in a world growing too small for her kind. She sighed deeply, and big tears ran down her face.

The etorphine had inhibited her blink response, so I took off my shirt and covered her eyes to keep the sun's ultraviolet rays from damaging her retinas. Delia and I quickly began measuring the elephant's height at the shoulder and her length and taking other essential data while Mike drew a blood sample. Then we began fastening her radio collar around her neck. I was tightening one of the bolts when I heard a crash and looked up to see the calf storming over a small bush as he charged us. We jumped to his mother's other side. He stopped at her belly, trumpeted, shook his head, and kicked up some dust to make his point. Then, as though having second thoughts, he turned, screwed up his tail, and ran a few steps away, turned back, and stood watching us, flapping his ears and wriggling his trunk.

"I really wish they wouldn't do that," Mike said, shaking his head.

Moments later the calf walked up to us and held out his tiny trunk in our direction. That his mother was so relaxed seemed to convince him that we were not a threat. While we worked on fastening the collar, he followed us around, now and then reaching his trunk in our direction to sniff our scent.

We finished measuring and collaring the cow in eighteen minutes. Then, while Mike gave her the antidote, Delia and I each grabbed up an armload of gear and bolted for the helicopter.

We were strapped in our seats and I was just starting the Bell's turbine when Mike shouted over the radio: "Aaaaggggh hh! Mark! Get this bloody elephant off me! Hurry!"

I immediately went to full throttle and yanked the chopper off the ground. We rose straight up, turned, and flew upslope to Mike and the elephants. The cow was struggling to stand up. Mike was crouched behind a skinny tree on the slope above her with his radio in his left hand, face to face with a much larger and very angry four- to five-year-old elephant, probably the cow's previous offspring, which had appeared out of nowhere. Mike was bouncing pebbles off its forehead to hold it at bay.

I hovered down until my right skid was nestled in the crown of the tree above Mike and turned on the chopper's antipoaching siren. Still the young elephant refused to back off. I turned the chopper left and right while hovering up and down. After several minutes of these maneuvers the brave not-so-little warrior backed off a few yards. The cacophony of noise also roused Mom to her feet. As she got up, Mike bolted down the slope, running for the clearing, with the four-year-old on his heels. I flew in behind him and again flicked the siren's toggle switch. Apparently convinced that he had saved his mother, the adolescent went back to stand at her side. She shook herself, leaving a great cloud of dust hanging in the trees, then hurried off to find the rest of her herd, her calf at her side.

We flew to the clearing, landed, and picked up Mike. Slipping his headset over his ears, he grinned. "I hope she teaches that kid some manners before he grows up."

After lunch and a rest back at camp, we returned at sunset to check the cow's radio signal. The *beep-beep* of her transmitter led us straight to her and her calves, back with their herd and support group, raising a cloud of red dust in the sunset as they trundled along a narrow trail toward the foot of the scarp and a drink of water at the upper Lubonga River. Unlike so many other Luangwa elephants that had been shot, she had risen again. From her we would learn much about how she and her society had been impacted by the stress from severe poaching, and what these secrets of the savanna might mean for us.

Mark and Delia on a ridge high above Zambia's northern Luangwa Valley, one of the most remote wildernesses in Africa.

Mark greets Cheers, one of the first bull elephants to accept us. One third of the elephants of North Luangwa National Park are tuskless because so many of those with tusks have been killed for their ivory.

When we arrived in 1986, the park's seven game scouts were demoralized and lacked the equipment they needed to do their jobs.

Retrained and fully equipped, the scouts began capturing more poachers than any other unit in Zambia did. Today North Luangwa is one of the most secure parks in Africa, and its wildlife is recovering.

Gift, a female orphan, wandered into our camp when she was only five years old. Over the years she led us to remarkable discoveries about elephants' resilience in response to stress and caused us to reflect on our own fractured society.

We radio-collared one female elephant in each of sixteen family units in order to monitor their reproductive responses to poaching. Sometimes an elephant's family members charged us as we fitted the collar.

We used toy elephants, drama competitions, and art to teach the value of conservation in village schools.

Delia performs a puppet show for village children.

Gift brings her firstborn, Georgia, to camp. Gift became a mother when she was about eight and a half years old—half the average age of first-time mothers in normal elephant populations.

Crossing the wild waters of the Mwaleshi River was only one of the many obstacles we had to overcome to reach camp.

A vervet monkey hitches a ride
—and studies Delia.

Below: Searching for elephants
on foot often led to close
encounters with other wildlife.

Hammer Simwinga, who works for the project,introduced more nutritious crops to villagers.

Below: Cookson's wildebeest, found only in the Luangwa Valley, were often playful and curious. When we first arrived there were no roads in the park, so we did a lot of walking.

Small enterprises started with loans from the project, like this sewing business, offer goods and services that have largely replaced the poaching economy.

A sunset over the Mwaleshi River brings new hope for the wildlife and people of the Luangwa Valley.

12 MARK

THE COMMERCE OF UNDERSTANDING

"Time" has ceased, "Space" has vanished. We now live in a global village.

— MARSHALL MCLUHAN

"THEY SAY YOU NEVER got a permit to run the project." Trish Boulton's thin high voice, salted with a British accent, fought through the hiss and crackle of the HF (high-frequency) radio. Trish, a soft-spoken teacher raised in Zambia, supervised our project's educational program and ran the office in Mpika. She handled everything from producing children's coloring books to ordering trucks from Germany and airplane parts from America and buying mealie meal with the fewest weevils. We'd hired her husband, Malcolm, a Brit with an impish face and a personality to match, from a photo-safari camp, where he had been a guide and naturalist. Now he was the project's field manager, who kept our trucks running, spare parts and supplies flowing, and solved just about every logistical problem that can possibly happen in the bush. I keyed the mike, watching Long Tail sweep the ground for marula fruits just beyond the window of our radio room at Marula-Puku.

"Says who?"

"The warden brought me the message this morning; it's from senior officials at Parks headquarters in Chilonga."

"Nonsense. Jan Zehner at the U.S. embassy arranged our permits, along with those for the National Geographic film crew, when we entered the country. It took a year to get everything. We have them on file — and Parks must have them too." Beyond the window in front of me a great elephant turd hit the ground with a resounding thud.

This query wasn't really about permits; it was a setup by someone much more powerful than a senior Parks official.

"Okay, so what do I tell them?"

"Tell them we'll send them copies of our permits shortly."

We did that and heard nothing more. Our enemies would have to think of some other ploy to get rid of us.

THE MEDIUM-SIZE MOPANE tree appeared to have fallen across the track, blocking Tom Kotela, Isaac Daka, and the other Mano scouts from driving on to Mpika, where they were to meet with the warden, get their salary checks, and buy supplies. Three of the scouts jumped down from the truck with their axes and began cutting up the tree so that they could pass. Not easy to do, because mopane wood is almost as hard as steel and just as heavy. The local Bemba tribesmen use small homemade hatchets with thin, razor-sharp blades to quickly nip small crumbs of wood with each stroke, felling a tree far faster than a chain saw could. I know, because I once spent half a day burning up a chain saw while trying unsuccessfully to cut down a big mopane that refused to give way for our airstrip. Now, as the scouts went to work, the man nearest the butt of this tree noticed some marks made with a Bemba ax.

"Bwana Unit Leader!" he called to Kotela. "This tree is meant to keep us from touching Mpika. It has been cut." After nearly an hour they had cleared the track and driven on. Soon another mopane blocked their way and another, until finally they turned back to Mano, intending to take the longer route through Mukungule to Mpika. But that track too had been made impassable with downed trees. "Poachers," Kotela muttered.

This had happened during the early phase of our village outreach programs, when for the first time scouts had begun arresting and prosecuting big-name poachers, and it signaled the start of the inevitable backlash against the game scouts by the more determined commercial poachers and their supporters in Lusaka. The scouts had to deal with this before it became more hostile and spread to other villages. But how?

For several years before that we had struggled to keep the scouts supplied with patrol rations, food for their families, uniforms, and other commodities — all hauled at great effort and expense from Mpika, miles away. The thought came to me one short sleepless night that we could persuade the subsistence farmers at Mukungule to grow extra maize and vegetables, raise bees for honey, make vegetable oil, and provide other foodstuffs to sell to the scouts. The villagers needed cash, and the scouts could spend their salaries in Mukungule instead of Mpika. Surely this would help ease tensions between the two communities.

But convincing the villagers, many of whom were ex-poachers themselves or had worked as carriers for them, to spend their hard labor raising more crops to sell to the game scouts would not be easy. And even if they agreed, would they follow through? If anyone could get them on board, it would be congenial, silver-tongued Sugar. The person to begin with was Chief Mukungule, the oldest living tribal leader in Zambia. As was the Bemba custom, we asked for a meeting through one of the chief's retainers. Days later a message came back with the date and time.

Tom Kotela, Sugar, and I drove along the dusty track to the chief's palace on the outskirts of Mukungule village, where his head retainer, a handsome, soft-spoken man with gray hair, met us. After greeting us in perfect English, he led us into a great stand of banana trees with several mud-and-thatch huts huddled underneath. The huts belonging to the chief and his wives stood behind the n'saka, which was built on a raised red clay dais and consisted of an oval frame of poles with half-walls and a roof of thatch. Inside the n'saka the retainer invited us to sit on squat stools that seemed to put my knees somewhere just below my ears. He left us for a few minutes, then returned with another man carrying the chief's throne — the now famous row of three seats from an airliner. They placed these facing us against the opposite grass wall of the n'saka. The head retainer led the chief, a small, stooped figure with rheumy blue eyes and gray hair, wearing a blue safari suit, from his hut to the n'saka, where he sat on his DC10 throne, leaning his walking stick beside him.

"Mopalayne, Mfumu," we said, bowing deeply and clapping our hands in respect. One of the chief's younger wives knelt before us and silently held out a woven basket with freshly cooked sweet potatoes and warm roasted groundnuts, their odor filling the n'saka with a delicious musty pungency, like the warm, moist air from the deep catacombs of a termite mound. On our behalf, Sugar presented the chief with bolts of white cloth to be tied in trees at their ancestral spirit place near Marula-Puku, a bag of mealie meal, another of sugar, and a tarry plug of tobacco.

Through his interpreter-retainer, we chatted with the chief for several minutes about how stingy the rains had been and about whether his people would have enough maize to sustain them through the dry season. As I watched this wise and kindly old man, born in 1910, a tribal chief since 1928, I wished I could somehow download from his mind to mine all that he knew about his people and the subtleties of their culture.

Finally Kotela raised the touchy subject of our visit. "Mfumu, are you aware that villagers have been dropping trees across the tracks leading out of the park?"

The chief's ancient, cataract-scarred eyes shifted slightly and then settled on a place far beyond the n'saka. "I have been told," he replied simply.

"Mfumu," Kotela said gently, "it is not our purpose to punish your people for using wildlife. But unless hunting is regulated, the animals will all disappear. No one will enjoy bush meat ever again or benefit from wildlife tourism development."

In an even voice as soft as a warm breeze in the early rains, Chief Mukungule pointed out that his people were poor and that bush meat had been a tradition for weddings and funerals — and in their everyday lives — since the beginning. Some could not understand, he said, why the scouts were interfering.

Kotela gently countered that surely the chief had noticed that animals were now very far from his boma, that it took many days to find and kill a buffalo for its nyama.

The chief agreed that poaching must be controlled, but he did not know how to explain this to his villagers so that they would be satisfied.

And now it was Sugar's turn. He said that he could show the villagers how to improve their yield of maize and other crops so that they could sell surpluses to the Mano scouts and their families. With the cash they earned, they could buy mealie meal from a privately owned mill that the project would help a village entrepreneur install and buy salt, sugar, soap, and other staples from a "wildlife shop" to be built and run by villagers. With their earnings, they could purchase low-cost hunting licenses so that they could continue enjoying bush meat, so long as they did not supply the black market. This commercial interdependence with Mano, in the interests of wildlife conservation, would help foster improved relations.

As Sugar described our plans, the old chief's eyes found focus back inside the n'saka, and he sat up on his DC10 throne. "This can be a very good thing." A new light flickered in his eyes. He agreed to meet with his people to enlist their support for this idea.

"Mfumu," I addressed the chief as we stood to leave, "have you ever flown above your chiefdom, I mean in a *ndeke,* an aircraft, to see it as a bird sees it?" He seemed confused as he listened to his retainer translate, as though such a thing were inconceivable.

"When these things of which we have spoken are happening in your village, I will come with the helicopter, and we will fly to see them." He smiled, leaned on his walking stick, and offered me his hand.

A WET, A DRY, and then another wet season later, Chief Mukungule's ancient eyes shifted nervously as the helicopter rose straight up. Beneath us his boma, with its quaint thatched huts, n'saka, and banana trees, and his younger wives, their smiling faces turned skyward as they waved merrily, telescoped to a miniature below us. Behind the chief his oldest wife sat in her emerald-and-yellow-print chitenje, her forehead pressed to the window, a weak smile on her face. Even though I had explained to him that the helicopter could carry four passengers, he had chosen her alone over his younger wives to accompany him on this, their first flight ever in an aircraft.

In less than a minute we were over the heart of Mukungule village, whose huts seemed to sprout like shaggy mushrooms from the red earth, with villagers waving and scurrying antlike below. Behind the dun adobe communal meeting house, or "town hall," a large field of tall green maize stalks strained skyward in the sun. Several farmers paused from weeding between the rows, leaning on their hoes and hailing their chief as he flew by. At the end of the rainy season weeks earlier, Sugar and his farmers had carefully stepped off the width and length of those fields, calculating the number of plants in rows that would yield enough maize to supply the village plus the sixty game scouts and their families in Mano for an entire year. They were already building stick cribs to store the corn after the harvest, until it was dry enough to be shelled by hand and bagged.

Ahead a cloud of white dust rose like steam through the ragged thatched roof of the millhouse, which stood just off the village commons near the brick school. Jason Mosolo and his assistant were hard at work milling tins of maize kernels to be sold to the Mano scouts and to fellow villagers. From the air it all looked so easy, so serene. But not long after the mill had been installed, Jason had been forced to raise the price for milling a tin of maize to compensate for the rising cost of diesel. "Profiteering!" the villagers had cried as they surrounded the millhouse one morning, threatening to lynch him and his assistant. I had quickly flown Sugar to Mukungule to help explain that the rise in price was justified, that this was free enterprise at work, that the operation had to make enough money to cover its costs and allow for a modest salary for the miller and his assistant. Still the troublemakers persisted until Jason removed the mill's drive belts, shutting it down. Almost immediately a chorus of complaints rose from the village women, demanding that the mill be reopened. They were not about to go back to "stamping" — crushing corn kernels in stumps with heavy wooden poles — no matter what their husbands said. The conflict was over.

From the millhouse we flew to a broad field of yellow sunflowers, merrily nodding their heads in the breeze. Banda Mulenga and several other farmers were growing them for sale to another man who, with a loan from the project, had bought a simple hand-operated ram press, a contraption with a long lever and piston that pressed the seeds to make cooking oil; it looked like some medieval torture machine. The oil is highly prized by the villagers and game scouts alike, and Banda sold the leftover seed cake to fish farmers to feed their fish — which villagers bought and fried in black pots with sunflower oil purchased from Banda.

Using nothing but hoes, shovels, wheelbarrows, and their calloused hands and spirits, barefoot teams of men and women had hacked at the rude red earth for weeks to dig large rectangular fish ponds near the river. Sugar had brought fingerlings in plastic bags all the way from Kasama, many hours away by track and then road. At first the farmers had eaten them before they could reproduce. But now, as the helicopter hovered slowly forward, sunflowers bending below us, Sugar stood on the rim of one of the ponds, waving his clipboard at us. Below him a line of women, each with a conical basket made of sticks, waded into the shallow end and began scooping up hundreds of pounds of flapping fish. Nearby another group of women cleaned the fish and placed thick slabs of it on pole racks over smoldering fires to dry, the savory smoke filtering into the helicopter's cabin.

"*Bwino.*" Good. The old chief smiled. Sugar had timed and coordinated a lot of these activities especially for this flight, and Chief Mukungule was obviously pleased by what he saw. His senior wife sat behind him with both hands on the window ledge, gazing at her village from a bird's perspective, her weathered old face beaming.

The fish ponds proved to be such a delicious and abundant source of protein, and so profitable, that the villagers, without further encouragement, dug thirty more of them in a few short weeks. People from other villages came to see and began digging fish ponds near their homes.

Next we flew to Mary Chongo's boma. Mary, the woman who had lost all her children to diseases and had been abandoned by her husband, refused to be defined by her grief. Always on fire with life, she seemed not to have a care in the world. Below us we could see her sitting under a shade tree, running a treadle sewing machine. A group of women were cutting bolts of green fabric to make uniforms for more than sixty game scouts at Mano. Irrepressible Mary and her clutch of seamstresses stood to wave at their chief and then fell to their knees in a line, clapping and ululating in his honor.

From there we followed the Mwaleshi River, first over quiet pools and lazy water among green folds of miombo woodland, then over rills and ripples, shoals and rapids as the water hurriedly cut its way along and through folds in the escarpment, finally plunging over a series of falls and through canyons that led to the foothills near the valley floor. And then, just where the Mwaleshi began meandering through this gentle landscape, we saw a herd of elephants bathing in its blue-black waters, some squirting themselves with their trunks while others pulled up great plugs of grass along the banks. These were, I would learn later, the first elephants the chief had seen in a very long time.

As we made a wide circle around the herd, he turned his head only slightly and said to me, still watching the elephants through the side window, "*Natotela.*" Thank you.

It was president's day, and Unit Leader Tom Kotela had brought his baby girl, all decked out in a frilly new dress and coat with matching cap and booties, to the marketplace celebration in Mukungule. The delicious odor of roasting groundnuts, smoked fish, and other essences distilled from Africa's baked red earth rose into the air and mingled with throbbing music and excited chatter as Tom moved easily about, greeting and being greeted.

"Mopalayne, Bwana Kotela," Sugar greeted him. They shook hands warmly. "Ah, but your baby is looking very pretty. Where did you get such fine clothes for her? Can it be in Lusaka?"

"Ah — no. My wife even bought these very great clothes from the seamstresses in Mukungule."

13 MARK
THE KAKULE CLUB

Oft in the stilly night
Ere slumber's chain has bound me,
Fond Memory brings the light
Of other days around me;
The smiles, the tears,
Of boyhood's years,
The words of love then spoken;
The eyes that shone,
Now dimm'd and gone,
The cheerful hearts now broken!

—THOMAS MOORE

FROM OUR CAMP we could see from one sweeping bend of the Lubonga River to the next, more than half a mile of lazy water upstream and down, with gravel bars, rocky shoals, reeds, and papyrus banks, as well as scattered herds of pukus, waterbucks, elephants, and buffaloes, all bordered by a tall gallery of mixed riparian forest, primarily mopane, acacia, and *Trichilia* trees.

Every morning with the rising sun, some of the *kakules*—ChiBemba for old male buffaloes—wandered into our camp from the long grasses along the riverbank. Those left behind wallowed half submerged in mud holes, looking like black granite boulders in a backwater; still others lay farther up the bank, waterlogged driftwood cast up by the floods. All day they methodically chewed their cuds—all in no motion or slow motion. Oxpeckers danced around their bulky bodies like riveters repairing a submarine's hull, checking here, pecking there, probing at a grub, a hole from another buffalo's horn, or other tender spots.

People who have stood eyeball to eyeball with Cape buffalo bulls will tell you that they are the very definition of ornery, and unpredictable as well. Add to those qualities a sixteen-hundred-pound tank of a body, a great black boss on the forehead with ebony horns that sweep out and then up at the tips like a medieval weapon, eyes that seem permanently pink with aggression but do not see well, big ragged ears, grand piano legs, and hooves like split tree stumps. If you meet such a creature at night on a footpath, you definitely want to have a tree handy. But whatever else a bull buffalo may be, he is awe-inspiring, and after working for so many years to stop their slaughter by poachers, I guess we were glad that they finally felt comfortable around us.

Over the years we spent many hours habituating brown hyenas, lions, elephants, and other animals to our presence so that we could observe them closely without stressing them unnecessarily. When a wild creature comes close because *it* chooses to, we can see more clearly into its world; a world unclouded by fear is more transparent, more easily understood.

We labeled this small group of old male buffaloes the Kakule Club. Because their testosterone levels had ebbed, they could no longer compete for females, and they were too tired and slow to keep up with their wandering herds. They seemed to have retired near our camp, safer there from poachers and lions. They were like a group of grumpy old men hanging out together, comparing aches and pains.

For years poachers had relentlessly targeted the buffaloes, so while we were setting up our Marula-Puku Camp, these battle-scarred hulks watched warily from a distance, snorting, stamping, and shaking their heads. Whenever they chanced upon us cutting thatching grass for our cottages or gathering stones along their Lubonga River, they would storm off through the thickets, huffing like steam engines.

But as the years went by, poaching decreased in North Luangwa National Park and a circle of sanctuary began expanding around Marula-Puku. The puku antelope led the way. They began showing up across the narrow riverbed from our n'saka in the early mornings, grazing the dewy grasses as they ambled along, their fawns scampering around them. And then one morning a pair of wart hogs showed up, rooting, snorting, and farting, their piglets running around camp, tails sticking straight up like lightning rods. Finally Survivor, Long Tail, Gift, and the other Camp Group elephants began stopping by. Our camp looked like Noah's staging area for the loading of the ark.

But still the buffs glowered, stamping their feet and staring at us suspiciously, from the deep, dark *Combretum fragrans* thickets on the far riverbank. After watching the pukus, wart hogs, and elephants for a few minutes, they would turn back into the shadows and gallop away. On our side of the river we sat partially secluded in the n'saka, watching them through binoculars, wondering when they would feel safe. It was a long, frustrating business, especially after our years in the Kalahari, when yellow-billed hornbills perched on our heads at teatime and lions slept outside our tents.

One morning in late June of 1990, four years after arriving in Luangwa, I was walking along the footpath from our bedroom cottage to the kitchen for breakfast when, near the big marula tree in the middle of camp, my left foot suddenly slid away in front of me and I nearly did a split.

"Delia! Come look at this!" I yelled over my shoulder after recovering my balance.

In the path at my feet, with my skid mark across its face, was a very fresh, almost steaming, buffalo flat. Cloven hoof prints were deeply embedded in the ground on either side of the trail. At last the buffs had begun accepting us.

Every night after bathing, Delia took the hot-water kettles back to the fireplace in the kitchen, more than a hundred yards away. She hated to ask Kasokola, our Bemba cook, to come get them from our stoop first thing in the morning.

One chilly July night, after bathing in our tub in the bedroom, she picked up a flashlight and the two fire-blackened kettles and headed for the door.

"I saw buffs near camp at dusk. Why don't you leave that for morning?"

"It'll take just a minute, and I'll be careful," she said, touching my arm as she stepped around me and slipped out.

Recently a tour operator in Zimbabwe had surprised a buffalo at close range in her camp one dark, rainy night. The buff had spun around and, with a single sweep of his horns, hooked her spine out of her back. She was dead before she hit the ground.

I closed the door and began to undress for my bath. I was sitting in a wicker chair unlacing my boots when the air reverberated with the deepest growl I have ever heard. This was followed by a metallic crash of kettles hitting the ground — and then the *thump-thump-thump* of running feet on the path.

"*Maaaarrrrrk!*" I jumped up, ran to the door, and jerked it open. Delia had not run track since high school twenty years earlier, but now her flashlight was a relay baton in her hand, with round yellow marula fruits rolling like billiard balls under her feet. She was rocking and rolling as though running through a violent earthquake, eyes lemurlike in the beam of my flashlight, hair streaming back and mouth open.

Behind her was the buff that moments before had been grazing peacefully along the path. Delia had almost literally walked into his backside without seeing him, and he had spun around and voiced his surprise. Now he stood, head lowered, eyes fixed on the quickly retreating *Homo sapiens.* Although he had chosen not to charge her, Delia had understandably not hesitated long enough to learn of his decision.

I stepped to the side as she flew through the doorway into the bedroom. "Oh my gosh! That was close." She sat on the edge of the bed for some minutes catching her breath. I held the flashlight to the bedroom window and watched Brutus continue grazing, lifting his massive head from time to time to check the door of the cottage. I gather he did not want that wild thing headed *toward* him.

The next morning I opened the bedroom door to see Kasokola

on the path through camp, fitting the lids back on the kettles before returning them to the kitchen. He chuckled all through breakfast.

The buffs' next visit came some weeks later, again in the middle of the night. The sound of something scraping the stone wall of our bedroom awakened us. A sweaty odor mixed with the sweet smell of marula fruits lay heavy on the still night air. And from just outside the window next to our bed came the sound of heavy breathing — *very* heavy breathing — mingled with the popping and squelching of fruits being trampled to a pulp. The buffalo moved along the wall until his bulk filled the window next to me. Slowly, so as not to frighten him, I leaned out of bed and looked at the side of his head and shoulders — so close I could hear him swallow. By moonlight I could clearly see the notches in his left ear, which was practically touching the window screen as he slowly cruised by, then disappeared around the corner of the cottage. We eased out of bed and tiptoed to the window as he wandered out of camp along our footpath.

The next morning he was back, with a friend who had just a stub for a tail. But they did not come into camp. Instead they stood under the winterthorn tree, staring as we moved back and forth along our trails: from the bedroom to the office, to the kitchen, n'saka, and workshop. The one with the stubby tail kept lowering his head and hooking the air with his horns. We began to call them Brutus and Bad-Ass.

Being scrutinized by Brutus and Bad-Ass became a daily ritual. And after a while they were joined by another buffalo with even less of a tail than Bad-Ass; he became Stubby. And then Nubbin joined the club, he of great boss but horns that looked to be made of wax and melting in the midday sun, running off the sides of his head.

So the Kakule Club grew, and as they gradually screwed up their courage, they began making more and more forays into camp, at first only at night, when all was quiet, but then staying through dawn and showing up for breakfast.

SINCE FEMALE MAMMALS are usually bound tightly together in their natal groups, they are almost always among relatives. Living with relatives confers great evolutionary advantages, because whenever one group member feeds another's young, helps defend the territory, or in any way spends energy helping a relative survive and reproduce, the helper also benefits indirectly; the beneficiary carries some of the benefactor's genes. Thus, helpers and their beneficiaries have, over evolutionary time and partly because of these benefits, survived in greater numbers than those not giving or receiving these seemingly altruistic favors. This genetic payoff suggests a primal ulterior motive for such apparently altruistic behaviors as feeding, grooming, defending, and teaching relatives and their offspring. And even when *nonrelatives* receive such helping behaviors, research in the animal world has shown that the providers almost always get an immediate or eventual reciprocal payoff, as when, during drought, Kalahari lions from different, unrelated social groups get more to eat by cooperating to kill larger prey than they could bring down alone, or when unrelated human neighbors work together to build a fort for their common defense or raise a barn with the expectation that the ones being helped will soon offer help in return.

Males would benefit by remaining in the natal group, except for one big drawback. If they bred with their female relatives, they would produce genetically unfit offspring with anatomical and behavioral defects that would make them less likely to survive. So most male mammals — elephants, lions, baboons — are forced to leave their birth groups.

One of the most dangerous times in a male mammal's life is that period when he must leave the sanctuary of his mother's birth group and strike out on his own. Almost as soon as male lions begin developing a mane at about two years of age, older males that have emigrated from other prides kick them out. On their own in unfamiliar terrain, young males suffer severe disadvantages compared with their sisters who stay in their home pride. These solitary males are at higher risk from almost everything in their environment: wandering around on their own, they can be beaten up or killed by older, stronger individuals or coalitions of territorial males; they are less successful in bringing down large prey; and initially they do not know where to find food and water in their strange new lands.

Males who are especially good at risk-taking — for example, those who travel as far as it takes to fight strange males for the best territories — are generally the most successful; that is, they leave more offspring to the next generation than males who slink around their old homesteads trying to avoid the immigrant males while staying close to their mothers. So natural selection has consistently favored and promoted the genes for risk-taking in males of almost all mammalian species, including our own.

Males have many more sperm than females have eggs, making eggs a valuable and limited commodity, probably the most sought-after and fought-over natural resource of all. Males, and even their sperm cells, compete with each other, fighting for females and their eggs, and the most aggressive males are often the most successful breeders and providers. Throughout the natural world risk-taking, aggressive males have generally left more offspring and genes, generation after generation. For the human animal, this has been our legacy as well.

But such behavior carries costs. Besides the obvious disadvantages of death, injury, and starvation, there is loneliness. Since most male mammals leave their home territories and groups, they do not spend their lives in close proximity to relatives. In many species the only company they keep are the females they seek, and even then they are often rather quickly displaced by other more competitive males. But in some species, wandering males form loose, temporary groups. The Camp Group of male elephants — Survivor, Long Tail, and Cheers — were an example of such a free-form alliance. By just hanging out together and feeding near each other, they accrued some group-related benefits. It is more likely, for example, that several pairs of watchful eyes will spot a poacher before a single pair will. But as harmonious as these groups can sometimes be, if a receptive female comes prancing by it quickly becomes "every bull for himself."

When males get older and their testosterone levels drop, they see each other less as competitors and more as cohorts. Males like our Kakules, who could no longer successfully compete for females and dominance in their herds, and the aging Kalahari lions we once knew, who were no longer strong enough to hold a pride, seemed to be aware of their solitude. Old lions often would stand on a termite mound or dune top, looking far across the landscape for minutes at a time, "cooing" into the wind, inviting social contact among pride-mates who were no longer there to hear them. And sometimes they would meet and hang out with other older males, even former enemies, just to be with someone, anyone, rather than spend one more minute alone. Years ago in the Kalahari we even knew a solitary bull wildebeest who, whenever he saw us driving along his section of the fossil riverbed, would plod right behind our Land Rover as it trundled along. Presumably this somehow made him feel less alone, though our truck hardly resembled a wildebeest. Individuals of a social species will do almost anything to avoid being alone in an empty desert — or in a river valley full of lions and poachers. Far away from their relatives for most of their lives, many male mammals are at first aggressive, adventuresome competitors, then finally find themselves alone and, perhaps, lonely.

Just a Farmer
Just a Builder
More than a Father
More than a Man

I learned of my father's death when I flew to Mpika for a village development meeting. One of our friends met me at the airstrip to give me the news. Alone with my thoughts on the flight back to camp, I was cruising through quiet air with beautiful thunderheads stacked around when I felt him beside me, sharing our romance with Africa one last time.

Ahead a storm was brewing clouds too big for the sky, towering pinnacles of vapor turning pink, purple, red, and blue-black in front of the setting sun. Below the clouds a crimson rain streaked down to the green and gentle hills going to sleep in the dusk along the edge of the escarpment. Wisps of vapor, like an old man's white eyebrows, perched over each peak.

A curtain of gray rain began pouring from a big thunderhead ahead on my left; another stood to the right. Between the storm cells a slip of lighter sky promised a way through. But it suddenly grew darker, and then closed off. I urged the plane forward; flying blind as spikes of lightning flashed on either side, rain hammering my windshield.

I kept the nose of my craft pointed toward where the lighter patch of sky had been, until finally my wings tore free from the ragged tatters of cloud. Ahead, shafts of golden sunlight were spilling and spreading like puddles of melting butter over the malachite green of the valley floor. Then I saw a rainbow — no, I swear to God, a *double* rainbow — arching from the hills of the scarp to the Luangwa River, with our camp directly beneath its center. Then I *knew* Dad was beside me.

"This is for you, Dad!" My cheeks wet with tears, I shook my fist at the sky as I shot the gap between the massive black shoulders of the two thunderheads. The rainbow reappeared, two dazzling ribbons of color.

I did not want to land, so I wandered around, cloud to cloud, watching the rain spill over the hills. Then I flew aimlessly along the sinuous, rain-swollen Mwaleshi River. I flew lower, and then very low, among the dead trees on the plains west of the river. Banking and twisting, I tortured the plane through a series of tight turns, daring the branches to pull me out of the sky.

"See the buffalo, Dad? Over there! And the wildebeest, and the snowy egrets near that round waterhole."

I hurried across the Mwaleshi to the plains, where I knew I would find elephants. As I crossed the river, the sun came out one last time before it slipped below the Muchinga Mountains. It turned the water to sparkle and the plains the most brilliant green that ever was. A herd of elephants hurried under the plane, some wheeling, shaking their heads in threat.

The sun setting beneath the storm was one of the most beautiful sights I have ever seen in Africa, but I did not regret not having my camera. I knew I would remember it better than a photograph could.

Ahead, along one of the turns in the river, and a few feet below the plane, stood a sward of tall *Phragmites* reeds, their feathery, cream-colored heads nodding to the crimson sunset.

I dipped my starboard wing, easing the Cessna lower, until its wingtip sliced through some of the tall, wavering heads. A stream of down followed the airfoil skyward again, turning to fiery incandescence before the dying sun.

I landed and strolled to the brow of Khaya Hill. Distant thunder grumbled over the purple scarp while a stream murmured from the meadow below. All around me were the beautifully honest, clean, clear truths of Nature, the truths my father had taught me. I knew that so long as I was in a wild place, he would always be with me.

I drove back to camp, parked the truck, and walked to the river's edge, where I sat down in the grass near the Kakule Club. Just another aging male hanging out in the park with his cronies.

14 DELIA
Too Much Sugar

The day is done, and the darkness
Falls from the wings of Night,
As a feather is wafted downward,
From an eagle in his flight.

— Henry Wadsworth Longfellow

The mountains are no more fixed than the stars.

— Annie Dillard

The squat black HF radio, our link to the rest of the world, sat on a wooden table in the open reed hut next to our cooking area, where it chattered to itself throughout the day. Except during scheduled conversations, we kept the volume low. Still, now and then we could hear the Catholic nuns at an isolated mission checking on the welfare of their even more remote sisters, or a guide from John Coppinger's safari camp on the Mwaleshi River ordering marmalade or beer from Lusaka — which was actually a secret code. For years safari companies could not operate in North Luangwa because of the poachers. Now John had established rustic yet elegant reed-and-grass camps offering old-fashioned walking safaris that meandered by herds of a thousand buffalo. His clients watched small herds of elephants, no longer timid, bathe in the rivers. His camps were remote, and between visitors the guides lived alone and became somewhat lonely. When John was sending a tourist group that included a pretty single woman out to one of the camps, he would tell the guide over the radio that he was including "marmalade" with the supplies. Or if it had been a long dry spell between tour groups, we would hear one of the safari guides begging John to send some "marmalade" his way.

At six-thirty every morning and four-thirty every afternoon we "did radio" with Trish Boulton at the project office in Mpika.

Soon after one of my trips to Fulaza with Sugar, Trish informed me one morning on the radio that she had bad news. Sugar was in the Mpika hospital, she said, in very serious condition. He had been diagnosed with diabetes and had slipped into a coma. I sat down hard on the old safari chair. Is there anything we can do? I asked. Can we fly him to Lusaka? Trish said no; the Cuban doctors, doing the best they could in Mpika, did not want him moved. We agreed to do radio again at noon.

Kasokola, who was cutting up onions on the table nearby, asked what was wrong with Sugar. He didn't know about diabetes, so I tried to explain.

"He eats too much sugar for his condition, and he's been under too much stress. He has gone into a deep sleep, and they can't wake him."

"What is stress?"

"You know how Sugar is, he worries too much. He's always upset about things not going well."

Sugar was no better at noon, and at four-thirty we got the news that he had died. I thought of his serious nature, of his determination to help his people. We would never be able to replace him, and I wasn't sure we could succeed without him. I walked to the river's edge, my face streaked with tears. I could hear the baboons barking in the distance and wished I had my own troop to call.

15 MARK
CHIPUNDU PRIDE

If I had a hammer.

— PETE SEEGER

WORRY RODE SHOTGUN on my drive from Marula-Puku Camp to Chipundu village that June morning in 1993. Sugar had been essential to our work with villagers. A Bemba himself, he had a magical way of reaching people, a knack for describing a sunflower press so poetically that the people could see a new future in his words.

His final performance had been at Koluba village, a tiny settlement of perhaps a dozen scattered mud huts surrounded by maize and sorghum patches, perched near the brow of the escarpment not far from the western boundary of North Luangwa Park. Except for a footpath to Mpika, miles to the west, the village was almost completely cut off from the outside world, and it was notorious as a staging area for some big-league poachers. Sugar had paced back and forth in front of a gathering of men on the bank of the nearby stream, calling and waving his arms like a circus barker, selling them on the need to build a rudimentary road and a pole-and-stick bridge so that they could haul their maize and other produce to market.

As news of Sugar's death spread from village to village, the Bemba people took it with their customary fatalism: "Ah, Bwana, again it seems we have been Bemba'd," a man said to me. "It is our way."

LIKE MOST AFRICAN TRIBES, the Bembas have not had an easy history. In the early 1800s in Lubaland, west of Lake Tanganyika in what is today known as Congo, King Mukulumpe ("the great forever") ruled their ancestors. In his *Short History of the Bemba,* P. B. Mushindo relates that one day, according to legend, a villager brought before the king a woman with ears like an elephant's. Mumbi Makasa claimed to be the daughter of a man named Liulu ("heaven") and the queen of the abeena-Ng'andu, the crocodile clan. But because of her unusual appearance, her many brothers and sisters had despised her from birth.

Despite the woman's very large ears, King Mukulumpe found her beautiful, and he married her. She bore him three sons, including one ChitiMukulu fwamamba UmuLuba ("rude basket made of leaves"). He and his brothers grew up to be thugs, hurting and killing many people. Their hearts hardened by their father's frequent punishments, ChitiMukulu and his brothers sought permission to leave Lubaland in search of their own country. Mukulumpe gave each of them an elephant's tusk, spat on them to bless them, and gladly sent them on their way.

ChitiMukulu and his brothers, along with a large following, roamed for many years in search of a place to start a colony of their own. In their travels they mostly subsisted off the land, but occasionally they plundered settlements along the way. They also paused for extended periods to cultivate many of the plants they needed for subsistence, some of which are still found in Bembaland today.

Boldly adventurous as well as industrious, they crossed the Lwapula River at the border of today's Congo and Zambia; over some years, they traveled about four hundred miles south, establishing villages as they went. Eventually ChitiMukulu began worrying that he and his brothers would die without leaving heirs. Mukulumpe, their father, had forbidden them to bring any of their sisters with them, and according to Luba custom, only a sister's son could be an heir — a custom adopted to ensure the integrity of the royal bloodline. So ChitiMukulu sent Mumbo, his cousin, and some carriers back to Lubaland to kidnap Bwalya Chabala, ChitiMukulu's sister, who was also Mumbo's half-sister, to be the mother of their successors.

Bwalya came willingly, but on the way back, while the others were fetching firewood and water, Mumbo and Bwalya made their own "fire." Soon after arriving at the boma of Chief ChitiMukulu and the others, Bwalya was found to be pregnant. Mumbo admitted to being the father of her unborn child. Upset that Mumbo had sullied their royal bloodline by impregnating his own half-sister, ChitiMukulu and his brothers banished him from the clan and renamed him Kapasa of the Membe ("male private parts") clan. His totem relations were to be the Nkashi ("female private parts") clan. Bwalya's baby died from neglect soon after it was born.

ChitiMukulu and his band of Bembas continued exploring from Lake Bangweulu all the way across the Luangwa River to today's border between Zambia and Malawi. But industrious Bisa people were already living there, and by the 1830s they were organizing caravans of a hundred or more carriers to transport ivory, gold, copper, and slaves to Kilwa, Zanzibar, and Mozambique Island on Africa's east coast, where the goods were traded to the Portuguese and Arabs. Bisa carriers returned to the interior with manufactured items, including bolts of cloth and dinnerware, for their own use and for trade with other neighboring tribes. Although they occasionally used donkeys as beasts of burden, human carriers transported the bulk of the goods, and since being a carrier was vital to trade and commerce, it was a respected and valued occupation.

Meanwhile the Arabs, not content with their coastal enterprise, and especially hungry for more ivory and slaves from Africa's interior, began extending their commercial interests inland, setting up outposts along the traditional trade routes used by the Bisa, Yao, Nyamwezi, and other tribes. By trading guns for ivory and slaves, the Arabs fomented conflict among inland tribes and then took advantage of the consequent political instability. Robert July describes this period in his *History of the African People:* "As time passed, the system fed upon itself — more guns and an ever-rising demand for diminishing supplies of ivory led to increased raiding and slaving with consequent breakdown of village life and the rise of bands of rootless adventurers all too ready to add their measure of violence to the turbulent times."

With guns obtained from Arab traders, the Bembas forced the Bisas east into the Luangwa Valley and west past Lake Bangweulu. ChitiMukulu's people eventually dominated the huge tract of land now known as the Northern Province of Zambia. And then in the late 1800s, the British arrived, along with other foreign governments that began colonizing the continent. The Bemba, no longer dominant, were dominated instead. The British brought with them even more sophisticated weaponry and transportation than the Arabs had used, exacerbating tribal conflicts and the slaughter of elephants and other wildlife. Western medicines led to declines in human mortality rates; that decline, along with immigration, spurred the growth of human populations. To conserve the dwindling wildlife, the British in Northern Rhodesia (now Zambia) enacted laws requiring hunters to have licenses and limited the number of animals that could be shot.

In 1963 Kenneth Kaunda ended fifty-two years of British rule with a largely bloodless revolt that led to the establishment of the independent state of Zambia. But to promote unity among the country's seventy-four tribes, Kaunda discouraged the expression of almost all tribal traditions. Instead of being freed, the Bembas and other tribal people were once again stifled. Kaunda also strongly discouraged capitalism and free enterprise, promising citizens that the state would provide free education, health care, and other fundamental community needs. But as well intentioned as these policies may have been, few services were actually delivered, and corruption flourished — including commercial poaching.

Highly organized poachers, their middlemen, and corrupt officials took over where the Arabs and colonists had left off, controlling and plundering the resources that the local people needed to sustain themselves and improve their lives. In the 1970s, '80s, and '90s, Bemba communities were once again subjugated by outsiders, this time by commercial poachers who often paid them little more than a kilo of meat for carrying a hundred pounds of ivory, skins, and other contraband sixty miles or more over the Muchinga Mountains to Mpika and to nearby Tazara, a village and railhead from which contraband was smuggled aboard trains north to Dar es Salaam and south to Lusaka, Zimbabwe, and South Africa.

By 1985, poaching of all wildlife species had escalated to the point that it was a national institution. The economy of Zambia had crashed with the loss of copper exports as the primary foreign-exchange earner, and many high-level civil servants and military personnel had turned to the slaughter of rhinos, elephants, and other wildlife, often using government equipment. I met contract pilots who told of flying air force helicopters into the bush to transport tusks, rhino horns, and meat, their decks awash with blood; honorary rangers (unpaid volunteers such as ranchers or farmers who provided petrol, food, and transport to scouts) who were threatened for stopping an official Mercedes, its trunk full of tusks, at a checkpoint; and too many other examples of corruption to mention. During our countrywide search for a study area, we found that only two or three of Zambia's nineteen national parks contained viable populations of large mammals.

But when, in 1992, Zambians elected their first truly democratic president, citizens were able, for the first time in decades, to engage in free enterprise, with the hope of bettering their lives. Suddenly there was a surge of interest in the new businesses our project was helping to start. People in many parts of Bembaland were asking questions, coming to see, wanting to participate — even in Koluba and other remote, hardscrabble poaching hangouts.

SUGAR HAD BEEN the best at answering these observers' questions. But now he was dead, and as I drove through the rocks and rubble of the Muchinga Escarpment headed for Chipundu village that morning in the dry season of 1993, I worried that unless we could quickly replace him with someone as capable as he, all our work could be undone.

Alston Watt, our community service adviser, had proposed hiring a Zambian named Hammer Simwinga, the son of a medical practitioner, who had training in small business and agricultural development. Even though he was supporting Kasonde, his wife, their three young children, and two AIDS orphans, Hammer traveled from his rural home to our office in Mpika to meet us. I immediately noticed that his entire being radiated, like the sunflowers he would plant, and that his aura of good will defined him more clearly than any of his physical attributes. He could not finish a sentence without laughing, and his most important goal was service to others. In him I saw a new dawn for our work with villagers and a better understanding between them and us. We hired him on the spot.

From that day on, Hammer rode his motorbike from village to village distributing fingerling fish in plastic bags for new fish farms, sunflower seeds and presses, chili pepper seeds to ward off crop-raiding elephants, plans for new beehives, soccer balls and crayons from America for the "Sister Schools," bolts of cloth for sewing co-ops, tools for carpenters, medical supplies for clinics and the traditional birth attendants, and much more — all in the name of wildlife conservation. Like a modern-day Johnny Appleseed, he left a wake of renewed hope, pride, and prosperity behind his bike wherever he traveled.

This morning I was to meet Hammer for the second time in Chipundu, where he had been working with farmers to grow more crops with better yields and to hold the village's second Field Day, an agricultural fair. Sugar had tried to organize such a fair a year earlier, but no one, not a single farmer with a single fruit or vegetable, had shown up. It had been one of Sugar's biggest disappointments.

At the outskirts of the village I turned onto a better track and began passing the mud huts of villagers I knew, including that of Miriam Malenga, who always greeted me as though ready to celebrate life for any reason. I could not help but feel happy whenever I saw her.

But today her reed door was closed and her cooking fire was cold, as was the case with the other bomas I passed. And where were all the children who usually flocked to the track when they heard our truck approaching? I drove on, worried that some catastrophe had befallen the village or that perhaps they were all at a funeral for the latest victim of AIDS. I crossed the stream and continued up the hill toward the center of the village. Ahead were villagers, lots of them, crowded around the common ground near their school.

As I stopped the truck, I heard gumba music throbbing not far away, and a flock of women and children, clapping and singing, skipped toward me, Miriam among them. She took my hand and dragged me through the crowd to an open-air market. Set up on the commons were stands made of reeds, sticks, and grass, each festooned with brightly colored squashes, gourds, pumpkins, shocks of corn, bunches of bananas, pans of groundnuts, combs of delicious black honey, bolts of boldly colored chitenje cloth, bottles of sunflower oil, and trays of kapenta (dried fingerlings).

"Mopalayne, Ba Owen!" people called to me.

And then Hammer walked toward me, handsome in his dark slacks and blue-and-yellow print shirt, his eyes sparkling, smile warm and unassuming. He took my hand and curtseyed respectfully in the traditional Bemba greeting, though he is in fact from the Nyamwanga tribe. "Hello, sir."

That morning in Chipundu, Hammer and I held hands for a long time, as is the custom in that part of Africa.

He and Alston Watt would continue to establish village enterprises throughout the region, eventually benefiting an estimated twenty thousand people.

16 DELIA
A Present from Gift

Each instant of life
one after the other
came rushing in
like priceless gifts.

—Anna Swir

Perhaps there aren't any grownups anywhere . . . Grown-ups know things . . . If only they could send us something grownup . . . a sign or something.

—William Golding

For nearly three years we had watched the little orphaned elephant Gift as she danced her jig in camp or wandered alone on the grassy plains. She was now eight years old, barely an adolescent. It would be another seven or eight years before she would be mature enough to have a calf of her own. Another three thousand days of being alone, with no sisters, aunts, or cousins.

One morning Patrick Mwamba came to me once again in the stone office cottage, where I analyzed elephant data.

"Madame, come see. The baby elephant, the one you call Giftee, has got a baby."

"That's impossible! Where did you see her?"

"By the hippo pool."

Patrick and I scrambled into the truck and drove to the hill overlooking a clear pool in a bend of the river. Scanning with binoculars, we looked in all directions, but Gift had disappeared. After searching for her for several days, Mark and I finally found her feeding near our airstrip. Hidden deep in the mopane brush, standing next to Gift's belly, was a tiny dark gray calf. Walking first one way and then the other, Mark and I tried to get close enough to see if the calf belonged to Gift or if it also was an orphan who had taken up with her. Finally we saw the wee infant suckling. At about eight and a half years old, Gift was a mother! Mark and I looked at each other, stunned.

Before the onslaught of poaching in Luangwa, elephant females had their first calf when they were about sixteen. Gift had reproduced at half that age. In the 1970s females did not ovulate until they were on average fourteen years old; the earliest age recorded for first ovulation was eleven years. Gift must have ovulated when she was about six and a half years old. Nature does not often cut the age of first ovulation in half. We thought this had to be some strange anomaly, perhaps because Gift lived alone in a male world.

The calf's pointed forehead indicated that she was a female, and we named her Georgia. They often ambled into camp together, looking more like young sisters than mother and offspring. Since Gift showed no fear of us, Georgia accepted us right away and, with her ears and trunk flopping about, trotted at her mother's side down the footpaths between our cottages. As Gift fed, Georgia would stand under her mother's belly and look up at us with swimmy, curious eyes, as though wondering if we were somehow part of their missing herd.

Researchers in East Africa had learned that in normal unstressed populations of elephants, allomothering — care given by female relatives other than the mother — greatly enhances calf survival, and the young ones learn a lot about mothering from older aunts or sisters. Relatives even assist in the removal of the birth sac from newborns. Adolescents, although they are not lactating, practice nursing infants before they have their own first calf. They defend calves, play with them, touch and teach them. They help newborns step over roots and gently help them stand when they fall down. When a distressed calf makes a squeaky cry, an avalanche of females rushes to its aid. Georgia had no one but Gift.

As often as we could, we hiked around the hills near camp with Gift and Georgia, observing how this single mom who had no female support group was coping with raising a calf. Gift was not a good mother. After the age of five she had not been part of a unit, so since then she had not experienced the frequent touching and gentle care ordinarily shared among family members. Gift rarely touched her calf and often hardly seemed to notice her.

In the first weeks of its life, a calf normally stays very close to its mother, usually within a foot of her, and sometimes leaning against one of her large legs as if it were a tree trunk. When it is a few months old it will begin to venture farther away, but if it strays too far, the mother or another female — one of many aunties — will follow it. Not so with Gift and Georgia.

One morning when Gift was feeding on fruits in camp, Georgia, now about three months old, experimented with feeding nearby. She was just beginning to eat grass on her own, but it seemed to take a lot of concentration. Georgia tried pulling up the stalks, but she could not wrap her trunk tightly enough around the grass to pull the stems from the ground. Eventually she sank to her knees, turned her head to one side, and nibbled on the grass. Meanwhile, Gift walked quickly from our kitchen area to Kasokola's cottage, about forty yards away. She stood out of sight of Georgia, on the opposite side of the hut.

Suddenly Georgia realized that she had lost sight of her mother. Squealing loudly, she dashed around camp, her little legs pumping, trunk wriggling. She trotted right up to us, stared at us for a few seconds, then ran toward the office cottage, in the opposite direction from her mother. We backed up so that we could see Gift. The young mother continued to feed on marula fruits, completely ignoring the shrill cries of her calf.

Kasokola, slinging dough from his fingers, rushed out of the kitchen, and together we watched Georgia scurrying one way and then the other, screaming the entire time. I had the urge to chase her toward her mother, to somehow usher her in the right direction. But we dared not interfere for fear of making the situation worse.

Finally, Gift nonchalantly walked toward the workshop, where Georgia could see her. The calf trotted to her mother's side and stayed very near her until they both ambled out of camp several minutes later.

"This Giftee is too 'moveous.' Both these elephants need a proper mother," Kasokola informed us as he went back to the bread dough.

Gift's mothering skills seemed to improve slightly over time. One morning when Georgia was five or six months old, Mark and I stood in a small stand of mopane trees near our airstrip, watching Gift and Georgia pulling leaves and branches from the mopane shrubs, stuffing them into their mouths, and munching loudly. Occasionally they would disappear in the thick brush.

The air was stagnant and hot, and single-minded tsetse flies swarmed around us, biting our arms and legs. Each bite was as painful as a bee sting and made us twist and jerk in a strange antifly dance. We cut small branches from the trees and waved them about as fly swatters. Losing sight of the elephants, we stepped around a large termite mound to look for them. Gift, her ears flapping and trunk extended, pounded the ground as she charged directly toward us from only twenty yards away. This was no jig. We had accidentally gotten too close, and Gift, who now seemed very large, was defending her calf. Mark and I stumbled backward. When she was ten yards away Gift settled down, throwing her trunk our way one last time before continuing to feed. Georgia, who was five feet behind her mother, flapped her tiny ears wildly at us. She lifted her trunk and let forth with a shrill squeak. From then on we gave them a wide berth.

BESIDES OBSERVING Gift and Georgia on the ground, we watched them, as well as the radio-collared elephants, from the helicopter. The bird's-eye view increased our ability to see newborn infants, group composition, and the specific vegetation types they frequented. One afternoon as we hovered near a small elephant family, we noticed a small female with a tiny new infant. As with many of the families, there were more infants than adult females in the group.

"Wait a minute. Gift's infant could explain everything," Mark said. "Maybe Georgia isn't a fluke. Since the adult females have been killed, maybe the adolescents are breeding." Mark banked the chopper in a tight turn, putting my feet against the horizon and my stomach near the floor, and we flew back to camp.

As Cheers chomped on fruit just outside the window of our office cottage, we scrolled through years and years of data. We had aged and analyzed 255 different family groups. Of these, only 27 percent were normal in the sense that they included enough adult females to account for the number of infants present. All the other families had more calves than adult females — but there were enough *subadult* females to account for the calves. The adolescents must be breeding.

Now we had a theory to explain the mystery of too many infants per adult female, but we had to get proof. Every day we took off in the chopper, soaring over the elephants and observing the families. We confirmed that in less than two decades poachers had shot 93 percent of the elephants, mostly adults, and that female adolescents between the ages of eight and fourteen were giving birth to more than half (58 percent) of the calves born.

Apparently, elephant females are biologically able to ovulate and give birth earlier than had been observed. Perhaps when the elephant population is stable, the presence of numerous adult females suppresses early ovulation in younger females, as is the case for some other mammals. In what biologists refer to as a density-dependent phenomenon, the age of reproduction is correlated with the number of elephants. After the mature females were shot, the drastic reduction in population density may have triggered hormonal changes in the younger females, stimulating early-age ovulation. This inherent ability to reproduce as adolescents might allow the elephant population to recover from the decimation by poachers. The elephants were playing their ace.

There were more surprises. After poaching, one quarter of the family units consisted of a single mother and one calf. In the 1970s, before poaching, families consisting of only two elephants made up a mere 3 percent of the total. So as it turns out, the torn and fragmented elephant society produces not only more aggression and gangs, but also single moms and adolescent mothers.

Standing on a sandstone bluff, Mark and I watched a young solitary female and her tiny calf as they moved along the still waters of the Lubonga. The pastel colors of the rock face danced in the clear water. Then I noticed that our own reflections, although we stood higher, were close to those of the elephants, even touching their shoulders. It seemed as if we were drifting with them, neither species knowing where the downstream current would lead.

IN THE DAYS when Georgia was still a small calf, we looked up one morning to see her and her mother walking boldly up to the low grass fence of the kitchen boma. Mark and I stood on the stoop watching them forage only a few feet from the cooking fire. Gift swept her trunk back and forth along the ground, making loud sniffing noises as she searched for fruits. Once she found one, she deftly curled the pointed tips of her trunk around the fruit and tossed it underhand, so to speak, into her mouth. Georgia was not quite so adept at this task. Her rubbery little trunk seemed to twitch about like an unattended garden hose until she finally located a fruit. Having watched Mom, she curled her trunk toward her mouth and let fly. However, the marula missed not only her mouth but her entire head, bouncing off somewhere behind her. Patiently she found another one. This time it sailed between her stumpy legs. Again and again she tried, fruits glancing off her body in all directions and rolling across the ground. Finally she scored a hit and chomped loudly.

From the porch we watched the two little elephants leave camp and wander along the river. Four years later Gift presented another calf, which we named Gem. She had no family, so she was starting her own. Gift turned out to be appropriately named, for she taught us more about the altered reproductive biology of North Luangwa elephants than did any other elephant. Perhaps her early motherhood was unconventional in elephant society, but it was the only hope for the elephants of Luangwa to recover. Little by little, "panono, panono," one elephant at a time, the great herds may return.

By nature, Nature gives.

17 Delia
A Dangerous Dinner

Come let us draw the curtains,
heap up the fire, and sit
hunched by the flame together,
and make a friend of it.

— Humbert Wolfe

Kasokola and I stoked up the wood stove hotter than it had ever been. "We must get it really hot," I said. "Much hotter than to cook a chicken."

The cooking area in our camp was a rambling hodgepodge of structures made of various materials, all stuck together in a row. The stone cottage had a roof of homemade tiles formed from a slurry of bark fiber, cement, and termite mud. Inside were two rooms: the storeroom, which was very important since we journeyed to Lusaka only two or three times a year, had wall-to-wall shelves stocked with tinned beans, peaches, peanut butter, large canisters of flour, rice, powdered milk, sugar, tea, and coffee. The other room had two tables for peeling and kneading, an old-fashioned cupboard where pottery dishes and glass jars were neatly shelved, and the freezer. African baskets, dried peppers, onions, and garlic hung from the rafters.

Jutting straight out from the cottage was a long porch, covered by a thatched roof; here we washed dishes on a heavy wooden table and clothes under a spigot. A solar pump drew water from a well by the river. At the end of the porch, stuck on like an afterthought, was the cooking hut, a round structure of reed half-walls with a thatched roof. Steaming, blackened kettles perched on a grid above an open fire that always burned cheerfully on the stone floor of the hut. An iron wood stove squatted near the fire; its chimney, topped by a little hood like a cocked hat, passed through the thatched roof. Every morning smoke belched from the stack as the old, retired male buffaloes lounged nearby.

The cooking area was almost in the center of the camp. No matter where we were going or what we were doing — returning from an elephant walk or a chopper flight — we passed by the kitchen, where Kasokola was always ready with a wave or a cup of coffee. This was the heart of our camp, the place where we ended up sitting on the wash table or around the fire, grabbing the steaming kettle for coffee, adding firewood, or watching elephants or buffaloes. Cheers and Long Tail or Gift and Georgia were often nearby, because a giant marula tree not only shaded the kitchen but also peppered the ground with fruit.

A fire marshal would never have approved of the chimney poking through the thatch or the open fire blazing on the floor beneath it. Rural Zambia had no fire marshals or building codes, of course, but on the advice of one of the Bembas we had insulated the chimney with bark from a baobab tree, which he assured us would not ignite no matter how hot the chimney became.

However, we had never before cooked a roast in our wood stove. Generally we don't eat meat, and our gas freezer, an old kerosene jalopy from our Kalahari days that never really froze anything, usually held only whole wheat flour and cereals to protect them from weevils, roaches, and ants. But when two very generous sponsors came to camp, we purchased an assortment of meat and transported it from Lusaka, a twenty-hour drive over potholed roads and rutted bush tracks. After the sponsors departed, there was meat left over and we invited our staff to share a pork roast with us. With three buffaloes grazing nearby, Kasokola put the roast in the oven at four in the afternoon and began peeling potatoes for dinner. I rummaged through the vegetable basket, searching for an edible month-old cabbage.

"So, what do you think, Kasokola? Is it going to rain soon?" Toward the end of the long, dry season, questions of rain flavored every conversation on the continent.

"That, madame, very much depends on the weather," he replied.

As Kasokola was putting potatoes in a pot and I was scraping the rotted, stinky leaves off a head of cabbage, Gift and Georgia walked up to the woodpile about ten yards from where we stood. The Camp Group males had eaten most of the marulas, but Gift must have remembered that sometimes the odd fruit rolled under the woodpile. With her trunk she picked up one piece of firewood after another, moving them aside and sniffing around the ground until the woodpile was spread out in a mess more than twenty yards wide. Georgia stood nearby.

"I hope she's going to put it back together again," Kasokola said.

Gift found no fruits, so she and Georgia walked down the main footpath and fed on tall grass by the river. I watched them pulling the long stalks, complete with roots, from the ground and swatting them over their backs to shake out the dirt. Then they stuffed the grass, roots and all, in their mouths.

I returned to the stone office cottage to continue writing an elephant report. Outside I could hear the *whack, whack, whack* of the elephants slapping grass on their backs. Now and then I checked on them through the window, and after an hour they disappeared into the long grass. I lost track of time but finally looked up to see the faint glow of a peach-colored sunset behind the flat-topped acacias. Then I heard a scream.

"FIRE! FIRE! FIRE!" Kasokola wailed from the kitchen.

I grabbed the large fire extinguisher in the office and ran. Small orange flames lapped at the chimney stack that poked through the thatch of the cooking hut. Mark was already spraying the fire with another extinguisher, and when he emptied it he grabbed mine. The flames had doubled in height and were roaring over a quarter of the roof. In a few seconds Mark exhausted the second extinguisher, and for an instant the fire went out, just vanished. My eyes darted back and forth. Suddenly the fire jumped back to life. Kasokola pushed another extinguisher from the workshop into Mark's hand, and again he covered the roof with white spray.

By now the staff, who had been bathing in the river, had run over from their camp, towels wrapped around their waists. They immediately set up a bucket brigade, taking water from the spigot and passing it to Mark, who threw it on the fire. The entire roof of the small cooking hut was engulfed in tall flames that reached hungrily into the marula tree.

"It's going to burn the porch roof!" I screamed. "Help me move the table!" Kasokola, some of the others, and I grabbed the long heavy table and dragged it out from under the roof. Sparks and burning embers shot wildly into the sky and rained down on us. If the other roofs caught fire, the entire camp could burn. I joined the bucket brigade, and in spite of the intense heat blasting our faces, we slung one bucket after another toward Mark.

A few small flames spread to the ten-by-fifteen-foot porch roof. Then *swush,* in seconds the entire roof exploded in flames thirty feet high. Instantly the great limbs of the marula and *Pericopsis* trees began to burn. No longer able to get to the spigot under the roof, the men ran thirty yards to the workshop to fill each bucket. But the raging fire shrugged off the water until the burning roof sagged against the exposed wooden beams, then fell against the door of the cottage.

I heard a roar behind me. I whirled around and saw flames racing through the dry grass toward the office cottage. Our data, our records, our journals were stored under thatch. Two of us grabbed shovels and beat at the base of the flames, which reared five feet high. Black soot and hot smoke choked our throats. The shovel quickly became too heavy for me to lift, but there was no time to grab anything else. Turning my face away, I darted forward, swatted the flames five or six times, then jumped back when the heat threatened to consume me.

Then the worst happened: the wind began to blow, sending a torrent of living sparks, thousands of hot, burning embers, through the air toward the rest of the camp. A red-orange glow lit the sky and reflected spectacularly in the lazy river, which ignored the frenzy, flowing leisurely past the turmoil.

I yelled for someone to help me kill the grass fire. Kasokola ran over with a large tarp and dragged it through the fire line, racing back and forth next to the flames. The tarp smothered the flames, but here and there they bounded back. I ran behind Kasokola and beat the upstarts to death. Finally, only twenty yards from the office, only a few yards from the solar panels, all the flames disappeared. We hurried back toward the main fire.

"The whole camp's going to burn — we gotta get this roof on the ground!" Mark shouted, as the wind continued to send sparks high into the air. The guys grabbed chains, threw them around the burning posts, then hooked them to the hitch on the Unimog, our huge all-terrain vehicle. Mark drove forward, pulling the flaming posts out from under the burning roof. The entire structure — blazing roof, rafters, and posts — crashed to the ground in a tornado of sparks and fire.

The flames burned lower now but still lapped at the trees and the rafters of the stone cottage. Within seconds the ends of the rafters began to burn, leading the fire inside the kitchen to the shelves and tables. Two men tore the screens from windows and crawled inside, smoke pouring around them. The Bemba men quickly passed buckets of water through the windows to douse the flames. The window shutters and door were ablaze, but the men stood their ground, pitching water to the ceiling and against the door.

Patrick Mwamba pulled the buried water pipe out of the ground, held it up like a fire hose, and sprayed the flames. Dense black smoke billowed out of the windows. I worried that the men inside would be asphyxiated.

My hair was singed, and we were all coughing and drenched

with sweat. The grass roofs had almost burned themselves out and lay in two huge smoldering piles of red ashes on the ground. A few small flames continued to flicker from the kitchen rafters, but they were soon drowned with water.

Searching for more fuel, the fire lapped at the branches of the marula tree above our heads. Before we knew what he was doing, Kasokola had shinnied up the tree and beaten out the flames with an inner tube. We looked around anxiously for any more flames jumping from the piles of debris. Smoke poured from the remains of the collapsed roofs, but minutes went by and there was no more fire.

"I think we've got it," Mark said finally.

My lovely, lopsided bush kitchen was a blackened pile of rubbish. We walked around, pulling out a burned pot here, a blackened tray there. I found my red enamel teapot, with hyena tooth marks from the Kalahari, crushed and blackened, sitting on the fire grate. Kasokola, shaking his head sadly, lifted the remains of his favorite pan from the wreckage.

And then we remembered the pork roast.

The thatch of the cooking hut had collapsed on top of the wood stove, burying it completely under a pile of charred rubble. Mark grabbed a rake and pulled away the burned debris. Underneath a layer of black ash and smothering remains, the iron stove glowed cherry red from the intense heat. Its dainty little feet had collapsed, and the stove sat flat on the ground, legs sticking straight out. Shielding his face from the heat with his arm, Mark pried open the oven door with the rake. A black-crusted blob, all that was left of the roast, rolled out and bounced across the ground, hissing like a hot cannonball.

Balancing the roast on the end of the rake, Mark carried it to the wooden table we had saved from the fire. Someone handed him a machete, and he sliced away the charred layer of crackling. Inside, the pork was white and succulent. Perfect — Julia Child could not have done better.

We ate our dinner as planned, in the n'saka by the river, smoke still belching into the night from the blackened remains of my precious kitchen. No one had been hurt, and the rest of the camp had been saved. Reason enough for a feast, and we were all hungry. The potatoes, of course, had not fared as well as the roast; we could not even find their carcasses. The Bembas brought a huge pot of mealie meal from their camp, and we sat by the river, plates in our laps. We decided against having a campfire.

WE HAD SO MANY important things to do that it took more than a year to rebuild the kitchen. But eventually the structures were constructed much the way they had been before. Now and then I teased Kasokola about the recipe for pork roast: "*Sprinkle roast with garlic salt, stoke fire, burn down kitchen, serve hot.*" But he took it very seriously, and if I jokingly suggested having a pork roast for dinner, Kasokola shook his head. "Ah, but-ee, that meat is a very dangerous thing."

18 MARK
WILDLIFE DRAMA

She would make her eyes see more today than they
ever did before.

— JULIA MOOD PETERKIN

HIDING IN THE TALL dry grass, two poachers stalked noiselessly toward an elephant feeding not thirty yards away. Unaware of the danger, the big bull reached down with his trunk, tore off more grass stems, and lifted them to his mouth, his ropy tail flicking contentedly.

Ka-Boom! The elephant's knees buckled at the shot. He pitched forward, driving his tusks into the ground and balancing on them for a moment. Then he hauled himself upright, and charged. The poachers fired again, but the elephant seemed determined to kill before he died. He quickly gained on one of the fleeing poachers, but just as he was about to crush the man, he stopped. His massive body convulsed, and he rolled onto his side, shivering in his death throes. In seconds the poachers began hacking at his tusks with their machetes.

But the tusks were as limp as rags — because they were, in fact, made of twisted cloth bound up with strips of bark. The tail was indeed a rope, and the machetes were wood.

The elephant itself was propelled by two schoolchildren, bent over and swaying under a gray sheet, their black spindly legs poking out beneath the cloth. Three other classmates played the poachers in this wildlife drama, which had taken Hammer weeks to arrange. The prize for the most original, creative, and best-acted skit among various village schools would be a safari into the North Luangwa Park, where the winners would get a chance to see real elephants for the very first time in their lives — even though none lived more than thirty miles away.

The poachers separated the fake tusks from the cloth body and began stealing off with them. But suddenly a tall boy ran in from the grassy perimeter of the Mpika playground. He wore a radio headset made of plastic cups, and, with his right arm and hand held high over his head, he twirled a staff with a horizontal stick attached, its ends painted white to simulate a helicopter's main rotor. His billowing chitenje mimicked the chopper's fuselage, and close behind him were three "game scout" passengers dressed in bits of green khaki.

The chopper circled, swept in, and landed as its pilot squatted down. The game scouts, brandishing their wooden rifles, leaped out and gave chase, tackling the poachers, handcuffing them, and then marching them to the magistrate, who held court from a school desk on another part of the playground. After they were sentenced to two years at hard labor, the poachers were led to jail behind a bench in yet another corner of the yard. There students held a sign reading: POACHERS DON'T STEAL OUR ANIMALS!

With the criminals safely locked up, one of the game guards solemnly stepped to the center of the stage area, stood tall, and declared: "Our wildlife is our heritage! We must protect it for future generations!" The crowd of teachers, students, and villagers from more than fourteen communities — all once notorious for harboring poachers — rewarded the players with rousing applause. Hammer beamed like a proud father.

After the poacher had apparently served hard time, he was led out of jail by a chorus of singers chanting

> "A dream of judgment!
> Away with poaching!"

The singers covered him with a white sheet and took him to the mattress, where he lay down as though sleeping. Next an orator stalked to the bed, stood tall, and shouted to the gathering: "As you can see, our friend Shaka, the convicted poacher, is fast asleep, and he has a dream. In his dream people tell him of the importance of nature." A boy wearing a cardboard mask of a kindly face advanced and stood over the recumbent Shaka. "But he did not listen and instead continued poaching."

At this point the chorus again chanted:

"A dream of judgment!
Away with poaching!"

In the next scene Shaka was up to his old tricks. Carrying a toy homemade rifle, he stalked and shot three students who were crawling on their hands and knees, pulling up grass as they pretended to be grazing animals. He hacked at their carcasses with his hands, and the chorus sang:

"Every time,
I see the poachers
killing animals,
I do cry. [gesture of wiping tears from their eyes]
Up on the mountains
Up on the hills
Behind the rivers
Up in the sky.
Every time
I see the poachers
killing animals,
I do cry."

After several stanzas, the poacher went to sleep under his sheet again. This time in his dream he saw a stern vision of justice — portrayed by a boy wearing a cardboard mask. His knees knocked as the chorus chanted:

"A dream of judgment!
Away with poaching!"

Justice dragged Shaka, howling and still wrapped in his sheet, away for good.

Another skit showed tourists paying money at a gateway into the park, then seeing elephants, zebras, and puku likenesses as they walked on safari. The money was given to a schoolmaster, a doctor, and a merchant, to show how revenues from wildlife tourism would benefit the community. While this was going on, another student paraded with a sign that read: OUR WILD ANIMALS ARE WORTH MORE ALIVE THAN DEAD! DON'T POACH!

In still another performance, a player asked:

"Is it wrong for an elephant to be born just like you?
Tell me, is your mother died [dead] like an [poached] elephant?
No! She is born like you, she had a mother like you, she prays like you.
Tell me why her mother died.
Why? Because of *you*, you selfish *you!*

You want her ivory,
Understand my position and love it
For my mother's death.
What is wrong, selfish *you?*
Yes, selfish *you!*"

The chorus sang:

"Trees are important
Animals are rare,
Minerals are precious,
So look after them.

Zambia's our territory,
Zambia's our land.
Air is delicate,
Hold tight for life.

Minerals are precious,
So look after them."

After watching the skits from fourteen villages, a panel of judges chose Mwamfushi village primary school as the winner for their depiction of the helicopter and dreaming poacher. We were pleased, because for years Mwamfushi had harbored some of the worst poachers.

Early the following Saturday morning, the students, together with teachers and parent chaperones — more than twenty in all — piled into the open back of our Unimog truck for their safari trip into the park. Three hours later, covered with red dust from the track, they arrived at Marula-Puku, where Delia met them with cookies and orange squash.

From the camp, Hammer and I drove the students south through the plains along the Mwaleshi River, where a thundering herd of almost a thousand buffaloes stampeded across the track in front of us. Farther on, at the confluence of the Mwaleshi and Luangwa rivers, we crept quietly to the bank above the water to see more than four hundred hooting, honking hippos, which made the kids giggle. While we lunched with the hippos Hammer quietly huddled with the children, explaining that someone could shoot and kill one of these beautiful animals only one time and benefit from doing so only once before it was gone forever. By keeping the animal alive, the people would benefit from it many times during its life by showing it to paying tourists. In this way, he told them, the animal could be worth much more to them alive than dead.

After lunch we drove through the mopane woodlands, looking for elephants. Wart hogs, zebras, waterbuck, and even a pride of lions showed themselves. But when I climbed onto the back of the truck to give them a little lesson on the habits of these animals, a little girl in a blue dress looked up at me and pleaded: "May we please see an elephant?"

Sadly, I explained that since poachers had killed almost all of

North Luangwa's elephants, we might not be able to see one that far from the sanctuary of Marula-Puku.

The sun was setting on the Muchinga Escarpment, so we turned around and began the long drive back to Mwamfushi village. As we drove north through mopane woodlands past the turnoff to Marula-Puku, I looked back through the cab's rear window into the Mog's bed. Most of the passengers were now wrapped up in their blankets against the relentless tsetse flies and billowing dust. But the girl in blue clutched the side of the lurching truck, her head sweeping back and forth, diligently scanning the landscape.

We were barreling around a turn in the track when suddenly he was directly in front of us, blocking out the mountains of the Muchinga and the setting sun. I slammed on the air brakes as Long Tail, the huge, tuskless bull elephant who often hung out in our camp, towered over our nine-foot-tall, eight-ton truck, shaking his head, flapping his ears, and blowing like a sounding whale.

I quickly switched off the Mog's diesel, leaned out my window, and warned my passengers: "Be perfectly quiet and still." And they were.

Long Tail shook his head and blew again, a cloud of dust snapping from his ears as he curled up his trunk to take our scent. And then, not fifteen feet from the little girl in blue, whose mouth hung open and whose eyes looked to be the size of billiard balls, he wrapped his trunk around the branch of a mopane tree, stripped its green leaves, and stuffed them into his mouth.

THE NEXT MORNING, as we stood up from the breakfast table, I said to Delia: "Today I'm taking you somewhere special."

We packed a picnic basket with a couple of bottles of Boschendal wine, some smelly cheese from the bottom of the fridge, camp bread, resolidified chocolate, and other goodies saved too long for a special occasion. We tied up our sleeping bags and drove to the airstrip. There we put everything in the back seat of the chopper, climbed into our seats, and buckled up. Just before lifting off, I pulled a bandanna from the pocket of my vest and blindfolded her.

We took off and flew west toward the Muchinga Escarpment. At the scarp wall I pulled up the collective lever, adding more power, and we climbed to more than three thousand feet. We flew for another ten minutes, and as we passed directly over a mountain peak I told her to take off her blindfold. Almost two thousand feet below us and slightly to the left of the chopper's nose, a pristine river flowed through the miombo woodland until it reached a great tear in the western wall of the Rift Valley. There it plunged over a series of waterfalls, each like a giant stairstep, dropping nearly two thousand feet in a mile. With no roads, no villages, no development of any kind, the scene looked the way much of Africa did not so very long ago.

At the base of the first major waterfall, at the downstream edge of its plunge pool, the river flowed around a large dome of rock before pouring over the next falls. I had wanted to land there for a long time, but the rock was usually inundated with raging whitewater. On a recent flight, I had seen that the river had ebbed, exposing a nub of the boulder.

I lowered the collective, and we began descending.

"I don't see where we can land." Delia sat tall in her seat, her head against the Plexiglas.

"See that little rock right below the upper waterfall?"

"We can't land there — it's *tiny,* and there's water swirling all around it!"

"Just wait a minute; it'll get larger."

"Mark Owens, if we crash, you had better be dead, or I will kill you myself."

"Trust me."

A hundred feet above the river, I circled the upper waterfall, checked the wind, and began the landing approach, coming in from downstream, flying directly into the turbulent air. We came to a full-power hover over the rock, a dizzying cauldron of whitewater boiling and surging all around.

I slowly lowered the skids until they contacted the rock. But as I eased the helicopter down, it began to tilt back. I rose back up to a hover and tried landing in a slightly different place. This time the aircraft rolled to the left. Finally I turned the ship ninety degrees, held the controls off against the crosscurrents of air, and felt around with the skids until they nestled onto a dry, level spot. I slowly dropped the collective and cut the power. We popped the doors and stepped out into a cool, refreshing paradise.

The river thundered over the falls above us into the crystal-clear waters of the large pool at our feet, surged around the boulder, and then, a few feet downstream, plunged over the next falls, and the next, and the next. After the heat and tsetse flies of the valley, the refreshing breeze tinged with spray tingled on our cheeks and noses. Paradise flycatchers and Nysner lories flitted among the crowns of tall *Uapaca kirkiana* and *Combretum imberbe* trees standing along the banks of the pools, their lower branches draped with wisps and wigs of lichen. Thick, brilliant green mosses covered the rocks at their feet.

What had looked like a boulder from the air was really the back of a larger outcropping that had once formed a ledge across the river. Over time the rushing water had cut it down along both banks, so during the lowest flows of the dry season this small spot was left high and dry. In the rainy season the outcropping was submerged and hammered with a maelstrom of wild water that had augered deep, perfectly round hydraulic holes in the rock along the pool's edge. Those same floods had rounded the back of the outcropping so that it quickly dropped off on the downstream side. We walked hand in hand along its steepening back until we could see over it to the pool below the next falls.

Protected from crocodiles and hippos by the succession of waterfalls, we stripped at the edge of our pool and plunged into the cool, swirling water. For the rest of the day we swam, sunned, snacked, and swam again.

After the sun disappeared behind the peaks, I built a small fire. Its smoke, carried by a laminar flow of air over the rock, crawled like a white snake along the camber of the outcrop for about fifty feet, then plunged over the side to follow the river as it descended through the gorge.

Delia surprised me with a tin of the smoked oysters we kept for special occasions, or sometimes just to give us a sense of celebration.

As we sat back to back, she sighed.

"Mark, we can't go on keeping umpteen balls in the air and living on two to three hours of sleep every night. Let's let Hammer, Malcolm, and the rest of the guys handle the day-to-day running of the project so we can focus on our elephant research."

"That's a great idea. Why didn't you think of it before?"

"Really? Do you mean it?" She sat up and searched my eyes as though she could not really believe what I had said — because I had agreed to this so many times before. And always before, something, usually poachers, had gotten in the way. This time I was determined not to let that happen. We toasted our new direction with glasses of wine, and then, after the fire had died to coals, we spread out our sleeping bags and crawled inside. We lay on our backs listening to the sounds of the river and staring speechless at the full moon rising over the trees.

"Mark! I swear this rock is moving."

"You've had too much wine. Go to sleep." I pulled her close. And the rock really did move.

19 DELIA

When I Close My Eyes I See Elephants

Find expression for a joy, and you will intensify its ecstasy.

—Oscar Wilde

For years I had had a little grass camp on the banks of the Luangwa River, from which I staged elephant walks on the east side of the park. Every woman should have her own camp.

Now it was to become home for Mark and me so we could concentrate on the elephant research. We would continue to work with Hammer on the village projects, but we could now turn over much of the logistics to Malcolm, Trish, Rex, Anne, and the rest of the team. First, though, Delia Camp, as everyone had called it, in spite of my insistence that its name was Nyama Zamara, had to be rebuilt. It had never been a fancy place, consisting only of my tent, a flat-topped grass shelter for cooking, another hut for storage, and a reed shower stall with a glorious view of the river. Now, after several years, the thatch was ragged and disheveled, making the small huts look like old haystacks. Bornface Zulu, my companion and guide on the elephant walks, assembled a team of workers from the villages to rebuild the camp. While he and his crew set to work building new huts, I continued to identify plants and age elephants. Mark stayed on in Marula-Puku, using the chopper to locate the elephants, until we could rebuild the shelters.

One morning, as I squatted to measure an elephant footprint on a sandbar, I heard the *whop-whop-whop* of the helicopter to the west. I switched on my radio, and Mark's voice crackled.

"Hey, Boo, I'm on my way to pick you up. I want to show you something."

I grabbed my daypack and trotted toward the riverbank. Just as I reached the edge of camp, the chopper settled onto the landing spot we had cleared. The freshly cut grass spiraled up in the rotor wash and blew around like a green blizzard. Lowering my head and shielding my face from the debris, I ran toward the chopper and hopped in. The glistening river and emerald lagoon fell away below us as we lifted.

Putting on my helmet, I asked over the intercom, "So what's this about?"

"Just wait. You're not going to believe it." He smiled at me. Flying over the rain-drenched plains, we spotted herds of zebra and buffalo as we flew north.

"There. Look up there." Mark pointed through the bubble window to a large green plain that sprawled for miles between two rivers.

Elephants — hundreds of elephants, long meandering lines of elephants — moved across the grassy savanna in a mass of gray, swaying bodies. It was a congregation of elephant families, melded together on the vast succulent plains, where they munched rich grasses. It was a scene once common in Africa, but we had never seen it before. North Luangwa had not seen it for years. During the poaching war the elephants had avoided the plains, where they were easy targets.

Small families of four to six elephants and many single moms with tiny infants kept their identities as distinct units. They did not quite mingle with other groups, but the family units fed within fifty yards of one another. Surviving orphans, who made up 9 percent of the population, still foraged alone, but they were *close* to other elephants. For a social animal to be rejoined with such a massive herd after years of being alone must have eased some longing. I risk being anthropomorphic, but I choose to believe that some type of joy spread among those souls. Youngsters frolicked about on small meadows; teenage bulls sparred with their tiny tusks; older, tuskless males, like Cheers, strutted their stuff with hunched backs and streaming scent glands.

We flew on and on, watching and counting more than five hundred elephants, taking notes and photos, recording the GPS readings and habitat types. But mostly I allowed myself to absorb this glorious moment and all it meant for the earth.

Five hundred elephants congregating on a plain was not confirmation that the Luangwa population had suddenly recovered from the slaughter. Only fifteen years earlier twelve thousand elephants would have gathered on this same plain. Indeed, our aerial censuses still showed that the total number of elephants had increased only slightly. But it was a good sign that they felt secure in the open terrain and that at least some aspects of their lives could return to normal, which might translate into more successful reproduction and the beginning of a recovery.

We tracked them from the air every day. We located the radio-collared families and noted their positions in relation to other groups. One day we landed near the herd and camped in a dense clump of trees next to a small stream. There we were able to age 260 elephants. Their energy, sounds, and pungent smells hung thickly on the hot air, and at night, instead of a few calls drifting on the wind, a chorus of trumpets resounded across the valley.

All the camp elephants had left Marula-Puku, and we guessed that they had joined the assembly. On every flight I searched for Survivor, Cheers, Gift, and her offspring. I imagined Long Tail attempting to impress females, Stumpie picking fights with other males. When elephants interact with one another, sometimes their facial scent glands secrete so much moisture they seem to be crying. I wished I could have seen the faces of Gift's calves, who had spent all their lives in their own small family, when they encountered five hundred elephants moving together through the grass.

After we camped with the elephants, Mark dropped me off at Delia Camp and returned to Marula-Puku to enter the data on the computer. I ate cornbread and cabbage alone on the riverbank, watching the hippos and listening to the barks of the baboon troop in the distance. Something about seeing the elephants joining with their own kind had made me happy but had also left me melancholy. The Southern Cross seemed dimmer than usual, its stars lost among the strays of the Milky Way's tail.

Later, when I closed my eyes to sleep inside my little pup tent, I saw elephants behind my eyelids, and I knew that in the morning they would still be there.

The new grass huts grew every day like birds' nests. Soon the men had completed the pole frames and raftered ceilings and had built a corral of thorn bushes as a hyena-proof hangar for the chopper. I counted the days until Mark and I could live here with elephants.

20 MARK

A Dance with Survivor

> Wonders happen if we can succeed
> in passing through the harshest danger;
> but only in a bright and purely granted
> achievement can we realize the wonder.
>
> — Rainer Maria Rilke

Early one morning I left Delia in her new, unfinished camp on the Luangwa and flew back to Marula-Puku, where I ate breakfast in the n'saka. Shortly I would begin loading the Unimog with drums of jet fuel and other supplies we needed to live at Delia Camp.

At Marula-Puku the ground was covered with a carpet of yellow marula fruits, so I had plenty of company around my table. The Kakule Club buffaloes lazed about the kitchen area, some sleeping, others still stuffing themselves. On the footpath near our office cottage Survivor, the young bull elephant with the hole in his left ear, plugged fruits into his mouth, his ears sweeping back and forth contentedly. Years earlier, in the midst of the intense struggle against ivory poachers, he had been the first elephant to sense sanctuary in our camp, the first to accept us. But then, mere yards from here, a gang of poachers had shot and killed one from his group, and for months, while the elephants avoided camp, we thought it had been him. Now he was still somewhat shy, less inclined to come as close to us as he had before, curling his trunk and sometimes his tail, holding up a foot, and even mock-charging when we came too near. But as he came into camp to feed every day, his fear of us was slowly ebbing.

After finishing my last mug of coffee in the n'saka, I got up to walk to the office. Survivor was still standing across the footpath, sweeping his trunk over the ground in search of fruits, and I walked slowly toward him, subtly asking him to move aside. He merely cranked up his tail slightly and continued feeding, the hollow *swoosh* of his breath sounding through his trunk as it swept the ground. He watched me carefully, easily, with his left eye.

I was within thirty feet of him. We had not been this close in a very long time, and I was not sure how he would react. He turned directly toward me and raised his trunk, his eyes a little wider, his tail a little more curled as he lifted his left front leg and held it off the ground, rocking forward and back, unsure of what to do. I raised my right hand and reached out to him. He stepped toward me, laid his ears back, raised his head, and arched his trunk forward. I reached as high as I could, until the tip of his trunk was only a foot or two from my fingers and I could feel his breath. Then, like two dance partners we pirouetted around each other for perhaps half a circle. It lasted only a few seconds, just long enough for me to feel again a rare and special bond and an awe that I have felt only when close to sensitive creatures of other social species, whether lions, brown hyenas, Cape hunting dogs, or elephants. As though realizing that he had done something foolish, Survivor snatched back his trunk, blew out my scent, and shook his head until his ears flapped. Then he turned and walked away.

AS WE STROLLED along the tree-lined boulevard from our hotel to the conference center one morning in November 1994, the caress of the sweet Florida sea breeze against my cheek seemed seductive after the dry heat of Africa. Our studies of the North Luangwa elephants, one of the most heavily poached populations in Africa, had shown not only how devastating poaching had been but also how well the ivory ban was working. The ban had lowered the black-market price of ivory and had thus severely curbed poaching, giving the elephant populations an opportunity to recover. Because of our research work, Delia and I had been invited to join six people from Zambia's Department of National Parks, the Anti-Corruption Commission, and the Ministry of Tourism as that country's delegates to the United Nations Convention on the International Trade in Endangered Species (CITES) meeting in Fort Lauderdale. For eleven long days and nights, with delegates from 112 other nations, we listened to lectures and paged through a thick catalogue of briefs describing the threatened or endangered state of listed species — including *Loxodonta africana,* the African savanna elephant — before voting on whether or not each species could sustain a resumption of trade.

Despite the devastation by heavy poaching, Zambia still had one of the largest elephant populations, so the collective voice of its candidates would carry considerable weight in the debate on whether to continue a strict moratorium on the trade in elephant products. Some countries, such as Zimbabwe and South Africa, wanted to resume the ivory trade, claiming that they needed money from the sale of tusks to support conservation. But historically the legal trade had been used to cover an illegal one. In fact, before the ban, up to 90 percent of the ivory sold legally on the world market was actually from illegally shot elephants. In other words, if you bought ten ivory bracelets at any shop in the world, nine of them would likely have come from poached elephants.

Because the ivory ban was so hotly debated, the elephant vote was left until the very last day of the conference. Tensions among delegates in the ivory "working groups" were running high. At one point a Tanzanian delegate demanded that delegates from Burundi, who were lobbying to sell their stockpiled ivory, explain how they could have such a stockpile when the country had no surviving elephants.

The night before the vote, our delegation stayed up until early morning writing Zambia's position paper. The next afternoon, Henry Mwimwa, National Parks' astute chief research officer, read it to the CITES General Assembly. In the paper our team argued strongly that the moratorium on the ivory trade should be extended, not just for two years but for up to ten, to give elephant populations time to recover; we suggested that dissenting nations with less than 2 percent of the continent's elephants were trying to establish a trade policy that would jeopardize the other 98 percent of the elephants. The convention voted with an overwhelming majority to continue the ban until the next CITES meeting, in two years.

Shortly after the CITES meeting, our testimony citing the results of our studies and their implications for elephant conservation were read before a United States congressional hearing attended by major international "ivory interests," some lobbying to resume the trade. These groups began intensifying their efforts to undermine our work.

WE HAD JUST sat down for a midmorning tea break by the river in Marula-Puku when a truck with government license plates rolled to a stop near our radio room. Two Zambians, city-dressed in slacks and dress shirts, got out. A cold cramp knotted my gut when the one with a twisted smile and a pit bull's face introduced himself as Romance Musangu, chief of security for the highest office in the land. He was "one of the Big Boys from Lusaka" that Talky, our informant, had warned me about, maybe even *the* kingpin in the web of officially sponsored commercial poaching that had targeted the park. He and his "assistant" had come to "visit" the North Luangwa Conservation Project.

Government dignitaries had often visited before; over the years we had entertained the minister of tourism, the director of wildlife, members of Parliament, numerous permanent secretaries, and local tribal chiefs. Only months before I had flown then president Chiluba to several villages during his reelection campaign. We kept our host government up to date on our activities at all times.

But this visit was different. Musangu wanted to see everything, including our office, bedroom, dining, and kitchen cottages. His eyes lit up when he saw our trucks, the motor grader, and especially the Cessna. When I rolled back the heavy door to the helicopter hangar, he gasped, "Ah, but that is a very beautiful machine!" He seemed to be making a mental inventory of everything he saw.

We invited the men to stay for lunch — what else could we do? — and while they sat in our n'saka by the river, I excused myself briefly and hurried to the kitchen, where Delia was chopping onions. I took her firmly by the arm and led her into the pantry, where we could not be seen.

"Be very careful!" I hissed. "These guys are not our friends. I'll explain later." Her face masked in fear, she tried to ask a question.

"Later! Just be careful, that's all! Let's just feed them lunch and try to get them out of here." I hurried back to our guests with a tray of cool water and orange squash while Delia and Kasokola broiled a chicken in a three-legged cast-iron pot, boiled cabbage, beans, and onions in gravy, and steamed mealie meal to make nshima.

Over lunch, Musangu's narrow eyes held mine in conversation, but I had the feeling he was seeing way beyond me to the camp buildings strung out along the river, as though making a mental map of its layout. Soon after they finished eating, they drove hurriedly out of camp, as we stood on the riverbank wondering — and worrying — about the meaning of this strange visit.

Two days later Talky arrived from Mpika in one of our project trucks. I had not seen him for a long time and was immediately concerned that he would jeopardize our clandestine relationship — and his own security — by showing up in camp where our Zambian workers would see him.

We had barely sat down in the n'saka before he began: "Sir, you and Dr. Delia are in very much danger. You can be put in prison or even killed anytime from now." Without touching the tea I had fixed him, he leaned forward in his chair and went on to tell me that high-level officials in Lusaka were upset because the project had shut down poaching and they could no longer get ivory or game meat from North Luangwa. Working through Banda Famwila, the Parks regional field commander in Mpika, they were planning to put an end to the project one way or another.

"Look, we've been through this sort of thing for years," I said, trying to brush off his warning.

"No, sir, this time is different. You must take care. Believe me. Bwana Musangu is a very powerful man. He even reaches the very top." And he named other officials who had been mentioned many times by our friends in the Anti-Corruption Commission. Then I knew he was right to worry.

I decided not to tell Delia of Talky's warning, at least not until she had had a little time to enjoy her new camp. We were scheduled to fly to the United States on leave in a few days; maybe I would tell her then.

21 DELIA

GRASS HUTS AND LEOPARD STUMPS

When it is dark enough, you can see the stars.

—CHARLES BEARD

MY TENT SHOOK. A lioness was slithering along the back wall, bumping the canvas with a swishing sound. An entire pride — ten lions — had walked into Delia Camp, where several Bembas and I were finishing up the straw huts. As usual, I had camped some distance away from the men. As usual, I regretted that decision.

Bornface and I had first seen the lions about a week before, lying along the riverbank at sunrise, their paws hanging over the edge, folded neatly. Heads swinging in unison, back and forth, back and forth, they had tracked us from about two hundred yards away as we built the camp. It was a group of females with their cubs. And since these lions had a social system similar to that of the East African lions, they were probably close relatives who had been together since birth, raising their cubs, hunting, hanging out on the beach — a typical mammalian social group. As with the female baboons and elephants, the lions derived advantages from being in a group of close relatives: as a team, the cats could bring down larger prey, communally suckle their young, defend a larger territory. And the fact that they were related meant that all these advantages were bestowed on their kin. No adult males were in sight. They would come and go, as male lions are wont to do, fighting for tenure, showing up for supper, or to copulate.

We came upon the lionesses again when Bornface and I walked to the lagoon one morning to watch a pair of fish eagles. The lions had climbed up on a good-size termite mound. It was about eight feet tall and fifteen feet wide at its base, but not nearly large enough for ten lions. The cats made a game of it, like kids playing king of the hill. There was not a square inch of the white, dusty hump that was not covered with paw, tail, or chin as the cats perched on the top, clung to the sides, and curled about the bottom.

And now, at eight-thirty at night, I listened to the lionesses pacing back and forth behind my tent. The lazy moon would not rise until after ten o'clock, so camp was dark except for my little flashlight beam bouncing around the shadows, illuminating one blond body after another. Ears erect, tail lashing about, each one walked about ten steps east, whirled around, and walked back again, sniffing the ground like a bloodhound. As always, the cats wore their thoughts on their tails: agitated, alert, definitely curious, probably hungry. This was not good. One lioness could topple my tent with a single blow; ten could demolish it like tissue paper — with me wrapped inside. They were not simply passing by, satisfying their curiosity. They were focused on my tent.

I sat in my small folding safari chair for more than an hour, listening to the lions, loving it and hating it at the same time. Meanwhile, the hippos sounded as if they were having a small war down by the river. Their loud splashing sounds and territorial roars mingled with the soft footfalls of lion paws. Great night out.

One lioness stopped just outside the flimsy gauze window. I stood inside, just out of view. She lifted her huge head until her nose was only one foot from my stomach. Nothing between us but cheap canvas — not even the rip-proof variety. Not daring to shout for Bornface, I waited. The frames of the new huts stood around my tent like reed-and-pole skeletons in the dim light.

I heard a muffled sound — like a cough — from the direction of the men's camp. The lionesses jerked their heads in that direction and trotted toward the noise. As soon as they left, I called out: "BORNFACE. CAN YOU HEAR ME? THERE ARE LIONS OVER HERE."

"Yes, madame," came the reply. "They are here also."

"What should we do?"

"We'll come to you once they leave our place." I could hear the men shooing the lionesses with shouts and saw their flashlights playing in the darkness. In a moment he continued, "We are coming to you, Dr. Delia."

I waited anxiously, and in a few minutes I could see a tight wad of men wobbling toward me, shining their lights in all directions. Finally they reached the door of my tent, and I stepped out. The tightness in my chest loosened — *my pride*, my side, had arrived.

"Thanks, guys. Is everybody okay?"

"Yes, madame, but these lions are very dangerous. They have been circling our camp for many times now."

"Let's move your camp over here," I suggested. "We can set your tents up inside the new huts. It'll be safer."

Scouring the bushes with our lights, we went to their camp, grabbed armloads of gear, and carried it back to my area. Looking for the lionesses all the while, we rigged the men's tents inside the pole frames, which were at least partly secured by the incomplete reed walls. The moon had risen by now, and we built a bonfire. The lionesses were nowhere to be seen, but we guessed they were still nearby, watching us with their keen amber eyes. For curious creatures this commotion was too good to miss.

When we had settled down in our tents, I listened for the sounds of soft paws plodding through the brush, but the only night noises were the throaty chuckles of hippos. Then, just when all was quiet, the lions walked into camp again. They stood no more than fifteen yards from my tent, and all ten bellowed forth with full roars. I laughed with the hippos now that I felt safe and thought of other lion times.

Among the shadowy dunes and white-hot sands of the Kalahari we had studied lions for more than seven years. Following their low-slung tawny bodies through the long grass as they hunted or watching them from behind a tree as they raided camp, we got to know the lionesses of the Blue Pride. We had our share of exciting moments with the lions, but what we remember best are the quiet times: the long hours of waiting with them for the Kalahari heat to break, for the slow-moving sun to finally sink behind the dunes, when the lions would begin their night shift. Many late afternoons found us waiting with the lions in some isolated spot, sharing the same lean shade of a twisted thorn tree, all of us lethargic, torpid, lightheaded, comatose. The Kalahari heat is a great equalizer, reducing all creatures to a sluggish heap.

At first we would sit in the truck with the windows open, under a tree close to the lions, and wait for them to stir. But the shade of Kalahari thorn trees is as thin as lace, and the sun always burned its way through the roof of the truck. Soon we would open the doors quietly, begging for a breeze. Then, if the lions' shade was better than ours, we would drive over and park near them, opening the doors as wide as they would go. Inevitably the lions would rise slowly, one by one and, as if they were sleep-walking, stagger over and plop down in the shade of the truck, lined up like so many throw rugs. Eventually, after years of sun-waiting, we found we could slide out of our truck and sit on the ground near them.

Late one afternoon the temperature seemed stuck at 120 degrees, and the air was almost too hot to breathe. Mark and I slid out from his side of the truck, away from the lions, and sat on the white sand. Happy, Blue, Sassy, and Chary of the Blue Pride were sleeping under a scraggly acacia bush about thirty feet away. Not a tail or an ear twitched as we moved to the ground. No one cared. The sand did not seem much cooler than the truck, but when we dribbled water from the canteen over our heads, the slight breeze brought goose bumps to our skin. As we wet our T-shirts and breathed in deeply, the moisture on our chests reached inside to cool our bodies. The lionesses had not had a drink of water for six months, getting the moisture they needed only from their prey or wild melons. I wished we could pass the canteen around the circle.

After a few minutes Happy stirred. She lifted her head and, through half-closed lizardlike eyelids, gazed at the truck. Nothing in her features expressed surprise or even awareness that we had entered her space on the sand. She worked her rough tongue over dry lips several times, then stood and took a step toward us. We were quite unprepared for this, and our bodies must have tensed slightly as we stared at her. She walked toward the truck and seemed to be heading for the rear bumper, which would take her on a path no more than two yards from us. We didn't move as we watched her giant paws lift and drop in the loose sand, her large head hanging low and relaxed. At one point her paw landed no more than an arm's reach from Mark's boots. She never looked at us but strolled to the back of the truck and stretched out under the bumper, her face turned away. I could count the individual hairs of her ear tuft. Turn up the heat; we will stay here forever. What does comfort matter with a lion at your toes?

Over the years we discovered that the social system of Kalahari lions was somewhat different than that of lions elsewhere. Yes, they lived in tightly knit prides of lionesses with their cubs and various consorts of unrelated males fighting for possession of the pride every few years. But when severe drought hit the desert and most of the large-bodied prey scattered into herd fragments over thousands of square miles, the prides of mothers, grandmothers, sisters, and female cousins disbanded. No longer able to find hefty gemsbok or stately eland, they hunted smaller prey — hares and guinea fowl — in pairs, then finally solitarily. Sassy, who for years had slept, groomed, and played with her pridemates every day, now stood alone on the dune top cooing into the harsh wind. Before the drought Spicy or Happy would have answered her call and sidled up to her, and the two would have rubbed their long bodies together from nose to tail.

But now no one answered her *coo,* and Sassy fed that night on wild tsama melons and old bones. Eventually the former pridemates dispersed over hundreds of square miles, some of them never seeing each other again, as far as we knew.

Years later, when the rains came again and the grasses greened, herds of two thousand springbok and five hundred gemsbok dotted the plains once more. Wandering lions came together and formed groups in order to bring down the large prey. But, breaking all rules of lion society, they did not necessarily rejoin their relatives. Raking in strays from the distant dunes, a female here, a female there, they came together to form new prides. Sometimes — many times — when you're out in the desert in need of a friend, any group is better than none.

SLEEPY-EYED, but more enthusiastic than ever to finish the huts of Delia Camp, the men and I roused ourselves before dawn. They crawled quietly over and through the pole frames, securing the crossbeams and rafters with strips of bark. One stalk at a time, they wove the bright red and green reeds tightly into very strong walls with twine. They tied long grass stems into thick bundles and threw them higgledy-piggledy onto the rafters, where one man straightened and fastened them into a rather floppy thatch.

As the days went by, each Bemba wove his imagination into the tying, twisting, and thatching, so that the huts acquired their own bush character. It was impossible for the men to simply bind a reed into place. Using bark, Jackson Kasokola made large cross-stitches on every two feet of wall, adding a bold geometric pattern to the exterior and interior. Bornface added his signature by bending reeds into arches and lashing them to the hip roofs. Patrick Mwamba outdid everyone by braiding three different species of grass stalks together into long garlands that framed the windows and doors.

We stood back to admire their handiwork. The bedroom hut, only five yards from the high riverbank, encircled a massive *Trichilia* tree. On three sides it was made of golden bamboo stalks held together with ropy red bark in large X patterns. The third wall, facing the river, had a large open window that offered a view of the slow-moving current and the distant shore. The branches of the tree spread like arms across the room and served as shelves for the water basin, books, and binoculars. A colorful cloth woven and dyed by Bisa women was draped across the bed, which was shrouded in an enormous mosquito net.

The dining and office huts were also built around large trees overlooking the river. I radioed Mark that at last the camp was finished and he should come home. He answered that he would be there by late afternoon.

I PLANNED a candlelight dinner: smoked oysters on crackers, a mock cottage pie made from baked beans, seasoned with piri-piri sauce and topped with mashed potatoes, and bread freshly baked in the black pot. By midafternoon I had completed the preparations. Sitting on the riverbank, I watched my favorite soap opera: the troop of baboons, who were scattered across the beach on the opposite shore.

A young female sashayed away from her troopmates toward a small, shallow pool tucked behind an old fallen tree, which formed a formidable fort against crocodiles. The Luangwa River swarms with one of Africa's highest densities of Nile crocodiles, but this little unnamed pool was a safe place to drink, and Ms. Baboon knew it. No doubt she had known it all of her life, having learned it from her elders.

Hesitating only briefly, she knelt to drink, her backside sticking up, tail elbowed down. After a few moments, she sauntered back toward her troop, which was moving slowly into the forest. As she left the beach, she passed an old stump tucked under a shrub and overgrown with dried grass. It looked very much like the straw-colored mane and head of a lion peeping from the undergrowth. But this stump had mimicked a lion's head for years, as long as I had been here, so neither the baboons nor I were fooled. None of the troop members wasted precious foraging moments by stopping to investigate the harmless stump and establish whether it was carnivore or grass. Knowing that a lump is not a lion reduces stress.

Suddenly, several of the baboons halted on the edge of the trees, forming a tighter group. Using my binoculars, I saw a strange form hunkered low to the ground under a bush. A few of the baboons began barking alarm calls. Some of the others rushed over to the mystery bump, while two large males bounded back and forth to get a better view. Long moments — precious feeding time — were spent as they shouted and sprang about, gathering data but also presenting a confused target to the possible predator. At last it became apparent that the lump was a freshly fallen tree limb bent in a weird leopardlike shape complete with spots of bark.

As the commotion died down and the primates moved on, the landmark was unconsciously sketched on their mental maps and mine: "This bump is not a leopard but a tree limb." Never again would they have to stop and investigate that fallen branch. Knowing that a limb is not a leopard is part of being home.

If this troop were suddenly transported to a different valley or a distant forest, all of the baboons would have to draw a map of the new neighborhood in their minds. Lion-looking stumps covered with weeds would have to be investigated one by one and plotted on their charts — and Africa's bush sprouts many, many stumps pretending to be lions. Diagrams scrawled in some primitive, wordless language would register: this waterhole dries up early; this floodplain has good grass during the rains. The survey would take years, as they roamed and searched for the closest Starbucks or the best salad bar in the unfamiliar suburb. Mapping one's range is an expensive endeavor, costing precious time and energy, high risks, and unpleasant emotions. In a new place the sense of security felt by Ms. Baboon as she knelt to drink at the familiar pool would be lost. She would rarely feel safe from lurking predators or lingering starvation. All of the troop members would be a bit more jumpy, and they would probably enjoy less quality beach time together. Mothers might be less attentive to infants; males might fight more often; adolescents might disperse sooner; single moms and gangs of young males might become more common; families might break apart. Of course, baboons and most other animals are smart enough not to leave their homes in the first place unless they are forced to do so.

However these concepts are formed in the mind, research has shown that being aware of the riches and dangers of the home range is one of the most ancient and primitive of all animal sensations. Feelings born of mapped spaces and familiar faces make a place into what we call home, and it has been a deep part of almost every creature on Earth, including ourselves, for a long time.

MARK ARRIVED in the late afternoon. I showed him around the newly constructed huts, pointing out Jackson's artwork and Bornface Zulu's hip roofs.

Later we sat at our little dining table, our faces reflecting the candlelight, and watched the ripples of the river swish against the faces of moonlit hippos. Every minute of our lives, every lion we had seen, every campfire we had shared, seemed to have led us to this place at this moment. The poaching had stopped, the village programs were working well, and the elephants were poised to make a comeback. Buffaloes, hippos, and elephants had been sighted in areas where they had not been seen in twenty years. We had a great staff living in Mpika and Marula-Puku to manage the project. Perhaps we could breathe more easily and laugh more often. We talked about how we would locate the radio-collared elephants and follow them on foot. We planned to dart and collar more of them. As the moon shadows embraced the river beaches and stretched their arms toward our shore, an elephant trumpeted in the distance.

Clinking our enamel mugs together, we toasted the elephants. We had no way of knowing that after nearly a quarter of a century, this would be our last night in the African bush for a long, long time.

22 DELIA
CAMP ARREST

I envy the animals two things — their ignorance of evil to come, and their ignorance of what is said about them.

— VOLTAIRE

"WHAT'S THAT?" I sat upright, my eyes searching the strange dark room. The clock read 4:30 A.M. A phone was ringing. Why? We had lived without telephones for more than twenty years. I hated their intrusive ring-anytime-they-please sound.

Mark leaped from the bed. I ran after him into another room and switched on the light. Yellow and cheerful, my mother's kitchen on plumb and nelly street in Americus, Georgia, popped into view.

"Yes, Malcolm," Mark answered, "I hear you. Go ahead." I slid to the floor, my back against the cabinets, and stared at Mark. Malcolm, our project manager, would not call at 4:30 A.M. unless something really bad was happening.

After our night in Delia Camp, we had left as scheduled on our annual leave in Europe and the States to raise money for the project. As we learned from Malcolm's call, a few days later, at ten in the morning, his wife, Trish, who supervised the educational program, heard a commotion outside their house in Mpika and ran to a window. A large flatbed truck loaded with armed men roared into their yard. Brandishing AK-47 automatic rifles and wearing an assortment of patched-up drab green fatigues and scruffy boots, they jumped from the bed of the truck and jogged into positions surrounding the house. Trish picked up her baby son and ran to the front door and locked it. Ronnie Hadley, who had shared the sacred dances of the

Katibunga women with me, was also in the house. Malcolm was in Lusaka on a supply run.

One of the men banged on the front door. Trish handed the baby to Ronnie and motioned for her to take him to the back room. Trish stepped onto the porch and demanded to know what they wanted. The man said he had orders from the field commander of National Parks, Banda Famwila, to hold everyone on the project under house arrest and seize its equipment. Trish, a Zambian citizen, knew most of the local game scouts by name. They often came to her house or the project office for fuel allotments, patrol food, or medicines. But she did not recognize the man who stood at the door or any of the others.

"Do you have a warrant?" she asked.

"No, we do not need a warrant. We are on official business."

Calmly but firmly, she told him that they could not put one foot inside her house without a warrant. "Zambia is a country with laws," she said, and stepped inside and locked the door. He shouted that he would return with official documents, then drove away, leaving the ragtag posse patrolling the garden. Malcolm returned to Mpika that afternoon to find his house surrounded by armed guards.

At about the same time that these men surrounded the Boultons' house, Hammer rode his motorbike to the project's office — a cream-colored building painted with dramatic gold and black patterns — and found strangers milling about the doors. The keys for the trucks, the checkbook, the documents — everything he needed to conduct the village projects — were locked inside, but another band of men refused to let Hammer enter.

FOR YEARS the game warden and others had warned us that Field Commander Famwila, working in league with his superiors in Lusaka, would try to end our project so that they could return to elephant poaching. Now that the villagers had become fish farmers and millers, the smugglers had no one to hire to shoot the elephants. The illicit trafficking of ivory had dwindled to a trickle. For their dirty business to continue, the project had to be stopped. Famwila and Musangu had obviously planned this illegal seizure for some time; the game warden, the magistrate, and most of the senior game scouts, all of whom had worked closely with our project for years, were in Lusaka for a meeting. As soon as we left for the States, the commander moved to end our project and take over all of its assets.

After hearing this news from Malcolm, we phoned the American ambassador to Zambia and explained what had happened. He knew our project well, having visited our camp and the village programs. Ambassador Kutchel was also well aware of our long-standing difficulties with Famwila and Musangu, but this time they had gone too far. Ronnie Hadley was a Peace Corps volunteer seconded to the project, and she had been put under house arrest by a band of paramilitaries. The ambassador firmly demanded that the Zambian authorities release Malcolm, Trish, their baby, and Ronnie. The senior bureaucrats with whom he spoke apparently knew nothing about the illegal seizure and house arrest, which made it seem even more likely that Famwila, Musangu, and several other higher-level officials were acting on their own.

Night fell in Mpika with Trish, Malcolm, Ronnie, and the baby huddled inside their small brick house while armed men skulked through the garden, trampling the poinsettias and moonflowers. No one slept except the guards. The next morning they refused to allow Malcolm or Trish to go to the open market for supplies for the baby.

MY MOTHER had been quietly offering us food, coffee, and soft smiles since the first phone call. "John Pope is Jimmy Carter's best friend, and I've known John all my life. I could get you a meeting with Jimmy."

Several hours later we sat next to former president Carter on his living room sofa in Plains, Georgia. Open on his lap was a large picture album, showing our village outreach programs, our game scout assistance, our elephant research. He nodded as we told him about the illegal ivory trade and the corrupt individuals who had been put out of business as poaching decreased. My mother looked on, rocking gently in a chair across the room.

"I know the president of Zambia," the president said. "I can't promise anything, but I'll do what I can."

THE NEXT NIGHT at 11:00 P.M. a truck rushed into Marula-Puku. Rex Haylock, the general manager for the project, and his wife, Anne, sat up in their bed. They were now living in our camp as they prepared to take on more of the logistical problems so that we would be free to study elephants from Delia Camp. The driver slammed on the brakes only feet from their cottage windows, and twelve men piled out, eerily backlit through the dust swirling in the headlights as they waved their weapons and shouted. Rex hurried out to meet the men, and Patrick Mwamba, Jackson Kasokola, Bornface Zulu, and the other Bemba tribesmen, many of whom had worked with us for ten years, crept from their cottages and watched quietly from the shadows, holding their axes loosely at their sides.

The group leader curtly told Rex and Anne that they were confined to camp and that if they attempted "escape," they would "be restrained." After demanding food and lodging for his men, he and two others pushed their way into our stone and thatch cottage and began rummaging through files and journals. The only documents that interested them were the truck maintenance records. An hour later they shrugged their shoulders and returned the data books to Anne.

AFTER THAT first phone call, we had not slept. We wanted to go back to Zambia immediately, but the ambassador advised that since a few high-level officials had taken such extreme — and illegal — action against our project, it would not be safe to return. Calling everyone who could help, we secured as much support as possible to free our friends and the project. Five embassies were now involved.

On the third day of the house arrests, some out-of-town friends — one Zambian, one Canadian — who were totally unaware of these events, arrived at Malcolm and Trish's house for a previously scheduled party for the baby's first birthday. The guards promptly put them under house arrest as well and impounded their vehicle.

A few hours later an American embassy diplomat phoned Malcolm to say that a truck was on its way from Peace Corps headquarters to free Ronnie and drive her to Lusaka. He added that the next morning officials from the American embassy and the British High Commission would arrive by plane to demand the Boultons' release.

That afternoon the Peace Corps representatives drove into the yard. Presenting official documents, complete with stamps and signatures, they told the guards that they were taking Ronnie and her belongings. The guards still did not have a warrant, so they did not try to stop the officials as they escorted Ronnie, who had helped train the midwives of Katibunga and knew many of the babies by name, through the garden gate laden with flowering bougainvillea and honeysuckle.

The next morning a large prop plane swooped low over the tiled roofs of Mpika. Malcolm ran outside and told the guards that American and British diplomats had arrived and that he was going to the airfield to collect them. He drove off before they could say a word.

At the airstrip an entourage from the two embassies as well as a Zambian attorney disembarked from the plane. Malcolm drove them and several policemen to the office of Field Commander Famwila and told him that everyone was to be released. His bluff was over.

The diplomats then flew to Marula-Puku and secured the release of Anne and Rex. Malcolm called us to say that all of them were safely in Lusaka.

THE ZAMBIAN GOVERNMENT was not responsible for the attempted takeover of our project. Only a few corrupt but powerful individuals from the Chiluba administration were involved. Several years later, in a concerted effort to clean up corruption, President Mwanawasa fired many dishonest civil servants and jailed others, including some of those who had sought to destroy our project. But in 1996, when this incident occurred, those men were still in office. We had worked closely and extremely well with many Zambian officials for years, so we did not want to speak out against the government in general. The Ministry of Tourism, which had issued permits for us to conduct the project for ten years, said we could continue our work. Even after all that had happened, Malcolm, Trish, Rex, and Anne were prepared to return to Mpika and Marula-Puku, and Hammer wanted to go on working with the villages. However, the U.S. ambassador advised us that since the people who orchestrated the illegal action were still in powerful positions, it would not be safe for us to return to Zambia.

All was set to continue, but when Malcolm and Trish returned to Mpika they found that Famwila had illegally seized much of our equipment, including trucks, the grader, radios, and computers. Hammer found that the project office was once again locked. Mpika is in the far north of the country, and there was no one to stop Famwila.

Every day we spent hours calling across the Atlantic on lines hissing with static, trying to reclaim the project. The police confiscated some of our equipment from the field commander and held it for us, but some of it disappeared. Now that Malcolm, Trish, and the others were safe it was more difficult to get the embassies involved. Weeks went by, then months. While the village farmers waited for seeds and the game scouts waited for diesel fuel, negotiations between international attorneys and officials bogged down over words and phrases. It became impossible for Malcolm, Trish, Rex, and Anne to conduct the project, and eventually they had to leave to find other employment.

Many of the farmers and small business people we had helped no longer needed outside assistance, but some still needed logistical support and loans, and hundreds of others had asked to join the programs. We were sure Hammer could continue to expand the village work, but we could not find him. As far as we knew, there were no trucks or even bicycles to support the village work — all had disappeared. We tried again and again to reach Hammer by fax, phone, and mail, but we could not get through.

It seemed that the ivory dealers had finally succeeded in closing down the project. I imagined Mary Chongo needing fabric for her sewing business but having no way to transport it from Mpika. The school in Fulaza would need books and paper. The midwives would need supplies, the farmers new seeds, the millers more diesel, but there was no way to help them. Famwila could continue to supply guns and ammunition to the villagers who did not have other jobs.

Like Gift, our dreams and efforts had become an ivory orphan.

23 MARK

ADRIFT

> See? See? That's what you'll get! There isn't a tribe for you anymore!
>
> —WILLIAM GOLDING

I HAD NOT BEEN BACK to the farm where I grew up for years. Now, driving a rental car and pulling a U-Haul loaded with the bits and pieces of our lives in Africa, we turned onto County Road J-6. It had been paved long ago, and the farmers had taken down most of the fences and plowed out the hedgerows bordering their fields, which now crowded the asphalt on either side. Without hedgerows, farming is closer to the bone, for every square foot of arable land that would otherwise serve as windbreaks and wildlife habitat is tilled. The gusty wind whipped up clouds of topsoil from plowed fields this spring day, casting it into the sallow yellow sky.

As we crossed the railroad tracks and drove along the county road I slowed down; everything seemed somehow familiar but foreign at the same time. Our neighbors' fields were smaller than I remembered, and their farm buildings closer together — as though the land had shrunk.

On a low hill across the fields near Swan Creek stood Fulton Union Church, white and pretty; when I was a kid, its steeple seemed almost near enough to our house that I could have hit it with a baseball from the yard. We stopped at its small, tidy graveyard to share some memories with my parents and other relatives buried there.

Standing at the foot of Dad and Mother's graves for the first time ever, I felt the lead weight of despair and a perfect darkness where their light had always been. But I knew at once, as though they had willed it, that this shadow, this drought, would be washed away by fresh drops of rain sweeping across my landscapes, my rivers and forests. I knew that I would never again watch a skein of geese headed south in an autumn sky or see fresh snow on a meadow or the lights in an old farmhouse at dusk without remembering my father's crooked pipe and impish smile and my mother's sweet, sad eyes and soothing embrace.

And then we drove on home — or where home should have been. Our old farmhouse had been razed, as had our workshop and the windmill that Dad and I had climbed. The woods where we had run in summer thunderstorms had been cut to little more than a huddled clump of maple, oak, and hickory trees. It took a minute to recognize this place where I grew up. I felt numb and melancholy as Delia and I walked hand in hand to the Gullywhumper — only to find it dry, its frogs and salamanders long gone. Someone had cleared the creek of trees and shrubs, and it was now a lifeless, muddy canal that looked fatigued by the load of sediment it carried. A few hundred yards away, across a field of stubble, a constant stream of traffic on the Ohio-Pennsylvania Turnpike cut through the carcass of the farm I had worked as a boy. The big old maples were gone from our front yard, and the wind whistled through the spare ribs of the old barn. Delia and I strolled into its cavernous interior and looked up to the high oak beams I had walked in my bare feet; for a moment I could see again the fresh stacks of sweet-smelling hay forty feet high and hear the echoes of laughter as I jumped with my brother and sisters from the oak beams into piles of cow feed on the barn floor. But then a gust of cold wind swept it all away.

Like the poached elephants of Luangwa, Kalahari lions in drought, and so many Americans, my siblings, and most of my extended family, were scattered. We received a warm welcome from an aunt who lived nearby, but there was nothing to hold us here, and for the first time since settling in the Kalahari Desert of Botswana more than twenty-two years earlier, we were without a home. We still planned to return to Zambia as soon as it was safe, and we had made repeated calls to the American embassy in Lusaka to try to determine whether it was. But in the meantime we had to find a place to live.

So we headed west, camping along the way, looking always for horizons that reminded us of Africa. But every time we found a likely valley, we also found a major road or a railroad passing through it, the rumble of the trains and traffic smothering the wild sounds coming from the countryside. Sometimes in the quiet just before dawn, I imagined that I could hear the thunder of hooves on the plains or the full-bellied roar of a lion splitting the night, or see platinum elephants crossing a river in moonlight. And as I rose every morning in yet another strange place, I found myself, coffee mug in hand, looking up to the mountains and ridgetops, imagining that the great horizons of Africa stretched beyond. I felt twisted, cracked, and dry, like the roots of a tough desert plant ripped out of the hardscrabble ground. How could we not go back to Africa? How does one decide not to breathe?

If we could not return, we wanted to find a last piece of wilderness in this country, but as we searched state by state, valley by valley, we gradually realized that there is no true wilderness left here — or anywhere else on Earth. In the more than two decades that we had been in Africa, the last of it had disappeared.

We would have to settle for second best by finding a troubled piece of *former* wilderness, one that we could begin to restore in what remained of our lifetimes. We would work to heal it, and it would heal us, make us whole and complete again, make us feel at *home* once more.

One day in the early fall of 1996, we turned onto a narrow gravel road that followed a creek bottom north for several miles to an old farm. It was near a crystal-clear lake and included a cabin on a meadow at the foot of the Rocky Mountains. The feet of too many cattle had stomped the meadow to dust and rounded down the creek's once proud banks; a complex of ditches leading to the creek had drained the marsh, and large bald spots showed where the forests had been clear-cut. But we bought "Thunder Mountain Ranch" and immediately started dismantling the web of barbed-wire fences, picking up and hauling off generations of junk, and restoring the marsh. We also began working to recover the grizzly bears that had roamed the mountains. In her way, Nature began rewarding us. As I later wrote in my journal:

> This evening the larches, sun-splashed and dazzling in their golden cloak of autumn, stood proudly forward on the rocky shoulders and ledge lines, looking down from the mountains on our new home at the edge of the meadow. Early snows on the high peaks and crags were pink cotton as the sun lay down for the night. The full moon rose through a blush of alpenglow into the sky above Windy Pass and sat on my left shoulder as I headed across the creek for the warmth of our fire, the new frost crisp under my steps. I cannot help it: I am falling in love with this new land, bewitched by its marshes, moose, mosses, mushrooms, and moons, its great horned owls hooting from deep in the dusk. A coyote calls, and then others, until their yips, yaps, and yowls fairly nip at the edges of the marsh. And finally a wolf's long, mournful song rises from the larches at the base of the mountains and soars across the valley. It is alone. I pause to savor the echoes of its last call until they are lost among the peaks and then head for the house again. But, in the gathering darkness, deep behind my soul, someone, something, whispers "Africa."

24 DELIA
THE STONES OF MY STREAM

> My right and left arms round the sides of two friends and I in
> the middle;
> Coming home with the bearded and dark-cheeked bush-boy
> . . . riding behind him at the drape of the day;
> Far from the settlements studying the print of animals' feet . . .
>
> — WALT WHITMAN

> If we have no peace, it is because we have forgotten that we belong to each other.
>
> — MOTHER TERESA

MARK AND I FOUND A PLACE of our own and mapped a territory, somewhere between snowfalls and moose tracks, but like any new home range, it didn't feel quite right. Most of the stars were different, some upside down, some missing altogether. With no Southern Cross, the sky seemed cut off at the knees. Leopard-looking stumps hid in grass clumps and peered at us with carnivorous eyes. For years now I had had no troop, no female group, as the women of Katibunga did. I wasn't even close to having the social support that a baboon or lioness has. I saw elephant families moving slowly through the gray space between the trees, but when I opened my eyes they were gone. We wondered how Gift and her small family were faring. As tiny as they were, they would still be targets for poachers. We kept trying to reach Hammer but finally gave up.

After growing in strength and maturity in distant waters, a salmon must return to the exact estuary where she hatched — a thousand miles through the open ocean, hundreds of miles of her native river, against the current of her natal tributary. Instinctual maps made partially from memories of the stones of her stream guide her homeward. At every bend and fork, without hesitation, she must make the correct decision and swish on toward her childhood address.

Could it be that like all the animals we had studied, in the end we just wanted to find our own troop and our home? Are we all salmon searching for our streams?

MONTHS AFTER leaving Zambia, we received this letter:

> Dear Mark and Delia, Greetings from Zambia, Mpika District, which has been your African Georgia. It has started getting much warmer. It could be that Luangwa Valley influence is slowly getting control of our plateau winds. Probably these are early signs of the begging of the rain season.
>
> How are you "guys?" It's sad the team is no longer here any more. At times I wished I could as well leave. But alas am not British or Scottish. I have to learn to take the pain courageously.
>
> I always get consoled as every week reports reach us at our homes that places like Nkobe and Mukungule, a place which is relatively populated with people, wildlife has finally forced its way. To us as former NLCP staff its great achievement.
>
> For weeks I tried to contact you by fax and email everything was difficult. Apparently every single item has been taken over by the "big boys" from Lusaka who have been "biting" the project complete hastily from people we loved so much and worked with. It was now the last storm which for sure we could not survive this time. No ways I had to surrender. I would not be bought to their side and I made a decision which is very costly. No job and no income with a wife I find it hard. Mark, Are you not coming soon?
>
> It's painful to be here in Mpika and continue to see what was

rightly under our project, equipment, buildings, etc completely under strangers — reaping where they never sewed. Believe me Mark I always hold back my tears. Because I know what it took for the project to be what it was. And how I loved the bike you bought me. It is no more.

I and Albert struggled to hang on with the community development programme. No one, however, cared for the continuing of the programme. Big guys were here but no one dared to introduce us nor could we have any audience. NLCP concept can't die that way. It is a model to be applied in community based conservation programmes.

Now at home this time waiting to hear from you. Don't feel I have lost hope and trust in what you have done to our park and the people here. The revolving fund which was the backbone of our success and continuity, to our surprise we were told there was nothing. I am only waiting to hear from you for further instructions. All the villagers did not want to see the project die.

Thanks. God bless.
Hammer.

We wrote to Hammer immediately, assuring him that we would continue our support for the village projects. He replied that he no longer had an office but worked under the banana trees the way we did in the beginning. Prince Bernhard of the Netherlands paid for a new motorbike for him.

A few months later he wrote again: "The established work structure still exists despite all what has happened. Activities in the communities are still going on and we are a focal point in development for our District. Some of the activities are tuck shops, cooking oil making, farming of fish, bee keeping. Women clubs are still active in sewing and baking industries."

Bit by bit, from the other side of the world we helped Hammer rebuild the village programs. He wrote applications for grants and raised funds from organizations such as Harvest Help, which supplemented our support for farmers. Hammer and his colleagues wrote their own charter, formed their own project. The news spread, and many other villagers asked to join their programs. Grace NG'ambi, using her special dance, taught the women of Nabwalya to be traditional birth attendants like those of Mukungule. Hammer moved back into the project offices. From its simple "one-man, one-woman" beginning the project had grown to reach the people of fifty-two villages. Fifteen hundred households had sustainable industries such as sunflower presses or beekeeping. Agriculture had been improved, and food security for families had doubled in some areas. There was a new school in Chilyaba, and there were supplies for the clinic in Nkomba. Sixty percent of the participants were women. Zambians were running the project, teaching each other fish farming and beekeeping. The beauty was they almost did not need us anymore. That was what we had wanted all along.

One afternoon Gift's daughter Georgia, who was less than nine years old, delivered a calf right in our old camp. So at the young age of sixteen, Gift, who would normally be giving birth for the first time, had three kids of her own and one grandcalf. From being a solitary orphan who wandered alone and could only watch elephant mothers and daughters from a distance, she was now the matriarch for a family of five. Kasokola would have said, "Panono, panono."

LYING IN A MEADOW under a mountain dusted with spring snow, so far away from Luangwa, I felt as if I were in a raft drifting on a shoreless sea. Under Hammer's leadership the village work had soared, and once again the elephants were safe. Our dream had spilled over, and again we found ourselves in the wild surrounded by vast beauty. Yet the space around us seemed as empty as the gray place where elephants hide.

In my mind I saw the baboons scampering across the river beach. I remembered the young female who often left her troop, scampered into my camp on her own, and watched me identify plants. One morning when the other baboons were nearby, I had a chance to watch her leaving the group. It was not a matter of walking away with cocky confidence. She stole a few steps in my direction and then looked back, as if reassuring herself that they were still there. When they moved away, she bounded back toward them and stood nearby for a few moments, torn between curiosity and camaraderie. Finally, she corraled the courage to jump into my tree, but she listened intently to their calls. She always knew exactly where they were.

I walked to our cabin and telephoned my childhood friends the Walker twins, Margaret and Amanda. I said, "Here's to'd ya. If I never see'd ya, I never know'd ya." It had taken all my life to understand what that means: baboons, elephants, and people belong with the ones they truly know. We need more than strangers around us. Mark and I had studied the significance of social systems of other species for decades, but in doing so, we had left our own families. And what we learned was that it is not so much that the troop is incomplete without some of its baboons or human beings, but that the individual baboons or human beings are incomplete without their troop.

Margaret and Amanda flew west to visit me, and a few days later we stood on the edge of the sweeping meadow. I pointed out that the white-tailed does had left their small herd and were almost evenly scattered across the field, each standing alone. This meant they either had had their fawns or would soon, I explained. The three of us spread out across the meadow and walked quietly through the lush grass shadowed by mountains. Minutes later we found twin fawns — their soft coats spotted with white — curled tightly in the grass. As instructed by their genes, they lay motionless, their huge brown eyes reflecting the sky. This strategy of stillness, along with their lack of odor, prevented predators from finding them. As long as we kept a few feet away, the fawns would not bolt, and their mother would return safely to them. Margaret and Amanda froze in awe, their hands covering their faces. Twins from my troop intertwined with twins from Nature.

My raft drifted closer to a shore. More friends, old and new, came to see the elk and cougars and us. Slowly a new group formed, loose at first, and wobbly, but becoming more solid with shared smiles and ski trails. Because most people are as scattered as desert lions, one can find plenty of strays in the dunes; all you need is a net to bring them in. To be complete, we need Nature and our troops, but both are slipping away beyond our reach. We must save what wilderness we can because it was our first home, and without it we will never fully understand who we are. Like Gift, we must put our troops and our families back together again. Like Kalahari lions at the end of drought, we must form a new pride.

Yawning cardboard boxes and crumbled newspapers surrounded me as I unpacked some of our stored belongings, many of them wedding presents we had not seen or touched in twenty-five years. Gingerly I opened the carton labeled DELIA'S THINGS. Wrapped in yellowing tissue paper was the china horse Grandpa had given me when I was ten. Nestled among old letters was the wristwatch he gave me when I learned to drive in the pecan orchard. I held them against my heart and then placed them on my shelf. They are the stones of my stream.

I remembered the last time I saw Gift and Georgia. Of course, I had no way of knowing that it would be my final encounter with them. I was driving to my camp from Marula-Puku and had just forded the Lubonga River. The grass was nearly as tall as the truck, so I could not see very far on either side. Suddenly they stepped into the track ahead of me, and I switched off the engine. Without hesitating, Gift walked gracefully to my open window. The still, hot air drifted with her movements — an elephant breeze. She was so close I could not see the top of her head, but by leaning slightly, I could see into her gray eyes, fringed with long lashes. Her trunk, usually so curious and busy, dangled loosely. I could have reached out and touched her, but instead I sat very still. How did I know to memorize her face, to make note of the "smile lines" creasing her cheeks, to notice that her eyes always seemed sad? Notes that will have to last me a lifetime. She stood there for only a minute or two and then glided by like a big ship. Georgia followed her, slightly farther away, glancing at me with her moist, deep eyes. It was a fine goodbye.

No elephants move through the thickets here, but the soft footfalls of deer and elk can be heard along the creek. The moon touches my face with the same light that smiles on the distant lionesses in the long grass. The stars are out of place, but soon they will become oriented to my new place until I am familiar to them. Time has allowed me to map my new space, and the honking of the Canada geese brings spring as heartily as the sparrow weavers' trill.

I lay on the warming ground until I could no longer feel where I ended and the earth began. The oneness I share with Nature, the women of Katibunga, and my own troop makes me whole. I pushed myself up from the ferns that were rallying with all their might for spring and dusted the last of the snowflakes from my sleeve. Impotent in this new season of warmth, the cold crystals fluttered through the air and literally disappeared before my eyes. As I emerged from the woods at an easy pace, the large meadow opened before me, offering a walk in any direction.

Maybe someday we will return to Marula-Puku and Fulaza, but that is not really important. What matters is that Gift keeps having babies, that Hammer is distributing seeds, and that the winterthorn still sings.

MARK

Epilogue

As of this writing (2005) the work we began in 1986 to conserve the wildlife in and around North Luangwa National Park by offering villagers alternatives to poaching is nineteen years old. Hammer Simwinga, whose heroic and selfless efforts sustained and preserved the North Luangwa Conservation Project (NLCP) during the attempted seizure by corrupt officials, has founded his own offspring organization, the North Luangwa Community Conservation Development Project (NLCCDP). In 2004 villagers in the Mpika area chose our project and NLCCDP as the model to follow for future wildlife conservation and wildlife-based remote rural development programs, and it is being replicated in other parts of Zambia.

On September 20, 2005, the National Geographic Society and the Owens Foundation for Wildlife Conservation cosponsored an evening with Hammer Simwinga and the best-selling author Alexandra Fuller at the National Geographic's auditorium in Washington, D.C. To get to America, Hammer had traveled more than eleven thousand miles, battling automatic doors, escalators, and hotel key cards like a Bembaland version of Crocodile Dundee. Then he rode horses in Idaho; saw bears, elk, bison, and the scenic grandeur of the Tetons; was interviewed on National Public Radio; toured the nation's capital; and ate his way across the country. Then he saw his name in lights on the National Geographic building.

"Ah," he said. "First I am an American cowboy, and now this! I can be telling stories for the rest of my life and never finish."

For more than an hour on his night, he, Alexandra, and Senior Editor Oliver Payne enchanted the audience with descriptions and impressions of village work and wildlife, which Alexandra had written about for the *National Geographic*'s September feature issue on Africa. And then Hammer returned to Zambia to continue the project.

ELEPHANT POACHING in North Luangwa decreased by more than 95 percent from 1986 to 1996. The Frankfurt Zoological Society (FZS), our funding partner for nineteen years, stepped in to continue elephant research and support for antipoaching programs, and Marula-Puku is now the home of Hugo van der Westhuizen and Elsabe Aucamp, who are managing those programs. NLCP is now one of the most secure parks in Zambia. In fact it is so well protected that the Conservation Foundation of Zambia is working with FZS to reintroduce black rhinoceros.

Gift and her family still stop by at Marula-Puku, as do Cheers, Long Tail, and Survivor — who not only eats the marula fruits but harasses the staff as well. More and more elephants can be seen walking along the rivers of the Luangwa Valley. Although Gift's grandcalf died, she and her three offspring are now the beginning of an extended family.

Sadly, Tom Kotela has died, but Mano Unit, under the leadership of Samushi Kamuti, has consistently been chosen as the best in Zambia at the wildlife officers' annual parade. For the past two years the scouts have been given more sophisticated paramilitary training so that they can handle any threat from poachers.

Isaac Daka, one of the top game scouts in Zambia, is now the unit leader of Chikwa/Chifunda, from which he and his officers are ably protecting the eastern flank of the North Luangwa Park.

Chief Mukungule has died, but his successor enthusiastically supports the community-outreach work of Hammer and his colleagues. One morning before he died, the old chief watched a group of elephants on the outskirts of his village for the first time in many years. He wrote us a letter thanking NLCP for making that possible.

Mary Chongo continues her sewing industry under the tree next to her home, though she recently wrote to say that she has worn out her Singer treadle machine. The traditional birth attendants trained by Dr. Philip Watt still practice in their villages, and the Owens Foundation recently funded the training of another group in Nabwalya. The small school in Fulaza is still operating, and villagers recently wrote to ask for help expanding it. In all, more than twenty thousand Zambians benefited from job training, agricultural assistance, small business loans, improved education, and rural health care provided by NLCP. To turn away from poaching and embrace the conservation of their wildlife resources, the people of North Luangwa needed only a new direction and a bit of help and encouragement.

Malcolm, Trish, Rex, and Anne now live and work in Tanzania, where they have set up a company converting crop wastes to a charcoal-like fuel as an alternative to cutting down forests for firewood.

In exchange for a large subsidy from the European Union, the Department of National Parks and Wildlife Services has been privatized in order to stamp out corruption; it is now known as the Zambian Wildlife Authority. Many of the senior officers have been replaced, including those who engineered the illegal seizure of NLCP. In fact, President Mwanawasa and his administration have fired or jailed many former officials, including the previous president. The new government is also making admirable strides in the conservation of its wildlife resources and the proliferation of community-based conservation projects.

It will take many years for the elephant populations of Luangwa to build back their former numbers after the severe poaching of the 1980s and '90s. They need room to grow, which will require a secure habitat, and they need time to grow old, to learn the lessons of life and pass them on to their young. A continued — and strengthened — United Nations moratorium on the international trade in ivory is crucial, at least until poached populations are reestablished.

But it is perhaps no more important than the need to stem the growth of the human population. In most of Africa, as in other parts of the world, human populations are now so dense that unrestricted hunting, even for subsistence purposes, especially with modern weapons, would quickly deplete the wildlife, bringing many animal populations to extinction. Unless human numbers are in balance with those of neighboring wildlife populations, the decline of wildlife will continue to be a hard reality. Despite the ravages of AIDS and a plethora of other diseases, Africa's populations continue to outstrip the carrying capacity of the continental resource base — as is the case in many other places on Earth. So long as this growth in human numbers continues, the misery for both human and wildlife populations will grow exponentially.

Elephants, buffaloes, and other animals are expanding farther and farther from North Luangwa, repopulating areas where they have not been seen in decades. The elephants and hippos have recovered from poaching to such an extent that their crop raiding has become an increasing problem. Hammer and his colleague, Moses Nyirendu, and their team have encouraged farmers to ring their fields with chili peppers and beehives, which seem to be effective ways to ward off the giant herbivores.

WHILE WE CONTINUE to support our project in Zambia, since returning to the United States in 1996, we have been working to recover remnant populations of grizzly bears and wetland habitats in the Pacific Northwest. For information on the Owens Foundation for Wildlife Conservation, contact our Web site, www.owens-foundation.org, or write to us at P.O. Box 870530, Stone Mountain, Georgia 30087.

APPENDIX

The North Luangwa Conservation Project

A Multidimensional Community-based Approach to the Conservation of Natural Resources

NLCP REFERS TO the project as founded and designed by Mark and Delia Owens in 1986 and directed by the Owenses until 1997, and to the community outreach work that continues to the present as an offshoot of the original NLCP model. The project included the following programs:

Microbusiness Development and Employment Opportunities
Agricultural Assistance
Rural Health Care
Conservation Education
Wildlife Law Enforcement
Wildlife Research and Monitoring
Tourism Development

NLCP was a multifaceted project designed to satisfy the basic needs of rural people living on the outskirts of Zambia's North Luangwa National Park and to restore and manage a depleted natural resource — the local indigenous wildlife — so that eventually it could benefit the people and the local economy. By 1985 highly organized commercial poachers had severely depleted the park's major wildlife species, including 93 percent of the elephants and all of the black rhinoceros. Our wildlife censuses revealed that two thirds of the park's area had been depopulated of its large mammalian species; had the slaughter been allowed to continue, the other third would have been killed off within five or six years. Poaching and the black-market wildlife trade made up the primary economy of the area. Poaching and working for commercial poachers were the only ways local people could benefit from the national park, which the Zambian government at that time did not have the financial resources or political will to protect or manage. Criminal elements and corrupt officials from outside the communities hired shooters to kill elephants for about ten dollars each; the organizers could get up to two hundred dollars a pound for the ivory. They hired villagers as carriers and paid them as little as two pounds of meat to transport hundred-pound loads of contraband meat, ivory, and skins on their heads up to sixty miles over the mountains to settlements along the Cape-to-Cairo Road. Poaching was not only illegal, it was also dangerous, unsustainable, and not very profitable for local people. It also eroded the moral fabric of entire communities. Poachers took children as young as ten out of school to work as virtual slaves and took young girls away from their families in exchange for favors.

Conceptually, NLCP was not an attempt to conserve North Luangwa National Park through the development of ecotourism in the short run. That approach was not possible because wildlife populations had been depleted to extinction or near extinction, and the area was not secure enough or the infrastructure developed enough to sustain visits by large numbers of tourists. Instead, we sought first to empower villagers and their communities economically and with improved health care, education, and security. At the same time we bolstered wildlife law enforcement so that the animal populations could recover and once again become a sustainable resource. The age-old symbiosis between wildlife and people could be recatalyzed only after the animal and human communities had been independently restored. NLCP conserved wildlife by helping villagers develop legitimate alternatives to poaching and by helping them realize direct and indirect *sustainable* benefits in exchange for conserving their natural resources. NLCP made a deal with them: "We will invest in you if you will invest at least sweat equity in yourself and if you will help conserve your wildlife." The project expected a measurable return: the repopulation of wildlife and improved quality of life for local people, including a reduction in the numbers of poachers in each village.

None of the assistance was a handout: the NLCP loan fund for startup enterprises operated much like those from commercial lending institutions, except that they were interest free. The loans were to be repaid so that we could invest in and help others from the same community. Any tangible or intangible assistance beyond what might be expected from a "good neighbor" was made conditional on an in-kind investment (usually labor) by the recipient in order to reinforce the self-help concept and to ensure that the enterprise would be self-sustaining. This concept was at first difficult for villagers to understand and accept. For decades foreign assistance programs had consisted of grants-in-aid, which did not require recipients to invest in themselves or to be accountable for the money they received. Eventually most of the local people understood the concept of self-help, and when they did, the pride they felt in their own accomplishments was truly remarkable.

Indirect Benefits of NLCP Programs to Local People

The direct financial benefits of tourism and associated jobs as well as other business opportunities coming from the park could not be realized until the wildlife populations were revitalized and until NLCP had built a rudimentary physical infrastructure, including roads, bridges, and airstrips. In the meantime the project stimulated indirect benefits to the local people *on behalf of the park and its wildlife,* including jobs, business opportunities, and community development through improved health care and education, for example. These programs, which were not directly related to the park and wildlife, were generated by and subsidized with resources from outside the area. The programs were expected to become self-sustaining and/or supported by entities within Zambia in ten to fifteen years.

These NLCP programs offered villagers alternatives to poaching and also demonstrated to them the value of wildlife conservation. Program administrators and their assistants were specifically asked to find creative ways to repeatedly reinforce the notion that opportunities and resources were being made available to villagers on behalf of the wildlife community in and around the park. For our pilot programs we initially selected fourteen villages near North Luangwa National Park that were known to harbor hardened commercial poachers.

Wildlife clubs are one of the most important tools for reinforcing the link between conservation and the programs offered in the villages. Initially, through NLCP, these clubs were a forum for discussing personal and community needs within the context of conservation and for assessing a community's available talents and resources to address those needs. But under the North Luangwa Community Conservation Development Project (NLCCDP) the clubs have become much more: they are now repositories for loan funds, training facilities, and the spearhead for expanding programs into other communities — all on behalf of wildlife. When villagers request that the project start a program in their community, they must first form a wildlife club and pay a fee to join it. They are charged an additional fee if they miss a meeting, and they lose their membership if they miss more than three meetings. The fees tend to weed out those who are not in earnest about addressing community problems. Each member's money is held in a sort of savings account until he or she decides, with the help of project advisers, on a worthwhile business enterprise. Then the money, in conjunction with a low-interest loan, is used to develop that business. Members of long-established clubs share their skills and training with the new initiates, which makes it unnecessary to hire more and more vocational trainers.

Because women are more likely than men to remain in their home community, NLCCDP requires that 68 percent of the members of each wildlife club be women before the project will set up a program for a village. Thus women have become economically empowered in developing businesses, and many are assuming leadership roles in their community for the first time. This elevated social status has made other opportunities more readily available to women, including access to family planning techniques.

Microbusiness Development and Employment Opportunities

The Village Approach to Microbusiness Development

Meeting with tribal leaders. According to tribal protocol, we asked the village headmen to request a meeting with the chief and his elders. At the meeting we and our Zambian community development officer explained that NLCP was a wildlife conservation organization commissioned by their government to help villagers find alternatives to poaching in and around the national park, so that their wildlife would return to benefit all their people. Because of poaching, few large wild animals were left in these areas, and in some cases people had been reduced to eating mice and other rodents for meat. We asked the chief and elders for suggestions on how we could best work with them and the villagers to improve their agriculture and community infrastructure and to stimulate job opportunities and sustainable commerce as alternatives to poaching. After the chief gave us his endorsement, he then instructed his elders and headmen to arrange meetings with interested villagers.

Explaining project objectives to villagers. In each village, after being introduced by the headman, we explained that NLCP was not an antipoaching entity, even though we were offering substantial assistance to wildlife scouts, and that no one was forced to participate in the programs we hoped to develop with them. We explained that we were there primarily to assist any and all villagers who refrained from poaching, including reformed poachers, and that we *represented* wildlife conservation interests and the national park, that we were speaking to them on behalf of the beleaguered wildlife community. We reiterated many times that our programs were designed to help them turn away from poaching by developing legitimate employment and business opportunities, so that more of them could again benefit from their wildlife as the populations recovered.

Assessing skills and interests. We began by surveying villagers about their interests, skills, and formal training. Even in the most remote areas we found some young men who had left their villages for training and had returned as mechanics, electricians, cobblers, carpenters, or farmers; and women who could sew, make crafts, garden, or in other ways provide goods and services to their communities.

Documenting available resources. We helped villagers survey the raw materials and other commodities available for use in microindustries.

Choosing appropriate small industries. After local interests, skills, levels of training, and resources were assessed, the NLCP revolving fund administrators (including local Zambians) screened applicants for interest-free loans to pay for additional training, acquisition of basic equipment, enrollment in small-business management courses, and advice from outside experts on the development of appropriate small industries.

Businesses were considered appropriate for loans if they met the following criteria:

Readily available resources and nearby markets. Because of the expense and general lack of transportation, NLCP emphasized the development of microindustries that used local raw materials to produce items or commodities that could be sold or traded locally.

Low startup costs. NLCP concentrated on industries that required low initial capital investment and simple machines. Spare parts and other support for the industry had to be readily available in Zambia, preferably in Mpika. NLCP did not encourage industries that relied on tractors or other large equipment that required high maintenance or imported spare parts.

Minimal environmental impact. NLCP did not encourage the raising of livestock other than rabbits, guinea fowl, and other small domestic animals. Large livestock require a lot of grazing land and represent substantial losses when killed by predators, which intensifies the conflict between humans and wildlife, leading to the destruction of the latter. Our objective was to *reduce* that conflict so that both wildlife and people could prosper in a harmonious synergy.

Satisfaction of basic needs. Industries supplying basic products immediately needed by villagers were encouraged. These included the following:

1. *Sunflower seed presses.* These provided jobs for many local farmers. The press operator purchased the seeds from the farmers, produced the oil with the press, and then sold the oil to villagers and game scouts or at the open market in the central village. The roughage (cake) from the pressed seeds could be used as feed for farm-raised fish, chickens, rabbits, and other small livestock.
2. *Maize-grinding mills.* The mills provided jobs for the millers and a service for the community. Grinding mills, even simple ones, require diesel fuel and some spare parts, so they were not the most appropriate industry for remote villages. However, we agreed to sponsor several mills in some of the larger, more easily accessible villages because they relieved scores of women of the task of grinding maize by hand — laborious, time-consuming work. The women were thus freed to start businesses, become more economically independent, and assume greater responsibility in the community.
3. *Fish farms.* The fish farms provided jobs for operators and a good source of protein for villagers who purchased the fish. The larger villages and the game scout camps provided good markets for the fish.
4. *Carpentry shops.* One village had six trained carpenters; supported by an initial loan for tools, they made and sold furniture locally, including desks that the project purchased for schools as part of the Conservation Education Program.
5. *"Wildlife" shops.* These provided a living for the shopkeeper and a much-needed service to villagers. Before these general stores were established, people in many villages had to walk for two to three days to purchase basic items such as matches, soap, cooking oil, and cloth. Wildlife clubs started by villagers sponsored some of the first shops with NLCP loans.
6. *Sewing.* Using foot-powered treadle sewing machines, women and men

were able to make clothing to sell to villagers, merchants in the central village, and game scouts. Making uniforms for the scouts catalyzed other forms of commerce between the game scout camps and local communities, improving relations that had been strained by clashes between poachers and the scouts' antipoaching activities.

7. *Beekeeping.* Beekeepers were taught at first to house their bees in wooden box hives instead of cutting down trees to access the honey of wild bees. Further experimentation resulted in environmentally sound hives made from mud and small amounts of cement. The beekeepers could eat the organic honey themselves and sell it to others, and the bees helped pollinate some crops. In some cases beehives were used to ward off crop-raiding animals, including elephants and hippos.
8. *Shoemaking.* Villagers made sandals from old tires and sold them locally and at the marketplace in Mpika.
9. *Mousetrap making.* Villagers made mousetraps from scrap metal and sold them to other villagers and to the expatriate community in Mpika.

Entrepreneurial loan program. Each year NLCP offered each village a 1-million-kwacha (this figure fluctuated with the U.S. dollar–kwacha exchange rate) entrepreneurial loan fund. Individuals applied for loans from their village's revolving fund and bought equipment, training, transport, and other support for startup industries. For example, a villager could apply for funds to purchase a sunflower-seed press and have it transported from Lusaka to his or her village. After the industry was up and running, loans were to be repaid in quarterly interest-free installments. If the loan was not repaid or if the borrower was in arrears, the delinquent sum was subtracted from the 1 million kwachas available to that village for the next year. This requirement created peer pressure for loans to be repaid and on time; only 15 percent of the borrowers defaulted. The project was both strict and lenient, insisting that payments be made but allowing extra time for repayment during drought and other hardships as long as the person was earnestly trying to repay the loan. All payments were returned to the revolving fund to support other worthy proposals.

Training. After a villager received his or her equipment, the community development officer provided free training in using it and periodic retraining. Many villagers did not understand the fundamentals of operating a for-profit business. NLCP taught them how to factor in production costs so they could set a fair market price that allowed them to realize a profit and how to do basic accounting so they could track the progress of their businesses.

Employment Opportunities

NLCP hired many local people — up to one hundred at a time — to accomplish its objectives. Villagers were hired as community service experts, agriculture experts, teachers, drivers, mechanics, road and airstrip construction workers, camp staff, research assistants, and secretaries. These jobs boosted the local cash economy and constituted an indirect benefit from the national park to the people. The project also offered valuable training, so that when the indirect-benefit phase of the project was over, people who had developed skills and training would be more likely to find jobs elsewhere.

Agricultural Assistance

The aim was not only to improve crop yields but to introduce crops, such as legumes, that required little or no fertilizer and were good sources of protein and in general were more nutritious. Proposals requiring tractors or other motorized machinery were not funded or encouraged because the equipment could not be supported in remote areas.

Expert advice and training. Zambian agriculture experts who were full-time employees of the project visited all villages to offer training, workshops, and in-field advice on what crops to plant, how to fertilize them with compost, how to use mulch, protect crops from wildlife, and harvest and store them with the least waste.

Agricultural fairs. Village fairs were encouraged so farmers could learn about new crops, farming practices, and markets for their produce.

New crops. Wherever appropriate for local soils, climate, and food preferences, new crops were introduced that could be fertilized adequately by composting and by rotating crops to avoid depleting soils of nitrogen and other key nutrients. Soybeans, groundnuts, peas, beans, and other legumes were emphasized because of their relatively high protein content and their nitrogen-fixing ability. Chemical fertilizers were too expensive and difficult to obtain and apply, as well as environmentally offensive. Villagers were not encouraged to grow crops that would have to be transported long distances to market. Some novel ideas that were tried included drying mushrooms for sale and planting chili pepper crops around maize and soybean fields to protect them from elephants, hippos, and buffaloes.

Markets. The project helped farmers find new markets by encouraging the government-paid game scouts as well as project employees to purchase produce from them.

Fruit trees. Very few fruit trees had been planted in the area, so growing bananas, guavas, avocados, and mangos was encouraged and supported.

Rural Health Care

This program emphasized disease prevention and the use of basic remedies and treatments. Complicated high-tech equipment such as X-ray machines, though much needed, were not offered because they were too expensive and too difficult to operate and maintain. Instead we trained villagers in simple first aid, lifesaving techniques, and family planning, so that they could assist others in remote locations with simple, easily obtainable, effective remedies.

Under-five clinics. Because dehydration from diarrhea is one of the leading causes of death among children in remote rural areas, NLCP periodically provided transportation for medical personnel from Mpika to outlying villages, where clinics were held. The project also sponsored a nurse who traveled to villages to teach basic rehydration methods.

Training of traditional birth attendants (TBAs). Perhaps the most successful program in the NLCP Rural Health Care Program was the training of two women from each of twenty-four villages to be traditional birth attendants, or midwives. A volunteer American doctor and a Zambian nurse taught the course in a remote village mission, where the forty-eight women stayed for two months. Along with midwifery, they were taught first aid, AIDS prevention, family planning, nutrition, sanitation, and early childhood development. Refresher courses were offered periodically.

Donation of medical supplies. In cooperation with AmeriCares, an American medical organization, NLCP donated medical supplies worth $1 million U.S. dollars to Zambia. The supplies were flown from the United States. Smaller donations of medical supplies have been sent periodically since 1997.

Conservation Education

Another indirect benefit from the national park was our NLCP Conservation Education Program, which served schools in the fourteen target villages. The program employed a full-time educational officer, a qualified Zambian teacher who worked closely with the government's Ministry of Education. Although the program emphasized conservation education, its services went far beyond that, offering curriculum development and basic materials to remote schools that in some cases had never seen such things before. NLCP was often the sole provider of these items.

The following were some aspects of the program:

Conservation education. The project's education coordinator traveled to each school at least once a month to present programs on the value of conserving natural resources and to offer basic lessons in the natural sciences. The officer also taught lessons, met with teachers, planned future visits, assessed the school's needs, and provided materials.

Educational materials. The project provided such items as floors and roofs for the school buildings, desks, chalkboards, textbooks, paper, pencils, notebooks, crayons, posters, maps, globes, and soccer balls, many of which were shipped from the United States, Australia, Canada, and Europe. The project also paid for teachers' salaries and housing.

Bookmobile. NLCP provided a five-hundred-volume mobile library that was made available to schools through the conservation education coordinator.

Sister School Program. The project set up an exchange program between American schools and remote Zambian schools. The children exchanged letters, materials, stories, reports, artwork, and a lot of joy.

Curriculum. The NLCP education coordinator wrote a conservation education curriculum and produced teacher packets for all the area schools that included wildlife conservation workbooks, activity books, and board games. The program was coordinated with Zambia's Ministry of Education.

School construction and maintenance. The project built a school for one village and hired villagers (including some ex-poachers) to make bricks and help with construction. Some of the roofing sheets and window frames were paid for by ADMADE, a government program that returned revenues from safari hunting to villages. The project also built a house for the teacher and bought desks from NLCP-sponsored carpenters. In some other villages the project paid for school maintenance and repairs.

Drama and art competitions. NLCP provided many extracurricular activities for the schools, including sports and drama and art competitions, which otherwise would not have been available. Winners were occasionally taken on "safari" into the national park, where they could see wildlife, a treat that the children had never experienced.

Integration of Programs

To jump-start a cash economy, we tried to develop synergy among businesses and programs so that they could buy from and sell to each other. For example, newly equipped carpenters in the jobs program made desks for the schools served by the NLCP Conservation Education Program (the project paid for the desks); game scouts bought food and clothing from the newly trained farmers and seamstresses; farmers who grew sunflower seeds sold them to the sunflower press operators, who in turn sold the oil to the villagers or game scouts and sold the pressed cake to fish farmers.

Direct Benefits of the National Park to Local People

Villagers living in Game Management Areas (GMAs) around the park benefited directly from the park or its GMA in sustainable legal ways, most notably from tourism, hunting, and park-related government jobs.

Tourism

Well-managed tourism in the national park can benefit local people directly in the following ways:

Jobs. Safari companies hire local people as drivers, safari guides, construction workers, road crews, cooks, staff, management, and biologists.

Markets for agriculture. Safari companies buy produce from local farmers.

Markets for arts and crafts. Safari companies take tourists to villages where they can purchase locally made arts and crafts such as baskets, clothes, and wood carvings, and products such as organic honey from local people, thus providing a market for these goods.

Infrastructure improvements. Any improvements to infrastructure, such as park roads and bridges for tourism, also benefit local people. NLCP built new airstrips, roads, and bridges and improved roads all the way from Mpika through several villages to the national park, which benefited all the people in this area.

It is often pointed out that tourism cannot financially support national parks, and that is almost always true, even in well-developed countries, because only the government has the resources to manage the parks. It is also stated that a national park cannot provide a living to all the local people in an area. But this argument ignores the value that many local people place on the park as a place that preserves their heritage. So long as a threshold number of people are able to make a living from the park, they will have an incentive to conserve it. More than anyone else, local people deserve to benefit from the park — but in ways that will not diminish the resource. We believe in the world heritage concept: that because ecosystems are interrelated, they belong to and sustain everyone, and it is therefore the responsibility of all the peoples of the world to help protect them.

Hunting

As in most other countries, hunting is not allowed in Zambia's national parks, but it is allowed in Game Management Areas and surrounding open areas. NLCP worked to sustain lawful hunting for villagers in the following direct ways:

Establishment of the Mukungule Game Management Area west of the park. As commercial poaching declined, recovering wildlife populations began spilling out of the park into the GMA. With wildlife regulations and routine game scout patrols in place, legitimate local hunters increasingly benefited from this expanding resource.

Transportation of licensing officers to remote villages. Prior to that service, villagers from isolated settlements had to travel for up to three or four days to reach one of the larger villages where licenses were sold — and the allotment was often sold out by the time they arrived. As a result, many villagers hunted without licenses. Illegal subsistence hunting declined when transportation became available, making it easier to get licenses. Hunting regulations and other wildlife laws, including those pertaining to quotas and licensing, are very important for the restoration of depleted animal populations. In the near term there is a need to augment, but not necessarily replace, the benefits from hunting with more nonconsumptive uses of wildlife.

After depleted wildlife populations have recovered sufficiently to allow professional safari hunting, local people can benefit from programs that return revenue and meat products to them, as well as from associated jobs. NLCP assisted neighboring safari hunters by supporting antipoaching operations in their concessions and by assisting game scouts and villagers in those areas. The project did not, however, support the trophy hunting of at-risk, threatened, or endangered populations because that practice targets the most genetically fit and reproductively active individuals — the very ones whose reproductive performance is needed for the recovery and sustainability of the population. In general, when trophy hunting is allowed, the wildlife resource must be closely monitored and regulations strictly enforced.

Improved relations between game scouts and local communities. NLCP encouraged the scouts to buy local produce and products rather than importing goods from distant markets.

Park-Related Government Jobs

Government jobs contribute revenue to the local economy. A viable national park provides jobs, opportunities, and revenue to local people. When NLCP was founded, there were only seven game guards living in one camp near the park's western boundary to patrol and protect the whole park. Using local labor and materials, NLCP revitalized seven additional game guard camps by building forty-eight traditional houses for more than fifty scouts. The Zambian government hired the new officers and paid their salaries, which greatly stimulated the local cash economy.

Wildlife management provides jobs and revenue. Prior to NLCP the game scout camp had no vehicles, and no vehicles or machinery were assigned to the park itself. NLCP supplied aircraft, trucks, tractors, trailers, fuel tankers, and a motorized grader to support the game scouts' work and maintain the park. This fleet of vehicles provided jobs for drivers, mechanics, and workshop managers. Other management activities provided jobs for radio operators, secretaries, wildlife research assistants, and biologists.

Wildlife Law Enforcement

In 1986, when NLCP began, the seven game scouts of Mano Unit had only one functioning rifle and a single round of ammunition to protect NLNP. The scouts had not been paid for months and did not have uniforms, boots, patrol food, trucks, fuel, medicines, compasses, camping equipment, or almost anything else needed to do their jobs. Morale was low, and the scouts themselves shot wildlife inside the national park for their own consumption and for sale.

Working under the auspices of the Department of National Parks and Wildlife Services (NPWS), NLCP revitalized the law enforcement program to protect the park from further devastation. While NPWS supplied additional scouts, NLCP covered much of the costs of law enforcement, including those associated with transportation, construction of housing, roads, and airstrips, as well as patrol food and other assistance.

The purpose of NLCP's assistance was to build infrastructure, provide transportation, and equip and supply enough game scouts to field patrols throughout the park and its surroundings. NLCP personnel did not accompany game scouts on patrol and were in no way involved in law enforcement except through financial and logistical support. We considered it essential to gather information on poaching from local villagers and from aerial reconnaissance, then quickly transport the better-equipped and -supported scouts to areas were poachers were active. At the same time we worked to increase the number of man-days spent patrolling each month to boost the presence of law enforcement officers on the ground. The use of aircraft and the construction of rudimentary roads, bridges, and airstrips were crucial to this effort.

Some of NLCP's contributions to law enforcement from 1986 to 1996 were the following:

1. Refurbishing of seven game scout camps and construction of a new one west of the park.
2. Provision of uniforms, general equipment, transportation, and radio communication.
3. Construction of roads, bridges, airstrips, and an operations center to facilitate antipoaching patrols, including a jail to hold captured poachers.
4. Payments to village operatives who gathered undercover information on the locations, plans, and movements of major poaching figures.
5. Airlifting of scouts into poaching areas with fixed-wing aircraft and a helicopter, and day and night aerial reconnaissance missions to detect poaching and locate poachers.
6. A grinding mill and a miller (an ex-poacher) for Mano Unit game scout headquarters.
7. A tractor and trailer, trucks, fuel, and vehicle maintenance for game scouts.
8. A park-wide radio communication system.
9. Promotion of commerce between scouts and villagers to enhance community relations.

Wildlife Research and Ecological Monitoring

The wildlife populations in the park were surveyed, monitored, and researched, and the relevant results and implications were presented to Zambia's National Parks and Wildlife Services.

NLCP's ten-year study of elephants in NLNP included biannual aerial censuses to monitor population density; determination of the ages of 60 percent of the herd, using the footprint technique for aging (Lee and Moss 1995 and Western, Moss, and Georgiadis 1983) to establish the age structure of the population; and the radio-collaring of one individual in each of sixteen family units to study range movements, habitat selection, social behavior, and reproductive biology. Reports on population density, distribution, and habitat selection relative to poaching pressures were submitted to NPWS. Scientific data are being published in technical journals.

NLCP hired a full-time botanist to conduct a two-year research project that produced the first vegetation map of NLNP, quantified the impacts on mopane woodlands by repeated forest fires (mostly set by poachers), documented trends in woodland/grassland competition, identified fungus species, and documented their importance for wildlife and human communities.

Tourism Development

The NLCP staff contributed to the writing of the government's official Tourism Management plan for NLNP. The plan emphasized low-impact tourism that included low-cost park visits for Zambian citizens. With the decline in poaching, several operators established successful safari operations within North Luangwa.

The goal of NLCP was to make its programs as self-sustaining as possible. The hope was that village entrepreneurs would continue to operate their own cottage industries and that the project itself would continue under the supervision of local Zambians after the expatriate NLCP directors and staff left the area.

As of 2006, the project is twenty years old and so successful that its model for community-based wildlife conservation is being adopted elsewhere. Hammer Simwinga and Moses Nyirendu's nongovernmental organization, the NLCCDP, is benefiting more than 1,500 families in fifty-two villages. The most successful microindustries continue to be beekeeping, fish farming, sunflower presses, general mercantile shops, and improved agricultural methods. Of course, the more remote villages have problems with transport, which has limited the productivity of some of their industries. However, the local people are still enthusiastic, and the project continues to attempt working in these areas.

Those programs that depend on foreign financial support and are not economically self-sustaining, such as conservation education and rural health care, are not as active as they were and are in need of additional sponsorship. The training of traditional birth attendants has required comparatively little outside support and the program continues today, though it too needs help. And help may be on the way. Hammer and Moses are already working with the Zambian Wildlife Authority to develop the oversight and the community infrastructure needed to receive and wisely spend future ecotourism dollars. The North Luangwa is becoming a bright new destination for people wanting a back-to-nature walking safari.

In our opinion, a project such as NLCP can be successful in many parts of the world. It must be seen as a very long term multidisciplinary endeavor that requires the cooperation of the national government and the local people and at least initial foreign financial support.

SUGGESTED READING

Barnes, R.F.W., and E. B. Kapela. 1991. Changes in the Ruaha elephant population caused by poaching. *African Journal of Ecology* 29: 289–94.

Bradshaw, G. A. 2005. Bringing down the gods: human violence, trauma, and their effects on elephant communities. Dissertation, Pacifica Graduate Institute, Santa Barbara.

Bradshaw, G. A., A. N. Schore, J. L. Brown, J. H. Poole, and C. J. Moss. 2005. Elephant breakdown. *Nature* 433: 807.

Douglas-Hamilton, I., and O. Douglas-Hamilton. 1992. *Battle for the elephants.* New York: Viking.

Eltringham, S. K. 1982. *Elephants.* Dorset, Eng.: Blandford Press.

Eltringham, S. K., and R. C. Malpas. 1980. The decline in elephant numbers in Rwenzori and Kabelega national parks, Uganda. *African Journal of Ecology* 18: 73–86.

Hanks, J. 1972. Reproduction of elephant, *Loxodonta africana,* in the Luangwa Valley, Zambia. *Journal of Reproduction and Fertility* 30: 13–26.

———. 1979. *A struggle for survival: the elephant problem.* Cape Town: C. Struik Publishers.

Ivory Trade Review Group. 1989. *The ivory trade and the future of the African elephant.* Interim report for the second meeting of the CITES African Elephant Working Group.

Jachmann, H., P.S.M. Berry, and H. Imae. 1995. Tusklessness in African elephants: a future trend. *African Journal of Ecology* 33: 230–35.

Laws, R. M. 1966. Age criteria for the African elephant *(Loxodonta a. africana). East African Wildlife Journal* 10: 251–72.

———. 1969. Aspects of reproduction in the African elephant, *Loxodonta africana. Journal of Reproduction and Fertility* Suppl. 6: 193–217.

Leakey, R. 2002. *Wildlife wars.* New York: St. Martin's Press.

Lee, P. C. 1987. Allomothering among African elephants. *Animal Behavior* 35: 278–91.

Lee, P. C., and C. J. Moss. 1995. Statural growth in known-age elephants *(Loxodonta africana). Journal of Zoology* (London) 236: 29–41.

Lewis, D. 1985. Population density of Luangwa elephants. *Report to Zambian National Parks and Wildlife Services.* Lusaka, Zambia.

McComb, K., et al. 2001. Matriarchs as repositories of social knowledge in African elephants. *Science* 292: 491–94.

Moss, C. J. 1988. *Elephant memories.* New York: William Morrow.

———. 2001. The demography of an African elephant *(Loxodonta africana)* population in Amboseli, Kenya. *Journal of Zoology* (London) 255: 145–56.

Owens, D., and M. Owens. 1992. *The eye of the elephant.* Boston: Houghton Mifflin.

———. 2005. Single mom, only child. *Natural History,* 22–25.

———. In press. Early age reproduction in female elephants after severe poaching. *African Journal of Ecology.*

Poole, J. H. 1989. The effects of poaching on the age structure and social and reproductive patterns of selected East African elephant populations. In *The ivory trade and the future of the African elephant,* vol. 2. Ivory Trade Review Group, prepared for the seventh CITES meeting.

———. 1996. *Coming of age with elephants: a memoir.* New York: Hyperion.

Poole, J. H., and J. B. Thomsen. 1989. Elephants are not beetles: implications of the ivory trade for the survival of the African elephant. *Oryx* 23: 188–98.

Renewable Resources Assessment Group. 1989. The impact of the ivory trade on the African elephant population. Report to the Ivory Trade Review Group for the second meeting of the CITES African Elephant Working Group.

Western, D., C. J. Moss, and N. Georgiadis. 1983. Age estimation and population age structure of elephants from footprint dimensions. *Journal of Wildlife Management* 47: 1192–97.

ACKNOWLEDGMENTS

HAMMER SIMWINGA is a hero not only to us but also to the village people for remaining true to the ideals of our work, for keeping those ideals alive despite the dark forces of corruption, and for carrying on in service to wildlife and to his fellow man. To this day he continues the village programs that offer many people near North Luangwa Park a better living through improved job opportunities, higher-quality agriculture, and better health care, so that they can afford to conserve their wildlife. Moses Nyirendu and Albert Chilambwe have also played major roles in ensuring that these programs continue, and Grace NG'ambi ably teaches basic midwifery and medical skills to the traditional birth attendants. We are deeply grateful for their contributions and loyal friendship.

Our love and heartfelt thanks to Mary Dykes, Delia's sister-in-law, who has worked long hours seven days a week for years to administer the Owens Foundation for Wildlife Conservation, based in Georgia. Mary bought and shipped to Africa everything from paper clips to airplanes, radio-tracking collars for elephants, and educational and medical supplies for villagers. Among many other tasks, she organized the Sister School Program and raised funds. Mary put the foundation at the center of her life, next to her family, and we would be lost without her. Her husband, Bobby Dykes, Delia's twin brother, kept our computers working and cared for our photographic material. In the early days Helen Cooper directed the Owens Foundation and supervised everything stateside. She and her husband, Fred, have helped us in many, many ways over the years.

We are grateful to the former governing officials of Zambia who gave us permission to create the project and conduct elephant research and, even more, to the current administration under President Mwanawasa for its efforts to eliminate wildlife-related corruption. We especially thank the dedicated game scouts of Mano Unit, who, outnumbered and outgunned by poachers, regularly risked their lives under the most difficult conditions to protect the wildlife of North Luangwa and, at times, us. Former Manu unit leader Tom Kotela, another Zambian hero, now gone, was remarkably courageous in resisting corrupt officials to stand with the project against commercial poaching, as were Martin Mwanza (deceased), Isaac Daka, Gaston Phiri, Samushi Kamuti, John Mosolo, Monday Mukwaya (deceased), and many others. Isaac Longwe, formerly the warden of Bangweulu Command, counseled and assisted us in countless ways for years. We appreciated the support of the honest, hard-working members of the Department of National Parks and Wildlife Services, and its Ministry of Tourism. Bornface Zulu, David Chile, and Godfrey Chikalipe assisted with field research. Thanks to Paul Russell, Norbert Mumba, Clement Mwale, and Charles Lengalenga at the Anti-Corruption Commission for their friendship in dark hours, and for their dedication and diligence in curbing ivory smuggling and associated corruption. They saved a lot of elephants in North Luangwa and in Zambia as a whole. There are no words to adequately thank these people. We literally owe our lives to some of them.

For more than thirty years Bob Ivey and Jill Bowman have been loyal friends, confidants, and our oasis in desert storms. They have always been there when we needed them, and we owe them a great deal for their unfailing support.

Jackson Kasokola (deceased), Mumanga Kasokola, Patrick Mwamba, Mwaba, and Harrison Simbaye (deceased) worked by our sides for more than ten years, doing everything from building airstrips to darting elephants. Along with Bornface Zulu, Milford, and our other Bemba staff, they will not be forgotten.

Our effort in Zambia could not have succeeded without the volunteers who dedicated years of their lives to assisting us. We thank Alston Watt for improving the village work tenfold; Dr. Philip Watt for introducing and expanding the Rural Health Program; Alex Haynes for expert flying and for building offices, bridges, and schools; Jay Cooper for bringing his amazing computer programs to the bush; Steve Hall for risking his life repeatedly to airlift everything from solar panels to boots for game scouts into muddy bush strips, often in the dark of night; Ronnie Hadley for extending our health care programs; Edward North for his unselfish work in Fulaza village;

and Ian Spincer for improving agriculture in remote villages. Marie and Harvey Hill and Tom and Wanda Canon gave much of themselves in the very beginning. From our Kalahari days to the years in the Luangwa Valley, Kevin Gill helped us identify plants and opened his home to us whenever we were in Johannesburg. Warren Powell, Mike Owens, and Chris Owens helped us in the field.

Some very special people sacrificed much to work with us in North Luangwa: Malcolm and Trish Boulton expertly handled communications, vehicle maintenance, accounting, and complex logistics; secured permits; and supervised the Conservation Education Program. Rex and Anne Haylock managed the field camps, entered data on the computer, supplied game scouts, and met with officials in Lusaka. The Haylocks and the Boultons risked everything to salvage the project during the illegal takeover by corrupt officials, and we will always admire and thank them for their bravery and loyalty to our ideals and us.

Dr. Paul Smith produced the first vegetation survey and map of North Luangwa. His wife, Dr. Debra Shah-Smith, conducted original mycological investigations of the park's mopane woodlands. Judith Hawke and Charlie Ross managed the project's complicated logistics in Lusaka. Our special thanks to David and Carol Harvey for helping us through the project's transition. Dr. Mike Kock is surely one of the most expert large-animal capture specialists of our time — and one of the bravest. He flew, hanging out of the chopper's doorway, into the mountains with Mark — and because he did, we learned a lot about a beleaguered elephant population.

We are grateful to the Frankfurt Zoological Society for financing our field work for more than nineteen years, and we applaud Elsabe Aucamp and Hugo van der Westhuizen for their hard work in continuing the elephant research, with funding from Frankfurt, and for supporting the game scouts of Mano.

The project was also financed by the Owens Foundation for Wildlife Conservation, and we owe so very much to the members for their generous contributions and letters of encouragement and for shipping thousands of pounds of materials to Zambia. A very special thanks to Hank and Margaret McCamish for their remarkably generous donation of a helicopter, pilot training, and operating funds, which literally transformed NLCP by allowing us to reach many more villagers with our programs, even in the rainy season. This aircraft was our single most effective conservation tool. The late Prince Bernhard of the Netherlands provided the park's first radio communication network, perhaps our second most useful conservation tool because it relieved Mark of the need to drop messages in tin cans from the Cessna and because it was essential for coordinating antipoaching patrols and arranging logistics and supply. HRH "PB" supported our work for years and offered his unqualified friendship and encouragement when times were tough. Thanks also to the Turner Foundation, the Williams Family Foundation, the Norcross Wildlife Foundation, the Golden Ark Foundation, the Emily Parker Baker Foundation, and the Frederick E. Cooper and Helen Dykes Cooper Charitable Foundation for generous donations. Special thanks to Diane Parker, H. Turney McKnight, Dick Burgheim, Andrew Filipowski, Mike and Liz Pura, Shana and Andrew Laursen, Elizabeth Holland, Dennis and Sue Umshler, Danny and Barbara Morris, Carol Wong, Jeff Short and the late Barbara Short, Avery and Gerry Doubleday, John and Jane Emrick, John and Theresa Cederholm, Robert and Emmy Cleaves, Phil Osborne, Lois and James Garner, and Alex Carson and the late Johnny Carson for their generous support. Harvest Help has been very supportive of the agricultural assistance programs for years.

Thanks to Paul and Sonja Tudor Jones for their generous contributions and for their vision and funding of the North Luangwa rhino reintroduction programs. Through their conservation fund, they are accomplishing profoundly important conservation work in many parts of Africa, much of it artfully choreographed by our friend Jeremy Pope. Thanks to Jeremy and to Athol Freylink and Adrian Carr of Tudor Safaris for their friendship, support, and dedication to the conservation of wildlife in Zambia, for hospitality in their safari camp, and for Athol's initial help in immobilizing elephants. They were great neighbors in the bush.

Dr. Philip Watt coordinated with AmeriCares to send more than one million dollars' worth of medical supplies to the Zambian people. Dr. Bob and Dana Davis sent thousands of dollars' worth of medical supplies for the Rural Health Care Program. Elefriends of Australia, a generous sponsor, personally delivered educational supplies to us in Luangwa. More than thirty American schools sent art supplies and educational materials to the schools of Mpika District. Delia and Hawk Dykes volunteered their time on numerous occasions to load airplanes or move medical supplies. Our thanks to the "Dear Everybody" volunteers, who stuffed thousands of envelopes over the years, and especially to Vicki Anderten and Ginger Salisbury (deceased) for all the hundreds of ways they helped.

We are forever indebted to the American ambassadors to Zambia

Roland Kuchel and Gordon Streeb, for their astute assistance, encouragement, friendship, and support for many years. They and their wives, Marianne and Junie, were gracious hosts whenever we visited Lusaka. Thanks to President Jimmy Carter for meeting with us to discuss our project and to Delia's mother, Mary Helen Hartley, who helped arrange that meeting. We are grateful to President George H. W. Bush, President Bill Clinton, and President George W. Bush for supporting the United Nations ivory ban.

Our special thanks to John and Carol Coppinger of Remote Africa Safaris for their longtime friendship, for hosting us and our staff at their camps, and for their support in many other ways. Andy Anderson and his family opened their home in Lusaka to us, lifted our spirits, and allowed us to safely park our trucks and trailers loaded with tons of supplies in his yard. Always smiling, Dick Houston offered us cold drinks, warm friendship, old movies, and great accommodations in Lusaka, as did Hal and M. K. Cope, who added more than a dash of moral support and good counsel. Thanks also to Richard Jeffrey for his friendship and support.

Jenny and Derrick Gordon always welcomed dusty travel-worn NLCP staff in from the bush and gave them the run of their home. Thanks so much to Mark Falstad for his professional videotaping of the project — and for his good humor when Mark flew the plane into the lens of his new camera. Oops!

Slim Suleman traveled long distances to help maintain and repair our helicopter in the bush and cooked curry for us in Nairobi. Thanks to Father Thomas for helping us in numerous ways in Mpika, Rick Richey for editing miles of video, and Tom Steeb for designing a great Web site. Thanks to Mwana Bermudes and Nelda Villiness at the American embassy for facilitating grants, shipments, and for offering advice. We are so very appreciative of Trish Parsons and Rob, her late husband, who assisted with our aircraft on special occasions.

The Dallas Zoo designed and shipped NLCP teacher packets for the Conservation Education Program, and Rich Lobello wrote the curriculum. Thanks to Cathy Chiesa and Dr. John King for library research. Thanks also to Bell Helicopter, Inc., for their support, and especially to Bruce Lane, who, though very ill, flew with Mark in our new helicopter during its maiden flight to Marula-Puku.

Delia's brother Lee Dykes drove her all around the state of Georgia whenever she returned home. Leslie Ann Keller designed the Owens Foundation logo, and Bonnie Barney donated her beautiful artwork.

For more than twenty years Dr. Joel Berger has always taken time from his international field work to advise us on scientific matters and has remained steadfast in friendship. We are very grateful to Bernie Lanigan, Brad Jackson, Dana Raybon, and Mary Lou Marocha of Lanigan & Associates for advising us on financial matters for decades. Tammy Johnson has helped with foundation matters in countless ways.

Besides the dedicated officers of the former NPWS and of ZAWA, many people who have worked for years to conserve the Luangwa Valley deserve special appreciation: Phil Berry, Dr. Dale Lewis, the late Norman Carr, Adrian Carr, John and Carol Coppinger, Robin and Jo Pope, Dr. Richard Bell, Dr. Hugh Jackmann, Paul Russell, Adam Pope, Jeremy Pope, Athol Freylink, Mark Harvey, David Shepard, Mike Faddy, and Rachel McRobb.

For comments on the manuscript we are very grateful to Bob Ivey, Jill Bowman, Doug Kim-Brown, Mary Dykes, and Helen Cooper. We are deeply indebted to Alexandra Fuller, one of the most remarkable literary talents of our time, for being a friend to us, to truth, and to Zambia. Thanks, Bo, for writing the foreword to our book.

We thank Harry Foster, our longtime editor and friend at Houghton Mifflin, once again for his talent, patience, and forbearance in helping us mold a ragged, thorny bush manuscript into a book. Peg Anderson did an incredible job of chasing down every redundancy and inserting lost commas. Thanks also to Richard Abate, our literary agent, for his advice and encouragement.

To our old friends and families who make up our roots and troops, our thanks for always being there for us. Our love and thanks always to Margaret, Amanda, and Barbara. And to our "new" friends in Idaho — Doug and Mona, Janet and David, Tim and Joanne, Mike and Jane, Dawn and Rob, David and Mechee, Pat, Wilma and Larry, John and Jen, Sam and Carolyne, Greg and Alicia, and the Pederson clan — thanks for including us in your troop.